OF THE ELEMENTS

SUBSHELLS BEING COMPLETED

8.75

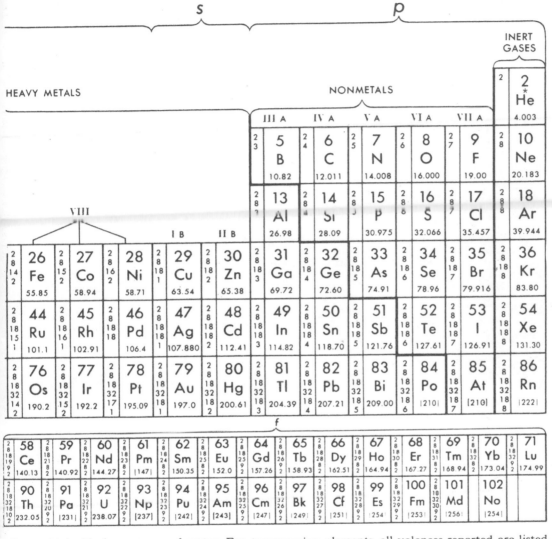

s   p

INERT GASES

HEAVY METALS

NONMETALS

| | | | | | III A | IV A | V A | VI A | VII A | 2 / 2* He / 4.003 |

| | | | | | 2 3 / 5 B / 10.82 | 2 4 / 6 C / 12.011 | 2 5 / 7 N / 14.008 | 2 6 / 8 O / 16.000 | 2 7 / 9 F / 19.00 | 2 8 / 10 Ne / 20.183 |

| | | | | | 2 8 3 / 13 Al / 26.98 | 2 8 / 14 Si / 28.09 | 2 8 / 15 P / 30.975 | 2 8 6 / 16 S / 32.066 | 2 8 7 / 17 Cl / 35.457 | 2 8 8 / 18 Ar / 39.944 |

VIII

I B   II B

| 2 8 14 2 / 26 Fe / 55.85 | 2 8 15 2 / 27 Co / 58.94 | 2 8 16 2 / 28 Ni / 58.71 | 2 8 18 1 / 29 Cu / 63.54 | 2 8 18 2 / 30 Zn / 65.38 | 2 8 18 3 / 31 Ga / 69.72 | 2 8 18 4 / 32 Ge / 72.60 | 2 8 18 5 / 33 As / 74.91 | 2 8 18 6 / 34 Se / 78.96 | 2 8 18 7 / 35 Br / 79.916 | 2 8 18 8 / 36 Kr / 83.80 |

| 2 8 18 15 1 / 44 Ru / 101.1 | 2 8 18 16 1 / 45 Rh / 102.91 | 2 8 18 18 / 46 Pd / 106.4 | 2 8 18 18 1 / 47 Ag / 107.880 | 2 8 18 18 2 / 48 Cd / 112.41 | 2 8 18 18 3 / 49 In / 114.82 | 2 8 18 18 4 / 50 Sn / 118.70 | 2 8 18 18 5 / 51 Sb / 121.76 | 2 8 18 18 6 / 52 Te / 127.61 | 2 8 18 18 7 / 53 I / 126.91 | 2 8 18 18 8 / 54 Xe / 131.30 |

| 2 8 18 32 14 2 / 76 Os / 190.2 | 2 8 18 32 15 2 / 77 Ir / 192.2 | 2 8 18 32 17 1 / 78 Pt / 195.09 | 2 8 18 32 18 1 / 79 Au / 197.0 | 2 8 18 32 18 2 / 80 Hg / 200.61 | 2 8 18 32 18 3 / 81 Tl / 204.39 | 2 8 18 32 18 4 / 82 Pb / 207.21 | 2 8 18 32 18 5 / 83 Bi / 209.00 | 2 8 18 32 18 6 / 84 Po / [210] | 2 8 18 32 18 7 / 85 At / [210] | 2 8 18 32 18 8 / 86 Rn / [222] |

f

| 2 8 18 19 8 2 / 58 Ce / 140.13 | 2 8 18 21 8 2 / 59 Pr / 140.92 | 2 8 18 22 8 2 / 60 Nd / 144.27 | 2 8 18 23 8 2 / 61 Pm / [147] | 2 8 18 24 8 2 / 62 Sm / 150.35 | 2 8 18 25 8 2 / 63 Eu / 152.0 | 2 8 18 25 9 2 / 64 Gd / 157.26 | 2 8 18 26 9 2 / 65 Tb / 158.93 | 2 8 18 28 8 2 / 66 Dy / 162.51 | 2 8 18 29 8 2 / 67 Ho / 164.94 | 2 8 18 30 8 2 / 68 Er / 167.27 | 2 8 18 31 8 2 / 69 Tm / 168.94 | 2 8 18 32 8 2 / 70 Yb / 173.04 | 2 8 18 32 9 2 / 71 Lu / 174.99 |

| 2 8 18 18 18 2 / 90 Th / 232.05 | 2 8 18 20 20 2 / 91 Pa / [231] | 2 8 18 32 21 2 / 92 U / 238.07 | 2 8 18 32 22 2 / 93 Np / [237] | 2 8 18 32 23 2 / 94 Pu / [242] | 2 8 18 32 24 2 / 95 Am / [243] | 2 8 18 32 25 2 / 96 Cm / [247] | 2 8 18 32 26 2 / 97 Bk / [249] | 2 8 18 32 27 2 / 98 Cf / [251] | 2 8 18 32 28 2 / 99 Es / [254] | 2 8 18 32 29 2 / 100 Fm / [253] | 2 8 18 32 30 2 / 101 Md / [256] | 102 No / [254] | |

those obtainable in presence of water. For transuranian elements, all valences reported are listed.

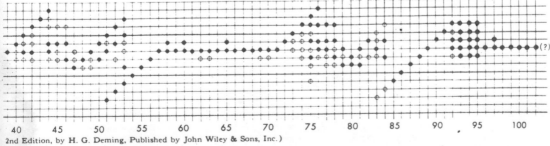

(?)

40   45   50   55   60   65   70   75   80   85   90   95   100

2nd Edition, by H. G. Deming, Published by John Wiley & Sons, Inc.)

TABLE OF ATOMIC WEIGHTS*   1961   (Based on Carbon-12)

	Symbol	Atomic No.	Atomic Weight		Symbol	Atomic No.	Atomic Weight
Actinium	Ac	89	(227)	Mercury	Hg	80	200.59
Aluminum	Al	13	26.9185	Molybdenum	Mo	42	95.94
Americium	Am	95	(243)	Neodymium	Nd	60	144.24
Antimony	Sb	51	121.75	Neon	Ne	10	20.183
Argon	Ar	18	39.948	Neptunium	Np	93	(237)
Arsenic	As	33	74.9216	Nickel	Ni	28	58.71
Astatine	At	85	(210)	Niobium	Nb	41	92.906
Barium	Ba	56	137.34	Nitrogen	N	7	14.0067
Berkelium	Bk	97	(249)	Nobelium	No	102	(254)
Beryllium	Be	4	9.0122	Osmium	Os	76	190.2
Bismuth	Bi	83	208.980	Oxygen	O	8	15.9994
Boron	B	5	10.811	Palladium	Pd	46	106.4
Bromine	Br	35	79.909	Phosphorus	P	15	30.9738
Cadmium	Cd	48	112.40	Platinum	Pt	78	195.09
Calcium	Ca	20	40.08	Plutonium	Pu	94	(242)
Californium	Cf	98	(251)	Polonium	Po	84	(210)
Carbon	C	6	12.01115	Potassium	K	19	39.102
Cerium	Ce	58	140.12	Praseodymium	Pr	59	140.907
Cesium	Cs	55	132.905	Promethium	Pm	61	(147)
Chlorine	Cl	17	35.453	Protactinium	Pa	91	(231)
Chromium	Cr	24	51.996	Radium	Ra	88	(226)
Cobalt	Co	27	58.9332	Radon	Rn	86	(222)
Copper	Cu	29	63.54	Rhenium	Re	75	186.2
Curium	Cm	96	(247)	Rhodium	Rh	45	102.905
Dysprosium	Dy	66	162.50	Rubidium	Rb	37	85.47
Einsteinium	Es	99	(254)	Ruthenium	Ru	44	101.07
Erbium	Er	68	167.26	Samarium	Sm	62	150.35
Europium	Eu	63	151.96	Scandium	Sc	21	44.956
Fermium	Fm	100	(253)	Selenium	Se	34	78.96
Fluorine	F	9	18.9984	Silicon	Si	14	28.086
Francium	Fr	87	(223)	Silver	Ag	47	107.870
Gadolinium	Gd	64	157.25	Sodium	Na	11	22.9898
Gallium	Ga	31	69.72	Strontium	Sr	38	87.62
Germanium	Ge	32	72.59	Sulfur	S	16	32.064
Gold	Au	79	196.967	Tantalum	Ta	73	180.948
Hafnium	Hf	72	178.49	Technetium	Tc	43	(99)
Helium	He	2	4.0026	Tellurium	Te	52	127.60
Holmium	Ho	67	164.930	Terbium	Tb	65	158.924
Hydrogen	H	1	1.00797	Thallium	Tl	81	204.37
Indium	In	49	114.82	Thorium	Th	90	232.038
Iodine	I	53	126.9044	Thulium	Tm	69	168.934
Iridium	Ir	77	192.2	Tin	Sn	50	118.69
Iron	Fe	26	55.847	Titanium	Ti	22	47.90
Krypton	Kr	36	83.80	Tungsten	W	74	183.85
Lanthanum	La	57	138.91	Uranium	U	92	238.03
Lead	Pb	82	207.19	Vanadium	V	23	50.942
Lithium	Li	3	6.939	Xenon	Xe	54	131.30
Lutetium	Lu	71	174.97	Ytterbium	Yb	70	173.04
Magnesium	Mg	12	24.312	Yttrium	Y	39	88.905
Manganese	Mn	25	54.9380	Zinc	Zn	30	65.37
Mendelevium	Md	101	(256)	Zirconium	Zr	40	91.22

This new table of atomic weights based on Carbon-12 replaces the former chemists' standard based on natural oxygen because of the needs of the atomic physicists. Natural oxygen is made of O^{16} with small proportions of O^{17} and O^{18}, proportions which are not constant but depend upon whether the sample comes from the atmosphere, the ocean or the earth's crust. The exact number 12 is taken as the relative nuclidic (atomic) mass of the isotope C^{12}. Natural carbon is made up of C^{12}, about 1% of C^{13} and sometimes a trace of C^{14}.

Most radioactive elements, regardless of origin, do not have fixed isotopic compositions. The approximate atomic weights of these elements are listed in parenthesis; they are *not* a part of the official table. Abstracted from the *Chemical and Engineering News*, November 20, 1961.

*Courtesy of the International Union of Pure and Applied Chemistry and Butterworth Scientific Publications.

PHYSICAL SCIENCE

A Study of Matter and Energy

VERNE H. BOOTH

Brooklyn College, Brooklyn, New York

THE MACMILLAN COMPANY
Macmillan New York, London
A Division of The Crowell-Collier Publishing Company

to my wife and daughter

. . . for the neglect that they
tolerated during the period of
writing . . .

© Verne H. Booth, 1962

First Printing

Library of Congress catalog card number: 62-7271

The Macmillan Company, New York
Brett-Macmillan Ltd., Galt, Ontario

Printed in the United States of America

PREFACE

Every college student today completes at least a year's training in science; if he is liberally educated, he will have undertaken a minimum of a year's training in physical, and a half-year in biological, science, in which basic principles are of primary concern, descriptive material secondary. In other words, the courses should be *in* science, not merely *about* science. A course in general physical science, designed to include some astronomy, physics, chemistry, and geology, should be thoroughly integrated and so have little regard for the boundaries between the component sciences, boundaries often hazy and commonly artificial. This textbook attempts to provide such a course in physical science for nonscience majors.

Today the selection of major topics to be included in the better textbooks in physical science has been reasonably well standardized. The order of treatment, however, will probably be endlessly argued, for there is no arrangement that will result in a consistent sequence throughout; any order will be artificial in some respects. On the other hand, some continuity must be attempted, and we cannot but strive to present one that will achieve the highest possible degree of integration. Each part—and here there are eight of them—leads to the next in one fashion or another, and each chapter, to the next. The degree of integration necessarily varies due to inherent unevenness among the parts. Nevertheless, without integration a course of this sort becomes atomized into a number of seemingly isolated topics, and hence proves merely confusing to the nonscience student.

We have therefore been mindful of the perplexing problem of integration, striving always to make visible to the student the continuous thread that holds the course together, gossamer though it may often be. How perplexing this can be at times may be illustrated by a few examples. Wave motion is a method of transferring energy from one place to another, and so it can be discussed along with energy. However, the methods of transferring energy—as well as mechanical waves themselves—are incidental at best in this course. They are presented chiefly as a preliminary introduction to light waves, a subject of primary importance in unraveling the structure of the atom. A similar problem is encountered with the structure of the nucleus. A seemingly logical place for a discussion of it follows presentation of Rutherford's nuclear theory, though before the Bohr theory. To do this means that one would have to go all the way to the modern hydrogen bomb before discussing fundamental chemical processes. Moreover, the return to the Bohr theory is then somewhat of an anticlimax. Once the Bohr theory and its modifications are introduced, good integration seems to demand that the electronic theory of chemical bonding and its role in explaining fundamental chemical processes follow in sequence. A third problem is that of integrating fundamental geologic processes into the course. There is no good way to do so, and most textbooks make no real attempt at it. The title of the present book, *Physical Science: A Study of Matter and Energy,* indicates a scope which necessitates discussion of how matter occurs here on earth. Such scope also seems to require an explanation of that energy and its transformations which we encounter at almost every turn in our daily lives. The common thread becomes tenuous here, but it can be followed.

Descriptive chemistry is given in one part and the electronic interpretation of chemical properties in another because a student needs the former before the section on the structure of the atom; indeed, the interpretation cannot be given until later if one of the prime objectives of the course is not to be nullified. If the two are given together, they interfere with each other. In this connection, the role of electronegativity in chemical bonding is strongly emphasized. The new atomic weight scale, based on C^{12}, is given in a textbook for the first time.

The importance of the periodic chart as a systematic list of all of the elemental kinds of matter cannot, of course, be overemphasized. The understanding of the basic reasons for this order and the relationship to it of the properties of the elements and the compounds they form is one of the crowning glories of science—and one of the prime objectives of this course. We have tried to present it in such a way.

The historical approach is used wherever there is, in the opinion of the author, a significant advantage to be gained. The history of the development of ideas, however, is never substituted for the ideas themselves, nor is it so interwoven with them that the latter become lost. The attitudes and methods of scientists, the mental climate of the times in which they worked, and the reasons for their successes or failures are considered in appropriate detail wherever appropriate.

Another primary objective has been that of clarity. Many of the concepts of science are difficult regardless of how they are explained; however, the author contends that most can be successfully presented at the level of the nonscience major. The language used here is at the student's level insofar as possible. Frequently, and wherever feasible, simple analogies and references within the student's experience are employed in an effort to simplify the subject matter. For the most part, the explanations of the diagrams are included in the captions, rather than hidden in the body of the text, in the hope that students will therefore make better use of the diagrams.

No mathematics beyond elementary algebra is presupposed. Even the development of the original Bohr theory requires no more than elementary algebra. The material on mathematics is placed in the body of the text as a separate chapter after that on Galileo's study of motion, rather than in an appendix, material in the latter tending to be lost insofar as the student is concerned. It follows consideration of Galileo rather than preceding, because the author believes the student must see a need for applying mathematics before he will apply himself to it. Similarly, a chapter on theories, hypotheses, and laws has been included only after two major theories have been presented. To discuss the former beforehand is to do so in a vacuum, the students having no background to orient them for understanding.

This text is the outcome of twelve years of planning and teaching a course in integrated physical science at Brooklyn College to nonscience majors, mostly under the direction of Bernhard Kurrelmeyer. Much of the material was used in mimeographed form before the final writing. The author is indebted to many friends and colleagues for help and advice. In particular, he is obliged to Professor Vincent Dillon of the Physics Department for detailed, constructive criticism of the first thirty and the last four chapters, and to Dr. Lewis Bodi of the Chemistry Department for doing the same with the chapters on chemistry. Mr. Mortimer L. Bloom of the Art Department made the drawings on the astronomy of the solar system, as well as a few in other areas. Mr. Richard S. Cappel, formerly with the City Planning Commission, prepared the remainder. For the final typing, the author is indebted to a neighbor, Mrs. Helen Lainen, and for an excellent job of proofreading, to Mrs. Lainen and to her husband, Arvo. To Dean Walter Mais goes very real gratitude for a critically helpful lightening of the teaching load during the final year of writing. Finally, the author is indebted to his copy editor, Miss Evelyn Cohn, not only for the excellent editing job she did, but for the making of many suggestions that improved the book.

VERNE H. BOOTH

CONTENTS

II. Force and Motion, 73

IV. The Electrical Nature of Matter, 267

V. The Structure of Matter, 317

VI. Atomic Structure and Chemical Combination, 457

VII. Matter and Energy in the Study of the Earth, 551

VIII. The Energy within Atomic Nuclei, 643

THE SOLAR SYSTEM

A study of matter and energy logically begins with the solar system, for within it we find all of the various kinds known to man. There must be other solar systems in a universe that includes over a billion billion suns, many of them more massive than our own, but we know only one, our own. It is highly doubtful that man will ever know any other, but it is likely that our solar system is a representative one, and so a study of it seems called for as a first step in understanding our environment. This environment is to a very large degree fashioned by the sun, without whose light and heat this earth would be a desert beyond compare. It is no wonder that so many primitive peoples have worshiped the sun, and if the sun did not have an apparent motion about the earth, it is likely that they would have placed this light and heat giver at the center of the solar system.

Our ancestors of long ago turned their attention to the skies in their attempts to understand their environment. The things near at hand—the mountains, the oceans with the ceaseless motion of their waters, the rivers and their valleys, the forests, the flowers, the animal life about them—all are much too complex for simple analysis. Matter in the ultramacroscopic state, i.e., matter in chunks the size of the sun, the planets, and the moon, is easier to analyze in some respects. Man could see one whole side of the moon all at once, whereas even from a mountain top he could see very little of the earth on which he lived. To learn the elemental facts of their own abode, these ancestors of ours turned to the heavens. It was there that they learned that basic tenet of all science—without which there could be no science—that there is law and order and simplicity in the universe. We will therefore attempt to follow in their footsteps.

CHAPTER I

Rise of the Ptolemaic System of the Universe

*Astronomy compels us to look upwards and leads us from this world to another.—*PLATO

EARLY MANKIND AND THE HEAVENS

Who was the first scientist? There is, of course, no answer to this question. It is probably more fruitful to ask, "What type of man gave the first scientific explanation to natural phenomena?" We cannot completely answer this question, either, but there can be little doubt that he was a man who was curious about his environment, and who attempted to explain his observations without reference to a supernatural being. We say this because supernatural explanations of *natural* phenomena can never be scientific.

The observations that suggested that our earth was a part of a solar system, part of a group of heavenly bodies set apart from the stars, was made several thousands of years ago. This differentiation between the true or "fixed" stars and the planets or "wandering stars" was probably made by shepherds guarding their flocks of sheep during the clear nights prevalent in the dry regions of the Middle East. They observed that most of the heavenly bodies maintained fixed positions with respect to each other but that a few wandered across the sky without regard to the fixed stars.[1] The sun and moon, of course, also appear to move without regard to the stars, but this was so obvious as not to cause comment. One of the wanderers was the planet earth, but several thousands of years were to elapse before man first became aware of this fact. The reasons for this long lapse of time were of two sorts.

THE ORDERLINESS IN NATURE

The first group of reasons was that man had not yet attained any concept of the basic orderliness in nature. Another way of saying this is that man had not yet arrived at the conclusion that a given set of causes is followed by a particular set of effects. In fact, many people have not yet arrived at such a conclusion; if they had, the sale of rabbits' feet, the hanging of horseshoes over doors to bring good luck, and the like, would long since have ceased.

Primitive man's first reaction to any natural phenomenon that was significantly different from the usual everyday events of his life, e.g., a violent thunderstorm, an earthquake or volcanic eruption, or an eclipse of the sun or moon, was that it was controlled by one or more angry gods who held his

[1] The separation of the sun's yearly apparent motion from its daily apparent motion across the sky is a sophisticated piece of scientific analysis that was accomplished only a few hundreds of years ago.

fate in the hollows of their hands. Moreover, primitive man always seems to have made the further assumption that these gods never acted in any orderly fashion, but always according to moods of anger or kindliness. Such attitudes could never lead to a belief that there was order in the universe because they began by assuming that such order did not exist.

It should be apparent that *every scientist must believe that the universe is one of law and order, and that man is capable of understanding this law and order*. There would be little point in making the many observations and the mathematical calculations necessary to plot the paths of the various planets as they revolve about the sun if these paths were not determined by natural laws rather than by some whimsical god who could change them at will.[2] Whether or not we realize it, all of us plan our lives to a large degree upon the assumption of this orderliness in nature; if we believe that the sun might not rise tomorrow morning or some succeeding morning unless some whimsical god decreed that it should, there would be little point in planning our days.

ISOLATION OF OUR SOLAR SYSTEM IN SPACE

The second group of reasons for the long delay in the recognition that the planet earth is part of a solar system is more in keeping with the ways of science. In part, the difficulty is that nothing in the universe is motionless. We make our observations from a moving observation post, so to speak, so all motion becomes relative. This is contrary to common sense, for we here on earth are aware of no such motion. In part, the second difficulty is our tremendous isolation in space, an isolation that is difficult even today for us to conceive, let alone perceive. The nearest "fixed" star to our sun (which is itself a star) is Alpha Centauri. It is so far away that it takes light traveling at 186,000 mi/sec a bit over 4 years to reach us. Put into more understandable terms, it would take a space ship, traveling at a speed of 25,000 mi/hr [3] the entire distance, about 130,000 years to reach Alpha Centauri. Even at a speed of 1,000,000 mi/hr, and assuming that this is an average speed for the whole distance, it would take nearly 3000 years. To reach Polaris, the North Star, would take eight times that long. The distances between individual stars in our galaxy are, for the most part, of this general order of magnitude.

EARLY MAN'S USE OF THE HEAVENLY BODIES AS TIMEPIECES

Among all of the early peoples—Egyptians, Babylonians, Chinese, and Hindus—astronomy seems to have been the first of the fields of scientific knowledge to develop. Apparently man discovered that he could use the various heavenly bodies as guides while traveling, and that he could tell time by the positions of certain stars or groups of stars (constellations) at night.

---

[2] It should be apparent that a belief in the orderliness in nature, i.e., a belief that a particular cause is followed by a particular effect, need not in any way detract from a belief in a Supreme Being.

[3] This is the *minimum* speed a rocket ship must have to escape from the earth. Its initial velocity would be continuously reduced by the earth's gravitational pull so that the actual time to reach Alpha Centauri would be several times that indicated.

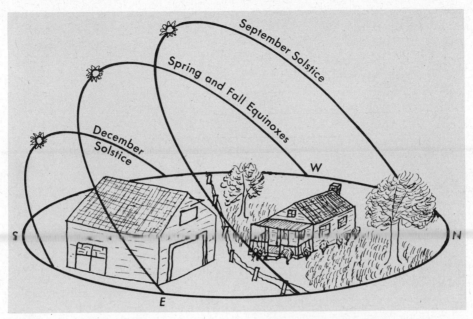

Fig. 1-1. Points of Sunrise and Sunset at Different Seasons in Northern Hemisphere. Note that the sun rises directly in the east and sets directly in the west only at the time of the equinoxes.

The appearance and disappearance of these constellations was observed to take place at regular intervals; they therefore provided a calendar to indicate the seasons.

The place of sunrise on the eastern horizon (Fig. 1-1), farthest north in summer, farthest south in winter, was also useful in indicating the seasons. The length of the *noonday* shadow of a vertical rod (Fig. 1-2) could also be used as a calendar, for the higher the sun in the sky, the shorter the shadow. The direction of the shadow of a vertical rod provided a crude clock, with the noon hour always correct. Eventually someone tilted the rod so that it was parallel to the axis of the earth, creating a true sundial with the hours correct at all times.

A calendar to indicate the seasons was of the utmost importance among peoples who lived by agriculture in regions where crops had to be planted at certain times of the year, particularly in regions where the seasons are alternately wet and dry and with the wet season much the shortest.

As early as 4700 B.C. the Babylonians had developed a 12-month calendar with 30 days to the month. To keep this calendar from getting too far out of step with the stars, they inserted an extra month every few years. It was they who initiated the 7-day week. By 4200 B.C. the Egyptians had also developed a 12-month calendar, each month with 30 days, with five feast days each year. This calendar was far better than that of the Babylonians, but it, too, eventually got out of step with the stars.

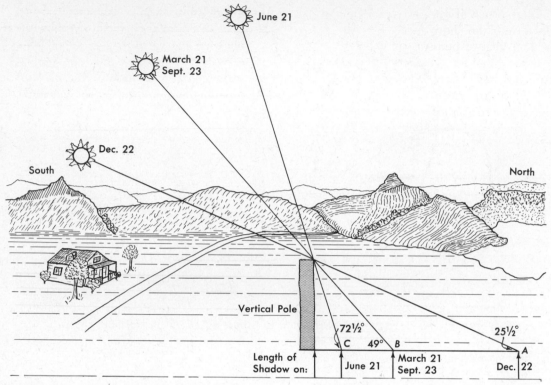

Fig. 1-2. Length of Shadow at Noon at 41° N lat. (New York City). Note that the angle of the sun's rays can act as a calendar. It takes six months for the end of the shadow to migrate either from A to C or from C to A.

RISE OF ASTROLOGY

Still another reason for man's early interest in astronomy was that the belief had arisen that the stars and the planets could be used to foretell the future, a belief that is still held by many ignorant people, some of whom are intelligent. Primitive man, in contrast with modern man, should not be criticized for such beliefs, for the sun gives light and heat during the day, the moon gives useful light at night, and the stars provide directions at night. The simple mind might reason that they could confer other benefits. The dog star, Sirius, rose at dawn in Egypt at the time of the Nile floods; the belief that Sirius caused the floods was perhaps inevitable, considering the propensity of people even today to assign wrong causes to events just because they happen in a given sequence.

SCIENCE OF THE ANCIENT GREEKS

The Greeks were the first to make real advances in science. The reason appears to have been grounded in the fact that their religion was not based on fear, as were the religions of most of the other peoples of the time. They could inquire into the natural order of the universe, they could delve into the "how" and "why" of things without fear of punishment by angry gods. Science liberates man from the terror of the gods, said Lucretius (*ca.* 60 B.C.).

1. Thales (*ca.* 580 B.C.) was the first of the ancient Greek philosophers. Some authorities have stated that he was the first scientist of record because his school was the first to break away from mythological traditions and assume that the universe is natural, and is potentially explainable by man.[4]

2. Anaximander (*ca.* 550 B.C.) was the first man of record to note that the heavens (in the northern hemisphere) appear to revolve about Polaris (Fig. 1-3). The simplest explanation of this observation is that the stars are lights embedded in a great overturned spinning bowl, i.e., half of a great sphere, with the earth motionless at the center. You would undoubtedly believe the same if you watched the sky for many nights—and had not been indoctrinated to believe otherwise. If you were a genius, you might even extend this bowl to a complete sphere, the other half of which could be viewed from a point directly opposite you on the other side of the earth.

3. Pythagoras (*ca.* 525 B.C.), better known as a mathematician, believed all matter to be composed of four elements—earth, water, fire, and air—rather than one. This concept may be naive but it certainly is not silly. For example, burn a piece of green wood. The fire coming from it can be seen, with the smoke vanishing into the air. The water it contains can be seen on the ends of the stick where it boils off and

also vanishes into the air. The final residue, the ashes, are similar to earth. Pythagorus also believed the earth to be a sphere that moved in a circle (like a stone on the end of a string). The rotation of the heavens was explained, apparently for the first time,

Fig. 1-3. Star Trails about a Point near Polaris. The curved trail near the center was made by Polaris. Exposure time was about two hours. The motion producing the trails is not that of the stars but of the camera which is anchored to a rotating earth. No stars appear to rise or set. Compare with Fig. 1-9.

by a moving earth rather than by a revolving sky. His followers thought that the lengths of the radii of the planets were proportional to the lengths of the successive strings on a stringed instrument. This gave rise to the expression "music of the spheres."

Plato (*ca.* 400 B.C.) conceived the sphere to be the most perfect of forms and therefore concluded that the universe was a perfect sphere. It followed that the circle must be the most perfect two-dimen-

---

[4] Thales is also thought to have originated the science of geometry (later developed and expanded by Euclid). He is also said to have predicted an eclipse.

sional figure, and that all moving celestial bodies must move in perfectly circular paths. Adherence to this purely esthetic concept was to cause untold trouble to Kepler nearly two thousand years later. Plato thought experimentation a base mechanical art and so condemned it. He thought it folly to try to figure out the paths of the planets by observation. By Plato's time enough observations of the apparent [5] motions of the sun, moon, planets, and stars had been made to reveal that they were highly complex, that there were certain apparent irregularities in the motions of the planets. Plato formulated the problem by saying, "Determine what uniform and ordered motions must be assumed for each of the planets to account for their apparent irregular movements." Note that he would account for apparent irregular movements by assuming certain uniform ordered motions. Plato believed this should be done primarily by speculation, with observation occupying a secondary role.

Eudoxus, a pupil of Plato's, followed his teacher's advice, and in doing so he rejected the moving-earth hypothesis of Pythagoras, and returned to the concept of an earth-centered universe. He postulated a series of transparent domes or spheres, one inside the other. The outermost dome carried the fixed stars embedded in them. Five of the inner domes had a planet embedded in each. The sun and the moon were each embedded in their own domes. He could not have all of these seven domes revolving on the same axis because the bodies embedded in them neither rose nor set at the same time nor in any ordered sequence.

[5] Apparent—what the motions seem to be, as opposed to their actual motions.

Consequently, he had to have different axes for each, and each at its own angle of inclination to the axis of the dome or sphere containing the fixed stars. All of these spheres revolved at the proper speeds to duplicate the observed motions of the planets, sun, moon, and stars. Eudoxus found he needed a total of 26 motions to make this duplication.

His theory was the first attempt to account for the apparently irregular movements of the planets. It was a good one considering the state of knowledge of the time. It had a comparatively few basic assumptions, which allowed him to derive a model that fitted the known facts reasonably well. It was a fruitful theory, for it allowed predictions to be made as to the approximate positions of the stars and planets at any particular time.

But you might ask, "Is it true?" If you had asked that of the Greeks, they would have wondered what you meant by "true." But if you had offered them a simpler and more fruitful theory, they would have welcomed it. The theory of Eudoxus was good, but not too good, for discrepancies soon appeared in it. Among other things, his model could not explain why the planets appeared to reverse their normal directions every so often, making an *apparent* backward loop before proceeding on their normal paths across the sky. This phenomenon is spoken of as retrograde motion; it is, of course, apparent, not real. (See Fig. 2-7.)

By Aristotle's time more and better observations of the planets had been made, increasing the amount and number of the discrepancies. Aristotle (384–322 B.C.) had to increase the number of apparent motions from the 26 of Eudoxus to 55. This was done without destroying the model, but it certainly greatly increased its com-plexity. Aristotle knew of one easily ob-served objection to the original model of Eudoxus as well as to his revised model. This was that the planets at some times seemed nearer the earth than at others. The fact that his model did not account for this did not bother Aristotle, because to him (and to most of the Greek scientists), observation was not the final test of a theory. To him a theory had not only to describe and predict observations, it also had to show that these observations were in accord with the assumptions of his whole philosophical system, a system that could not be given up just because a few observations contradicted it. In other words, he confused philosophic truth with scientific truth. Many people still do the same today, although no modern scientist does; to him, facts are the supreme arbiters of the value of a scientific theory.

Aristarchus (*ca.* 250 B.C.) came closer to the modern concept about our solar system than did any other Greek. He considered the earth moved about a fixed sun. Thus his was a truly heliocentric hypothesis. He thought the stars immensely far away because he could observe no parallax (Fig. 1-4),[6] i.e., the relative positions of the stars with respect to one another did not change as the earth revolved in its orbit about the sun (Fig. 1-5). He also calcu-lated that the diameter of the sun was about seven times that of the moon (a fig-ure we now know to be much too small) even though they appear to be about the same size. This was a remarkable con-

clusion considering the time. In fact, the views of Aristarchus were too advanced for his time. The pressure of common sense [7] combined with the fact that others of greater reputation held to an earth-centered universe prevented him from gaining many converts to his revolutionary ideas.

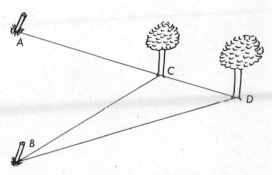

Fig. 1-4. Parallax. Formally defined, parallax is the *apparent* displacement of objects due to shift of position of the ob-server. Viewed from A, C and D are in a straight line; viewed from B, D appears to have shifted its position relative to C.

Eratosthenes (*ca.* 200 B.C.) calculated the circumference of the earth and came up with a figure of about 25,000 mi. His method is shown in Fig. 1-6. It is essen-tially the method in use today.[8]

Hipparchus (*ca.* 150 B.C.) was another great physical geographer. He rejected the

[6] As an observer moves about, the relative posi-tions of distant objects seem to change. This ap-parent change of position of distant objects, due to the actual change of the position of the observer, is known as parallax.

[7] See p. 15 for a discussion of common sense applied to this problem.

[8] Eratosthenes wrote that a man sailing west far enough would come to India (reached at that time by going east). This statement eventually led Co-lumbus to test the truth of it. From the similarity of tides in the Indian and Atlantic oceans Eratos-thenes reasoned that the two oceans should be con-nected around the southern tip of Africa. He was the first great physical geographer.

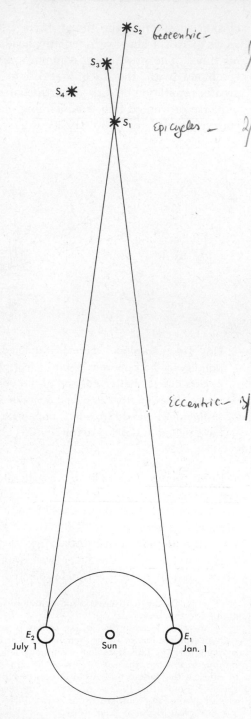

S₂ Geocentric —

S₃

S₄

S₁ Epicycles —

Eccentric —

E₂
July 1

Sun

E₁
Jan. 1

heliocentric hypothesis of the solar system because he could observe no parallax. He accepted the geocentric model of Eudoxus and Aristotle, which he altered so as to bring it into line with the latest observations of the movements of the planets. He invented the concept of epicycles (Fig. 1-7) to explain the apparent reversal of motion of the planets (retrograde motion) against the background of fixed stars [9] (see p. 26). The number of epicycles traversed by a planet depended upon its period, i.e., its time of revolution about the earth. Jupiter, with a period equal to nearly 12 of our years appears to retrograde 12 times per revolution, i.e., it had 12 epicycles. Saturn with a period equal to 30 of our years had 30 epicycles.

The use of epicycles destroyed the scheme in which all celestial spheres were concentric to the earth, but at least the deferents (Fig. 1-7) were, so not too much violence was done to the concept. However, the use of epicycles was not successful in explaining the variable distance of a planet from the earth, simply because there was no relation between the supposed position in the epicycle and the nearness or far-

[9] Hipparchus also calculated the distance to the moon as 33⅔ times the diameter of the earth. The actual figure is 30.2. He also originated latitude and longitude as a means of determining location on a spherical earth.

Fig. 1-5. Stellar Parallax. When the earth is at E_1 in its orbit, S_1 and S_3 appear to be in line. Six months later when the earth is at E_2, S_1 appears to be in line with S_2, i.e., the position of S_1 appears to have shifted with respect to the more distant stars. The angular scale is enormously exaggerated.

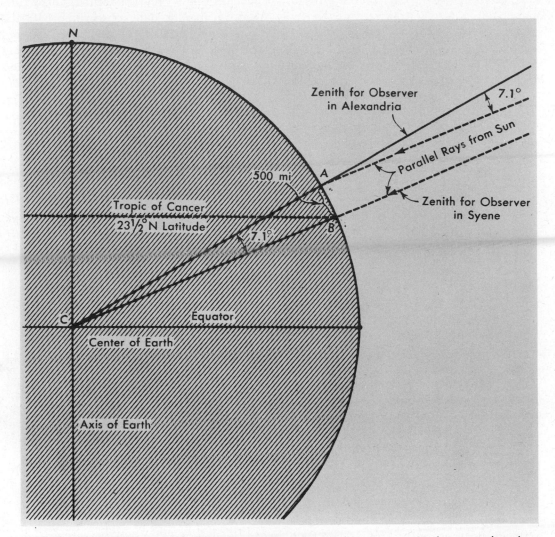

Fig. 1-6. Eratosthenes Measures Circumference of Earth. On June 21 the sun is directly overhead at noon at B. At the same moment a vertical rod at A, 500 mi to the north, makes an angle (A) of 7.1° with the sun's rays. The angle at A equals the angle at C. AB is a measured distance. The circumference is given by

$$500 \text{ mi} \times \frac{360}{7.1} = 25,300 \text{ mi.}$$

ness of the planet from the earth. Hipparchus therefore introduced the concept of the eccentric. This placed the earth somewhat off the center of revolution (Fig. 1-8). This did great violence to the concept that the earth was at the exact center

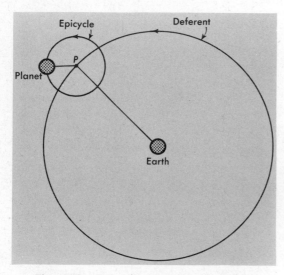

Fig. 1-7. Epicyclic Motion. The planet was supposed to revolve about a point *P* as a center, as *P* revolved about the earth. The supposed circle about *P* is the epicycle, and the circle described by *P* is the deferent.

of the universe but it was necessary to bring theory into accord with observations.

By use of these ideas Hipparchus could prepare planetary tables from which the positions of the sun, moon, and planets could be predicted for any time with a considerable degree of accuracy. Furthermore, solar and lunar eclipses could be predicted. This revised hypothesis seemed a good one, and certainly explained the observations of the time—which, after all, is the real test of a theory. At any rate,

his hypothesis, revised from time to time to keep it up-to-date, i.e., in line with the known observations of the time, endured for over sixteen hundred years. During these centuries it successfully interpreted the known phenomena of the solar system, and guided the labors of countless astronomers up to and beyond the time of Copernicus (*ca.* A.D. 1500).

PTOLEMY'S SYNTHESIS

Yet this hypothesis is not named in honor of Hipparchus, as it might well have been.

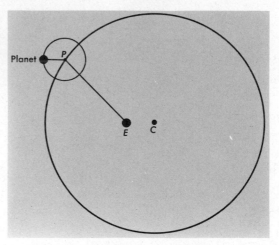

Fig. 1-8. The Eccentric. *E* is the earth, *C* the center of the deferent. This concept was devised to explain the varying distances of the planets from the earth.

Instead it is known as the Ptolemaic hypothesis in honor of Claudius Ptolemy, the last of the great Greek astronomers. He lived about A.D. 140 in Alexandria, then the intellectual center of the world. He collected the works of Hipparchus, added the more recent data and his own observa-

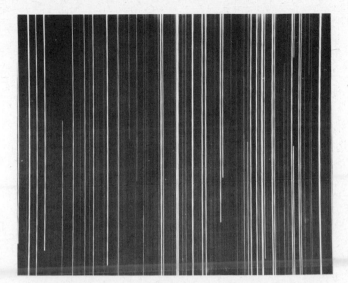

Fig. 1-9. Star Trails Viewed from the Equator. All stars appear to rise and set. Compare with Fig. 1-3.

tions, to formulate a really good theory.[10]

Ptolemy still retained the concept that considered the sun, moon, and the five planets that are visible to the naked eye as embedded like gems in separate crystal spheres, all concentric with the central stationary earth, and each rotating on a north–south axis inside a larger celestial sphere, which carried the stars. The spheres containing the sun and the stars were assumed

[10] He added only one concept that was really new. This was the concept of the equant, designed to reconcile the planetary movements with the hypothesis of uniform velocity about the earth. The concept is somewhat involved, and we will not explain it here. It is enough to say that new observations had indicated that the planets did not move with uniform speed in their supposedly circular orbits, and that the concept of the equant allowed their deferents to move with uniform velocity with respect to one point and with circular motion with respect to another. Thus, in some fashion the Platonian concept of uniform circular motion of the planets and the stars was retained. It was still unthinkable that celestial bodies could have any other type of motion. This is an excellent example of what a preconceived notion, alien in origin to the problem concerned, can do to the thinking of even learned men.

to rotate at slightly different speeds on their axes once every day to account for their rising and setting. Polaris was considered to be located very near to the north end of the axis of the crystal sphere containing the stars, so that all of the other stars revolved about it. Those stars close to Polaris revolve in small circles (Fig. 1-3), those farther away in larger circles. To an observer in the middle latitudes those stars close to Polaris would not rise and set, while those farther away would. To the observer at the equator all stars would rise and set (Figs. 1-9 and 1-10).

The sun created a set of difficult problems of its own. For one thing, it does not rise and set in the same place on any two successive days. It rises directly in the east, as viewed from the latitude of Greece, only two days a year (on the equinoxes) (Fig. 1-1). At the time of the June solstice it rises 23½° north of east and at the time of the December solstice 23½° south of east. For another thing, its time of rising or setting is not synchronized with the rising

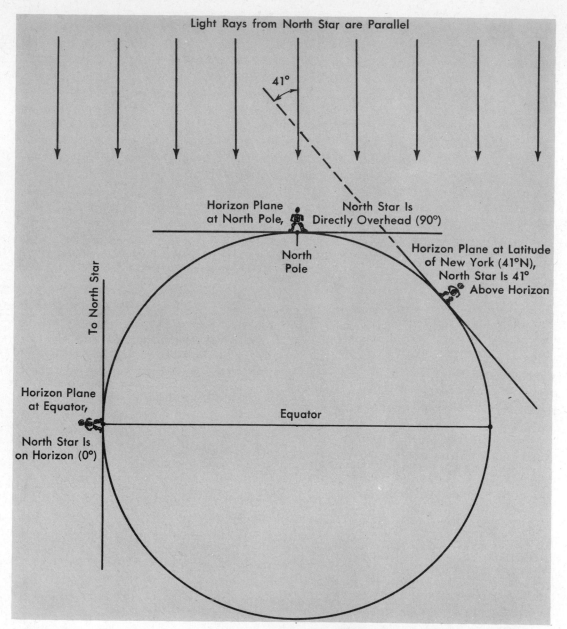

Light Rays from North Star are Parallel

41°

Horizon Plane at North Pole,   North Star Is Directly Overhead (90°)

North Pole

Horizon Plane at Latitude of New York (41°N), North Star Is 41° Above Horizon

To North Star

Horizon Plane at Equator,

North Star Is on Horizon (0°)

Equator

Fig. 1-10. Altitude of Polaris above Horizon Plane at North Pole, New York City, and the Equator. The observer at any point on the earth's surface sees all stars above *his* horizon plane. The altitude of Polaris above the horizon gives the latitude for any place in the northern hemisphere. (Why not in the southern?) The observer at the pole sees no stars rise or set, one at the equator sees all stars rise and set. (What about the observer at New York City?)

and setting of the stars. Thus, the rate of turning of its crystal sphere on its axis had to be slower than that of the crystal sphere containing the stars, so that the *apparent eastward drift* of the sun among the stars could be accounted for (see Fig. 2-9). This eastward drift is such that Ptolemy's crystal sphere containing the stars had to gain one complete revolution on the sun in exactly one year. The moon also presents its problems, for it similarly loses about fifty minutes a day to the sun. Its crystal sphere had to turn at such a speed that it lost one revolution to that of the sun every 29-and-a-fraction days.

These and other deviations of all of the bodies concerned made it necessary for Ptolemy to adjust the axes of the various celestial bodies, their directions of motion, their rates of rotation, the radii of their orbits, the number and sizes of the epicycles, eccentrics, equants, and various combinations of them, to bring them into harmony with the best observations of his time.[11] This he did by a straight trial-and-error method. The whole scheme called for more than seventy different simultaneous motions. He published the whole of his information and data, along with a set of planetary tables, in a single volume, an encyclopedia of astronomy called *The Almagest.* This remained the standard treatise to the time of Copernicus and beyond. The planetary tables enabled predictions of solar, lunar, and planetary positions that were better than those of Hipparchus. These tables were particu-

larly useful in navigation. Similar tables are used even today.

It is worth noting that in *The Almagest* Ptolemy stated a fundamental principle of science (not original with him) that holds to this day: *In explaining phenomena, it is best to adopt the simplest hypothesis that will coordinate all of the known observations.*

Let us examine the Ptolemaic geocentric hypothesis (Fig. 1-11) in terms of this principle. Doing so will also help us understand how an hypothesis can be so completely wrong and yet win acceptance by those most expert in the field for so long, if it is in accord with the observations of the time. We must always bear in mind when evaluating the accomplishments of the past the necessity of doing so in the light of what was known at the time rather than in light of what we now know.

Ptolemy's system prevailed for fifteen hundred years because:

1. It described the observed paths accurately enough considering the methods of observation in use.
2. It predicted the future paths with a reasonable degree of success.
3. It explained the lack of parallax.
4. It coincided fairly well with the philosophical ideas of celestial bodies.
5. It had common-sense appeal.

COMMON SENSE vs. "UNCOMMON" SENSE

Let us consider the problem of common-sense appeal. Ask yourself the question, "Why do I believe that the earth revolves about the sun?" There is only one answer —because you have been taught so from childhood. Could you have reached the correct answer by your own observations?

[11] That better data was obtained as time passed despite the lack of better instruments is not surprising if we remember that it takes Jupiter 12 years to complete one revolution and Saturn 30 years. Thus, during his lifetime a man could take scarcely more than one complete set of observations of Saturn.

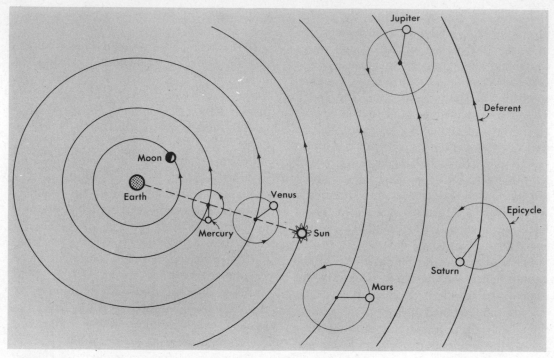

Fig. 1-11. Ptolemaic System of the Universe. The dome of the stars lies outside of Saturn. An epicycle and a deferent is associated with each planet.

You see the sun appear to rise in the east, move across the sky and appear to set in the west.[12] If you believe the evidence of your own eyes, you would think that this apparent motion was the real motion. If anyone questioned this observation you would say that your common sense tells you that the sun moves around the earth, and defy anyone to tell you differently. You would be doubly convinced that you were right because you could detect no motion of the earth.[13] You would probably

[12] The terms sunrise and sunset are holdovers from the days of widespread belief in the geocentric theory. They imply a stationary earth. In fact, the whole terminology that we use to describe movements not only in our solar system but also in the whole universe is based on a stationary earth. This is because no terminology has been developed to describe the actual movements. In fact, no simple terminology can ever be developed to describe them, for nothing is stationary in the whole universe; all movements are relative and highly complex. Their apparent movements are comparatively simple, and so we use an "apparent" terminology. No harm is done so long as we remember that it is apparent motion, not real motion, that we are talking about.

[13] Actually if you live on or near the 40th parallel, you are moving at a speed of about 600 mi/hr due to the rotation of the earth on its axis. You are also moving at a speed of about 66,000 mi/hr due to the revolution of the earth about the sun. Also, the whole solar system is moving through space at a speed of about 1,000,000 mi/hr. Despite this latter speed, there is practically no danger of a collision with some other stellar body, first, because this solar system of ours is tremendously isolated in space, and second, because all the

wonder why, if the earth traveled so fast through space, that there were no strong winds blowing in the opposite direction, and why birds were not left behind in their flights. The answer is, of course, that our atmosphere moves with the earth. In this respect, it is just as much an integral part of the earth as the soil and rocks. If you watched the sky all night, you would note that the stars near the North Star would appear to revolve about it (Fig. 1-3) and those farthest from it would appear to rise and set once a day. If you did not know that these apparent motions were due to the earth's rotation, you, too, would believe that the earth was stationary at the center of the universe, a universe that had been created especially for the benefit of man.

You might also believe that the surface of the earth was flat, particularly if you lived in a plains country. The Greeks, however, believed the earth to be spherical. There were several reasons. Plato had conceived the sphere to be the most perfect of all objects, and the sun and the moon, as we see them, appear to be cross sections of spheres. It was therefore natural for them to think the earth spherical, too. They had some concrete evidence also. Ptolemy made a list of them in *The Almagest*, about A.D. 150. It is instructive to quote directly from him:

We are best led to the concept that the earth is sensibly of spherical form by the following considerations. We observe that the sun, the moon, and the other heavenly bodies do not rise and set at the same time for all inhabitants of the earth, but rather first for those to the east and later for those to the west. For we find that the phenomena of the eclipses, particularly those of the moon, which always occur at the same absolute time for all people, are not, for all that, seen at the same hour relative to noon; that is, at an hour equally distant from the middle of the day; but that, in every case, the times are later for eastern observers and earlier for those further to the west. Now since the differences between the times when one observer and another see these eclipses is proportional to the [east–west] distances between their respective locations, one can conclude that the surface of the earth is certainly spherical, and that the uniformity of its curvature extends to the whole; it results that each of its parts makes an obstacle to the following parts and limits the view in a similar manner for all. This would not happen if the earth had any other shape as can be seen from the following reasoning.

If the terrestrial surface were concave the inhabitants of the western part would be the first to see the heavenly bodies rise; if it were a plane, all its inhabitants would see them rise and set together; if it were composed of triangles, quadrilaterals or polygons of any shape, all of the inhabitants of the same plane face would see the phenomena at the same time; things which are not observed to occur. It is also evident that the earth is not a cylinder whose surface views the rising and setting and whose bases face the poles of the sky, an assumption which one might judge more probable; for if such were the case, there would be no stars which are always visible, but on the contrary, some stars would rise and set for everyone on the earth, and certain stars up to an equal distance from each pole would be invisible to everyone. However, the further we go towards the north, the more stars we discover which never set, and at the same time, southern stars disappear from view in the same proportion. Therefore, it is evident that here too, along the north–south direction, by an effect of the uniform curvature of the earth, each part forms an obstacle

---

other stellar bodies with which it might collide are also moving in the same general direction at comparable speeds.

to the adjacent parts due to the uniform curvature of the earth, which proves that the earth has in every direction a spherical curvature. Finally, on the sea, if at any point and in any direction, one travels towards mountains or other elevated places, one sees these objects as if coming out of the sea where they were apparently hidden by the curvature of the surface of the sea.[14]

SUMMARY

The science of astronomy was the first to develop because of the curiosity that simple observation of the night skies has always invoked in man. The division of the heavenly bodies into three groups, the fixed stars, the planets, and the sun and the moon was made long before written records were kept. The belief that the universe is one of law and order and the assumption that man is capable of understanding this law and order came much later and were not fully developed before the beginnings of Greek science.

Several thousands of years before the ancient Greeks, man had used the apparent movements of the planets and the stars to formulate calendars, much as we do today. The pseudoscience of astrology developed before astronomy as an outgrowth of the tendency of all primitive peoples to call on the supernatural for the explanation of natural phenomena.

The concept of the earth as one of the planets was considered by the Greeks, and rejected, partly because no parallax could be observed and partly because of the common-sense appeal of a stationary earth. The great isolation of the solar system in space was not suspected by them. Eudoxus (*ca.* 370 B.C.),

[14] Translated from the Greek and the French by T. A. Ashford and T. L. Page, used by permission of Holt, Rinehart and Winston, New York, 1946.

a pupil of Plato's, was the first to devise a model of the universe in an attempt to explain the apparent motions of the sun, moon, planets, and stars. This model was revised from time to time, first by Aristotle, then by Hipparchus (*ca.* 125 B.C.), and finally by Ptolemy (A.D. 140), the revisions being necessary to account for the more accurate observations. Most important were the revisions of Hipparchus, who, among other things, invented epicycles to account for the periodic apparent retrograde motions of the planets. Ptolemy, essentially a mathematician and a compiler of data, put the geocentric hypothesis in a form that was not much altered before being discarded some fifteen hundred years later.

Aristotle interwove his science with his philosophy, so that science was included in his philosophy. In any conflict between them, philosophic truth was given precedence over scientific truth.

The Greeks believed in a spherical earth for a number of reasons. Eratosthenes measured the circumference of the earth with a remarkable degree of accuracy for the time, using essentially modern methods. The Greeks also believed that all celestial bodies were spherical and that all moved with uniform speed in perfect circles. The latter was a conclusion based not on observation but on esthetic grounds.

EXERCISES

I. TERMS AND CONCEPTS

Planet	The four "elements"
"Fixed" star	
Crystal spheres	Retrograde motion
Apparent motion	Epicycle
	Deferent
Heliocentric	Parallax
Geocentric	*The Almagest*

II. PROBLEMS

1. Suggest a reason why astronomy, rather than physics, chemistry, biology, or geology was the first science.

2. How does a satellite differ from a planet? What is another name for a natural satellite?

✓ 3. In what major respect does a star differ from a planet or a satellite? p.3

4. How many celestial bodies aside from the fixed stars did the ancients recognize? Name them in order from their *supposed* distances from the earth.

✓ 5. Did the term fixed star mean to the Greeks that these stars did not move? Explain.

6. How do you know that the earth goes around the sun instead of the sun around the earth?

7. What is the distinction between apparent and real motion? Illustrate.

✓ 8. What is meant by parallax? q,

✓ 9. What is meant by apparent retrograde motion? p. 8

✓ 10. What are epicycles? Why were they invented? Are they apparent or real? 12

✓ 11. What is a deferent? Why were they considered necessary? 12

✓ 12. If you travel northward a distance of 70 mi the North Star appears 1° higher above the horizon. Assuming the earth to be approximately spherical; what is the length of its circumference?

13. Suppose that you are on the equator. You observe a certain star directly overhead.
  a. Where did it rise?
  b. Where will it set?
  c. In what part of the sky would you look to locate the North Star?
  d. Would you see any stars that did not rise or set?

14. Associate the following men with the statements, concepts, etc.

a. Hipparchus
b. Ptolemy
c. Eratosthenes
d. Thales
e. Aristotle
f. Plato
g. Eudoxus
h. Aristarchus

A. Originator of a heliocentric hypothesis.
B. Formulated the first geocentric model of the universe.
C. Advanced the concept of perfect circles for planetary motions.
D. Invented the epicycle.
E. Calculated the circumference of the earth.
F. First of the Greeks to break away from mythological explanations of natural phenomena in favor of rational ones.
G. Put the geocentric theory in nearly its final form.
H. Best known of the Greek philosophers and scientists.

15. Arrange the above philosophers and scientists in approximate chronological order.

16. List the heavenly bodies in order of their distances from the earth according to the Ptolemaic hypothesis.

✓ 17. List the various pieces of evidence *Here* given by Ptolemy (see quotation on p. 17) for a spherical earth.

18. Would you expect the earth to show an apparent retrograde motion if you could view it from Mars? From Venus?

CHAPTER II

Some Basic Astronomical Observations

One of man's most persistent and revealing pre-occupations has been his attempt to fashion for himself an adequate conceptual model of the Universe.—GERALD HOLTON

INTRODUCTION

We have presented the Ptolemaic system of the universe, which accounted well enough for the motions of the various celestial bodies insofar as they were known at the time of Copernicus and beyond. Top-heavy though it was, and seemingly ready to crash under its own weight, it had a common-sense appeal that no heliocentric hypothesis could possibly have. As previously implied, we would all be geocentrists if we relied exclusively on the evidence of our own senses. Since we are going to have to replace a common-sense universe with one that is very "uncommon-sensical," we are going to postpone the story of this replacement until we learn something about our solar system as we

know it today. We will be concerned chiefly with the earth in space.

ROTATION OF THE EARTH ON ITS AXIS [1]

If we believe that the earth revolves about the sun, then we *must* also believe that it turns on its axis once every 24 hours. Otherwise we have no explanation for the apparent rising and setting of the sun, moon, and stars. The direction of rotation is from west to east (Fig. 2-1), a fact made obvious by the rising of the sun and moon in the east and by their setting in the west. As viewed from the North Star, the rotation is counterclockwise.

Rotation also accounts for the apparent turning about Polaris of those stars and constellations that do not rise or set, as viewed from the middle and low latitudes (Fig. 1-10). As viewed from either pole no stars rise or set; all appear to turn about a point in the heavens directly above that pole (Fig. 1-3). It should be realized that these observations can all be explained by assuming a stationary earth and a revolving sky.

No evidence, direct or indirect, that indicated the earth was actually rotating was forthcoming until about 1735. Newton, in his great scientific work, the *Principia*, published in 1688, showed that a rotating spherical body should be flattened at the poles. If this were so, a degree of latitude in the polar regions should be somewhat greater than a degree in the equatorial regions. Evidence that this was so came in

[1] We must distinguish carefully between revolution of the earth around the sun and rotation of the earth on its axis at all times in order to prevent confusion.

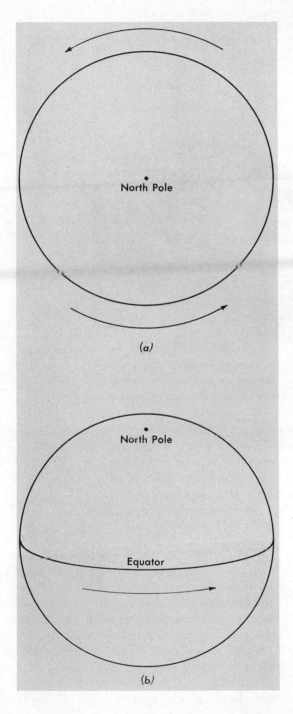

(a)

North Pole

North Pole

Equator

(b)

1735–1736 when the French sent expeditions to measure a degree of latitude [2] in both Peru and Lapland (northern Scandinavia). This evidence did not constitute conclusive proof, however.

Experimental proof came about 1850 when the French physicist, Foucault, demonstrated rotation of the earth by suspending a large iron ball by 200 ft of wire from the dome of the Pantheon in Paris. Friction at the point of support was reduced to a minimum. The ball suspended by the wire constituted a gigantic pendulum (Fig. 2-2a). It was carefully started swinging parallel to a line marked on the floor beneath the pendulum (Fig. 2-2b). This line was actually a segment of a meridian [3] and we will henceforth designate it as such.

As time passed, the direction of the plane of the swinging pendulum changed with respect to the meridian segment at a uniform rate. There was no force operating to change the direction of this swing. Therefore, it must have been the direction of the meridian that was changed with respect to the plane of the swinging pendulum. In other words, the floor of the Pantheon, and hence the building and the earth, must have been turning beneath the

[2] Distance north or south of the equator measured in degrees.

[3] A meridian is a half circle extending from pole to pole. They are used to indicate longitude, i.e., distance east or west of the prime meridian (0° meridian) measured in degrees.

Fig. 2-1. Direction of Earth's Rotation. **(a)** As viewed from any point above the north pole the direction is counterclockwise, and **(b)** as viewed from above the equator is from west to east.

Fig. 2-2. Foucault Pendulum. (**a**, *above*) Its demonstration in the Pantheon of Paris in 1851. The heavy ball swings from a 200-ft wire suspended from the dome of the building. (Courtesy The Bettman Archive.)

(**b**, *opposite*) The swing of the pendulum in relation to the floor beneath it. Started swinging parallel to the 0 line, in a vertical plane *AA'*, after some hours the pendulum appears to swing in the vertical plane *BB'*. Actually it is still swinging in the plane *AA'* because there is no force acting to change its direction. It is the floor of the Pantheon, firmly attached to the earth, that has turned.

ball. The end of the meridian segment that was nearer the equator was carried eastward at a faster *linear* rate than the end nearer the north pole.

If this demonstration were made at either pole (Fig. 2-3), the direction of the meridian would be changed at the rate of 15°/hr, 360° in 24 hours—for the point on the segment directly over the pole does not shift at all, whereas each end of the segment completes a circle in that time. At the equator, the deviation of the direction of the meridian segment with respect to the plane of the swinging pendulum is 0° because every part of the meridian segment is shifted eastward at the same rate (Fig. 2-4). If this rate of change of direction is 0° at the equator and 15°/hr at

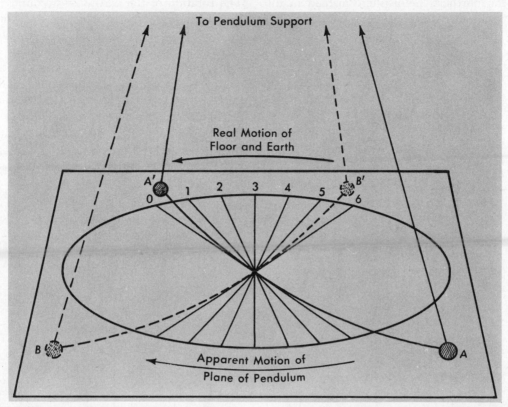

the poles, it should be obvious that the rate should be somewhere between 0° and 15°/hr at places between.[4] The deviation is clockwise in the northern hemisphere, counterclockwise in the southern. This experiment conclusively proves that the earth rotates on an axis once every 24 hours.

Other indications that the earth rotates are obtained from the firing of artillery shells long distances. Since all parts of the spherical earth complete one rotation in the same time, it is obvious that the *linear* speed varies with the latitude.[5] If we

[4] The actual rate of change per hour is 15° times the sine of the latitude.

[5] Thus the speed of a point is a bit over 1000 mi/hr at the equator, 0 right at the poles, and about 750 mi/hr at New York City.

neglect air resistance, the artillery shell retains, at all points in its trajectory, the rotational speed *of the place from which it was fired.* If it is aimed directly at a target north of the gun in the northern hemisphere, and then fired, it is moving towards a region of slower rotation, and therefore arrives ahead (east) of its target. If it is aimed and fired at a target south of it, the shell is moving toward a region of faster rotation, and so arrives behind (west of) its target. In any case the deflection is to the right of the observer when he faces the target. In the southern hemisphere the deflection is to the left of the observer. Obviously, artillerymen must allow for the deviation by aiming to the left of the target in the northern hemisphere instead of directly at it.

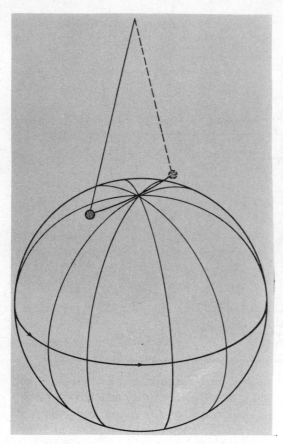

Fig. 2-3. A pendulum suspended from a "sky hook" directly above the north pole apparently changes its direction 360° in 24 hours, the time of one rotation of the earth.

This deviation occurs not only for artillery shells, bullets, and missiles, but also for the major wind systems of the earth.[6]

[6] Artificial satellites also carry with them the component of rotational motion of the place from which they were launched.

The rotation of the earth also accounts for the direction of the spiraling of the winds in cyclones (the lows of our weather maps), in hurricanes, and in tornadoes. In conjunction with the configuration of the continents, it controls the directions of the great ocean currents like the Gulf Stream. Furthermore, the weight of an object is less, by about 1 lb in 190, at the equator than it would be if the earth did not rotate.

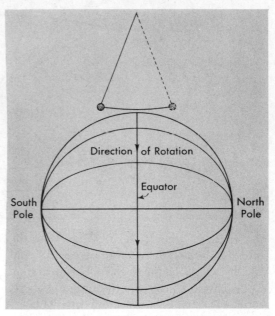

Fig. 2-4. A pendulum suspended from a "sky hook" directly above the equator makes no apparent change in its direction as the earth rotates.

REVOLUTION OF THE EARTH AND THE PLANE OF THE ECLIPTIC

The earth moves in a slightly elliptical orbit about the sun. At its farthest point (about July 4) the earth's distance is

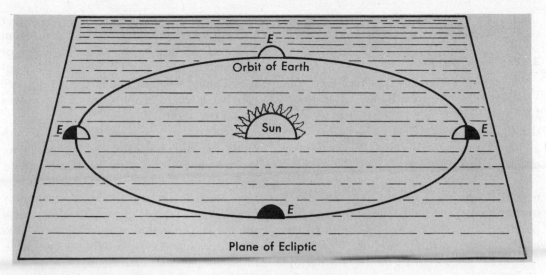

Fig. 2-5. Plane of the Ecliptic. Note that it passes through the centers of the sun and the earth, *E*, so that it includes the orbit of the earth.

94,500,000 mi from the sun,[7] and at its nearest point (about January 4), its distance is about 91,500,000 mi. The average of 93,000,000 mi is sometimes referred to as *one astronomical unit,* a unit of distance that is useful in comparing the distances of the other planets from the sun. The orbit of the earth is thus 186,000,000 mi across. The earth moves faster when it is nearer the sun than it does when farther away. *The plane that includes the orbit of the earth is called the plane of the ecliptic* (Fig. 2-5). It passes through the center of the earth and the center of the sun. It is a plane of reference to which all other points in the solar system may be referred. This is just as necessary as it is to have the

north and south poles as points of reference for location here on earth.

EVIDENCE FOR THE EARTH'S REVOLUTION

Some of the evidence for the earth's revolution is comparatively simple, some very complex. We need here to differentiate between evidence that can be used to support either the heliocentric or the geocentric theory, and that which supports one theory while denying the other.

1. Parallax

There are two pieces of evidence of the latter sort that support the heliocentric theory. The most direct is that of stellar parallax (Fig. 1-5. See also footnote, p. 9). Parallax is, however, undetectable for those stars more than 300 light years away, and even for those nearest, it is so small (less

---

[7] The point in the orbit of any member of the solar system when it is farthest from the sun is called *aphelion.* The nearest point is called *perihelion.* The corresponding points of a satellite in orbit about its planet are called *apogee* and *perigee,* respectively.

than 1/10,000 of a degree) that it is not very convincing to the nonscientist.

2. Phases of Venus

Far more convincing is the fact that Venus can be observed by means of a telescope to have a full set of phases as does the moon. The pertinent observable facts about Venus are as follows: Venus is seen either in the western sky (as the evening "star") up to about three hours after sunset, or in the eastern sky (as the morning "star") up to about three hours before sunrise, depending upon the relative positions of the earth and Venus in their orbits (Fig. 2-6a). *It is never seen high in the sky during the night;* it always crosses the high part of the sky during daylight hours, and when it is brightest it may sometimes be seen during the day if atmospheric conditions are right. The reason for these observable facts is that Venus is so close to the sun that, viewed from the earth, it can never get more than about 46° away from it, i.e., the angle formed by a line from the earth to the sun and a line from the earth to Venus is never more than 46° (Fig. 2-6b).

It should be realized that the sun always illuminates only one-half of Venus at any one time, just as it illuminates one-half of the surface of the earth or moon at any one time. When Venus is at V_5 (Fig. 2-6b) we can see almost all of the illuminated surface; this is the full phase. When Venus is at V_3 the illuminated face is turned precisely away from the earth, and so we see none of it; this is the "new" phase.

According to Ptolemy, Venus had its orbit (Fig. 2-6c) about the stationary earth inside the orbit of the sun. To have a full phase Venus would have to be at V_5 when the sun is at S_1, or at V_5' when the sun is at S_2. Now this distance is approximately 160,000,000 mi, and Venus is found never to be more than about 65,000,000 mi from the sun. Hence it can never be at V_5 or V_5', and so there can be no full phase unless Venus revolves about the sun; there can be only crescent phases if it revolves about the earth.

However, if Venus and the earth both circle the sun, as postulated by the heliocentric theory (Fig. 2-6d), it can be at V_5, and still not be over 65,000,000 mi away from the sun, for its orbit is approximately circular, so that this distance is almost constant. An inspection of the diagram shows that the angle SEV_4 or SEV_1 is the maximum angle that can be made by lines drawn from both Venus and the sun to the earth (the position of the observer's eye). Therefore, Venus can never be more than 46° above the horizon at either sunrise or sunset.

Venus is only 26,000,000 mi from the earth at the new phase, and some 56,000,000 mi away at the crescent phase; whereas it is some 160,000,000 mi away at the full phase. The result is that the amount of light reflected to the earth from Venus is 2½ times greater at the crescent phase despite the fact that the area of the illuminated surface that is turned towards us is far less.

3. Apparent Retrograde Motion of the Planets

A geocentrist must of necessity believe that the planets periodically reverse their motions, for that is what they appear to do. For example, Mars travels in an orbit considerably larger than that of the earth, and at the same time travels at a slower speed, so that it takes nearly two of our years to complete one revolution. It therefore covers a smaller fraction of its orbit

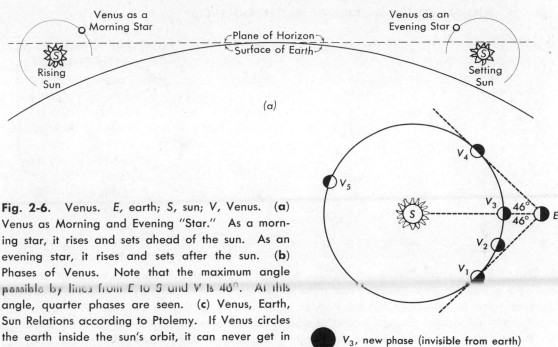

Fig. 2-6. Venus. *E*, earth; *S*, sun; *V*, Venus. **(a)** Venus as Morning and Evening "Star." As a morning star, it rises and sets ahead of the sun. As an evening star, it rises and sets after the sun. **(b)** Phases of Venus. Note that the maximum angle possible by lines from *E* to *S* and *V* is 46°. At this angle, quarter phases are seen. **(c)** Venus, Earth, Sun Relations according to Ptolemy. If Venus circles the earth inside the sun's orbit, it can never get in position for a full phase without exceeding the *observed* angle of 46°. **(d)** Venus, Earth, Sun Relations according to Copernicus. Venus circles the sun inside the orbit of the earth and so can get into positions for phases ranging from quarter to full.

(a)

● V_3, new phase (invisible from earth)

◐ V_2, crescent phase

◑ V_1 and V_4, quarter phase

○ V_5, nearly full phase

(b)

(d)

(c)

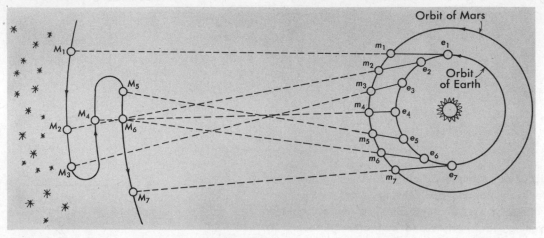

Fig. 2-7. Apparent Retrograde Motion of Planets. Successive positions of the earth in its orbit are shown by e_1, e_2, etc., and those of Mars at the same times by m_1, m_2, etc. Note that earth (e_1) starts off behind Mars (m_1), catches up to it when at e_4, and then passes it. Viewed against the background of stars, Mars appears to move in the path indicated by M_1, M_2, etc. This apparent retrograde path, believed to be real by the Greeks, gave rise to the concept of epicycles.

per unit time than does the earth. The result is that if we "let" Mars "start" out a bit ahead of the earth, the earth will catch up with and pass Mars, making it appear that Mars is moving backwards for a time (Fig. 2-7). All of the planets with orbits greater than that of the earth appear to retrograde every time the earth catches up with and passes them. Venus and Mercury, with orbits inside that of the earth, appear to retrograde when they catch up with and pass the earth. Hipparchus invented epicycles to explain what to him were real retrograde motions.

The heliocentrist needs no epicycles, for, as we have seen, these motions are only apparent. Given different periods for the various planets the apparent retrograde motions become inevitable, i.e., the apparent paths are just what we would expect them to be. If it were useful to do so,

we could plot them for years to come, just as we do their actual paths. If prediction is the test of a theory, there can be no question about the heliocentric theory.

ROTATION, REVOLUTION, AND TIME

The measurement of time from the very beginning of civilization has been dependent on the space relations of the earth and the stars. The rotation of the earth on its axis, with the resultant changing pattern of the stars in the sky, furnishes the fundamental "clock" mechanism on which the civilized world still depends. So accurate is this standard clock that it is estimated to lose not more than 1 second in 100,000 years.

While it is the rotation of the earth that gives us our standard clock, it is the revolution of the earth about the sun and the revolution of the moon about the earth that gives us our calendar. While our best clocks keep precisely in step with the rotation of the earth because they are designed to do so, our calendar is not, and never can be, in step with the revolution of the earth. This is because the time of revolution is not an even number of days. If, instead of being about 11 minutes short of 365¼ days, it were exactly 365 or 366 days (or better still, 360 days), we would not have an extra day every 4 years. This extra day overcompensates, and so we omit a leap year every 400 years. This overcompensates the other way and so it goes.

The exact time that it takes to complete one revolution is 365 days, 5 hr, 48 min, 45.68 sec. This is the time that elapses between two March equinoxes, i.e., it is twice the time between two successive appearances of the sun directly over the equator. Put another way it is the time the sun takes to *apparently* shift from the equator to its most northerly position (the Tropic of Cancer), then back to its most southerly position (the Tropic of Capricorn), and then northward again to the equator (Fig. 2-8). This length of time is called the tropical year and our calendar is based upon it.

The sidereal year is based upon the stars instead of the sun; it is the time required for the earth to return to a given point in its orbit with reference to any selected star (Fig. 2-9). The stars make a perfect timepiece; our sun does not, for its apparent speed is not constant (p. 50). We do not use the stars directly as our timepiece, however, for the length of our day is determined by the sun, and the stars do not operate according to our conventional system of days and hours. Our conventional

system averages out the sun's "errors." The stars are used to check the accuracy of this averaging.

EASTWARD DRIFT OF THE SUN

Directions here on earth are defined with the poles as reference points. When facing the north pole, east is on the right. Out in space the poles of the earth cannot be used as reference points. We do, however, have need for directions in space. Westward is therefore defined as clockwise [8] as viewed from the North Star. Eastward is therefore counterclockwise as viewed from the North Star.

The apparent eastward drift of the sun and moon with respect to the stars is easily explained by a revolving earth. Consider the following: The ecliptic plane passes through the center of the earth and the center of the sun, and may be considered to extend beyond the stars. A band of stars that form the constellations of the zodiac (Fig. 2-10) extends about 10° on each side of the ecliptic plane. Most of the stars of the Milky Way are in this belt, which is divided into 12 parts each 30° long, containing the astrologer's signs of the zodiac. It is used to roughly indicate the plane of the ecliptic in the sky.

The dashed line, *AB*, in Fig. 2-10 passes through the centers of both the earth and the sun. If we consider the earth to be revolving in the direction indicated, we will see that one end of *AB* will pass successively through Virgo, Libra, Scorpius, etc., while the other passes through Pisces, Aries, Taurus, etc. At the position shown

[8] The early timepieces were sundials. Clocks were invented in the northern hemisphere, and their hands were made to turn in the direction that the shadow of a sundial turned.

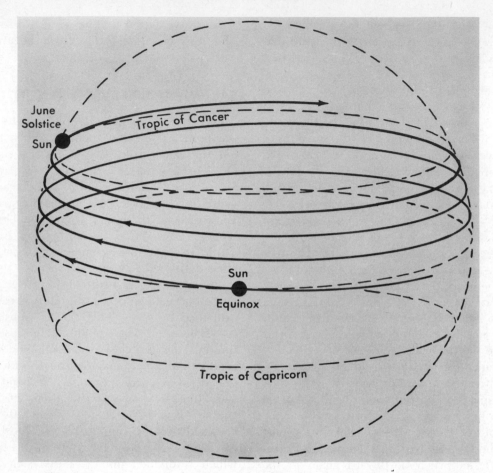

Fig. 2-8. Apparent Path of Sun about Earth. Starting from a position above the equator at the March equinox the sun appears to describe a low ascending spiral (northern hemisphere) until the June solstice, after which it appears to describe a low descending spiral until it is over the Tropic of Capricorn at the December solstice. It then appears to start an ascending spiral again. Thus the sun appears to migrate back and forth between the two tropics. (After Strahler, *Physical Geography*, Wiley, New York, 1960.)

we say the sun is in Cancer and the earth is in Capricornus. We on earth can look outward along the line and see Capricornus at night, but we cannot look the other way and see Cancer during the day because the sun is too bright. To see Cancer we will

have to wait until the earth gets around to the other side of the sun, i.e., to A, six months hence.

Let us select an easily identifiable star that rises directly in the east a bit after sunset, say at 7:00 P.M., and check its position once a month at 7:00 P.M. At the end of the first month it will be about 30° above the horizon at that hour. At the end of two months it will be 60° above the horizon at 7:00 P.M., and at the end of about six months it will be setting with the sun. It will have gained a full 180° on the star, that the sun appears to

drift eastward with respect to the stars. In another six months we may observe the same star once more rising at 7:00 P.M.

The geocentrists explained this apparent eastward drift of the sun with respect to the stars by assuming that the dome containing the fixed stars (p. 8) moved at a faster rate than the dome containing the sun, a rate sufficiently faster to allow the

Fig. 2-9. Sidereal vs. Mean Solar Day. These differ by nearly 4 min because the earth moves forward in its orbit as it rotates. Assume that at noon (first day) both sun and star X were directly overhead to an observer at a. The earth rotates counterclockwise (as viewed from a point above the North Pole) through 360° in 23 hr 56 min to bring the star directly overhead again, but must rotate through about 1° more to bring the sun directly overhead again. The angle (1°) is enormously exaggerated.

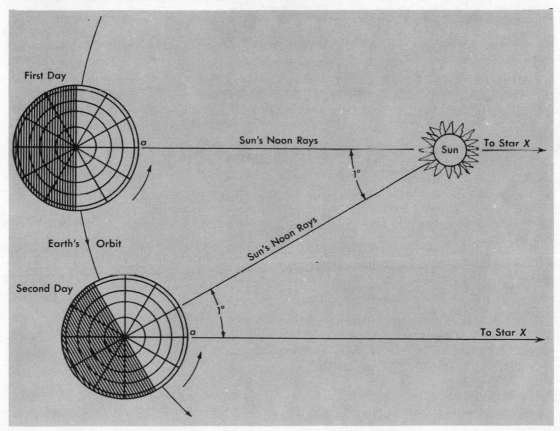

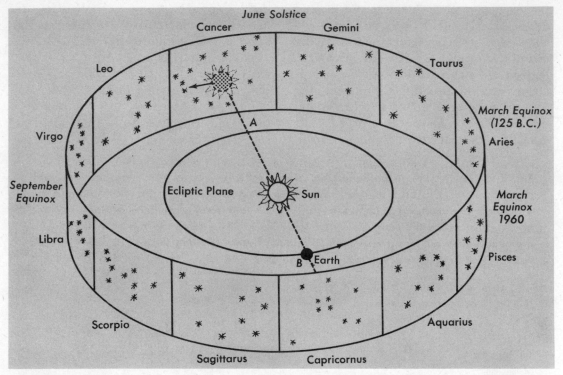

Fig. 2-10. The Zodiac. The band of constellations called the zodiac roughly mark both the plane of the ecliptic and the Milky Way. As shown the sun is said to be in Cancer (as viewed from the earth) or the earth in Capricornus (as viewed from the sun). As the earth revolves, the upper end of the line *AB* shifts to the left (counterclockwise) which is defined as eastward, as viewed from Polaris. Therefore the sun appears to drift eastward among the immobile stars. (After Ashford, *Atoms to Stars*, Holt, Rinehart and Winston, New York, 1960.)

star dome to gain one complete revolution on the sun per year. The heliocentrists explain it by the earth moving forward in its orbit 30° per month while the stars apparently stay fixed in position.

AXIS OF THE EARTH IN RELATION TO THE PLANE OF THE ECLIPTIC

The axis of the earth is inclined 66½° to the plane of the ecliptic. More commonly we use the complement of this

angle, so that we say the axis is inclined 23½° to a perpendicular to the plane of the ecliptic. We who live north of the Tropic of Cancer, can determine this angle by measuring the altitude of the sun above the horizon at noon suntime [9] on

[9] Noon suntime is the time of day the sun is at the highest point in the sky for that day. It is midway in its apparent path from horizon to horizon. The altitude of the sun is defined as its elevation above the horizon at noon suntime, measured in degrees.

both solstices. The difference between these two altitudes (47°) is twice the angle of tilt. If we were on the equator, the difference in the altitudes of the sun at noon suntime at an equinox and a solstice would give us the angle of tilt directly. If there were no tilt, i.e., if the earth's axis were perpendicular to the plane of the ecliptic, the altitude of the sun at noon suntime would be constant the year round for any one place.

This inclination has important consequences to the human race, for it makes more of the earth's surface habitable than would be without the tilt. The axis main-

tains this angle as the earth revolves, so that in any one position it is parallel to what it is in any other position (Fig. 2-11). This is called *parallelism of the axis*.

FACTORS CONTROLLING THE SEASONS

A combination of three factors operating together give us the seasons as we in the middle latitudes know them. All of them have already been discussed. They are (1) the inclination of the axis, (2) the parallelism of the axis, and (3) the revolution of the earth about the sun in about

Fig. 2-11. Parallelism of Earth's Axis. In its revolution about the sun, the earth's axis, A, not only maintains a constant angle of inclination to a perpendicular to the plane of the ecliptic, but also remains parallel to itself in all positions in the orbit.

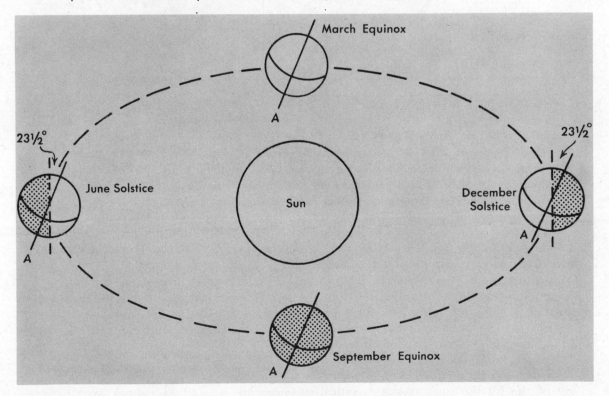

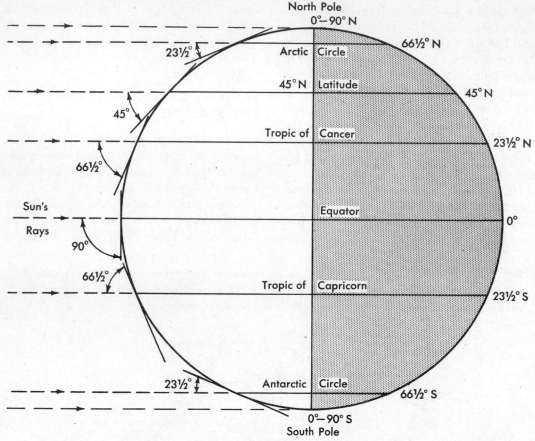

Fig. 2-12 (a). Angle of Sun's Rays at Equinoxes and Solstices. The sun's rays (from the left) are parallel. At the equinoxes they make an angle of 90° with the plane of the earth's surface at noon at the equator, 66½° at either tropic, 45° at a latitude of 45° N or S, 23½° at either the Arctic or Antarctic Circle, and they arrive parallel to the earth's surface at either pole.

365 days. Change any one of them significantly and our seasons would change. Of greatest importance to people living in the middle and high latitudes is the inclination of the earth on its axis, for when the axis is inclined towards the sun (Fig. 2-12b) they have their summers, a season that would be absent from those regions if there were no tilt (Fig. 2-12a). As a result of the tilt the sun's rays are vertical about June 21,[10] at the Tropic of Cancer, 23½° north of the equator.

The Tropic of Cancer is the farthest north the vertical rays of the sun ever get (Fig. 2-12b) just as the Tropic of Capricorn is the farthest south the vertical rays

[10] Since our calendar is not quite synchronized with the apparent movements of the sun, the hour varies so much that the date of any solstice or equinox may occur on either of two days.

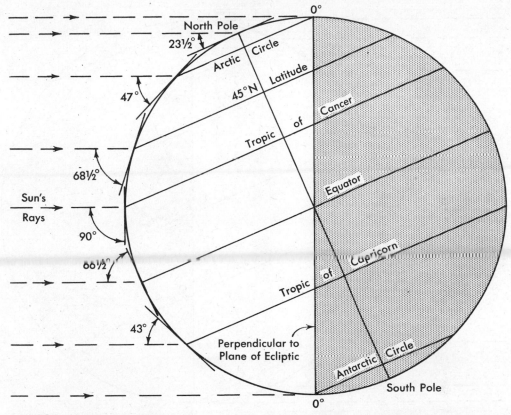

Fig. 2-12 (b). The angle of the sun's rays at noon at the June solstice at any given place is $23\frac{1}{2}°$ more than at an equinox in the northern hemisphere and $23\frac{1}{2}°$ less in the southern hemisphere.

ever get (Fig. 2-12c). *The sun is never directly overhead anywhere in continental United States.* The tilt affects our seasons not only by increasing and decreasing the angle of the sun's rays (Fig. 2-12 *a, b, c*) but also by regulating the length of day and night. Thus, in the latitude of New York City the earth has a day of about 15 hr and a night of about 9 hr at the June solstice—15 hr to heat up and 9 hr to cool off. At the December solstice the situation is exactly reversed. The inclination of the axis causes the sun to rise and set once a year at the poles; thus their day (the time between two successive sunrises) is equal to their year. The six months of steady sunshine makes the polar regions far warmer during the summer months and far colder during the winter months than they would be otherwise.

PRECESSION OF THE EQUINOXES

We shall have to retract to some extent our statement about the parallelism of the axis. Any deviation from one year to the next or even during a man's lifetime is relatively insignificant and so what we said is

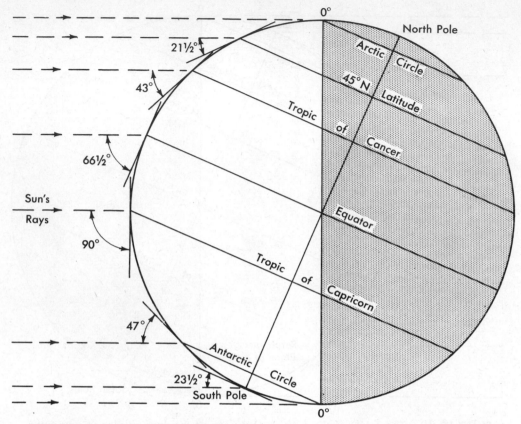

Fig. 2-12 (c). The angle of the sun's rays at noon at the December solstice at any given place is 23½° less than at an equinox in the northern hemisphere and 23½° more in the southern hemisphere.

essentially true for all practical purposes. Over a long period of time (12,000 to 13,000 years) the cumulative effects of deviation from parallelism could cause our seasons to be completely reversed, if our calendar were not adjusted to take care of the situation.

By careful measurement Hipparchus (*ca.* 125 B.C.), determined that the sun was in Aries at the time of the March equinox (Fig. 2-10). Today measurements show that the sun is in Pisces (the earth in Virgo) at that time. This does not mean

that Hipparchus was wrong. We know today that the March equinox occurs about 20 min earlier each successive year. Thus, in the time of Hipparchus, two thousand years ago, the equinox was 30 days later than it is now, i.e., in terms of our calendar it was about April 20. And two thousand years from now the March equinox would be about February 19, and so on, if our calendar did not correct for it. Obviously the dates of the September equinox and the solstices tend to shift likewise. This regular shift in the dates of the equinoxes is called the *precession of the equinoxes.*

What is the cause of precession? We cannot investigate precession in its entirety here since the explanation involves some rather difficult mathematics. We will content ourselves with the following: If the earth did not rotate, the gravitational pull of the sun and the moon on the earth's equatorial bulge would tend to eliminate the tilt of the equatorial plane to the plane of the ecliptic, i.e., to make the two planes coincide. The bulge is slightly nearer to the sun and the moon than other portions of the earth and so the effect of gravity on the bulge is a little greater than on other parts. However, the earth does rotate and any spinning object resists a change in the direction of its axis of rotation, i.e., it takes a force to change it. The slightly greater gravitational pull on the bulge is not sufficient to overcome the resistance to a change in the angle of inclination of the equatorial plane. Instead, the earth's axis performs a slow conical motion, a precession, around an axis perpendicular to the

Fig. 2-13. Precession of the Equinoxes. Precession of the earth's axis may be compared to the wobbling of a top as it spins. Note that the earth's axis changes the direction in which it points as it revolves about the perpendicular to the plane of the ecliptic. This change is so slow as to be negligible in any one year since it takes the axis 26,000 years to complete one "wobble."

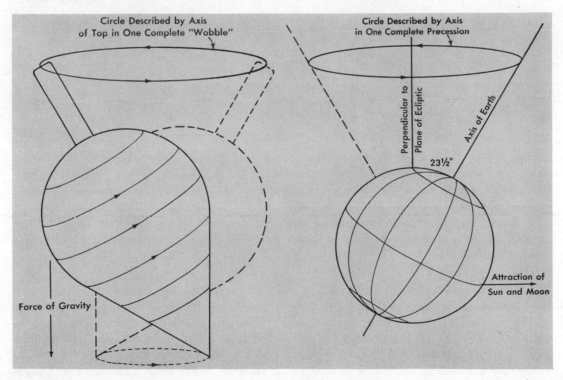

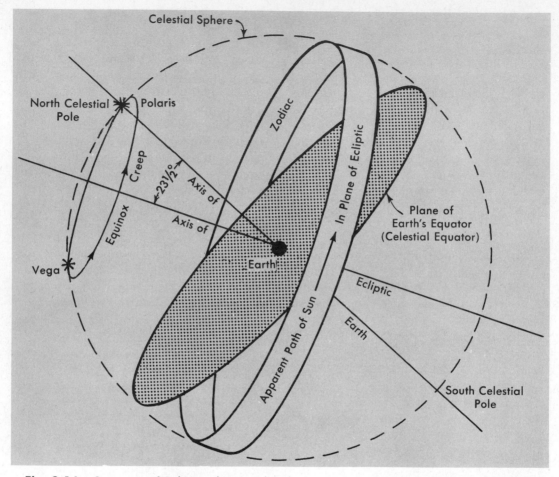

Fig. 2-14. Summary of Relations between Earth, Sun, Ecliptic, and Precession of Equinoxes in Conjunction with Concept of Celestial Sphere. The sky appears at any instant to be a dome of infinite radius—half of a great celestial sphere—with the earth at the center. The stars appear to be embedded in the inner side of this great sphere; they appear to describe circles about the celestial poles. Note that Vega will be our north star some 13,000 years hence—due to precession of the earth's axis. The diagram is oriented for the altitude of Polaris at New York City, 41° N latitude.

plane of the ecliptic (Figs. 2-13 and 2-14). This motion is the same as that of a slightly inclined spinning top which, instead of falling, precesses in a cone about the vertical. It takes nearly 26,000 years to complete one precession.

The fact that precession takes place contradicts the statement we previously made about the earth's axis maintaining a constant orientation in space. The justification is the same as that for referring to the stars as being fixed. During the lifetime of the average individual the precessional change is insignificant, too small to be noticed except by astronomers. One effect of precession is that Polaris is becoming less and less our pole star. Even today it lacks being directly over the axis by one to two degrees. Certain other nearby stars which are at a proper distance from the axis of precession will in turn become "pole stars" until, some 25,000 years hence, Polaris will again be our pole star.

MOTIONS OF THE MOON

The actual motion of the moon is not a simple revolution in an elliptical orbit about the earth. When we say that it moves in an elliptical orbit we are reverting to the geocentric concept of a stationary earth (Fig. 2-15). Actually the earth is moving through approximately 30° of its orbit, a distance of nearly 50,000,000 mi, while the moon completes one revolution about the earth. The result is a path like that in Fig. 2-16. We will, therefore, consider the moon's orbit relative to the earth, i.e., we will, part of the time at least, consider ourselves good geocentrists. This merely means that we are talking about apparent motions rather than real motions.

The orbit of the moon is, therefore, an ellipse with the earth at one focus. The eccentricity is small, the long axis being about 253,000 mi and the short one 221,500 mi long. The mean distance is about 239,000 mi, roughly 240,000 mi. This is about 60 times the radius of the earth.

Astronomically, the month is the period of the moon's revolution. There are two kinds of months, depending upon our point of reference. The sidereal month is the time of a complete revolution with any particular star as the reference point. This

is about 27½ days. The synodic month is the time of a complete revolution with respect to the sun, i.e., it is the time from one new moon to the next. It is about 29½ days. The longer time is due to the fact that the earth has moved forward nearly 30° in its journey about the sun during that

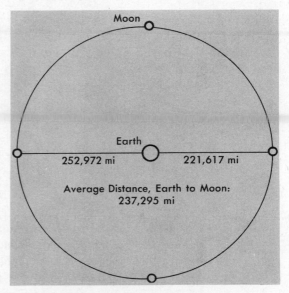

Fig. 2-15. Orbit of Moon. The earth is considered stationary.

27½ days and so the moon has a longer distance to travel. With respect to the stars the moon gains 12.2° per day on the sun. It therefore gains a full lap on the sun each synodic month. But with respect to the diurnal (daily) motions of the earth, the moon falls behind the sun about 50 min a day. Thus moonrise, on the average, comes about 50 min later each day. The speed of the moon relative to the earth averages a bit over ½ mi/sec. Its actual speed is, of course, much greater, for the earth is moving forward in its orbit at an average speed of about 18.5 mi/sec.

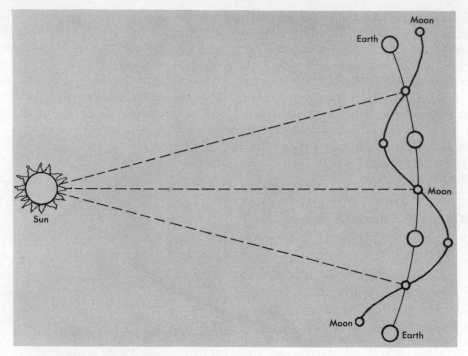

Fig. 2-16. Real Path of Moon Relative to Earth. Because of the exaggerated scale of the drawing, the moon's path appears to be sinuous instead of always concave towards the earth.

The moon rotates on its axis in exactly the same time that it takes to complete one sidereal revolution. The result is that the moon always keeps the same side toward the earth; we always see his "face," never the "back of his head."

PHASES OF THE MOON

At any one time the sun illuminates one-half of the moon's surface just as it illuminates one-half of the earth's surface. If the moon is rising in the east as the sun sets, we on earth can see that fully illuminated half (Fig. 2-17, position 5). This is the full phase. If the moon is setting with the sun, the illuminated half is turned away from us, position 1, so that we cannot see the moon at all.[11] This is the new phase. If the moon is high in the sky at either sunrise or sunset, we have one of the quarter phases (position 3 or 7), for then we see only half of the illuminated half. As the moon progresses from third quarter (position 7), towards the new moon, we see the *waning* crescent (position 8), and as it progresses from new moon to first quarter (position 3), we see the *waxing* crescent (position 2).

[11] Actually, if atmospheric conditions are right we may dimly see the moon by reflection of the sun's light from the earth to the moon.

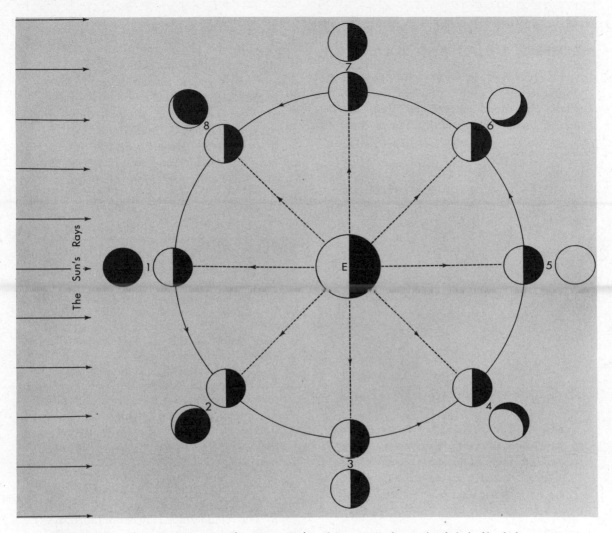

Fig. 2-17. Phases of Moon. The inner circle of "moons" shows the left half of the moon illuminated by the rays of the sun coming from the left. Note that only one-half is illuminated at any one time. You can see it this way only from a position far out in space beyond the moon and between it and the sun. An observer on earth, however, sees the moon as it appears in the outer circle of moons. Thus in position 1 he sees none of the illuminated side. This is the "dark" of the moon (new moon). Two weeks later the moon is in position 5 where the full illuminated half can be seen (full moon). Halfway between, in positions 3 and 7, half of the illuminated half may be seen; these are the quarter phases. At position 2 we see the waxing crescent, and at position 8 the waning crescent. Positions 4 and 6 show the gibbous phases. Of the infinite number of phases possible, these are the only ones that have special names. As an aid in seeing the relationship between the two circles of moons, try looking along the line of sight at each pair, remembering that you can see only that part of the illuminated half which is turned towards the earth.

ECLIPSES, LUNAR AND SOLAR

The plane of the orbit of the moon is inclined about 5° to the plane of the ecliptic. Thus, the moon crosses the plane of the ecliptic twice each month.   The two points

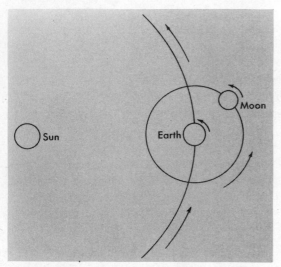

Fig. 2-18. Directions of Rotation and Revolution of Earth and Moon. Note that all four motions are counterclockwise as viewed from a point high above the north pole, e.g., from Polaris.

of intersection of the two planes are called *nodes*.   If the moon is at or very near one of the nodes at the time of full moon, it is eclipsed by the earth's shadow, for the earth is between the moon and the sun then (Fig. 2-19).   If the moon is new when it is at or near one of the nodes, the sun is eclipsed by the shadow of the moon falling on a portion of the earth.   Eclipses of the sun are rarer than eclipses of the moon because the shadow of the moon is only about 232,000 mi long, not long enough to reach the earth on the average.

Only when the above conditions prevail at a time when the moon is closer than 232,000 mi will there be a solar eclipse.   Since both the earth and the moon are spheres far smaller than the sun, their shadows are cones with the apex directed towards the earth (Fig. 2-19).   In an eclipse of the sun only the tip of this cone sweeps across the earth in a belt never more than 167 mi wide.[12]

SUMMARY

Some basic astronomical observations must be understood if we are to understand the heliocentric solar system and the reasons for the final victory of the heliocentrists over the geocentrists.   Included are:

   1. The rotation of the earth on its axis and the pieces of evidence thereof.

   2. The revolution of the earth in its orbit and the pieces of evidence thereof.

   3. The plane of the ecliptic and its use as a reference plane for all bodies of the solar system.

   4. The explanation of the phases of Venus.

   5. The explanation of the apparent retrograde motion of the planets.

   6. The relationships between rotation, revolution, and time.

   7. The explanation of the eastward drift of the sun.

   8. The relationship of the axis of the earth to the plane of the ecliptic, and the consequences thereof.

   9. The precession of the equinoxes.

   10. The motions of the moon, revolution and rotation.

   11. Eclipses, solar and lunar.

[12] This is the maximum width of the band in which any total eclipse may be observed.   A partial eclipse may be observed in a band up to 2000 mi across.

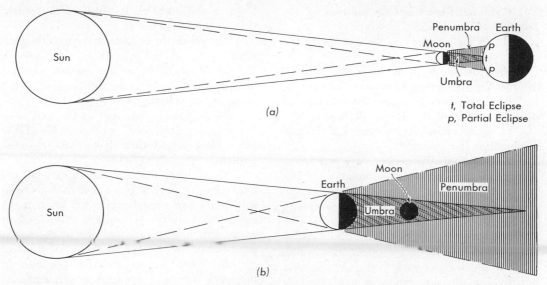

t, Total Eclipse
p, Partial Eclipse

Fig. 2-19. Eclipses of Sun and Moon. **(a)** Eclipse of Sun. The solid lines from the sun to the moon meet to form a cone whose tip is intercepted by the earth. When the moon is farthest from the earth (Fig. 2-15), this tip fails to reach the earth and so there is no eclipse. This explains the rarity of eclipses of the sun as compared to eclipses of the moon. Note also that only a small part of the earth intercepts this tip. Thus a total eclipse of the sun can be seen only in the areas intercepting this tip.

(b) Eclipse of Moon. Note that the moon is on the opposite side of the earth from that during an eclipse of the sun, and that the moon is completely within the cone formed by the solid lines from the sun to the earth. Thus a total eclipse of the moon may at times be seen from all of the dark side of the earth at the same time.

EXERCISES

·I. TERMS AND CONCEPTS

Rotation	Phases of Venus
Revolution	Period
Plane of the ecliptic	Equinox
Tropic of Cancer	Solstice
Tropic of Capricorn	

II. PROBLEMS

1. What determines the positions of the north and south poles?

2. How are day and night accounted for by the geocentric theory? The heliocentric theory?

3. If the earth is flattened at the poles instead of being truly spherical, why should a degree of latitude as measured in miles be greater in the polar regions than at the equator?

4. List the pieces of evidence that the earth rotates on a north–south axis. All should consist of phenomena that cannot be explained by a geocentric stationary earth.

5. What is the plane of the ecliptic? Of what use is it in our study of the solar system?

6. What is the orientation of the axis of the earth to the plane of the ecliptic?

7. What determines the positions of the Tropics of Cancer and Capricorn?

8. What is meant by the altitude of the sun?

9. How is the altitude of the sun related to the above two Tropics?

10. Is the sun ever directly overhead at any place north of the Tropic of Cancer?

11. How many days a year is it directly overhead at the equator?

12. On earth the north pole is our frame of reference for our compass directions. Out in space these directions have no significance, yet we need the terms eastward or westward. How are these terms defined?

13. Suppose you could get the midday sun to vanish by the wave of a magic wand. What would the sky look like? Do you ever actually see the sky somewhat like this? If so, when?

14. Explain why Venus is never seen high in the sky (midway between the two horizons) at midnight.

15. An artilleryman fires a shell from a long range gun at a target 20 mi due south. In what direction does he aim his gun? (Be as specific as the question will allow.) Explain.

16. What is the zodiac?

17. What is meant by the apparent eastward drift of the sun?

18. What is one astronomical unit?

19. What is a tropical year? How does it differ from a sidereal year?

20. What effect does the varying distance of the sun from the earth have on our seasons?

21. What is the *fundamental* reason for colder weather in the middle and higher latitudes in the northern hemisphere in January than in July?

22. What three factors control the seasons?

23. What effect on the seasons would a 90° tilt of the earth's axis with respect to the plane of the ecliptic have?

24. Suppose that the earth took two years to complete one revolution about the sun. How would this change our seasons? Explain.

25. Suppose that the earth's axis did not retain its parallelism but constantly changed so that the axis was always tilted towards the sun in the northern hemisphere. What effect would this have on the seasons in the northern hemisphere? In the southern hemisphere?

26. What are the relative positions of the earth, sun, and moon at new moon? At full moon? Why is new moon called the "dark of the moon"?

27. Suppose that the apparent periods of the sun and the moon were exactly the same. Would you see a complete set of phases of the moon? Explain.

28. What is the approximate average distance of the earth from the moon?

29. At what time of day (suntime) would you expect to see the full moon rise?

30. What is the effect of the precession of the equinoxes?

31. Suppose the plane of the moon's orbit coincided with the plane of the ecliptic. What effect would this have on lunar and solar eclipses?

32. Why do lunar eclipses occur more frequently than solar eclipses?

33. Why are total solar eclipses never seen from all parts of the illuminated half of the earth at the same time?

CHAPTER III

Establishment of the Copernican System

The object of all science is to coordinate our experiences and bring them into a logical system.
—ALBERT EINSTEIN (*Nobel Prize, Physics, 1921*)

FROM THE GREEKS TO COPERNICUS

Ptolemy died about A.D. 150, Copernicus in 1543. The interim of about fourteen hundred years was twice that in which Greek science was developed to a high level. During this interim natural science just about vanished from the earth. The Romans made no progress in theoretical science, largely because their viewpoint was clearly a utilitarian one. New ideas never develop when men's minds are ruled by the "What's the use of it?" philosophy, for how can one know the use of an idea in advance of its development? (Thus, friends of Benjamin Franklin asked him why he "fooled" around with electricity. What's the use of it? they asked.) Science flourishes best when ideas are advanced for their own sake and not for any possible utilitarian value. The true scientist wants to know, and that is enough justification for his researches.

The barbarian hordes overran Western Europe as Rome declined. With the destruction of the Roman Empire, the whole western world collapsed. There was little else to fill the void. It took centuries for an intellectual world to rise again. Christianity spread, and as it did, it naturally came into contact with Greek science and philosophy, and for a time the chief work of the early Christian Fathers lay in combining the two philosophies. Until after the time of St. Augustine (d. A.D. 430) Christian doctrines were fluid, and alternative ideas could exist peaceably side by side. In time men came to rely more and more on authority. Vague hopes and fears of heaven and hell, the hope of salvation in one and the fear of damnation in the flames of the other, dominated scholars more and more. With their firm belief that the day of judgment and the second coming of Christ was very "near," their efforts naturally went into preparation for them. Small wonder that little interest was shown in secular knowledge for its own sake. "To discuss the nature and position of the earth," said St. Ambrose, "does not help us in the life to come." Secular learning became identified with paganism, and ignorance was exalted as a virtue. Slowly the desire to objectively investigate natural phenomena passed away. The sole use of a knowledge of nature was in illustrating the passages from the Scriptures, and almost anything was believed if it accorded with them. By the end of the sixth century the darkness was complete in Western Europe. The writings of the Greek scientists, Aristotle chief among them, passed out of fashion and were forgotten.

During the eighth, ninth, tenth, and eleventh centuries, the flame of learning was kept burning chiefly by the Arabs. They kept alive the memory of Greek science and made some original contributions of their own, chiefly in chemistry. Arabic became the classical language of learning. Much of the work of the Greeks was translated into Arabic, from which it was later translated into Latin. A revival of learning began in Europe in the twelfth century. Slowly the innate curiosity of the human mind began to rebel against the enslavement of medieval theology. Signs of breaks with the medieval habit of mind began to appear. The axioms that "doubt is the road to inquiry," that "by inquiry we perceive the truth," and that "it is necessary to understand in order to believe" grew slowly in the confused jungle that had taken over the once cleared fields of scientific thought. The complete works of Aristotle were rediscovered and translated into Latin between 1200 and 1225. Roger Bacon [1] stood out from the other philosophers of his time because of his clear understanding that experimental methods alone give any adequate degree of certainty in science.

Bacon was

. . . in spirit a man of science and a scientific philosopher, born out of due time and chafing unconsciously against the limitations of his own restricted outlook, no less than against the external obstacles at which he rails so openly and so often . . . for all his comparatively advanced outlook, [he] accepted most of the medieval attitude of mind. No man can do more than advance a little way in front of the ranks of that contemporary army of thought to which, whether he will or no, he belongs.[2]

St. Thomas Aquinas accepted the Ptolemaic system of astronomy as a working hypothesis. His successors, however, welded the whole of Aristotle's science with geocentric theory and Christian theology. The result was a rigid structure in which the parts were so interdependent that to doubt Aristotelian science was to doubt the Christian faith. Such a structure led naturally to reasoning by authority,[3] and once again progress in inquiry ceased, this time because all of the answers were "known." This setting up of Aristotle as the supreme arbiter of scientific thought caused Bertrand Russell to call Aristotle one of the great misfortunes of the human race—through no fault of his (Aristotle's) own.

As the revival of learning and the Renaissance progressed, the courage that is born of knowledge, the calm strength begotten by a positive attitude of mind began to assert themselves. Gradually there arose a new concept of man, a man of some confidence in himself, a man of growing curiosity, a man who ceased to devote his whole time to contemplating the life hereafter, and who started to live in the present. The search for the knowledge of the past increased to a comparatively high tempo, especially in Italy. The spirit of adventure drove men to exploration of the world about them, culminating in the dis-

[1] Not to be confused with Francis Bacon who lived 350 years later.

[2] Dampier, *A History of Science*, Macmillan, New York, 1942, pp. 100–102.

[3] Not to be confused with acceptance of responsible authority. In all fields of knowledge, none more so than in science, acceptance of what has been done previously by competent men is a necessity if further progress is to be made. For a more complete discussion, see p. 149.

covery of the Americas by Columbus [4] and the circumnavigation of the earth by Magellan.

NICOLAUS COPERNICUS

Such was the world into which Nicolaus Koppernigh (1473–1543) was born of a Polish father and a German mother. His name was latinized as Copernicus. That this world into which he was born was different from that of the thousand years preceding may be seen from a scanning of the names of some of his contemporaries and near-contemporaries: da Vinci, Gutenberg, Michelangelo, Dürer, Erasmus, Columbus, Luther, Henry VIII. It was an exciting world in which he lived, a world that was breaking rapidly from the fetters of the past, a world in which new ideas had some chance of eventually succeeding.

Still the Ptolemaic hypothesis of the universe reigned supreme. Some observations of greater accuracy than before were made during the revival of learning, and these increased the difficulty of fitting the motions of the sun, moon, and planets into the already highly complex system of Ptolemy. However, the astronomers of the time had no thought of discarding it and starting anew to see if a more satisfactory system could be developed. Instead they added

[4] The concept of a spherical earth was not original with Columbus. He got it from the rediscovered works of the Greeks. His estimate of the circumference was not gotten from the data of Eratosthenes (p. 11). Instead he used the figures of another Greek, which gave a much smaller circumference. The result was that he thought he had reached the East Indies when he actually had not sailed half the distance to them. The concept of a flat earth had arisen and spread during the dark ages.

more complicated assumptions to it so that the 70-odd motions in the time of Ptolemy were increased to 80 or more.

Copernicus studied mathematical science, took a degree in canon law, studied medicine, and found time to study astronomy. He was a devout Churchman and spent most of his time in the service of the Catholic Church. The amazing intricacies of the Ptolemaic system appalled him. He found it difficult to believe that an intelligent creator would create such a top-heavy system. By 1450, 19 epicycles were needed for Mars alone. More than one devout man jokingly intimated that if he were present at the time of creation he could have made simpler suggestions to the Creator. Copernicus saw that the observed phenomena could be more simply explained if he followed Aristarchus in assuming that the sun was at the center of the universe. A corollary would be that the celestial sphere containing the stars was a fixed one, i.e., the stars were motionless. The planets revolved about the sun in perfect circles. The moon revolved about an earth rotating on an axis as both revolved about the sun.

Copernicus wrote,

In the midst of all, the sun reposes, unmoving. Who, indeed, in this most beautiful temple would place the light-giver in any other part than whence it can illumine all other parts? . . . In this orderly arrangement there appears a wonderful symmetry in the universe and a precise relation between the motions and sizes of the orbs which is impossible to attain in any other way.

Copernicus was well aware that his system would not be readily accepted. For one thing, it was contrary to human experience, for we are not aware of any motion, and we can observe the sun, moon, and planets rise and set. Moreover, it was not only comforting to think of man on an unmoving earth, but it also bolstered his ego to think that he lived at the center of the universe. Copernicus did not seriously attempt to answer these objections directly; he could only hope that the advantages of his system over the rival one would eventually win the battle for him. He knew that the absence of parallax among the fixed stars would have to be explained; his was the same answer as that of Aristarchus—that the stars were many times farther away than even the farthest planets. He could not prove that they were, nor did he think that they were anywhere near as far away as they actually are. He faced the argument that the rotating earth on its axis should burst like a fly wheel when driven too fast with the rejoinder, "Why does the defender of the geocentric theory not fear the same fate for his rotating celestial spheres—so much faster because so much larger?"

He also had to bring his system into accord with the religious and philosophical dogmas of the time. He tried to show how much more harmonious and orderly his system seemed than that of Ptolemy, how the observable world was but a symbol of the working of God's mind, and that it was a reverent duty to find symmetry and order amid the apparent chaos of the planets and stars. He felt that the reduction in the number of elements needed in his system (from over 80 to about 34), and the resulting simplification of practical astronomical problems, was a renewed proof of the Deity.

He also calculated the relative radii and speeds of the various bodies in his system

so that planetary tables could be prepared for use by astronomers and navigators. These tables were as good, but no better than, those of Ptolemy for predicting future positions of the planets. Both were equally correct within the current error of the time of about $\frac{1}{6}°$ of arc. (Even today the geocentric system is preferred for calculations in navigation.) From the scientific viewpoint the chief merit of his system *at that time was that it was simpler*. Science has learned that there is merit in simplicity if the observable facts can be equally well explained. Even Ptolemy recognized this principle, as we have already stated (p. 15).

Copernicus died in 1543, the year his work was published. He had dedicated his book to the Pope. There was little opposition at first, probably because the churches failed to see what it would do to their philosophic-religious beliefs. They disliked the concepts of the stars being so far away, for that made heaven—which was supposed to be among the stars—far, far away, while hell—supposed by most to be at the center of the earth—was uncomfortably close beneath their feet. The contention that the Creator had worked from a heliocentric blueprint was not at all convincing to most Catholic, Protestant, and Jewish religious leaders, most of whom forbade it to be taught in their schools.

The common-sense objections (p. 15) together with the conflict of religious and philosophical dogmas, interwoven with Aristotelian science, were sufficient to prevent acceptance for a time, especially in the face of a lack of any observable parallax. The only sound evidence that Copernicus could present was based on logic: His system was simpler and just as much in accord with the facts as the opposing theory. This argument was not at all convincing to people who had not yet developed our modern way of viewing scientific evidence.

Moreover, an additional scientific objection was soon presented. It could be shown that if Venus revolved about the sun it should show a full set of phases (Fig 2-6), whereas if it revolved about the earth only crescent phases should be observed. Observations of Venus by the naked eye showed no evidence of a full phase. There were variations of apparent brightness, but at the time of greatest brightness, it was not in the full phase position. There was no answer to this problem at the time (For the answer, see Fig. 2-6b).

TYCHO BRAHE

Even an unbiased astronomer like Tycho Brahe (1546–1601) rejected the Copernican system because he could observe no stellar parallax. Tycho was a high-born Dane of great talents who spent nearly a lifetime making careful observations of planetary motions, most of them in the finest observatory of all Europe. He invented new instruments with which he could make measurements with the naked eye that were accurate to less than ½ minute of arc. Compare this with the 10 minutes of arc probable error prevalent during the times of Copernicus. Tycho was clearly the naked-eye observer supreme, an excellent example of a scientist who collects data. He developed a geocentric hypothesis of his own which gained favor briefly. His own stated purpose of his work was to construct better planetary tables. Despite his high birth and his very considerable education, he was as full of superstition and of belief in occult influ-

ences as the rest of the people of his time. While he was the greatest of observers, he had little theorizing ability, and so at the time of his death his two volumes of data were just that—two volumes of data.

JOHANNES KEPLER

Tycho Brahe willed this enormous collection of data to his assistant, Johannes Kepler (1571–1630), when he died. Kepler, a German with a considerable talent for mathematics, knew that he could not improve on the accuracy of Tycho's observations. He therefore used Tycho's data in an effort to bolster the Copernican heliocentric hypothesis, in which he was a devout believer. It is interesting to note why.

To Kepler, a mathematician, the mathematical labyrinth of the Ptolemaic hypothesis was as abhorrent as the simplicity of the Copernican hypothesis was delightful. His motivation was the perfection of the heliocentric theory, but the ultimate reason was not, despite what we have said above, simply a desire for truth. Kepler's mind was a curious mixture of the old and the new. He was convinced that "God created the world in accordance with the principle of perfect numbers, so that the underlying mathematical harmony, the music of the spheres [p. 7], is the real and discoverable cause of the planetary motions." This harmony, was, of course, not to be found in the Ptolemaic hypothesis. Kepler was, in the beginning, a symbol-seeking mystic who made his living as an astrologer, but somewhere within him were the makings of a true scientist, for eventually he fashioned his laws from Tycho's data alone, and afterwards looked for his symbolism. Kepler started with the orbit of Mars.

His object was to determine its exact path about the sun. His problem was threefold: to find the center of the orbit, to find its distance *relative* to the earth–sun distance, and to find the inclination of the plane of the orbit to the plane of the earth's orbit. After four years of calculation he found that he could not fit Tycho's data into a

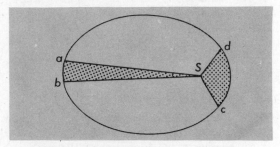

Fig. 3-1. Kepler's Law of Equal Areas. The sun, *S*, is one of the foci of the ellipse. A planet moves from *a* to *b* in the same time that it takes to move from *c* to *d*. The area *ASB* is equal to the area *CSD*. Thus, a planet sweeps out equal areas in equal times.

perfect circle in which Mars moved with uniform speed. The difference was only 8 minutes of arc, less than $\frac{1}{7}$ of a degree, but he knew that Tycho's data were far more accurate than that. If he had been a man of less integrity, he could have hidden the difference behind some convenient assumption. This failure of the data to fit his theory distressed him, for he was a devotee of the uniform circular motion concept. Eventually and reluctantly he tried an ellipse with the sun at the center, but without success. Then he put the sun at one focus of the ellipse—and everything fell into place. He formulated the Law of the

Ellipse: *Planets move in elliptical paths, with the sun at one focus of the ellipse.*

Gratified though he was, Kepler soon saw that the law would not allow him to calculate the position of Mars at any particular time, for Tycho's data had also shown that the speed of Mars varied within narrow limits. He therefore set out to discover a law that would relate the speed of a planet at any point in its orbit to its speed at any other point, the evidence for which Kepler was sure must be hidden in Tycho's data. Years of labor went into the effort before he was able to announce the Law of Equal Areas: *During equal time intervals a line from the planet to the sun sweeps out equal areas* (Fig. 3-1). This means that the planet moves faster when nearer the sun, slower when farther away. The two laws together made astronomical predictions possible.

Still Kepler was not satisfied, because neither law revealed any connection between the radius of the orbit and the speed of one planet and the radius of the orbit and the speed of any other planet. We might ask, "Why should there be?" Kepler believed firmly that there must be an overall pattern in the solar system, that the spacing of the planets was not haphazard, that there must be uniformity in nature to reflect the orderly mind of the Creator. After several more years of work he was able to announce his third law, sometimes called the Harmonic Law: *The square of the time for one complete revolution of a planet about the sun is proportional to the cube of the mean radius of its orbit,* i.e., the cube of its mean distance from the sun. Symbolically, $T^2 \propto r^3$, where the symbol $\propto$ means "proportional to." If we use a proportionality constant, *K*, to take care of the difference in the units of T and r, we can write

$$T^2 = Kr^3 \qquad \text{(Eq. 3-1)}$$

(See p. 99.)

Suppose we apply the law to Jupiter, whose observed period is 11.87 of our years. We need to know the value of K, for a unit of time can never equal a unit of distance. We do this by applying the equation to the earth, for which we know both T and r. We use the average distance of the earth from the sun (93,000,000 mi) which we will call one astronomical unit (A.U.). For the earth, r in astronomical units then becomes 1. If we use our year as the time unit, then $T = 1$ also. We have for the earth,

$$T^2 = Kr^3$$

Substituting, $\qquad 1^2 = K(1^3)$

Whence $\qquad K = 1$

This value of K is good for all planets as long as we use the units stated above for T and r. For Jupiter we have already expressed T in terms of our years—11.87 years. Therefore,

$$(11.87)^2 = Kr^3$$

Since $K = 1$, $\qquad r^3 = (11.87)^2 = 140.9$

$$r = \sqrt[3]{140.9} = 5.2 \text{ A.U.}$$

The average radius of the orbit of Jupiter thus becomes $5.2 \times 93{,}000{,}000$ mi $= 483{,}600{,}000$ mi. The actual distance in round numbers (calculated in other ways) is 483,000,000 mi.

The period of Pluto, our outermost planet, discovered in 1930, could be calculated once its distance was measured without waiting the 248 years necessary for it to complete one revolution. Conversely, if

we wait that long in order to get its period, we can use it as a check against the distance.

It took Kepler 17 years of hard labor to arrive at these three laws. He was then able to construct tables of planetary motions, tables which remained in use for over a century. Kepler showed himself to have some of the attributes of a true scientist by his attitude towards observations. He made the observations the supreme arbiter of his theory; the theory lived or died according to how well it explained the observations. His overall view, his great overriding purpose was, however, to show that an intelligent Creator would never have made the universe according to that unnecessarily complex device that was called the Ptolemaic hypothesis of the universe. Kepler's laws helped to convince only those who were already more or less favorably inclined to the Copernican system. It failed completely with the active opponents of the theory. To them it was merely a neat mathematical scheme that permitted calculations of the positions of the planets in their orbits at any particular time. Furthermore, there was still no positive evidence for the lack of observable phases of Venus, nor for the lack of observable parallax. More convincing evidence was needed.

GALILEO GALILEI

Kepler published his first two laws in 1609 and his third law about ten years later. A friend and avid reader of his was Galileo Galilei (1564–1642) of Italy. They corresponded, keeping each other informed of the latest scientific events in their own parts of Europe. Both were Copernicans living in a world that was still Ptolemaic.

Between them they very nearly succeeded in turning it into a Copernican world.

Galileo's contributions consisted of the invention of a telescope and the observations he made with it. He had heard of the invention of a telescope in Holland. He deduced its principle, and made one of his own, and so brought astronomy to the practical test of a telescope. With it the phases of Venus were clearly seen, including the full phase. This was a triumph of the greatest importance for the Copernicans, for in the Ptolemaic system, Venus could never get far enough away from the sun to show a full phase (compare Fig. 2-6c with Fig. 2-6d). The fact that Venus displays a complete set of phases constitutes the one conclusive proof that it revolves about the sun.

Far greater numbers of stars were visible with the telescope. All still appeared as mere points of light, which bolstered the argument of Copernicus that they were extremely far away. The telescope revealed that Jupiter had four moons revolving about it. (We now know it has 12.) This came as a shock to the Ptolemaic world, for here were clearly four celestial bodies that revolved about a center other than that of the earth. Furthermore, the celestial bodies were supposed to be perfect spheres, but Galileo could see mountains on the moon, spots on the sun, and bulges at the equator of Saturn. These facts annoyed his opponents, for they meant the collapse of the perfect-sphere concept.

The battle, however, still was not yet won, for the authoritarians refused to be convinced, proving once again that man can believe only what he is ready to believe. Even the concrete evidence meant nothing. Most refused to look through the telescope, for they did not wish to be convinced. The following argument from the Italian astronomer Francesco Sizzi (1611) will serve to illustrate the type of reasoning that Galileo and Kepler had to contend with:

There are seven windows in the head, two nostrils, two ears, two eyes and a mouth; so in the heavens there are two stars, two unpropitious, two luminaries, and Mercury alone undecided and indifferent. From which and many other similar phenomena of nature such as the seven metals, etc. which it were tedious to enumerate, we gather that the number of planets is necessarily seven. Besides, the Jews and other ancient nations, as well as modern Europeans, have adopted the division of the week into seven days, and have named them from the seven planets: Now if we increase the number of planets, this whole system falls to the ground. . . . Moreover, the satellites are invisible to the naked eye and therefore can have no influence on the earth and therefore would be useless and therefore do not exist.

From 1616, when the Inquisition warned Galileo to cease teaching the Copernican theory as truth (rather than as an hypothesis) because it was contrary to Holy Scripture, until his death in 1642, Galileo's life was a constant warfare waged in behalf of the revised heliocentric theory of Copernicus. We say revised theory, for Kepler had destroyed the concept of uniform circular motion. The extent to which Galileo had advanced beyond either Copernicus or Kepler can be seen in that he urged acceptance of the heliocentric system on its own merits of simplicity and usefulness rather than on how well it satisfied religious views, or reflected the mind of the Creator.

THE FINAL TRIUMPH

Forty-four years after Galileo's death in 1642 (the year of Newton's birth) Newton's *Principia* was published, and with this event the opposition among the educated to the heliocentric theory of the solar system began to crumble. We would like to be able to say that the overwhelming evidence that had developed by 1700 in favor of the theory had convinced even its staunchest opponents. The truth, however, is that in the interim most of these staunch opponents had died, leaving the field largely to those less indoctrinated with the authoritarian attitude and more ready to accept the evidence from observation and experiment. We must not think that the warfare between authoritarianism and science is yet dead. This warfare as well as the warfare between ignorance and knowledge still goes on, but with somewhat diminished intensity. We have only to witness the so-called Monkey Trial in Tennessee in the early 1920's and the banishment of textbooks in the 1930's because of Einstein's Jewish faith. Thus, the ultimate success of the heliocentric theory hinged as much on a gradually changing mental climate as on the works of Kepler and Galileo and Newton. The final scientific objection, that of the lack of observed parallax, was removed in 1838 when Bessel observed parallax of a "fixed" star, Proxima Centauri, 2.4×10^{13} mi away.

SUMMARY

The Romans contributed almost nothing to science, largely because of their utilitarian attitude. After the fall of Rome and the overrunning of western Europe by the barbarian hordes, the progress of science was brought virtually to a standstill. Chiefly responsible was the spread of Christianity and its concern with "how to go to heaven" rather than "how the heavens go." The Scholastics in the thirteenth century, on the rediscovery and translation of the complete works of Aristotle and the other Greek scholars, interwove Aristotelian physics, astronomy, and philosophy with Christian theology so intricately that to doubt one was to doubt the other. Thus it became heresy to question the geocentric hypothesis of Ptolemy.

Copernicus, a Polish Churchman, doctor, mathematician, and astronomer, disliked the complexities of the geocentric hypothesis so intensely that he returned to the heliocentric theory of Aristarchus. He developed this theory in detail, still maintaining the circular orbits for all celestial bodies. His work on the system was published the year of his death in 1543. It failed to win many adherents, for, aside from the common-sense objections, there were no proofs and no overriding advantages over the geocentric concept. Its only advantage was that it was much simpler.

In the early 1600's Kepler, using the volumes of data collected by the greatest naked-eye observer that ever lived, Tycho Brahe, deduced and formulated his three laws of planetary motion, which still hold today within very narrow limits. Still there were few additional converts. Then Galileo, a contemporary and friend of Kepler's, invented a telescope, discovered that Venus had a full set of phases (the first direct observational evidence of the heliocentric theory), and discovered four satellites circling Jupiter. The opposition still was able to prevent acceptance of the heliocentric theory until after Galileo's death in 1642. What giants like Kepler and Galileo could not do, a changing mental climate, aided by Newton, did. Those steeped in the learning and traditions of the Scholastics died, their places being taken by those brought up in the rapidly changing atmosphere of the Renaissance, where there was much less tendency to accept the authoritarianism established by the Scholastics. Moreover, the layman began to play a bigger and bigger role in the search for knowledge. Modern science, we can truthfully say, began with Galileo, largely because of his clear formulation of the problems, his experimentation, and his mathematical approach.

EXERCISES

PROBLEMS

1. The Ptolemaic system reigned undisputed for nearly fourteen hundred years. State four scientific reasons for its long reign.

2. What advantage, if any, did the Copernican hypothesis have over that of Ptolemy at the time of its formulation?

3. List three scientific objections to the Copernican hypothesis.

4. For what was Tycho Brahe noted?

5. How were day and night explained by the geocentric theory? By the heliocentric?

6. What change did Kepler introduce into the Copernican hypothesis? Why was it necessary?

7. State Kepler's three laws, which accounted for the varying speed of a planet in its orbit.

8. What were the contributions of Galileo to the heliocentric hypothesis?

9. List the following in the proper time sequence: Kepler, Brahe, Galileo, Copernicus.

10. The discovery of the phases of Venus spelled ultimate doom for the geocentric theory. Why?

11. What answer did Copernicus have to the fact that no parallax could be detected among the stars?

12. When was stellar parallax first discovered? Do all stars show it? Explain.

13. A hypothetical planet is 4 astronomical units distant from the sun. What is its period?

14. How did the Ptolemaic hypothesis explain the seasons?

CHAPTER IV

The Solar System

The most incomprehensible thing about the universe is that it is comprehensible.

—ALBERT EINSTEIN

INTRODUCTION

Our solar system consists of the sun, 9 planets, 31 satellites, about 1500–2000 planetoids (asteroids), myriads of meteors, and several hundred thousand comets. The mass of all the planets and minor bodies taken together equals only about 0.15 per cent of the sun's mass. Almost all of these bodies are arranged within a relatively thin, slightly elongated disc that is about 7.5 billion mi in diameter. The plane of

the ecliptic is parallel to the disc and passes through its center (Fig. 4-1). The orbit of Pluto deviates more than those of the other planets from the plane of the ecliptic. This deviation causes the disc to be thicker than it would be otherwise. The orbits of the comets deviate far more widely than does Pluto's, but these are minor bodies which, despite their great numbers, do not have a total bulk mass anywhere near that of the earth.

Large as the sun and the larger planets may seem to be, almost all the volume of this huge disc is empty space. It is also tremendously isolated in space (p. 4). It takes light traveling at 186,000 mi/sec a bit less than half a day to cross the disc, but over four years to reach the nearest body outside the disc. That nearest body is the star Alpha Centauri. A planetary system like the solar system revolving about this nearest star could not be seen or photographed by any telescope we now have, nor any of the light-gathering type that we are likely to ever make, for planets have no light of their own.

Our solar system is a part of an immensely greater galactic system, which we call the Milky Way. Like our solar sys-

Fig. 4-1. Orbits of Planets Viewed Edgewise. Note that they are all nearly in the same plane except Pluto. Thus they traverse the same relatively narrow band in or near the plane of the ecliptic.

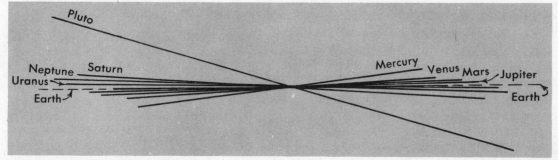

tem, most of the stars of our galaxy, more than 30 billion of them, are also arranged in a disc, which lies parallel to that of our

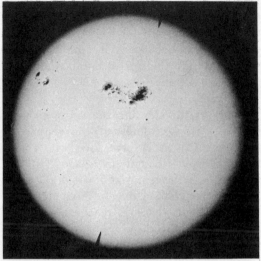

The Sunspot of April 7, 1947

Fig. 4-2. Whole Solar Disc (above) Showing Sunspots. Below is an enlargement of the large sunspot group. (Courtesy Mt. Wilson and Palomar Observatories.)

solar system. This disc is more than 100,000 light years across (light travels about 6 trillion mi in one year) and about 10,000 light years thick. Our solar system disc is far off the center of this galactic disc but is deep enough in it so that if

we look out in directions parallel to the "flat" sides of it we see very large numbers of stars,[1] whereas if we look in directions at right angles to the plane of the disc, we see comparatively few.

Almost all of the planets and most of their 31 satellites revolve in the same direction (counterclockwise as seen from outer space) about the sun. A few minor satellites are exceptions. Furthermore, all except Uranus rotate in the same direction (counterclockwise). Planets inside the orbit of the earth exhibit phases because they can get between us and the sun, thus preventing us from seeing all of the illuminated face at all times. Those outside the earth's orbit never exhibit phases because we can always see the whole illuminated face at all times.

THE SUN

The sun is a star, a rather average star. It is a great sphere of intensely hot glowing gas, 864,000 mi in diameter. Its volume is about $1\frac{1}{3}$ million times that of the earth, but its mass is only $\frac{1}{3}$ of a million times greater. Its average density is therefore much less than that of the earth, about one-fourth as great. The temperature of the outer part is about 6000° Centigrade (10,000° Fahrenheit); the interior is far hotter. Thus, every substance on or in it exists in the gaseous state.

The only features that can be observed on the sun are sunspots and prominences (Figs. 4-2 and 4-3). Sunspots range from 500 to 100,000 or even 150,000 mi across. They are huge areas that look black be-

[1] The light from these myriads of apparently closely spaced stars gives a hazy whitish appearance to this belt. Hence the term Milky Way.

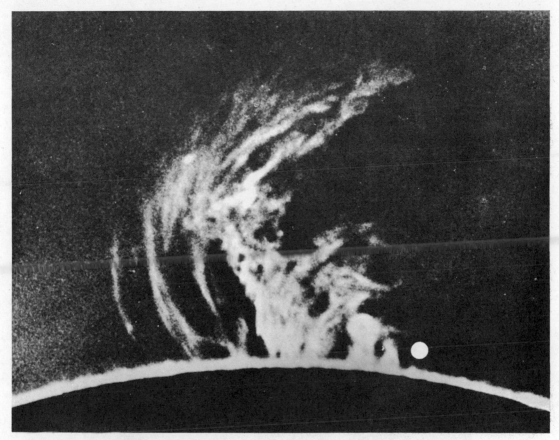

Fig. 4-3. Large Active Prominence, 140,000 Miles High. Photographed in the light of calcium, July 9, 1917. The white spot shows the size of the earth to the same scale. (Courtesy Mt. Wilson and Palomar Observatories.)

cause they are cooler than the areas surrounding them. They are still intensely hot, however. Their cause is not definitely known. It is by watching them as they move across the sun's face that we know that the sun rotates slowly on an axis. The period of rotation increases as the distance from the equator increases, which can be possible only if the surface is entirely gaseous. Prominences are huge streamers of glowing gases rising great distances above the surface (Fig. 4-3).

THE PLANETS

Many of the statistical facts about the planets are summarized in Fig. 4-6. We will therefore confine our attention here to brief descriptions that cannot conveniently be put in the form of tables.

Mercury

Mercury is close to the sun, rising and setting either a little before or a little after it, and so is never above the horizon in

Fig. 4-4. Sun at Time of Near Total Eclipse, December 9, 1929. The whole edge of the sun is seen, with several prominences. (Courtesy Mt. Wilson and Palomar Observatories.)

complete darkness. This adds to the difficulty of studying its surface details. It is also the smallest of the planets, being only a little larger than the moon, and thus difficult to see. Because of these circumstances, few people have ever seen it.

Its period of rotation is equal to its period of revolution, therefore it always keeps the same side towards the sun. The result is that the side towards the sun has a temper-

ature as high as 770° F, higher than the melting points of lead, tin, and sulfur. The temperature of this side is somewhat variable, for the orbit of Mercury is more elliptical than that of any other planet save Pluto. The other side is extremely cold—several hundreds of degrees below 0° F.

Mercury has very little or no atmosphere, and seems to be at least as mountainous as the moon. As an environment for the development of life, that of Mercury is about as forbidding as anyone would expect to find in the whole solar system.

Venus

Venus as viewed from the earth is the brightest of all of the heavenly bodies except the sun and the moon. It is only 26,000,000 mi away from us at the closest approach (Fig. 2-6b), and would appear many times brighter than it does if we could see the whole of the illuminated face in that position. Actually we can see only a thin crescent phase, but even so Venus is far brighter than any star (15 times as bright as Sirius, the brightest star), and 2½ times brighter than when it is in full phase but on the opposite side of the sun from us.

The orbit of Venus is about twice as far from the sun as that of Mercury, approximately midway between the orbits of Mercury and the earth. This is not far enough for it ever to be seen for more than two or three hours before sunrise or after sunset. It is thus either a morning star when it rises ahead of the sun (Fig. 2-6a) or an evening star when it rises later than the sun (and so sets later than the sun).

Because of its nearness to the sun, the

Fig. 4-5. Solar Corona at Time of Total Eclipse, June 18, 1918 as Seen from Green River, Wyoming. The corona is the luminous region about the sun which may be seen during a total eclipse. (Courtesy Mt. Wilson and Palomar Observatories.)

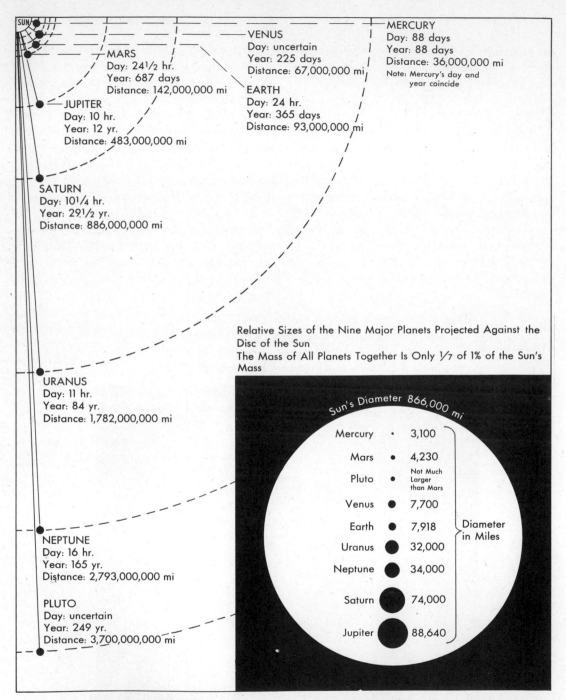

SUN

MARS
Day: 24½ hr.
Year: 687 days
Distance: 142,000,000 mi

VENUS
Day: uncertain
Year: 225 days
Distance: 67,000,000 mi

MERCURY
Day: 88 days
Year: 88 days
Distance: 36,000,000 mi
Note: Mercury's day and
year coincide

EARTH
Day: 24 hr.
Year: 365 days
Distance: 93,000,000 mi

JUPITER
Day: 10 hr.
Year: 12 yr.
Distance: 483,000,000 mi

SATURN
Day: 10¼ hr.
Year: 29,½ yr.
Distance: 886,000,000 mi

URANUS
Day: 11 hr.
Year: 84 yr.
Distance: 1,782,000,000 mi

NEPTUNE
Day: 16 hr.
Year: 165 yr.
Distance: 2,793,000,000 mi

PLUTO
Day: uncertain
Year: 249 yr.
Distance: 3,700,000,000 mi

Relative Sizes of the Nine Major Planets Projected Against the
Disc of the Sun
The Mass of All Planets Together Is Only ⅐ of 1% of the Sun's
Mass

Sun's Diameter 866,000 mi

Mercury	•	3,100
Mars	•	4,230
Pluto	•	Not Much Larger than Mars
Venus	•	7,700
Earth	•	7,918
Uranus	•	32,000
Neptune	•	34,000
Saturn	•	74,000
Jupiter	•	88,640

Diameter
in Miles

Fig. 4-6. Summary of Planetary Data. The scale is approximately correct. The length of
a planet's day is expressed in our hours, and its year in terms of our year. (After Menzel,
Stars and Planets, used by permission of The University Society, New York.)

temperature is considerably higher than that of the earth. Venus is completely blanketed by clouds, so that man has never seen its surface. These clouds seem to consist chiefly of carbon dioxide. Oxygen is definitely not present and the probability that water vapor is present is extremely slight. Since Venus has a mass about four-fifths that of the earth, and is so near the earth, it would seem probable that it should have about the same atmosphere. The fact that it does not is at present unexplainable.

Since the clouds prevent us from seeing any of the surface features, the period of rotation is unknown. It has been estimated to be about one month. If so, the surface temperature, below the blanket of clouds, late in its two-week-long day is probably above the boiling point of water. During its two-week-long night the temperature would drop to several hundred degrees below 0° F if it were not for the heavy blanket of carbon dioxide, a gas that is especially effective as a heat trap. Even so, it drops to below 0° F every "night" of its year. The prospect for life on Venus is considered zero.

Mars

From two standpoints Mars is the most interesting of the planets. For one thing, it is the only planet that man can hope to land on and survive for any length of time, if at all, even with all of the devices that have been invented to aid him. For another, it is the only one on which there is any prospect of life, primitive though it may be.

It is the first planet whose orbit lies outside that of the earth. Its somewhat ruddy color makes it easy to recognize. Its diameter is about twice that of our moon, big

enough to hold an atmosphere by its gravitational force. However, it is unlikely that the density of the atmosphere is much more than half that at the top of Mt. Everest (where man must carry a supply of oxygen in order to live). Furthermore, the percentage of oxygen in Mars' atmosphere seems to be less than 1 per cent of the earth's, and it has been determined that the total amount of water vapor would, if condensed, form a liquid layer only $\frac{1}{300}$ in. thick if spread over the entire surface. Any space traveler to Mars would probably find that the so-called polar ice caps, which appear in the Martian winter and disappear in the summer, are not much more than layers of frost on the ground. At their greatest extent they reach more than halfway to the equator. Mars appears to be about three-fifths desert. The reddish color is believed to be due to layers of reddish sand mantling these deserts.

Its day is very nearly the same length as ours, but its year is twice as long, so its seasons are six months long. The greater distance from the sun, about 50 per cent greater on the average than the earth's distance, means that Mars has a comparatively cold climate. During the long summer the temperature rises from a little above the freezing point of water to a maximum of about 50° to 60° F (about 13° C) in its hottest part. Nevertheless, there is a possibility of plant life of the lichen–moss variety in the slightly more humid lower areas. Animal life as we know it is out of the question, for there is no reason to believe that there is animal life with a metabolism based on an element other than oxygen, and which could originate or exist without water. Life on earth, plant and animal, originated in the oceans. How it could originate on a planet with

MARS 1956

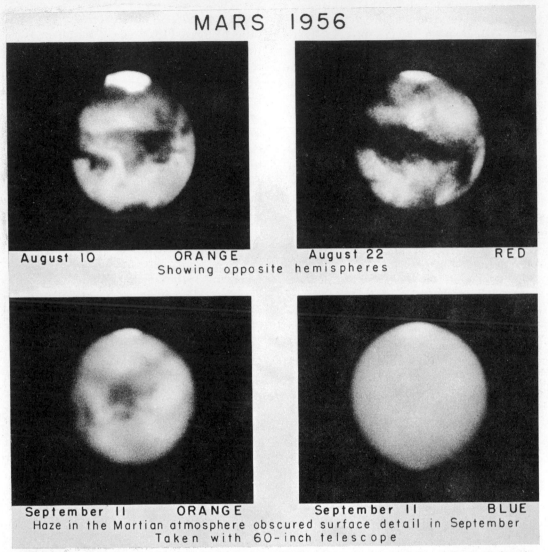

August 10   ORANGE   August 22   RED

Showing opposite hemispheres

September 11   ORANGE   September 11   BLUE

Haze in the Martian atmosphere obscured surface detail in September

Taken with 60-inch telescope

Fig. 4-7. Mars During Closest Approach to Earth. Four views taken in different-colored light. (Courtesy Mt. Wilson and Palomar Observatories.)

so little water is difficult to imagine. The difficulty is increased by the temperature factor. A maximum temperature of 50 to 60° F in the warmest part during the day suggests a drop to near or below freezing at night every night of the year over the whole of the dark side, especially in view of the rare atmosphere. For life to originate, carbon, nitrogen, oxygen, and hydrogen atoms must have combined in some way. Since low temperatures slow down the rate of chemical combination, the probability of life originating on Mars becomes still smaller. Furthermore, Mars must have lost its hydrogen very early in its history because of its small mass.

Jupiter

Nearly half a billion miles from the sun is Jupiter, with a volume greater than that of the other planets put together. There is a marked difference in the average densities of the planets from Jupiter outward, as compared to the inner planets. The earth, with a density of 5.52, is the densest planet. Mars has a density of 3.3, but Jupiter drops to 1.34. Aside from atmospheres, the four inner planets therefore must consist largely of rock. If any part of Jupiter does consist of rock—and this is extremely likely, as its density cannot be accounted for otherwise—the rock must be in an inner core not much more than one-third the diameter of the whole planet. Studies seem to indicate that this is the case, and that one would have to penetrate 25,000 mi into Jupiter before rock would be encountered.

What is this outer 25,000-mi-thick layer surrounding the core composed of? The outermost part is the atmosphere, composed of hydrogen and helium, with ammonia and methane increasing with depth. Beneath this atmosphere is a layer of ice thousands of miles thick, ice consisting of frozen ammonia and methane (like our cooking gas).

It goes without saying that life on Jupiter is impossible. It is far colder than Mars because it is so much farther away from the sun, over three times the distance of Mars. The average temperature is $-140°$ C.

Saturn

Saturn, second in size, holds the distinction of being the only planet that is less dense on the average than water. It is,

however, far more famous because of its three rings. The rings are formed by billions of small bodies, probably similar to small asteroids. Their origin is not known. They are invisible to the naked eye and so were not known before the time of Galileo. The composition of Saturn is similar to that of Jupiter, but there is less ammonia in its atmosphere and presumably not much of a rocky core—the low density of 0.71 gm/cm^3 would forbid that. The solid part is largely frozen ammonia and methane. Its average temperature is $-155°$ C.

Uranus

Uranus differs from the other planets in its orientation to the plane of the ecliptic and its direction of rotation. It rotates clockwise on an axis that is very nearly parallel to its direction of revolution. Its four satellites also revolve clockwise instead of in the more common counterclockwise direction. The density of Uranus is nearly equal to that of Jupiter. Its composition is similar but with no ammonia in the gaseous state. The ammonia has all been frozen out by the intense cold to form a layer of ice thousands of miles thick. Its average temperature is $-180°$ C.

Neptune

Neptune is somewhat smaller, but has a greater density than Uranus. Its rotation is normal but the direction of revolution of one of its two satellites is retrograde. Its composition is about the same as that of Uranus, but it probably has a somewhat bigger rocky core.

Pluto

Pluto, discovered in 1930, is about the size of Mars, but there is considerable un-

Fig. 4-8. Saturn and Its Rings. Photographed with 100-in. telescope. (Courtesy Mt. Wilson and Palomar Observatories.)

certainty about it. Since its period of revolution is about 248 years, it has traversed less than one-eighth of its orbit since its discovery. Its orbit is highly eccentric and inclined more to the plane of the ecliptic (Fig. 4-1) that that of any other planet. It will be closest to us in 1989, at which time it will be inside the orbit of Neptune by about 35,000,000 mi. It will, however, be 240,000,000 mi away from Neptune at that time so that no collision is possible.

THE MOON

The moon is not the largest of the 31 planetary satellites, but it is much the largest in proportion to the size of the planet about which it is revolving. Its diameter is a bit over one-fourth that of the earth. It is not large enough for its gravitational force to hold an atmosphere. Its average distance of 240,000 mi, 60 times that of the earth's radius, makes it much the nearest of all the celestial bodies.

The lack of an atmosphere is attested by the fact that when the moon passes between the earth and a star, the star disappears suddenly without any gradual fading as it would if there were an atmosphere to refract the light. Moreover, during an eclipse none of the effects that can be ascribed to an atmosphere show up. It would seem unlikely that the moon did not have an atmosphere at the time of its "birth." If so, why did it lose it? This involves the velocity of escape.

The gaseous molecules which form the atmospheres of the planets are all moving at speeds that depend partly on their masses and partly on their average temperature (p. 208). At 0° C this velocity would range from the neighborhood of 1800 ft/sec for the heavier molecules like oxygen and nitrogen to 5000 ft/sec for hydrogen, the lightest of all gases. At higher temperatures the speeds are greater. Gravitational attraction holds the molecules to the planet, and if it is not great enough, the lighter, faster-moving molecules in the outer atmosphere escape for good. This is the reason that the earth has no hydrogen in its atmosphere, whereas the more massive planets with a greater force of gravity do. The velocity of escape on the moon is scarcely more than one-fifth that on the earth due to its lesser mass, so that even oxygen, nitrogen, carbon dioxide, and water vapor have long since escaped.[2]

[2] This velocity of escape is an important factor in firing rockets into far outer space. A rocket must leave the earth with a minimum speed of about 25,000 mi/hr if it is to escape permanently. This does not mean that it will continue at this speed. As soon as its fuel is exhausted, it starts to slow down because of the opposing force of gravity. By the time it gets far enough out, where this opposing force is negligible, it has a relatively low velocity.

The lack of an atmosphere has extremely important consequences for an astronaut attempting to land on the moon. It means that he not only would have to carry his own oxygen supply, but also would have to wear a pressurized suit at all times, or his blood would literally boil in his veins. There is no atmosphere to cause friction and vaporize the countless meteors that must be striking the moon, and if a meteor did no more than puncture the pressure suit, it would be fatal to the astronaut. Lack of an atmosphere also means that there is no water either on the moon's surface or below it. Thus, there are no clouds, and the sun's rays beat down on the surface during its two-week-long day with an intensity unknown on earth, raising the temperature above that of the boiling point of water. It means that as soon as the sun sets—to begin its two-week-long night—the temperature plummets to below zero, eventually reaching the neighborhood of −250° F. It also means that there is no atmosphere to filter out most of the deadly ultraviolet rays emanating from the sun. While protection from some, if not all, of these dangers may be possible, life on the moon by earth-born visitors will be extremely hazardous. Life native to the moon is, of course, impossible.

A visitor to the moon would be treated to a view of outer space that is very unlike that from the earth. The sky *in daylight hours* would not be blue but black, because there is no atmosphere to scatter the sun's rays; blue is scattered more than the other colors of the spectrum by the atmosphere. Thus, not only the sun, but also the earth, and all of the stars and the other planets that are above the horizon would be shining out of a perfectly black sky at the same

Fig. 4-9. Northern Portion of Moon at Third Quarter. The larger craters are some tens of miles across. (Courtesy Mt. Wilson and Palomar Observatories.)

time, with a brilliance that is difficult to imagine. Next to the sun, the most brilliant would be the earth, especially after sunset. Its apparent diameter would be four times that of the full moon as viewed from the earth.

The surface of the moon has been de-

scribed too frequently to go into much detail here. In places there are mountains, most of which seem to be volcanic in origin rather than of the folded type which form most of the earth's mountain ranges. There are thousands of high peaks, some of the order of 25,000 ft above the surrounding plains. These plains have been called "seas" by earlier astronomers who had less knowledge than we now have. More than 30,000 craters, ranging from ¼ mi to about 150 mi across, have been mapped. They have been thought to have originated from impacts of meteors in the early days of the moon's history, but their association in groups with the mountain ranges seems to preclude this. They are more probably volcanic in origin, but the evidence is by no means conclusive.

Fig. 4-10. Enlarged Portion of Moon Showing Density of Craters. (Courtesy Mt. Wilson and Palomar Observatories.)

ASTEROIDS

The first asteroid (or planetoid) was discovered the first night of the year 1800 by an astronomer who was searching for a planet that should, according to the Titus-Bode law,[3] revolve in an orbit between those of Mars and Jupiter.

This asteroid, too small to be called a planet, was the first of some 1500 to 2000 that have since been discovered. It was the largest, a bit less than 500 mi in diameter. The others range down to masses as small as ½ mi across. None of them has the characteristic oblate spheroidal shape of the true planets. Many thousands probably exist that are too small to be detected with our present instruments. Many of them have highly eccentric orbits. It is possible that some of the meteorites that fall to the earth were asteroids whose orbits eventually brought them too close to the earth. They may be the remains of a planet that was shattered by some unknown catastrophe.

COMETS

Comets were once believed to be stars with long hairy tails. Up to the time of Galileo and even later they were widely regarded as omens of evil, and often caused panic among superstitious people. They were thought to be balls of fire flung by an angry Creator to warn the peoples of their

[3] If we take numbers 0, 3, 6, 12, 24, 48, 96, etc., doubling at each step from 3 on, add 4 to each, and divide by 10, we obtain the distances of the planets in astronomical units (p. 25), with reasonable accuracy. These distances, called Bode numbers, are 0.4, 0.7, 1.0, 1.6, 2.8, 5.2, 10.0, 19.6, (38.8), and (77.2), all in astronomical units. In Bode's time (*ca.* 1780) there was no planet to occupy the 2.8 position. Perhaps, he thought, one was there but had been overlooked.

wicked ways. Not until the discoveries of Tycho Brahe, Kepler, and Galileo did the people's fears begin to be allayed.

What these astronomers did was to establish the fact that comets are members of the solar system just as much as the planets are, but the paths that they describe are usually very different from those of the planets. Most comets pass very close to the sun and then go out to enormous distances, taking scores or even hundreds of years to return. Thus, their orbits are commonly highly elliptical. A few have relatively small ellipticities, i.e., small for a comet. About half move clockwise around the sun, the other half counterclockwise. The inclinations of their orbits to the plane of the ecliptic varies from 0° to 90°.

The head or nucleus of a comet consists of an immense number of small particles varying in size from specks of "dust" to particles some yards across. It is never composed of one solid mass. Surrounding the nucleus is a foggy mass of gases sometimes hundreds of thousands of miles across. The tail is composed of dust particles and gaseous molecules which trail off behind the nucleus sometimes for hundreds of millions of miles. As the comets approach the sun, the heat vaporizes some of the particles, thus causing the tails to increase in size. The gases become luminescent under the action of the sun's ultraviolet rays, thus "lighting up" the gaseous parts of the comet. The sunlight exerts a radiation pressure on the gaseous and finest dust particles, so that the tail of a comet always swings away from the sun. Thus, when the comet approaches the sun, the tail is behind the head, as all respectable tails should be, but when it is receding from the sun the tail precedes the head.

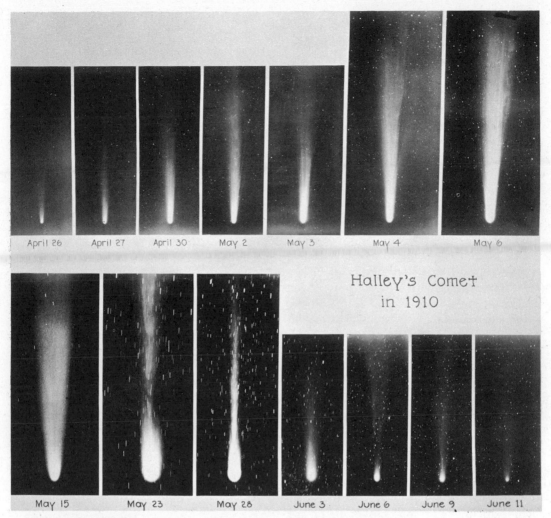

April 26 April 27 April 30 May 2 May 3 May 4 May 6

Halley's Comet
in 1910

May 15 May 23 May 28 June 3 June 6 June 9 June 11

Fig. 4-11. Halley's Comet. Fourteen views made during its last appearance in 1910. It will reappear again in 1986, reaching its nearest approach on April 29 of that year. (Courtesy Mt. Wilson and Palomar Observatories.)

The masses of comets vary widely. Vast numbers of them are too small to be seen with the unaided eye. Halley's Comet (Fig. 4-11), one of great ones, last seen in 1910 and expected to reappear in 1985, has a mass that has been estimated to lie be- tween 30 million and 10 million billion tons. Halley, a contemporary of the great New- ton, calculated the orbit of the comet now known by his name when it appeared in 1682, and predicted that it would appear again in 1835. It arrived on schedule.

METEORS AND METEORITES

Meteors are the so-called "shooting stars" and have nothing whatever to do with stars. Most are tiny specks of matter no bigger than a grain of sand, or at most a pea. Every day many tens of millions encounter the earth's atmosphere. Traveling at high speed they develop a considerable amount of heat because of friction with the air; they become white hot and are burned up in a second or two. They get hot enough to glow about 60 mi above the earth and are burned up within another 20 mi.

The bigger ones fail to get burned up completely and so strike the earth. They are then called meteorites. One of the largest, brought from Greenland, is in the American Museum of Natural History in New York City. It weighs 36½ tons. Still larger ones have struck the earth, causing devastation for miles around. The largest ever known landed in Arizona not more than five thousand years ago. A crater 4200 ft in diameter and 570 ft deep was formed when it exploded as it struck.

These bigger meteorites are all of metallic composition, largely iron, with several per cent nickel and small amounts of many other metals. Some are made of low-silica igneous rocks. The minerals in them are the same as those formed from molten "lava" here on earth.

There is a close association between most meteors and comets. Many well-known meteoric showers have been caused by the earth passing through the tails of comets. A comet "discards" part of its matter as it revolves about the sun. This debris continues to revolve about the sun in a manner similar to that of Saturn's rings. This debris cannot be seen until it encounters the earth's atmosphere, and is heated to incandescence. None of the large meteors that have struck the earth came from the tails of comets.

SUMMARY

The isolation of our solar system in space and its position in our galaxy, the Milky Way, is emphasized. The descriptions of the planets follow but their motions are not discussed here, for that has been done in Chapters II and III. The four inner planets have average densities that are somewhat greater than those of average rocks at the earth's surface, whereas the low average densities of the outer planets, considerably less than half that of the inner planets, must mean a great difference in composition. The inner planets are largely made of rock, whereas the outer ones, with the possible exception of Saturn which may lack a rocky core, probably have relatively small cores of rocky material. These cores are certainly surrounded by layers of ice thousands of miles thick, ice made chiefly of frozen ammonia and frozen methane. This ice, in all except Pluto, is surrounded by an atmosphere that contains some ammonia and methane and also some hydrogen and helium.

The inhospitable conditions on the moon have been described in some detail because of the possible attempt to send an astronaut there.

EXERCISES

PROBLEMS

1. Fundamentally, what condition must be met if a planet, or our moon, is to show a complete set of phases?

2. Why do the outer planets (planets with orbits outside that of the earth) not show phases like those of the inner planets?

3. From the earth we see the phases of the moon. If you were on the moon, could you observe phases of the earth? Explain.

4. If we consider the length of a day to be the time between two successive sunrises, how long is the day on the moon?

5. Mars, as seen from the earth, varies greatly in brightness. Why?

6. Why do the planets never eclipse one another?

7. Few people have ever seen Mercury. Why?

8. Assuming that Venus is visible on a particular date, where would you expect to see it an hour or two after sunset?

9. When, on that same date, did it rise with respect to the rising of the sun?

10. What is meant by the velocity of escape?

11. How do we know from the earth that the moon has no atmosphere?

12. The composition of the atmospheres of the planets is determined from the character of their spectra, which you will learn about in Chapter XXIV. What gases have been detected in the atmospheres of the other planets? What is the most general and striking difference between these atmospheres and that of the earth?

13. List the advantages that the earth has over any and all of the other planets with respect to the development of life.

14. Why do the so-called shooting stars disappear so quickly?

FORCE AND MOTION

The choice between the heliocentric and the geocentric theories could not be made with finality much before 1620. There were no dynamic principles to help, no clear understanding of force and motion. What force, or forces, kept them moving? What kept them in their elliptical paths? The latter question was easily answered by the followers of Ptolemy. They were embedded in crystal spheres or domes which held them in their courses. To turn these great transparent but solid domes Aristotle postulated a supernatural Prime Mover. Much later, after comets from far out beyond the sun were seen to cut paths through the supposedly hard crystal spheres, the planets had to be assumed as floating in empty space. Without the domes it was extremely difficult to see how they could follow exactly the same paths in their revolutions about the earth. The early Christian followers of the Ptolemaic system supposed the planets to be composed of light fluffy materials carried along in their orbits by angels. The earth, however, was obviously made of heavy materials which would require a great force to move at all—all the more reason for believing it motionless. Copernicus and his followers had no answer to this problem of a moving earth than to point out that the moving system of stars in the Ptolemaic system presented an even greater problem because they were so much farther away.

Many realized, the philosopher René Descartes among them, that a new start in science as a whole, a new manner of attack upon the unknown, was needed. A scientific revolution was being called for, even though no one knew what kind of a revolution was needed. From the time of Copernicus onward men of the western world began to take more and more of a part in shaping their own destinies. They became less and less willing to leave it all to the theologians and philosophers. Whereas for thousands of years it had been the countries in or near the eastern end of the Mediterranean that had dominated world history, western Europe now began to take command. The scholars became less and less concerned with the mystical "essence" of a thing; instead they wanted to know how things worked. The influence of the ecclesiastics declined and that of the laymen increased. Men of leisure and money, along with many craftsmen, turned to science. The artists, in part at least, led the way. They were often the "engineers" and the inventors, often artisans as well as artists. For an outstanding example, there was Leonardo da Vinci (1452–1519), painter, sculptor, goldsmith, engineer, architect, physicist, biologist, geologist, philosopher—and a master of each. He was unquestionably the most versatile genius that ever lived.[1]

The first to use a new manner of attack upon the unknown openly, consistently, and effectively was Galileo (1564–1642). Hence, more than anyone else, he deserves to be called the father of modern science. To be sure, Kepler had showed a tinge of modernity by his acceptance of the explanation of observable facts as the criterion of the worth of a theory, but beyond this he did not progress far. Kepler could not divorce his science from medieval mysticism. We feel far more at home with Galileo, for with him the last vestiges of mysticism had disappeared. Galileo clearly formulated his problems, a necessary first step towards their solution. He was able to correct a fallacious view of motion because he was able to restate the problem in very different terms. It is therefore to him that we first turn in our efforts to understand the causes of motion, not only among the celestial bodies, but here on earth.

[1] His many notebooks were not published for well over a century after his death. If they had been immediately published, it is probable that science would have been advanced a hundred years in a single step.

CHAPTER V

Galileo's Study of Motion

Nothing in Nature is more ancient than motion, and the volumes that the philosophers have compiled about it are neither few nor small; yet have I discovered that there are many things of interest about it, that have hitherto been unperceived."
—GALILEO (1636)

Nothing is more familiar to us than motion. We see it everywhere, from the apparent motions of the sun, moon, stars, and planets to the real motions of clouds drifting across the sky and the raindrops and snowflakes that sometimes fall from them. We see it as the winds rustle the leaves, as the streams flow toward the sea, as the waves lap gently on the shore or pound it with savage fury. We see it in all of man's activities, in the transportation not only of ourselves to and from our work or play, but in that of our daily needs of every sort. We ourselves, or some part of us, are in constant motion from even before birth to the time we die. So used to motion of many kinds are we that if we rise at dawn on a still summer morning, we look out upon a world that seems unnatural because of the lack of motion, and we are often moved to comment on it. Not only is motion a charac-

teristic of much of our macroscopic and microscopic worlds, but it is even more a characteristic of the submicroscopic world of atoms and molecules. It may truly be said that there is not a single completely motionless atom or molecule in the whole universe. Yet man for thousands of years believed that rest was the natural state of matter. Let us inquire into the reasons for this belief.

Primitive man had long been concerned with the problems of motion, chiefly because he needed more efficient means of transportation of his goods as well as himself. This concern with transportation led to the early invention of sails, the wheel, and the horse collar. Yet a true insight into the fundamental concepts of force and motion was long delayed. Looking backward, we can see why, for these concepts are extremely subtle, so much so that it might well be said that the average intelligent and educated person is intuitively an Aristotelian unless he has had special instruction. So subtle and contrary to common sense are many of the aspects of ordinary motions, and so great is the tendency for us to therefore draw the wrong conclusions concerning them, that one of the foremost contemporary historians was moved to say,

Of all the intellectual hurdles which the human mind has been faced with and has overcome in the last fifteen hundred years the one which seems to me to have been the most amazing in character and the most stupendous in the scope of its consequences is the one relating to the problem of motion.

ARISTOTLE'S CONCEPTS OF NATURAL MOTION (FREE FALL)

Aristotle appears to have been the first to attempt to give rational explanations to the phenomena of freely falling bodies. Before considering these concepts we must clearly understand that the scientific concepts, not only of Aristotle but of all the early Greeks, were intimately tied into a comprehensive philosophical-religious system whose main function was to interpret nature and its processes in terms that could be understood.

Science had begun in magic. Early man lived at the mercy of uncontrolled nature, and his first attempts to control it were by magic. The Greeks were the first to make any large-scale attempt to understand and interpret nature. If man could do that, he would feel more at home in this world. The first step in this direction concerned the constitution of matter, for its behavior would depend, in large part, upon its composition (and in other large part upon its structure). Therefore, we need to understand Aristotle's concept of matter in order to understand his views on its "natural" motion.[1]

Aristotle had accepted the Pythagorean concept of four basic elements, earth, water, fire, and air. In an attempt to explain why solids and liquids free to move always fell towards the earth, whereas fire and air seemed to rise, Aristotle conceived that each of these four elements had a natural home. That of earth and water is the earth itself; that of air is obviously above the earth, as was also that of fire, for does not one see the flames leaping upward? All of the various kinds of matter consisted of combinations of these four elements. Each kind took on the characteristics of the particular element or elements that it had

in greatest abundance. Thus, when fire was added to water (i.e., when the water was heated) the water turned to vapor, and escaped upward because it now had one of the characteristics of fire. When the vapor lost the fire, i.e., when it cooled and condensed, it became water again and returned to earth (its natural home) as rain. Thus, the concept of what Aristotle called natural motion was intimately related to matter itself.

The utmost confusion reigned in the minds of the early Greeks with respect to this natural motion. It is easily observed that when compact heavy objects are dropped, they seem to fall faster and faster, whereas small light objects such as feathers, snowflakes and raindrops seem to fall with speeds that are constant.[2] Aristotle held that falling objects fell because the earth was their natural home. The bigger and more massive the object the more rapidly it fell, because it had within it more of a "desire" or tendency to reach its natural home. According to this concept a 100-lb ball would fall 100 ft in the same time that a 1-lb ball fell 1 ft, because it had 100 times the tendency to return to the earth that the 1-lb ball had. There is no evidence that Aristotle checked this by experiment.[3]

[1] By natural motion Aristotle meant the motion of a body falling freely through space towards the earth. Today we refer to such motion as free fall.

[2] Democritus held that heavy objects would fall faster in a vacuum than would light objects. Aristotle held that they would fall at the same speed in a vacuum, but since the concept of their falling at the same speed was inconceivable, the concept of a vacuum was absurd.

[3] Aristotle preached the checking of concepts by observation or experiment insofar as it was possible but he commonly failed to follow his teaching. An example is the report that he once said that women had more teeth than men. This statement could easily be proved false by an observation, for even in those days he should have been able to find some woman with her mouth open.

It is doubtful that the failure of such an experiment would have changed his views, for to him and his followers, observable facts did not have to be strictly in accord with the postulates of his comprehensive philosophical system. He considered the postulates more important than the observations, and so gave philosophic truth precedence over scientific truth. Contrast this with the modern concept that all scientific theorizing must proceed from observed facts, and that if other pertinent observable facts are not in accord with the theory, then the theory must be altered or abandoned.

Aristotle's belief that the speed of any particular body was proportional to its weight meant that its speed was constant regardless of the time or distance of fall. This concept may be written as an equation,

$$v = K,$$

where v stands for velocity and K is a constant. He never checked this hypothesis by experiment.

GALILEO, THE FATHER OF MODERN SCIENCE

Galileo is important and interesting to us in the study of force and motion for several reasons. For one thing, he not only had to criticize, alter, and eventually destroy faulty theories and replace them with better ones, but he also had to destroy a whole intellectual world and replace it with another. He had to evolve a new concept of science which was completely independent of the philosophical and religious dogmas of the time. Like Copernicus with respect to the relative motions of the earth, sun, stars, and planets,

Galileo had to replace a common-sense approach to motion by one that is "uncommon-sensical."

He may also be truly called the father of modern science, for he was the first to use modern experimental methods throughout. If Galileo could return to earth today, he probably would, after a period of study, feel right at home in many fields of science. Compare this with Kepler, who, despite his new attitude towards observed facts and his successful attempt to formulate physical laws in mathematical form, would have found it far more difficult, more likely impossible, to make the transition, for he still had far too much of medieval mysticism bred into him.

Galileo first studied medicine at the University of Pisa, but soon changed to the physical sciences and mathematics. At the age of twenty-six he was appointed to the University Chair of Mathematics. His unusual mental qualities, his independence of spirit and his intellectual integrity, alloyed with a testy temper, a gift for ridicule, and no semblance of patience or tact, were soon displayed in his refusal to accept the reasoning by authority in scientific matters (see p. 46) that had pervaded all institutions of learning in western Europe for over three hundred years.

Despite his almost constant warfare with scientific authoritarianism, he managed to escape arrest and trial for heresy until the last few years of his life. At no time was he forced to discontinue his experiments. His quarrel with the Jews and with the Christian churches, Protestant and Catholic, was over his insistence on teaching the Kepler version of the Copernican hypothesis as truth rather than as an hypothesis. Eventually he was forced to recant.

He spent the last few years of his life under "house arrest."

GALILEO'S EXPERIMENTS ON FREE FALL

The legend that Galileo tested the Aristotelian viewpoint that the rate at which an object falls is proportional to its weight, by dropping large and small balls made of metal and wood from the Leaning Tower of Pisa, is an old and repeatedly told one. If he did, neither he nor any of his contemporaries recorded it. We can be confident, however, that he did test it, not only because the Aristotelian viewpoint was taught at the University of Pisa, but also because any true scientist would do so. We might as well assume that it was as likely done there as anywhere else.

According to Aristotle a 1-lb ball should be only halfway down at the instant a 2-lb ball, dropped at the same instant, strikes the ground. This is easily disproved by experiment, for the two strike the ground almost at the same instant. We attribute the slight difference to the greater effect of air resistance on the smaller ball, for today we can demonstrate that in a near vacuum a feather and a lead ball will drop together. If one is medieval-minded, one can deny the experiment proves anything by insisting the experimenter has bewitched either the two balls or the eyes of the observer, so that the balls appear to fall together. This is what some of Galileo's colleagues said with respect to his experiments. Some also refused to look through his telescope, for they said they would be bewitched into seeing what Galileo wanted them to see.

We must not suppose that Galileo was the originator of all of the ideas that are associated with his name. No large intellectual enterprise ever starts from nothing; there are always previous investigators who contribute an isolated bit here and another there. What every great innovator does is take these bits, check them, add to them his own, and shape them all into a consistent whole. James R. Newman put it aptly when he said, "Great ideas emerge from the common cauldron of intellectual activity, and are rarely cooked up in private kettles from original recipes."

True scientist that he was, Galileo was not content merely to prove that light and heavy bodies fell at the same rate if air resistance was neglected; he set out to find out how they fell. He wanted to know the relationships between the distance fallen, the speed, and the time. It is an easily tested fact that an object falling through a distance of 20 ft has a greater final velocity than one falling through a distance of 2 ft. You can test the truth of this statement by jumping first from a chair to the floor, and then by jumping from a second-story window.[4]

The "force" of your impact with the floor compared to that with the ground is a measure of the increase in velocity. This *time rate of increase of velocity is called acceleration,* a concept with which we are all familiar because of our experiences with automobiles.[5] Galileo reasoned that this rate of increase in velocity should be uniform. If so, a freely falling body should have uniformly accelerated motion. Galileo's problem was to find out whether the average velocity—which is all that we can hope to *measure* even today—was propor-

[4] Do not reverse the steps in this experiment, for if you do, you may be unable to complete the test.

[5] Aristotle seems to have been wholly unaware of the concept of acceleration.

tional to the distance of fall or to the time of fall. He reasoned that it had to be proportional to one or the other. He also had to consider Aristotle's hypothesis that the velocity (hence the average velocity) was a constant (p. 77). We may list the three hypotheses in mathematical form in Table 5-1. The letter K is a constant, the same

TABLE 5-1

Aristotle	Galileo (A)	Galileo (B)
	$\bar{v} \propto d$ *	$\bar{v} \propto t$ *
$\bar{v} = K$	$\bar{v} = Kd$	$\bar{v} = Kt$
also, $\bar{v} = d/t$	also, $v = d/t$	also, $v = d/t$
$\therefore \quad d/t = K$	$\therefore \quad d/t = Kd$	$\therefore \quad d/t = Kt$
and $d = Kt$	and $1/t = K$	and $d = Kt^2$

* Any proportionality may be converted into an equation, as we do here, if we insert a proportionality constant (see p. 99).

for all times (t) and distances (d); $\bar{v}$ (to be read "v bar") is the average velocity, and $\propto$ is a symbol to be read "is proportional to."

Inspection of the final form of Galileo's A hypothesis shows it to be an absurdity, for time obviously varies as the distance of fall changes. Hence $1/t$ cannot be a constant. Galileo therefore discarded this hypothesis. This left him with the other two to check. Note carefully that by performing the mathematical operations in the table a change is made in the quantities to be measured. Galileo now had to be concerned only with distance and time, quantities that can be measured far more easily than velocity. Note also the difference between the two remaining hypotheses.

Aristotle's states that the distance is proportional to the time, and Galileo's to the square of the time. In other words, Aristotle states that if a body falls 16 ft in 1

sec, it will fall a total of 32 ft in 2 sec, a total of 48 ft in 3 sec, etc., whereas Galileo states that if it falls 16 ft in 1 sec, it will fall a total of $16 \times 2^2 = 64$ ft in 2 sec, and a total of $16 \times 3^2 = 144$ ft in 3 sec, etc. You should clearly realize that both of the above are hypotheses. Neither can be proved by any sort of reasoning, mathematical or otherwise. One is just as logical as the other. Falling bodies are not required to fall in accord with the reasoning of man, as one might suppose if one were a follower of Aristotle. The only way to determine how they fall is by experiment, and this is what Galileo now set out to do.

Like any modern scientist, Galileo began by planning an experiment (Fig. 5-1). His difficulties were, however, enormously greater than those of any modern scientist. His greatest was the lack of a good timing device. Consider that the time of fall from the ceiling to the floor of your classroom is less than one second, and we can appreciate his difficulty. Moreover, the clocks of his time had only hour hands. He tried using his pulse but found it unsatisfactory. A more successful device was a vessel of water from which water was allowed to escape through a tiny jet which he could open or close with his finger. He could then weigh on a balance the water that escaped during short time intervals. This balance was the most accurate instrument he possessed, even though crude by modern standards. Still the time rate of free fall was too fast to measure directly with an accuracy sufficient to prove or disprove either hypothesis.

He resorted again to reasoning and invention. His invention was a pendulum "clock." His reasoning resulted in his conviction, reached after extensive experimen-

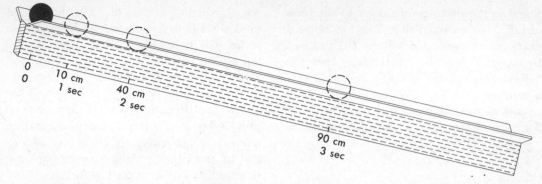

Fig. 5-1. One Version of Galileo's Inclined-plane Experiment. The ball rolled with uniform acceleration of 20 cm/sec².

tation with inclined planes,[6] that a ball rolling downhill is really "falling" downhill. In other words, a ball rolls downhill for the same reason that it would fall vertically if free to do so.[7] By adjusting the tilt of this inclined plane to a low angle so that the velocity of the ball was small, he found that he could measure the time of "fall" quite accurately with his pendulum "clock."

He found that the ball rolled four times as far in two swings of the pendulum as in one, and nine times as far in three, etc. This was in accord with Galileo's B hypothesis. He varied the steepness of the inclined plane; the ball rolled faster and faster as the steepness increased, but in every case the distance rolled was proportional to the square of the time. As the angle of tilt was increased until it was near the vertical, he found that the speed of the ball became too great to measure accu-

[6] For his inclined planes he used long straight strips of lumber in which he cut narrow grooves the full length. Since he lacked modern tools to make a smooth groove, he eliminated its irregularities by lining it with parchment paper.

[7] How do you think Aristotle would have explained the tendency of a ball to roll downhill?

rately. Again he had to resort to reasoning, somewhat as follows: "If, finally, I increase the steepness until the plank is vertical, the ball would hardly touch the plank at all, but rather would fall freely alongside of it. I shall then have a freely falling body, and the distance should still be proportional to the square of the time." Modern experiments prove that he was right. Put formally, Galileo's Law of Free Fall states that *a uniformly accelerated body, starting from rest, traverses a distance proportional to the square of the time of travel*. Mathematically stated it is $d \propto t^2$. Using a proportionality constant it is

$$d = Kt^2 \qquad \text{(Eq. 5-1)}$$

Since free fall is a typical case of uniformly accelerated motion, this equation applies to all uniformly accelerated motion.

You are probably wondering about that K in the law. Since it is a constant which does not change as d and t are varied, it will have a definite value as long as the conditions under which the experiment is performed do not change. When Galileo changed the angle of the inclined plane,

K = new angle.

K

metric system —

he changed one of the conditions of the experiment. Therefore, the value of *K* changed with each new angle. Yet intuitively we may feel that there should be some order in this change, that *K* cannot change randomly. We feel the need to know what *K* really is.

There are two ways of solving the problem, one by mathematical calculation and deduction, and the other by experiment. Galileo used both methods. The one should, of course, check the other. Either method will involve the use of, and the relationships between, the concepts necessary in any quantitative treatment of the subject of motion, namely, those of distance, time, speed, velocity, and acceleration. Before proceeding further we will make a short diversion to make certain that our understanding of them is sufficient to make either method meaningful.

DESCRIPTION OF LINEAR MOTION

There are various kinds of motion, but for the present we will concern ourselves only with linear motion, i.e., motion in a straight line. Later, when we have need for it, we will introduce circular motion. In this textbook we will be concerned with two kinds of linear motion, (1) uniform motion, by which we mean motion with a constant speed, and, (2) uniformly accelerated motion, of which free fall is a classic example. We will always carefully state the type with which we are dealing.

The concepts of distance and time are so familiar that they need no explanation, except for the units in which they are stated. We will at times use the centimeter-gram-second (cgs) system of units, and at times the foot-pound-second (English) system. Thus, distances will be

metric system

either in centimeters (in rare cases, meters) or in feet. Masses or weights will be either in grams (occasionally in kilograms) or in pounds. Distances, masses, and weights are easily measurable if they are appreciably large; Galileo had no difficulty with them. The accurate measurement of time is far more difficult, as we have seen; but modern electrical timing devices can measure intervals of time that are small fractions of a second long.

You may have noted in the past few pages that we have sometimes used the term speed and sometimes the term velocity. These terms are synonymous to the average person, but never to the scientist. The scientist uses the term speed, as you do, to mean *the time rate of motion,* but to him velocity means speed in a straight line, i.e., *speed in a given direction.* To say that a body is moving with uniform velocity means that it is moving in a straight line with unchanging speed. In such motion the distance traveled is *directly proportional to the time.* Algebraically, *d* = a constant × *t*, i.e.,

$$d = Kt \qquad \text{(Eq. 5-2)}$$

Obviously, we cannot say *d* = *t*, for that would be ridiculous. The *K* is a proportionality constant, which takes care of the difference in units.

Average speed is defined as the total distance divided by the total time, i.e., $\bar{v} = d/t$ (as will be explained shortly). For uniform motion, speed and average speed are the same. For nonuniform motion they are distinctly different. Suppose you drive 10 mi along city streets to visit a friend, slowing down and speeding up according to traffic conditions, or even stopping at red lights. To speak of your speed on such a trip is meaningless, but your average speed is obviously d/t, the distance divided by the time. Your average speed in the above example is a statistical speed, just as statistical as it is to say that the average number of children in an American family is 2.5. It is, however, a useful concept.

There is another kind of speed, instantaneous speed, that we may occasionally use. It is, of course, the speed of a body at a given instant. It is, for all bodies, impossible to measure. Unlike average speed, it can never be calculated for non-uniform motion. It can, however, be *calculated* for uniformly accelerated motion.

These concepts must be very clear if you are going to appreciate the meaning of acceleration. As previously stated, we all have an intuitive understanding of acceleration because of our experience with automobiles. This, however, is not enough for our purposes; we must have a precise understanding of it. It is a very difficult concept, first developed by Galileo, and one that the ancient Greeks never had. The difficulty arises from the fact that it is a time rate of a time rate. It is not a change in speed or velocity—which are themselves time rates of motion.

Acceleration is time rate of change of velocity, i.e., it is a rate of change in a rate of motion. In other words, it is change in velocity per unit time. Mathematically,

$$a = \frac{v_f - v_i}{t}$$

where v_f and v_i are the final and initial velocities, respectively. If the body starts from rest, v_i is 0, and we have $a = v_f/t$. Since we will be dealing only with accelerated motion when $v_i = 0$, we may write $a = v/t$.

If we know the acceleration and the time, we can calculate v, simply by transposing:

$$v = at$$

This is a highly useful equation which you should thoroughly understand rather than memorize. It applies only to uniformly accelerated motion in which the initial velocity is 0.

We need to be concerned about the units in which acceleration is expressed. Bearing in mind that velocity is time rate of motion (in a straight line), and that acceleration is time rate of change of motion, we can see that if velocity is expressed in distance units per unit time, acceleration must be expressed in distance units per unit time per unit time, i.e.,

$$a = \frac{d/t}{t}$$

A more convenient but equivalent way of stating it is distance units per unit time squared, i.e., d/t^2. Thus, we say that the acceleration is 5 ft/sec/sec ($= 5$ ft/sec^2), or 10 cm/sec/sec ($= 10$ cm/sec^2). Note carefully that neither the 5 nor the 10 is squared in these examples.

We need now to return to the concept of average velocity as applied to uniformly accelerated motions. In these cases the concept of average velocity is not statistical. Consider a car starting from rest and accelerating uniformly until the instant it reaches 40 mi/hr—which we will designate as the final velocity. In this case the average velocity is exactly half the final velocity, i.e.,[8] $\bar{v} = v_f/2$. If this is not obvious to you, consider the following:

Suppose that it takes a car 10 sec to ac-

---

[8] This equation holds only if the body starts from rest, i.e., if the initial velocity (v_i) is 0. Otherwise, $\bar{v} = (v_f + v_i)/2$.

celerate from rest $(v_i = 0)$ to 40 mi/hr. Since $v_f = at$, $a = v_f/t$ or $40/10 = 4$ mi/hr/sec. Therefore, at the *end* of 5 sec it will be moving at 20 mi/hr, which is half the final velocity. During these 5 sec it will be moving at less than half the final velocity, and during the last 5 sec it will be moving with more than the final velocity. The excess during the latter 5 sec just balances the deficiency during the first 5.

MATHEMATICAL TEST OF GALILEO'S HYPOTHESIS

With these concepts firmly in mind we can now return to Galileo's work on free fall. You will recall (p. 79) that we were inquiring into the characteristics of K in Galileo's law of free fall, $d = Kt^2$. Again we remind you that free fall is the classic example of uniformly accelerated motion. We stated that Galileo calculated this equation and then checked it by experiment. His method of calculation was as follows:

$$d = \bar{v}t$$

where $\bar{v}$ is the average velocity.

$$\bar{v} = \frac{v}{2}$$

where v is the final velocity.

Substituting for $\bar{v}$,

$$d = \frac{vt}{2}$$

Now $v = at$; substituting for v,

$$d = \frac{at \times t}{2} = \frac{at^2}{2} = \frac{1}{2}at^2 \quad \text{(Eq. 5-3)}$$

Since $d = Kt^2$ and $d = \frac{1}{2}at^2$, it is now clear that $K = \frac{1}{2}a$.

In Galileo's experiment the acceleration obviously increased as he made his inclined plane steeper and steeper. Therefore the value of K increased. Although mathematical deduction indicates that K does equal $\frac{1}{2}a$, it is necessary to find out by experiment if this is really so. Before we do this, however, let us make some predictions from this equation, and then see if they are borne out by experiment.

Let us choose an arbitrary value for a, say 20 cm/sec². Substituting for a in the equation $d = \frac{1}{2}at^2$, we see that d is 10 cm if t is 1, 40 cm if t is 2, 90 cm if t is 3, 160 cm if t is 4, etc. What we will really be doing in our experiment is checking predictions derived from a theory against observable facts. We have already described Galileo's experiment in a loosely quantitative way. We will now describe a modern version of this experiment, record the data in a table, and then see what conclusions may be drawn.

A MODERN EXPERIMENT TO TEST GALILEO'S HYPOTHESIS

Let a straight aluminum bar about 15 or 16 ft long be mounted on edge so that one end is 8 or 10 in. above the other. The upper edge has a smooth groove cut in it so that a steel ball can roll down the bar freely. An electrical device (electromagnet) holds the ball at the high end of the bar. When a switch is pulled, the ball starts rolling and another electrical device starts clicking off the seconds.

Our hypothesis (p. 79) predicts that if the ball rolls 10 cm the first second, it will have rolled 40 cm at the end of 2 sec, 90 cm at the end of 3 sec, etc. We therefore measure off and mark on the bar these distances: 10 cm, 40 cm, 90 cm, 160 cm, 250 cm, 360 cm—all from the starting point. We now carefully adjust the angle of inclination so that the ball will actually roll 10 cm the first second. Next we start the ball rolling to see if it is at the 40-, 90-, 160, 250- and 360-cm marks at the end of 2, 3, 4, 5, and 6 sec, respectively. We find that it is, and so observation checks with theory. If we put our data and the information gained from it in the form of a table, we will understand it better.

The first two columns in Table 5-2 constitute the data obtained in our experiment. From this data we can gain all of the information in the other columns. Make certain that you see how this is done. Column 5 is derived by dividing column 2 by column 4. This gives us the value of K in $d = Kt^2$, and it will hold for all values of t as long as we do not change the value of a by changing the tilt of the bar. The steeper the tilt, the greater the value of a.

Let us continue increasing the tilt. As we do so, we will find that we have increased our experimental difficulties because of the increased acceleration of the ball—our eyes are not good enough to mark the position of the ball at the end of the first second, let alone the second or third. We saw how Galileo had to give up and resort to reasoning (p. 79). Modern elec-

trical devices enable us to easily overcome Galileo's difficulty. With such a device we can measure the value of a when the bar is *vertical*. Actually, we dispense with the grooved bar since we are now measuring free fall (Fig. 5-2). The value of a in free fall, commonly called the acceleration due to gravity, and hence assigned the special letter g, is very nearly 980 cm/sec^2 at sea level. This is slightly more than 32 ft/sec^2. These two figures should be memorized. More important, you should know how to use them, just as you should know how to use the equations $d = \bar{v}t$, $v = at$, $d = \frac{1}{2}at^2$. Merely memorizing them is not learning science. You can learn to use them only by solving a number of problems in which they are essential. For this purpose, solve the problems at the end of the chapter.

While Galileo did not have the concept of force that we have today, he reasoned that in the case of a body thrown vertically upward, the cause of the slowing down on the upward journey should be the same as that which speeded it up on the downward journey. If this is so, the same law ($d = \frac{1}{2}at^2$) should apply, for the slowing down is just as much a time rate of change in velocity as is the acceler-

TABLE 5-2

Time, t (sec)	Measured Cumulative Distance, d (cm)	Distance Ratio	t^2	$\dfrac{\text{Col. 2}}{\text{Col. 4}} =$ $K = \frac{1}{2}a$	a	$d = \frac{1}{2}at^2$
1	10	1	1	10	20	10
2	40	4	4	10	20	40
3	90	9	9	10	20	90
4	160	16	16	10	20	160
5	250	25	25	10	20	250
6	360	36	36	10	20	360

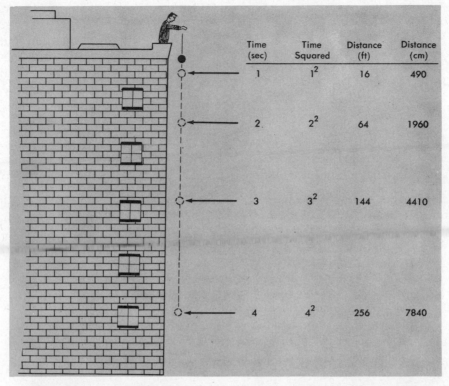

Time (sec)	Time Squared	Distance (ft)	Distance (cm)
1	1^2	16	490
2	2^2	64	1960
3	3^2	144	4410
4	4^2	256	7840

Fig. 5-2. A ball dropped from any place on earth will fall in accordance with the law governing uniformly accelerated motion, $d = \frac{1}{2}at^2$. (Air resistance is neglected.)

ation while the body is on its downward journey. The slowing down might be called deceleration; the physicist calls it negative acceleration.

ARISTOTLE'S VIEWS ON HORIZONTAL MOTION

Aristotle was less successful in his attempts to arrive at plausible conclusions regarding horizontal motion, which he called forced or violent motion, in contrast to free fall, which he called natural motion. He believed that a continually acting cause (which we now call a force) was necessary to keep a body moving horizontally at a uniform velocity. Inherent in this belief is the concept that rest is the natural state for terrestrial bodies. This is a common-sense view, for, according to the Aristotelians, if you leave a moving body alone, it will come to a stop.

The Aristotelians had to postulate a continuous force to act on a ball thrown by a pitcher to a catcher if the ball was to continue moving after leaving the pitcher's hand. They thought the eddies of air that developed behind the ball as it moved onward supplied this force for a brief time.

This view was a great stumbling block

for two thousand years in the effort to arrive at a true concept of horizontal motion.

GALILEO'S VIEWS ON HORIZONTAL MOTION

Galileo contributed a wholly new point
of view. Instead of continuing to try to
answer the Aristotelian question concerning the cause of continued forced motion,[9]
Galileo asked the more fruitful question,

---

[9] The reader must bear in mind the difference
between Aristotle's natural motion and forced motion. Free fall was natural motion and needed no
force to keep a body in motion. All other motion
was forced motion.

"What would make it stop?" He could devise no experiments (nor can we today)
to test the Aristotelian question, but found
it easy to test his more fruitful question.

Almost too obvious to be noticed is the
observation that objects at rest stay at rest
unless disturbed. Equally obvious is the
necessity of a force to put them in motion.
Galileo's experiments attempted to compare the effort to put in motion a body
which is at rest with the effort needed to
stop it. These he found to be nearly equal.
What he did was to let a ball roll down
one inclined plane and up another (Fig.
5-3a, b, c). No matter what weight ball
he used, no matter whether the two planes

Fig. 5-3. Galileo's Experiment on Horizontal Motion. Neglecting friction, a ball rolling down any incline will rise to the height
from which it started but no farther. In (d) he generalized that
if the plane were horizontal and infinitely smooth, the ball
should roll on forever.

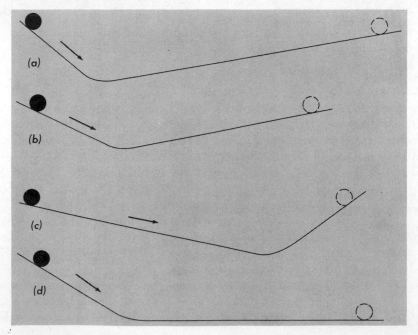

were inclined at the same or at different angles, the ball would always roll to a height that was a little less than the height at which it started. He found that the smoother the planes and the rounder and smoother the ball, the less this difference in heights was. He reasoned that if the planes and the ball were infinitely smooth, there would be no friction and the difference in heights would become zero.

In another experiment he used a single inclined plane with long level boards as an extended horizontal plane (Fig. 5-3d). Given the same initial force, a ball rolling on a rough plane did not roll so far as on a smoother one. The smoother the plane and the rounder the ball the farther the ball rolled. Galileo came to the conclusion that if a ball that was perfectly round and perfectly smooth was rolled along a perfectly smooth horizontal endless plane, there would be nothing to stop the ball (assuming no air resistance), and so it would roll on forever. We know now that it is friction between the ball and the surface, and between the ball and the air that stops the rolling. By stating that uniform motion is just as natural as is rest for bodies here on earth, Galileo gave these terrestrial bodies an attribute heretofore reserved for celestial bodies. Note also that Galileo here once more invoked *the method of the limiting case*,[10] a method in which he first reasoned from motion on an inclined plane to motion in the vertical path of free fall, and then from a rough horizontal plane to a perfectly smooth frictionless one. On Galileo's actual smooth horizontal plane no negative acceleration was discernible, i.e., the velocity appeared to be uniform.

[10] This method has ever since been one of the standard tools of scientific thought.

The conclusion that in the absence of a net force, whether of friction or otherwise, a body will remain in unchanging motion or else at rest, was first given precise form in 1644 (two years after Galileo's death) by Descartes:

We may remark that any velocity once imparted to a moving body will be rigidly maintained as long as there are no causes of acceleration or retardation, a condition that is found only on horizontal planes where the force of friction has also been minimized; for in case of planes that slope downwards there is already present a cause of retardation; from this it follows that motion along a smooth horizontal plane is perpetual.

PROJECTILE MOTION

Watch the path of a long high fly ball hit by a baseball batter on a windless day, or that of a football on the kick-off, or the throw of a volley ball. If you are a careful observer, you will be struck by the near symmetry of its path, i.e., the second half of the path appears to be the same shape as the first half, except in reverse (Fig. 5-4). The path of a cannon ball (a projectile) is similar, especially that of a slow-moving old-fashioned one.[11]

To an inquiring mind, this symmetry of the path might suggest that the upward and the downward paths are traversed in equal times. This seems reasonable enough, and it can be checked by experiment.

There is, however, far more to projectile motion than this. Consider the path of a bullet fired *horizontally* from a modern

[11] The faster a body moves through air the greater the air resistance, and so the true path deviates more and more from the ideal path in which air resistance is zero.

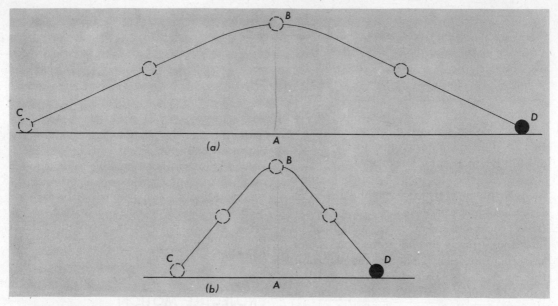

Fig. 5-4. Paths of Shells Fired from an Old-fashioned Cannon, or of Baseballs Batted on a Windless Day. Note the symmetry of the paths. If the height *AB* is the same, the time it takes to move from *C* to *D* is the same regardless of the distance *CD*. (Air resistance is neglected.)

high-powered rifle, say one with a muzzle velocity of 3000 ft/sec. Assume that the ground surface is level and that the barrel of the gun is 4 ft above the ground when you fire, and that you are out in the wide open spaces. Where and when will the bullet hit the ground? What will its path be like? When will the bullet start to fall to the ground? Suppose at the exact instant in which the bullet left the barrel of your gun, your friend dropped an identical bullet from the same height (4 ft) to the ground (Fig. 5-5). Would it strike the ground before, at the same time, or later than the bullet fired from the gun?

All of the ancients up to Galileo would have failed these questions just as dismally as you. Galileo worked out problems such as these when he solved the closely related problem of projectile motion. He did this

by recognizing the fact that the path of a projectile was a combination of vertical and horizontal motion, and *that these two motions are completely independent of each other.*[12] This means that in Fig. 5-4, the vertical motion indicated by *AB* is governed by the law of free fall, and that the horizontal motion indicated by *CD* will, if we neglect air resistance, go on forever if there is nothing to stop it. There is, of course, something to stop it—the earth—for every body thrown into the air at any angle whatever is acted on by a force which starts to act to bring it to earth *the*

[12] One should not read into this statement the concept that projectiles have separate vertical and horizontal motions. In our analysis of motion we split the real motion into two parts to understand it better (Fig. 5-6). The rules for doing this are discussed under vectors, p. 106.

instant that it leaves the propelling instru-ment.[13] You should now go back and try to answer the questions concerning the firing of the rifle bullet.

The concept that bodies in motion will remain in motion forever if there is nothing to stop them is incorporated in the Law of Inertia (later known as Newton's first law of motion). This law and the Law of Uniformly Accelerated Motion (of which the law of free fall is a special case) are Galileo's two great contributions to the understanding of the problem of motion. In the hands of Newton their inherent potentialities led, as Galileo himself predicted, "to wonderful new knowledge." Of equally

great importance was his emphasis on clear, well-formulated problems capable of being analyzed mathematically and checked carefully by experiment. He, more than anyone else, established the necessary conditions for the great growth of science that took place in the seventeenth century, a century justifiably called the century of genius.

SUMMARY

Aristotle's concepts of motion were not derived from experiments performed but from the postulates of a philosophical-religious system that encompassed the whole range of natural phenomena. He conceived of two kinds of motion, one which refers to the fall

---

[13] This means that no object can ever be thrown horizontally through the air, for the instant it leaves the hand (or the gun barrel) it starts to drop with an acceleration of 32 ft/sec/sec.

Fig. 5-5. A bullet emerging from the horizontal gun barrel and another dropped from the *same height* at the *same instant* will strike the *level* ground at the same time regardless of the velocity of the bullet fired from the gun.

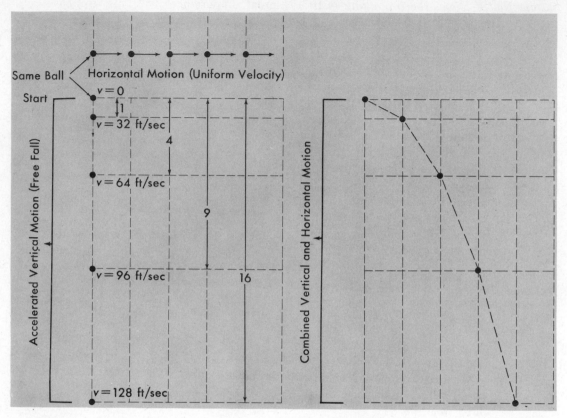

Fig. 5-6. Analysis of Projectile Motion (motion possessing both horizontal and vertical components). A batted ball is assumed to have reached its highest point (labeled start). Its vertical speed is zero at that instant. It then falls (left) according to $d = \frac{1}{2} at^2$ even as it moves forward.

of unsupported bodies to the earth and which he called natural motion, the other to horizontal motion which he called forced or violent motion. The concept of natural motion involved the nature of matter itself. Matter was made up of various combinations of four elements—earth, water, fire, and air—each with a natural home. No force was needed for any of them to return to their natural homes. Thus, natural motion presented no problems to him.

A consequence of Aristotle's philosophy was that he had to believe that heavier bodies fell faster than light bodies. Galileo found Aristotle wrong by dropping heavy and light objects side by side. He then proceeded to find out how objects actually do fall by letting balls roll down inclined planes. He reasoned that they rolled down the planes for the same reason that they would fall freely; the distances covered per second should therefore be in the same ratio as in free fall. His results showed that the distance was proportional to the square of the time.

Horizontal motion presented a different set of problems both to Aristotle and his followers, even up to the time of Galileo two thousand years later. The chief problem was what kept a body in motion after the propelling force was removed. Little progress was made until Galileo reformulated the question. All who had tried to find out what kept a body moving found the question led to a dead end. Galileo asked instead the very fruitful question, "What would make it stop?" This question can be answered, and it points up the fact that the ability to ask the right questions is a mark of the great scientist.

By a series of actual experiments aided by some thought experiments in which he imagined away friction and air resistance, he came to the conclusion that if there were no friction and no air resistance, a body set moving on a level surface would keep on moving forever.

Galileo was the first to recognize that horizontal and vertical motions were independent of each other, i.e., a ball thrown from one person to another possessed both kinds of motion, and they are completely independent of the other. Galileo's work on motion was completed by Isaac Newton, who was born the year that Galileo died.

EXERCISES

I. **Terms and Concepts**

Natural motion

Forced or violent motion

Free fall

Law of free fall

Projectile motion

Speed

Velocity

Acceleration

The symbols: d, t, v_i, v_f, v, $\bar{v}$, a, g.

The equations:

$$d = \bar{v}t$$

$$a = \frac{v_f - v_i}{t}$$

$$d = \tfrac{1}{2}at^2$$

$$v^2 = 2ad$$

$$\bar{v} = \frac{v_f + v_1}{2}$$

$$v = at$$

$$d = Kt^2$$

$$g = 980 \text{ cm/sec}^2$$

$$= 32 \text{ ft/sec}^2$$

II. **Problems**

1. Every equation has its limiting conditions, i.e., no equation is valid under any and all conditions in experimental science. The above equations, considered as a group, are valid for what type or types of motion?

2. You should not so much memorize the above equations as understand them. Memorizing science is not learning science. What two equations (above) are different forms of the same equation?

3. If $v_i = 0$, what do $\bar{v}$ and a, respectively, become?

4. Why may Galileo be considered the father of modern science?

5. How did Aristotle explain free fall?

6. Why did Galileo use inclined planes in his experiments on free fall rather than let objects drop from high places?

7. How did Galileo progress from the steepest inclined plane that he could use to completely free fall?

8. What limited the steepness of the inclined planes Galileo could use in his experiments on motion?

9. Before Galileo came to his final conclusions regarding either free fall or horizontal motion, he was forced to indulge in some thought experiments. What were these thought experiments, and why were they necessary?

10. In the equation, $d = \tfrac{1}{2}at^2$, what is the value of K in general? in free fall?

11. A car starting from rest is uniformly accelerated to 60 mi/hr in 12 sec.

   a. What is its acceleration?

   b. How far did it travel in those 12 sec?

   c. What was its velocity at the end of 5 sec?

12. Why are two time units necessary in any quantitative statement about acceleration, e.g., 15 cm/sec/sec or 5 mi/hr/sec?

13. A car travels 40 mi at 40 mi/hr and 40 mi at 60 mi/hr. Calculate its average

speed for the 80 mi. Show how you arrived at your result. (The answer is *not* 50 mi/hr.)

14. A ball is dropped from the top of a building. It takes 8 sec to reach the ground.
   a. How high is the building?
   b. What, neglecting air resistance, will the velocity of the ball be the instant before it touches the ground?

15. You wish to measure the depth of a deep well but have no line long enough. You drop a stone and time it until you hear it strike the water. If the time is 5 sec, how deep is the well? (Neglect time for sound to travel back to you.)

16. A ball is thrown vertically upward with an initial velocity of 128 ft/sec. Neglect air resistance.
   a. What will be its velocity after 1 sec?
   b. How long will it take for it to rise to its highest point?
   c. How high will it rise?
   d. How long will it take to return to the thrower's hand?
   e. What will be the velocity of the ball as it returns to the thrower's hand?
   f. Was the acceleration constant throughout its journey?

17. You are in an elevator at the fiftieth floor of the Empire State Building when something goes wrong with the mechanism. The elevator drops with an acceleration of 32 ft/sec/sec. On the way down you accidentally let go of a package you have been carrying. Will the package drop to the floor, rise to the top of the elevator, or remain stationary relative to you? Explain.

18. An object is given both an initial horizontal velocity and a vertical velocity. What effect will these two velocities have upon each other, if any?

19. A rifle is fired while being aimed horizontally from a window 16 ft above level ground. The muzzle velocity of the bullet is 3000 ft/sec. How far from the window will the bullet strike the ground? Neglect air resistance.

20. An airplane flying at an elevation of 5000 ft and with a velocity of 300 mi/hr drops a package weighing 50 lb. After dropping it the plane continues to fly in the same straight line at the same elevation and the same speed. Where will the plane be when the package strikes the ground with respect to the spot where the package lands? Neglect air resistance.

21. Using the data in Table 5-2, make a plot of t (*horizontally*) against d (*vertically*) choosing an appropriate scale (neither too small nor too big. There is a section with material about graphs in Chapter VI). Describe the kind of graph you get. Is d directly proportional to t? How do you know?

22. Now plot t^2 horizontally and d vertically, using appropriate scales. Is d directly proportional to t^2, i.e., does $d = Kt^2$? How do you know?

23. Plot time against velocity. Describe your graph and state the proportionality that it shows.

Mathematics and Mathematical Symbolism

No mathematician can be a complete mathematician unless he is also something of a poet.
—K. WEIERSTROSS

THE LANGUAGE OF SCIENCE

Science without mathematics is impossible, for mathematics is the language of science. Mathematics expresses in a few symbols ideas, concepts, or laws that often require one or more paragraphs to state in words. This simplified representation and economy of thought combined with the logic inherent in mathematics is necessary for the comprehension of many natural phenomena. Physical science, first physics and astronomy, and later, chemistry, have long been mathematical, and geology is following in their footsteps, some branches far more rapidly than others. Biology, and even the social sciences, are also learning that some areas in their fields are better investigated by the use of mathematical tools.

Mathematics, however, should not be thought of solely as a tool for the scientist. Hogben, in his book *Mathematics for the Millions,* states that mathematics should be thought of as a language of size, in contrast to ordinary language of sort or kind. Our everyday life is far more concerned with the language of size than most of us are aware. Hogben states,

The first men who dwelt in cities were talking animals. The man of the machine age is a calculating animal. We live today in a welter of figures: cookery recipes, railway time tables, unemployment aggregates, fines, taxes, war debts, overtime schedules, speed limits, bowling averages, betting odds, billiard scores, calories, babies' weights, clinical temperatures, rainfall, hours of sunshine, motoring records, power indices, gas meter readings, bank rates, freight rates, death rates, discount, interest, lotteries, wavelengths and tire pressures. Every night when he winds up his watch, the modern man adjusts a scientific instrument of a precision and delicacy unimaginable to the most cunning artificers of Alexandria in its prime. So much is commonplace. What escapes our notice is that in doing these things we have learned to use devices which presented tremendous difficulties to the most brilliant mathematicians of antiquity. Ratios, limits, accelerations are not the remote abstractions dimly apprehended by the solitary genius. They are photographed upon every page of our existence. . . . We constantly find that we have no difficulty in answering questions which tortured the minds of very clever mathematicians in ancient times. This is not because you and I are very clever people. It is because we inherit a social culture which has suffered the impact of material forces foreign to the intellectual life of the ancient world. The most brilliant intellect is a prisoner within its own social inheritance.[1]

---

[1] L. Hogben, *Mathematics for the Millions,* Norton, New York, 1937, p. 13.

If the very mention of mathematics throws you into some sort of a mental panic, perhaps you should read *Mathematician's Delight* by W. W. Sawyer, a book which is "designed to convince the general reader that mathematics is not a forbidding science but an attractive mental exercise." You should not allow the mention of mathematics as a tool of science to convince you that science must remain an enigma to you. In an elementary course the use of mathematics need not go beyond the use of simple arithmetic and the most elementary concepts of algebra and plane geometry. A clear understanding of ratios and proportions, and the use of the powers of 10 to express very small or very large numbers is absolutely necessary. It is assumed that you learned how to add, subtract, multiply, divide, and use decimals in grade school. In fact, none of the mathematical techniques used in this text are above those taught in grade school and the first two years of high school. Students who learned them there should have no trouble here. Above all, the student should understand ratios and proportionalities, direct and inverse, for a great many of the concepts and laws of science involve simple relationships between numbers. To this end a sizable section on proportionality and a considerable number of problems are included in this textbook.

THE SCIENCE OF MEASUREMENT

Measurement has been appropriately called the science of approximation. Shocking though this may seem to you at the moment, it should become clear during the following discussion. Qualitative statements such as, "It is cold out today," and, "This article is heavy," are of little use in science. Quantitative statements, such as, "The outside temperature is 30.3° F," and, "This jar holds 453.6 gm of sodium chloride," are much preferred. We say that they are more precise. But what do we mean by precise? Do we mean they are more exact? And what does exact mean?

Consider the temperature measurement. The precision of the reading depends upon a number of things. First, there is the quality of the thermometer itself. Is the tube containing the thread of mercury uniform in diameter? Are the gradations of the scale uniformly spaced? What is the value of the smallest division? We are not justified in ever reading any scale closer than to one-tenth of the smallest division. No instrument is perfect, hence all have limitations which govern their use. The scientist is always aware of the limitations of whatever instruments he may use. A ten-cent-store ruler is good enough for the measurements the average person makes, but it is useless for measurements that must be correct to the hundredth or thousandth of an inch. For such measurements instruments with a vernier, or a micrometer caliper, are needed, for the unaided human eye cannot detect such small differences.

This introduces a second factor governing precision, the human factor. This includes not only the quality of our vision, but the experience, skill, and judgment of the observer. The trained eye is far better than the untrained. Moreover, the physical conditions under which a measurement is made will influence its precision. It is more difficult to measure a moving object than it is a still one, more difficult to read a measuring instrument that cannot be held steady than it is to read a motionless one.

There are other factors, but we have seen enough to convince us that no measurement is exact if by that we mean that there is no possibility of error no matter how many decimal places we wish to use. The scientist recognizes the shortcomings of measurement by always assuming that the last decimal place is subject to question. Furthermore, he is always certain that the next-to-last decimal place is *not* subject to question. For example, suppose a properly trained observer puts a 1-lb weight on a scale that registers grams. Assume also that the smallest division on the scale is 0.1 gm. Suppose the observer records a weight of 453.6 gm. To the scientist this means that the 6 could be either a 5 or a 7, that the probable error is ±0.1 gm. If the smallest division is 0.01 gm, so that the observer is certain that the 6 could not be a 5 or a 7, then he records the weight as 453.60, for the zero here has significance. By simply adding the zero the probable error has been reduced from ±0.1 gm to ±0.01 gm. If we wish greater precision we will have to use a more sensitive scale. Suppose we do so. The observer might now record the weight as 453.592 gm. Since the 2 could now be a 1 or a 3, the probable error is now ±0.001 gm.

Only on a balance of the highest quality and great sensitivity could it be expressed as 453.592427 gm—which is the legal definition of a pound in the United States. But even here the scientist recognizes the doubtfulness of the last decimal place. But surely, some one of you might ask, if one made a sufficiently large number of different measurements of or on the same object, would not one of them be exactly right? Possibly so, but which one? How could one ever know that? Thus, we are forced to return to our original premise that measurement is the science of approximation, an approximation that comes closer and closer to truth as the expert uses better and better tools, and larger and larger numbers of measurements.

SIGNIFICANT FIGURES

The accuracy of any measurement is given by the number of significant figures. Thus, in the legal definition of a pound there are nine significant figures. This is a degree of accuracy which is uncommon in science. For most purposes we state that a pound weight weighs 453.6 gm, which has four significant figures. The proper use of significant figures constitutes a kind of rounding off, not a haphazard rounding off, but one done by following certain rules.

Most measurements in science are made with an accuracy that does not extend beyond six significant figures. Consider the equatorial radius of the earth, 3963.34 mi. This is expressed in six significant figures. Rounded off to five significant figures it is 3963.3 mi, to four it is 3963 mi, to three it is 3960 mi, and to one it is 4000 mi. This figure is close enough for most purposes; to use the radius or the diameter to six significant figures, or even to four involves needless expenditure of time and mental effort. We do the same with the moon. Its diameter is about 2160 mi. Rounded off to one significant figure it is 2000 mi, about one-fourth the diameter of the earth.

How would you express the volume of a box which measures $9.3 \times 4.7 \times 6.5$ in.? Most people think that 284.115 cu in. (which is the product of the three numbers) is more accurate than 284 cu in. It is not, however, for it implies an accuracy that is not warranted by the measurements. We have already learned that the measurements of the box could be as much as $9.4 \times 4.8 \times 6.6$ in. or as small as 9.2×4.6

× 6.4 in.   Now 9.4 × 4.8 × 6.6 = 297.792 cu in., and 9.2 × 4.6 × 6.4 = 270.848 cu in. Therefore, the volume of the box can be anywhere between 298 and 271 cu in. If you state it as 284.115 cu in., you are saying that it lies between 284.114 and 284.116 cu in., obviously an untruth. So we may round it off to 284 cu in. Even then there is uncertainty about the 4. The figure of 284 is gotten by rounding off only when we make the final calculation. Actually one can—and should—round off at each step in the calculations. The rule is never to have more significant figures in your answer than there are in the least accurate measurement. In the case of our box, all measurements are presumed equally accurate. Thus, 9.3 × 4.7 = 43.71. We round off to 44. 44 × 6.5 = 286.0 cu in. Since we have only two significant figures in any of the actual measurements, we want only two in our answer. The expert would therefore report the volume of the box as 290 cu in. If the measurements were made to the hundredth of an inch instead of to the tenth, how should the volume be reported?

UNITS OF MEASUREMENT

The process of measurement consists of comparing one item with another which has been selected as a standard. The world of primitive man demanded no accuracy. His first "standards" were those of his own body, e.g., his outstretched arms, the length of his forearm, the length of his foot or his hand, and the length and width of his fingers. There were no tribal or community standards, and there was little need for them. The first standards to be developed were those made by the Egyptians and the Chaldeans six thousand years ago for the purpose of land measure. These measurements were astronomical in origin, and so good that even modern science has not greatly improved on them. The Chaldeans worshipped the numbers 6, 60, 600, etc. Thus, the circumference of a circle is divided into 360° (6 × 60°), the hour into 60 minutes and the minute into 60 seconds.

In areas other than land measure confusion reigned even down to the seventeenth and eighteenth centuries A.D. In Germany in the sixteenth century the rod was established as the total length of the left feet of the first 16 men out of a church on a certain Sunday. The yard was defined by Henry I as the distance from the tip of his nose to the end of his thumb when his arm was outstretched. The poppyseed became a means of precise measure in the 1700's. In France nearly every city and province had its own system of weights and measures. As time passed there was an increasing need for standardization.

In 1790 the decimal metric system was imposed by law in France; it was to go into effect three years later. In this system the meter was defined as one ten-millionth the distance from the pole to the equator. Seven years were spent in measuring that part of a meridian which runs between Barcelona in Spain to Dunkirk in France. On the basis of these measurements a standard meter was established as the distance between two microscopic hair lines on a platinum-iridium bar. This bar is kept in a carefully guarded vault in Sevres, a suburb of Paris. Today the length of half a meridian (distance from pole to equator) is known to be 22,288.3 m longer than the 10,000,000 originally assigned to it. The error does not matter, so long as we know the length of the standard.

The metric system introduced a new unit

of mass,[2] called the gram. It is defined as the mass of a cubic centimeter of water at the temperature of its greatest density (about 4° C). A standard mass of 1000 gm (1 kg) equivalent to the mass of 1 liter (1000 cubic centimeters) of water at 4° C, was fashioned of platinum and iridium alloy. This standard is kept in the vault along with the standard meter. The great advantage of the metric system is that it is a decimal system (see Appendix). A further advantage is the fact that the gram is defined in terms of the cubic centimeter; this relates the units used for mass not only to those used for volume but also to those used for linear measurements. Thus, the metric system is an interlocking system which has advantages too numerous for us to discuss here. Many will become apparent as we proceed. This system is used by scientists throughout the world.

Compared to the metric system the English system is clumsy indeed (see Appendix). Several attempts have been made to make the use of the metric system mandatory by law in this country, but all failed. It is permitted, however, and is not only used almost exclusively in scientific work but is also widely used in industry. There are two chief objections to it. The first is the difficulty of retraining 150,000,000 people in its use, and the second is its cost. All present measuring instruments based on the English system would have to be scrapped if the metric system were imposed by law. The total cost was estimated in 1949 at about $200 per worker.

As an alternative we have defined our units in terms of the metric units. We have

already stated that the pound is equal to 453.592427 gm. In 1933 the American Standards Association defined the inch as exactly 2.54 cm. Attempts were made to enact this definition into law but opposition from civil engineers, map makers and the United States Coast and Geodetic Survey defeated it. All national, state, county, town, etc., boundary lines, and the elevations of mountains, etc., had been made with an inch that was 2.540005 cm long. Changing the inch to 2.54 cm would throw thousands of these boundaries off by as much as 3 or 4 ft.

We have also decimalized our inch-foot system. Inches are divided in tenths, hundredths, thousandths, ten-thousandths and millionths. There is still some confusion in highly precise work, for the English, Canadian, and American standards for the inch are not quite the same. The English inch is two parts in a million shorter than the Canadian and that adopted by the American Standards Association, and is four parts in a million shorter than that defined by the United States Bureau of Weights and Measures. International accord is soon expected on the use of the wavelength of the orange line in the spectrum of the element krypton-86 as the standard of linear measurement. In some modern machine-tool industries, accuracies to one-millionth of an inch per inch are not only desirable but imperative.

The decimal system does not apply to measurements of time. This is because the basic unit of time, the day, rests upon the time it takes the earth to complete one rotation about its axis with respect to the sun. The solar day is arbitrarily divided in 24 equal parts, each 1 hour long. Each hour is further divided into 60 minutes and each minute into 60 seconds. This unit

[2] Commonly called the standard of weight. For the difference between mass and weight see p. 137.

does not fit into any metric system—nor any other system. Attempts were made to divide and subdivide the solar day into units of 10, but these all failed. The decimal system is, however, applied to the second. Thus we speak of tenths of a second, hundredths of a second, milliseconds (thousandths of a second), and microseconds (millionths of a second).

Having defined the three basic units for distance, mass, and time, we can derive the units for all other physical quantities from them. Thus, we express velocities in centimeters per second, accelerations in centimeters per second per second, density in grams per cubic centimeter, etc. This system is referred to as the cgs system of units. It is used almost exclusively in scientific investigation. In this textbook we will occasionally lapse into the English system in those situations where it will profit the student to relate the units to his everyday experience.

UNITS IN CALCULATIONS

Every quantity in science consists of two parts, a number and the name of the unit. Many students have the bad habit of reporting only the number. To state the volume of a box as 290 is meaningless. In solving equations the units themselves are treated in exactly the same way as algebraic quantities, i.e., they are multiplied, divided, squared, etc. Any algebraic statement in quantitative determinations must be consistent with respect to the units. For example, consider a cube of brass, 3 cm $\times$ 4 cm $\times$ 5 cm. Its volume is given by $3 \times 4 \times 5 \times$ cm $\times$ cm $\times$ cm = 60 cm^3 (to be read 60 cubic centimeters). Suppose that it weighs 504 gm. Density = mass/volume.

Hence the density of the brass cube is given by 504 gm/60 cm^3 = 8.4 gm/cm^3.

Consider another example, that of momentum, mv. If m is in grams and v is in centimeters per second, then mv is expressed in gram-centimeters per second. In solving a problem, units may sometimes cancel, as do numbers, but you can never just drop them.

RATIOS, PROPORTIONS AND PROPORTIONALITY CONSTANTS

Ratios

Ratios imply comparisons. In its simplest terms a ratio is one number divided by another. The ratio of 8 to 16 is $\frac{8}{16}$. It is also $\frac{4}{8}$, $\frac{2}{4}$, and $\frac{1}{2}$. It tells us that 8 is half as large as 16.

Direct Proportions

Any proportion simply states the equality of two ratios. Thus $\frac{8}{16} = \frac{4}{8}$. Simple proportions of any kind deal with pairs of quantities in which the magnitude of one depends upon that of the other. Another way of stating this is to say that one quantity is proportional to another if their quotient (ratio) is constant. Thus, in a circle, circumference/radius = constant, regardless of the size of the circle. If we double or triple either the circumference or the radius, we double or triple the other. This is a *direct* proportion, for the quantities vary directly with each other, i.e., if one quantity is increased, the other increases proportionately. In buying commodities we often encounter direct proportions, e.g., the total money to be paid for pencils depends on the number of pencils bought, i.e., $x = Ky$ where x is the total money, y the number of pencils, and K is a proportionality constant that depends on the price per pencil.

Inverse Proportions

In some cases of proportionality, one quantity decreases as the other increases. Thus, the time it takes to travel a given distance decreases as the average velocity increases. Double the average velocity and we halve the time. This inverse relationship is expressed by writing one of the quantities as a reciprocal.[3] Thus, we may write, $v \propto 1/t$, or, if a constant is used, $v = K/t$.

Proportionality Constants

By means of proportionality constants we may change any proportionality into an equation. In doing so we replace the proportionality sign by an equal sign and add the symbol K to represent a fixed number. This number does not change as long as the conditions giving rise to the proportionality do not change.

In science and mathematics we encounter two kinds of proportionality constants, those that do not depend upon the conditions of the experiment and those that do. An example of the first is that of our circle, in which $C/R = K$ (where C is the circumference, R the radius). Here the value of K is 2π under any circumstances whatever, as long as the units in which C and R are expressed are the same. If C/R is not equal to 2π, then the figure in question is not a circle. An example of the second kind of proportionality constant is the price of pencils: Money = $K \times$ Number of pencils, where K is the price of one pencil.

[3] A reciprocal of any quantity is 1 divided by that quantity. Thus, the reciprocal of 2 is ½, that of x is $1/x$, etc.

This holds for the same kind of pencil and at any time as long as the price does not change.

Later we will learn that the volume (V) of a given quantity of gas is inversely proportional to its pressure (P) if its temperature (T) does not change. Thus, $V \propto 1/P$. Changing to an equation, $V = K/P$. Transposing, $PV = K$, for any given quantity of gas at constant temperature. For example, let the volume be 1 cu ft and the pressure 15 lbs/sq in. Hence $15 \times 1 = 15$. If we increase the pressure by a factor of 2, the volume decreases by a factor of 2. Hence $30 \times \frac{1}{2} = 15$. If we triple the pressure, $45 \times \frac{1}{3} = 15$. If we halve the original pressure, $7\frac{1}{2} \times 2 = 15$. There is one qualification; the units must not be changed. Familiarity with proportionality constants is an absolute necessity for this course.

There are two ways in which proportionality constants are determined. In the case of an object moving at a constant velocity of 100 m in 5.0 sec, determined by direct measurement, we can use $\frac{100}{5} = 20$ as a constant in the equation $d = Kt$. The constant, 20, is, of course, the distance traveled in 1 sec. As long as the velocity does not change, and the units are meters and seconds, the value of K does not change.

A few constants determined by experiment hold under all conditions, and so are called universal constants. An example is the one in Newton's Law of Universal Gravitation (p. 135).

The second way in which constants are determined has nothing to do with experiment; the constant is the result of the units used. The value of such a constant is always 1. Consider Kepler's third law (p. 50), $T^2 = KR^3$. We cannot write $T^2 = R^3$, for time is certainly not equal to distance.

The K has to take care of the difference in the units. It can do this only if we define our unit of time in terms of our unit of distance, or vice versa. Thus, if we take as our time unit the time that it takes the earth to complete one revolution about the sun, i.e., the year, and take as our distance unit the average distance between the earth and the sun, i.e., one astronomical unit (A.U.), we can write

$$(1 \text{ yr})^2 = K \times (1 \text{ A.U.})^3$$

Solving for K,

$$K = \frac{(1 \text{ yr})^2}{(1 \text{ A.U.})^3} = \frac{1^2}{1^3} = 1*$$

* Strictly speaking this should read $1 \frac{\text{yr}^2}{\text{AU}^3}$ for the units do not cancel. We commonly omit them for convenience only.

We can now use the equation $T^2 = KR^3$ for all other planets, provided we use the same units. Since $K = 1$, we can now write $T^2 = R^3$. The K, however, is still present in the equation, but because it is 1, it does not change the equation any, and we can omit mention of it. You will encounter many other equations in which K becomes 1 because of the way the units are defined.

Proportionalities in Which One Quantity Is Squared

Examples are the areas of squares and circles. The area (A) of a square is proportional not to the length (d) of one side, but to the square of one side, i.e., $A = Kd^2$. Let one side have a length of 1 (cm, in., ft, etc.). $A = K \times 1^2 = 1$ sq cm, sq in., sq ft, etc. Now let us double the length of one side, making $d = 2$. Then, $A = K \times 2^2 = 4$ sq cm, sq in., sq ft, etc. If $d = 3$, $A = K \times 3^2 = 9$ sq cm, sq in., sq ft. The same is true of the area of a circle as given by $A = KR^2$ where $K = \pi$ and R is the radius of the circle.

More important to us are the inverse-square relationships, for we will encounter them at least four times. Consider yourself reading at a distance d from a light source. You now double the distance so that $d = 2$ and find that the brightness has decreased by considerably more than a factor of 2. A light meter would show that it had decreased by a factor of 4 (the square of 2). The same light meter would show that if you increased the distance to $3d$, the brightness (B) of the light would be only $\frac{1}{9}$ that when $d = 1$. Thus, $B \propto 1/d^2$, and $B = K/d^2$. The reason for this is shown in Fig. 6-1. This general principle holds for all inverse-square laws.

SOME RULES OF PROPORTIONALITY

1. If $F \propto m$, then $m \propto F$, other things remaining unchanged.
2. If $F \propto m$ and $a \propto 1/m$, then $F \propto a$ if m remains the same.
3. If $F \propto m$ and F is also $\propto a$, then $F \propto$ to the product ma, or $F = Kma$.

The equation $F = Kma$ contains two direct proportionalities and one inverse proportionality (if solved for a). Make certain that you see that this is so.

GRAPHS

A common and extremely useful way of showing proportionalities is by graphs. Every student should be able to read and interpret simple graphs, for we encounter them in every walk of life. Graphs are in one sense pictures. They allow consider-

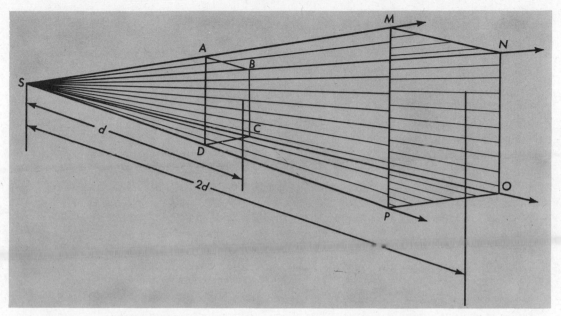

Fig. 6-1. Inverse-square Relationship. Consider the two squares *ABCD* and *MNOP*. The area of *MNOP* is four times that of *ABCD* if the distances from the light source *S* are *2d* and *d*, respectively. A certain amount of light falls on *ABCD*. If *ABCD* is now removed, the same amount of light falls on *MNOP*, where it is distributed over four times the area. The intensity has been reduced to one-quarter by doubling the distance from the source.

able information to be taken in at a glance, they help us to understand what we are talking about, they help us to detect errors in experimental data, etc.

Graphs are easiest to plot on graph paper on which a horizontal and a vertical axis are drawn. Their intersection is called the *origin*. Values of quantities plotted parallel to the vertical axis are called *ordinates*, these plotted parallel to the horizontal axis are called *abscissae*. The ordinate and the abscissa of a point are called its *coordinates*.

Every graph must have a scale for both the ordinates and the abscissae; the scales are arbitrary, within limits. They should be such that the arithmetic involves divi-

sion or multiplication of simple numbers only, and they should be of a size to fit on the page, yet large enough to plot and to read with the precision given by the data. Experience only will teach you how to choose satisfactory scales.

In making a graph the ordinates and the abscissae of the quantities are plotted and marked by a fine point. This point is then neatly circled for ease of finding. A smooth fine line is then drawn so that the plotted points will be as symmetrically arranged on either side of the line as possible. If our data is perfect the line will pass through all of the points. Since errors are present in all experimental work, some of our measurements will be a little

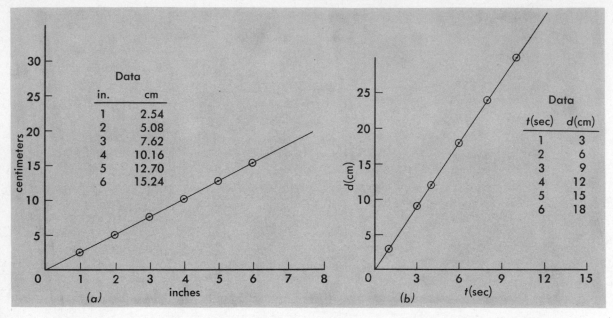

Fig. 6-2. Direct Proportionality Graphs in Which Two Quantities Increase at Same Rate. **(a)** Here, if we double the number of inches, we double the number of centimeters. Algebraically, inches = K centimeters, where K is the number of centimeters in 1 in. If either the relative scale or the proportionality constant were changed, the slope of the curve would change. The requirements for a direct proportion are that its graph must be a straight line and that it must pass through the origin. **(b)** Distance is plotted against time in motion with uniform velocity.

too big, some a little too small. Thus, our graph averages out these errors.

Once the graph is drawn we can proceed to obtain information from it—which is why we drew it in the first place. A graph in which centimeters have been plotted against inches can be used to convert inches to centimeters or centimeters to inches quickly and easily (Fig. 6-2). The shape of the curve (all lines on graphs are called curves whatever their shape) tells us something about the way the two quantities vary. Direct-proportion graphs are straight lines passing through the origin. A moment's thought should show you why

this is so. The slope of the curve will depend upon the relative lengths of the scales used in plotting the points.

If one quantity increases at a faster *rate* than the other, as in uniformly accelerated motion, the curve cannot be a straight line because we no longer have a direct proportion. Our graph is a curved line which passes through the origin, as in Fig 6-3. Note that this is a graph in which distance is plotted against time, not against time squared. If we plot d against t^2 (Fig. 6-4), we get a straight line through the origin, for here again we have a direct proportion $(d = Kt^2)$.

Graphs that represent inverse proportions cannot pass through the origin, for the value of one of the quantities is greatest when the other is least. Such a graph will be a curve which looks like that in Fig. 6-5. Here we plot pressure of a gas against its

either axis. If we plot one of these quantities against the reciprocal (p. 99) of the other, we turn the inverse proportion into a direct one whose curve starts at the origin. This happens because the proportionality, $P \propto 1/V$, means either that P

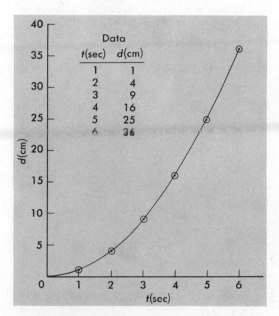

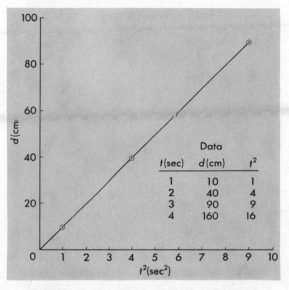

Fig. 6-3. Grapth in Which Two Quantities Increase at Different Rates (as in uniformly accelerated motion). Here, distance is plotted against time. Note that increase in distance during the third second is greater than it is during the second second, and this in turn is greater than it is during the first second. The curve of such a graph cannot be a straight line. The graph proves that distance is not *directly* proportional to time in uniformly accelerated motion.

Fig. 6-4. Graph in Which One Quantity Increases as Square of the Other (as in uniformly accelerated motion). Note that here the graph is a straight line—which proves that distance is directly proportional to the square of the time in uniformly accelerated motion.

volume at constant temperature (see p. 183). Since neither zero volume nor zero pressure is possible, the curve never touches

is inversely proportional to V, or that P is directly proportional to $1/V$ (Fig. 6-6).

Variety among graphs is enormous. The ones shown are those with which you should be familiar in this course. You should study them until you understand why the curves are shaped as they are. The problems at the end of the chapter include work on graphs.

VECTORS AND SCALARS

All quantities in science may be said to be either vectors or scalars. Scalars are quantities that are completely described

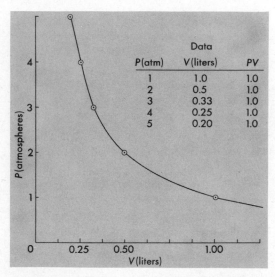

Fig. 6-5. Inverse Proportionality Graph. The curve of an inverse proportionality does not pass through the origin, for it is concave upwards. Here, the pressure of a *given weight* of a gas confined within a receptacle is shown to be inversely proportional to its volume (size of the receptacle). In other words, $P \propto \dfrac{1}{V}$, or $PV = K$.

by giving the magnitude only. Mass, volume, speed, and time are examples. Vectors are quantities that need not only magnitude but also direction in space in order to be completely described. Examples are displacement, velocity, acceleration, force, and momentum. In general discussions the vector nature of these quantities is often overlooked, but in many spe-

cific situations, it cannot be. The normal mathematical rules for addition and subtraction do not apply to vectors. Vectors are represented by arrows whose lengths are proportional to the magnitudes, and which point in the appropriate direction. Obviously the length of the arrow must be drawn to scale. Once this is done for one vector, all other vectors in the same problem must be drawn to the same scale.

Addition of Vectors

The use of vectors may be understood from the following: A plane flies 50 mi east

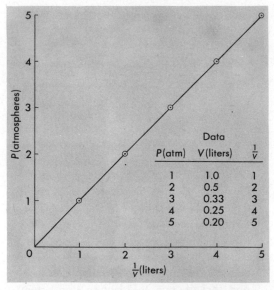

Fig. 6-6. An inverse proportionality is turned into a direct proportion if we plot one quantity against the reciprocal of the other. Its graph is therefore a straight line. Here P is plotted against $1/V$.

and 50 mi north. What is its displacement, i.e., what is its new position? Obviously this cannot be given in miles only; direction must be included. We have two vectors given us, both of the same magnitude. First we choose a convenient scale, say 1 in. = 50 mi, and draw an arrow 1 in. long with its head pointing either east or north, say east. Then we draw another arrow the same length pointing north with its tail at the head of the first vector (Fig. 6-7). These two arrows have been added by placing the tail of one at the head of the other. Then we connect the tail of the second arrow to the head of the first and put a head on this end, so that it points northeast (north 45° east in this case). This arrow now points in the direction of the displacement, and if we now measure

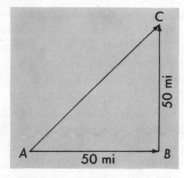

Fig. 6-7. Vector Diagram. This diagram shows displacement of a plane that has flown 50 mi east and 50 mi north from a starting point, A. The direction can be measured by a protractor and the distance measured on a scale.

the length of this arrow we would find it to be about 1.4 inches long (= $\sqrt{2}$), since in a right triangle $a^2 + b^2 = c^2$. Thus, the new position of the plane, i.e., its displacement, is about 1.4 in. × 50 mi/in. = 70 mi N 45° E from its initial position.

We call this third vector the *resultant,* because flight along this line for a distance

of a bit over 70 mi would produce the same result (displacement in this case) as a flight of 50 mi east and then 50 mi north. We have added two vectors to produce a resultant. We can, of course, add (or subtract) as many vectors as we wish. Suppose the plane was delivering passengers

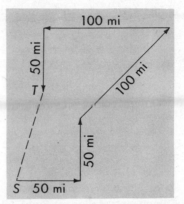

Fig. 6-8. Vector Solution of Airplane Flight Problem. All true directions are measured in the horizontal plane of the earth's surface and from a line running from the observer to the north pole. Thus the angle gives the direction as of the true north line.

and mail at a number of places on a scheduled route. Suppose that it flew first 50 mi east, then 50 mi north, followed by 100 mi N 45° E, then 100 mi west, and then 50 mi south. How far is the plane from its home base S and in what direction? For the solution see Fig 6-8.

Resolution of Vectors

We have already determined the resultant of two displacements (they could just as well have been two forces of given magnitude and direction) at right angles to each other. Frequently we may wish to do the reverse, i.e., to determine the two vectors at right angles to each other, which would produce the same result as a given vector if the two acted simultaneously. For example, in Fig. 6-9, an object is moved from A to B. This object can be moved along a straight line from A to B either by a force of a certain magnitude acting along AB, or it can be moved along

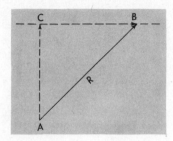

Fig. 6-9. Resolution of a Vector into Two Components Acting at Right Angles to Each Other.

AB, by a combination of two forces acting at right angles to each other simultaneously. The force AB is first drawn. Then a line is drawn through either A or B in any desired direction except that it may not be perpendicular to AB. Let us draw it through B. A perpendicular is dropped from A to a point C on this line. The lines AC and CB are at right angles to one another and their lengths represent the magnitudes of the two desired forces. There are an infinite number of pairs of forces such as AC and BC that will add up to the single vector AB.

This process is called the resolution of a single force into two components operating at right angles to each other. Since the triangle formed by the three vectors is a right triangle, the sum of the squares of

the two components is equal to the square of the single force.

SCIENTIFIC NOTATION

In many areas of science the use of very large or very small numbers is essential. These areas vary from the distances of stars and galaxies to the mass of an atom or an electron. The distance to some stars is of the order of 1,000,000,000,000,000 mi or even thousands of times that. The number of atoms in a gram atomic weight of any element is somewhat greater than 600,000,000,000,000,000,000,000, and the mass of a hydrogen atom is 0.00000000000000000000000166 gm. To multiply or divide such a number is an exceedingly cumbersome process; to state it in words is almost impossible. Hence these numbers are reduced by scientists to a standard form, a form with just one number in front of the decimal point, and multiplied by some power of 10. Consider the number 50,000. The significant figure here is the 5; the zeros merely indicate where the decimal point is. In the standard form it is written 5×10^4. The exponent indicates the number of places the decimal point should be moved to the right. Thus, 51,400 is 5.14×10^4 in the standard form; 1,000,000 becomes 1×10^6, or simply 10^6. The number of atoms in a gram atomic weight of any element is 6×10^{23}.

Very small fractions are always converted to decimals and written with a negative power of 10. Thus, 0.003 may be written 3×10^{-3}, 0.00001 simply as 10^{-5}. The exponent indicates the number of places the decimal point has been moved to the left. The mass of a hydrogen atom is 1.66×10^{-24} gm, etc. With a few minutes' practice you should be able to write any number in the standard form.

Multiplication in the Standard Form

Multiply the significant figures and add the exponents. Thus, 9.3×10^7 multiplied by 5.1×10^9 is $9.3 \times 5.1 \times 10^{16} = 47 \times 10^{16} = 4.7 \times 10^{17}$. Note that to compensate for moving the decimal point one place to the left (equivalent to dividing by 10) we had to multiply 10^{16} by 10.

Let us try another example. Let us multiply 6.02×10^{-4} by 7.5×10^{-8}. This gives us $6.02 \times 7.5 \times 10^{-12} = 45 \times 10^{-12} = 4.5 \times 10^{-11}$.

Suppose we wish to multiply 3×10^{10} by 5×10^{-5}. The only possible source of trouble here is with our exponents. The algebraic sum of 10 and -5 is 5. So our answer is 15×10^5 or 1.5×10^6. Note that we multiplied a number greater than 1 by a number less than 1. The product must therefore be less than the larger number.

Division in the Standard Form

Divide the significant figures and subtract the exponents. For examples let us use the same numbers we used in multiplying.

$$\frac{5.1 \times 10^9}{9.3 \times 10^7} = 0.55 \times 10^2$$

$$= 5.5 \times 10^1 = 55$$

$$\frac{7.5 \times 10^{-8}}{6.02 \times 10^{-4}} = 1.2 \times 10^{-4}$$

$$\frac{3 \times 10^{10}}{5 \times 10^{-5}} = 0.6 \times 10^{15}$$

$$= 6.0 \times 10^{14}$$

Suppose we wish to find the kinetic energy of a nitrogen molecule at room temperature, and want our answer in joules (pronounced jowls). The equation is, K.E. $= \frac{1}{2}mv^2$. The mass of the nitrogen molecule is 0.0000000000000000000000465 gm and its average velocity is about 52,000 cm/sec. Hence,

$$\text{K.E.} = \frac{4.65 \times 10^{-23} \times (5.2 \times 10^4)^2}{2 \times 10^7}$$

$$= \frac{4.65 \times 5.2 \times 5.2 \times 10^{-23} \times 10^4 \times 10^4}{2 \times 10^7}$$

$$= 1.2 \times 10^{-22} \quad \text{joules}$$

Work this out for yourself.

SUMMARY

Aside from its many other virtues, mathematics is a most important tool of the scientist. Most physical laws can be stated in mathematical form. The science of measurement and the units in which they are made have their roots in mathematics. The calculations made from these measurements involve the understanding and correct use of significant figures. Of particular importance to students in an elementary course in physical science are the concepts of ratio and proportionality. The latter involves both direct and indirect proportionalities and proportionality constants. Proportionality constants are quantities that do not change while the experiment or discussion is going on. They are determined in either of two ways: (1) by experiment, or (2) by the way the units are defined. In the latter case the constant becomes 1, and calculations are simplified. Constants valid for one system of units are invalid for any other system. Graphs are useful in demonstrating proportionalities.

Vectors are quantities that have both magnitude and direction. Displacements due to the action of certain forces may be determined by the addition and/or subtraction of vectors. Certain types of problems are best solved by the resolution of vectors.

Use of very large or very small numbers are unavoidable in many areas of physical science. They are best handled by the use of the powers of 10, sometimes called scientific notation for numbers. The standard form is to have one integer to the left of the decimal point. The ability to handle the powers of 10 is a "must" for all students of physical science.

EXERCISES

I. TERMS AND CONCEPTS

Significant figures	Standard form
Direct proportionality	Vectors
Inverse proportionality	Scalars
Proportionality constant	Resolution of
Scientific notation	vectors

II. PROBLEMS

1. The dimensions of a block of wood are 1.2 in. $\times$ 2.2 in. $\times$ 1.6 in. What volume of the block should be reported?

2. Your grades on quizzes during the term are 82%, 61%, 75%, 72%, 77%. What is your average grade?

3. Did you have proper respect for significant figures in your answers to the problems above?

4. What is the metric system of measurement? What are its advantages over the English system?

5. How many centimeters are there in 1 in.? In a meter? In a kilometer?

6. The cgs system is a decimal system. This fact is brought out in the following two problems:

    a. What is the sum of 2.05 m, 2 km, 34 cm, and 23 mm?

    b. What is the sum of 176 gm, 112 mg, and 5.13 kg?

7. a. Approximately how many grams are there in a pound?

    b. In a kilogram?

    c. How many pounds are there in a kilogram?

    d. Express your weight in kilograms.

8. Express the following in centimeters:

    a. 1 ft   b. 1 yd

    c. 1 mi   d. 1 km

9. a. How many centimeters are there in a meter?

    b. How many millimeters in a meter?

    c. How many meters in a kilometer?

10. Which is the greater distance, 100 yd or 100 m? By how many feet?

11. Estimate the distances between the various dots below *directly* in centimeters. Do *not* first estimate in inches and then convert to centimeters. Making such an estimate involves having a mental picture of how long a centimeter is.

    .   .   .

  A   *B*   *C*

AC —— *AB* ——— *BC* ———

Now measure them with a ruler to see how nearly right you are.

12. Write the following, using the powers of 10:

    a. 500   e. 0.03

    b. 2000   f. 0.007

    c. 32,000   g. 0.00092

    d. 758,400   h. 0.000000016

13. Multiply the following:

    a. 3×10^{10} by 6×10^5

    b. 3×10^{10} by 6×10^{-5}

    c. 3×10^{-10} by 6×10^5

    d. 3×10^{-10} by 6×10^{-5}

    e. 3×10^{10} by 1.5

14. Square the following:

    a. 10^5 d. 10^{-10}

    b. 10^{13} e. 3×10^7

    c. 10^{-5} f. 7×10^{-6}

15. Cube the following:

    a. 10^2 d. 10^{-6}
    b. 10^7 e. 2×10^5
    c. 10^{-2} f. 4×10^{-3}

16. Divide the following:

    a. 3×10^{10} by 6×10^5
    b. 3×10^{10} by 6×10^{-5}
    c. 3×10^{-10} by 6×10^5
    d. 3×10^{-10} by 6×10^{-5}
    e. 3×10^{10} by 1.5

17. The mass of a hydrogen atom is about 1.66×10^{-24} gm. How many atoms are present in 1 gm of hydrogen? Use powers of 10.

18. The radius of the earth is about 4000 mi. Express this distance in centimeters, assuming 5000 ft/mi and 30 cm/ft. Do the *whole* calculation by powers of 10.

19. The distance to the nearest star is 25 trillion mi. Express this distance in centimeters, using same assumptions as above.

20. Using the symbols given, show that there is either a direct or an inverse proportionality or both in each of the following by writing the proper equation. (Use K as the proportionality constant.)

    a. Monthly milk bill (B) versus the number (N) of quarts delivered.
    b. The weekly income of an hourly wage earner (I) versus the number of hours worked (H).
    c. The time required (T) to fly from New York to Chicago versus the average speed (S) of the plane.
    d. The rent of an automobile or bus per person (R) versus the number of persons in the group (P).
    e. The number of slices of bread (S) cut from a loaf of bread of a certain size (L).

21. A boat whose speed is 6 mi/hr in still water is traveling downstream where the current is flowing 2 mi/hr. Show the boat's velocity by a vector diagram. Do the same for it traveling upstream.

22. A boat is steered due east across a large river at a speed of 4 mi/hr but is carried north by a strong current flowing 3 mi/hr. Draw a vector diagram to show the boat's velocity.

23. A delivery truck makes a number of stops where the blocks are each 0.2 mi long in any direction. From his first stop he goes 6 blocks east, then 3 north, 4 east, 5 north, and finally 7 west. Show by a vector diagram how far he is from his first stop.

24. An airplane whose normal speed in still air is 300 mi/hr must travel due west. What course must the pilot set if there is a 50-mi/hr wind from the north? Solve by vectors.

CHAPTER VII

Newton's Laws of Motion

No one must think that Newton's great creation can be overthrown by Relativity or any other theory. His clear and wide ideas will forever retain their significance as the foundation on which our modern conceptions of physics have been built.
—ALBERT EINSTEIN (*Nobel Prize, Physics, 1921*)

THE CHANGING MENTAL CLIMATE

It was fitting that Isaac Newton was born in the year Galileo died rather than in the year Galileo was born. It is unlikely that Newton would ever have published a thing if he had encountered the same sort of opposition as that which Galileo had to contend with. He was a shy introspective man who disliked intensely the controversy that Galileo thrived on.

In the fifty years that followed Galileo's death there occurred a striking change in the mental climate of the time. Experimental science became a respectable tool, with men like Boyle, Huygens, Pascal, Torricelli, von Guericke, Halley, Roemer, Hooke, Descartes, and others to use it. The new attitude of these men led to an impressive array of discoveries, theories, and inventions, an array responsible for the seventeenth century being called the century of genius.

This is not to say that the religious opposition and its yen for strong reliance on tradition had died. It had, however, become less intense, less intolerant, more willing to attempt to reconcile traditional views with a Copernican universe. This change came about, not by any change of heart among Galileo's opponents, but by their deaths, which left a younger generation, born, reared, and educated in a world of quickening cultural, political, economic, and scientific changes, less ready to condemn for heresy. Medieval mysticism, medieval habits of thought still lingered on, even to some limited extent among the scientists themselves, for every man is a prisoner to some extent of the mental climate of his time. Astrology was still almost universally accepted; even Newton seriously investigated it.

We must not look back with scorn on the beliefs of the literate people of the seventeenth century, for we have only to look around us to see that many literate people of today, including hosts of college graduates, still accept one or more of those mystic beliefs. We might almost say that most people would rather accept a supernatural explanation than a natural one. To many the fact that a satisfactory natural explanation is not at hand at the moment is evidence that the cause is a supernatural one.

One other thing differentiated the scientific world of Newton from that of Galileo. This was the emergence of scientific societies where the scientists could meet to discuss, debate, and cooperate or quarrel, and which published scientific journals in which they made public their discoveries and their theories. These journals also played a leading part in making science international, for previously scientists could in-form others of their discoveries only by writing long time-consuming letters.

NEWTON (1642–1727), A BIOGRAPHICAL SKETCH

Isaac Newton, son of a small English farmer, has been called the greatest genius that ever lived; certainly there are few that could contest with him for that honor. If he had died at the age of twenty-six his name would still have gone down through the ages as one of the greatest scientists of all time, for he had already formulated his laws of motion, invented both differential and integral calculus, laid the groundwork for his famous law of gravitation, and made fundamental discoveries in optics. He had also done extensive work in astronomy, chemistry, and logic. Throughout his lifetime he spent fully as much if not more time on theology and biblical research as he did on scientific research. When he was about forty, and after much urging, he published the results of his researches in the *Principia,* said by many to be the greatest book in science ever written.

Newton's genius was recognized in his own lifetime, for as a reward for his scientific contributions, he was made Director of the Mint in 1699 and was knighted in 1703. In addition, he served in Parliament and was president of the Royal Society from 1703 until his death in 1727. He was buried in Westminster Abbey.

NEWTON'S FIRST LAW: THE LAW OF INERTIA

As we already know, this law was not original with Newton. He took it over almost verbatim from Galileo. Newton's contributions to the law were that he defined inertia, and he generalized beyond all experience when he stated that *every body continues in a state of rest, or of motion at constant speed in a straight line, unless disturbed by a force acting on it.* The first proposition is as apparent to us as it was to Galileo and Newton. So certain are we that a body at rest will remain so unless disturbed that if we see movement without noticeable cause, we feel impelled to investigate.

The second proposition in this first law is far more subtle, even difficult, for some to believe. It means that *the velocity of a moving body does not change unless a force acts on it.* In still other words, *a force is not needed to keep a body in motion.* This seems contrary to experience. Neither Galileo nor Newton could prove it. Galileo reasoned it out from one of his inclined-plane experiments (Fig. 5-3*d*). He reasoned that if he kept the left inclined plane at a constant angle as he reduced the angle of the plane on the right, the ball would roll farther and farther before it reached the height from which it started. If the plane on the right were horizontal, the ball could never rise to its original height. Therefore, he reasoned that it should go on forever. Note that he "reasoned away" friction and air resistance. This was one of his "thought" experiments. We can never isolate our experiments from friction and air resistance, so this second proposition seems contrary to experience.

To nail the meaning of this law down let us consider the following: Suppose that you had filled a cart with groceries at a supermarket and were taking it to the check-out station. Let us assume that there is no friction, either by the wheels on the axles or by the wheels on the level floor. The cart with its load weighs 50 lb and is moving at a constant velocity of 100 ft/min (Fig. 7-1). What force must you exert on it as long as it moves in a straight line at this constant speed? The answer is, "None." You needed to exert a force to start it from rest. You will also

F = 10 lb

F = 10 lb

Fig. 7-1. Cart in Supermarket. Regardless of how heavily loaded, the force needed to *keep it moving in a straight line at uniform velocity* is that needed to balance friction. Thus, if the frictional force is 10 lb, the force the man needs to exert is 10 lb even if the cart is loaded with 50 lb of groceries.

need to exert a force if you want to change its direction or to change its speed or to stop it, but you need no force to keep it moving at constant velocity if there is no friction.

The situation is, of course, a hypothetical one, but let us consider one of our artificial satellites in orbit about the earth—which is not hypothetical at all. What keeps it moving after the fuel supply has

been exhausted? Note the question carefully. It does not ask what keeps it in its elliptical orbit, but simply what keeps it moving. The answer is, "Nothing"—because there is nothing to stop it.[1]

Let us return for a moment to our cart in the supermarket. There are no frictionless carts, so you do have to exert a force even if you push it in a straight line at constant speed. How much force? Just enough to counterbalance the opposing frictional force. The net force, sometimes called the resultant force, is then zero. The net or resultant force is defined as the *vector sum* (p. 104) of all the forces acting on the cart. If the frictional force is 10 lb, then you need to exert a force of 10 lb to keep it moving at constant velocity. If you exert a greater force than this, the cart will accelerate. We say again, an object with zero *resultant* force acting on it stays either at rest or moves with constant velocity. Newton's second law will give us a clearer insight as to how this comes about.

CONCEPTS OF FORCE, MASS, AND INERTIA

We have been talking somewhat glibly of these terms without defining them precisely. Intuitively we know what a *force* is. We might simply call it push or pull. More formally, it is anything that tends to accelerate a body either positively or negatively, i.e., anything that tends to slow down or speed up the motion or change the direction of motion of a body. The

[1] This is true for those that are beyond the farthest reaches of the atmosphere. Those that are not will eventually be burned up by the heat of friction with the atmosphere if they are not too massive.

acceleration is always in the direction of the force, for force is, as we have already intimated, a vector quantity. If the resultant force is in the direction of motion, the body will be speeded up; if it is opposite to the motion, it will be slowed down, and if the force is at right angles to the motion, the body will be continuously deflected from a straight line (see p. 122 for discussion of circular motion).

Mass is another term with which we all feel some familiarity, even though our ideas about it may be somewhat vague. Most of us think of mass as quantity of matter, and many confuse it with weight. Matter is anything that requires a force to accelerate it. Thus we identify electrons as particles of matter because they require a force to accelerate them. Newton states that a fundamental property of all matter is its ability to resist any change in its state of motion, i.e., it resists acceleration. This resistance to a change in its state of motion is called *inertia*. Anything that has inertia has mass. In fact, the mass of a body may be measured by the amount of inertia it possesses. We might refer to the mass determined in this way as the inertial mass.[2] This inertial mass may be determined by measuring the force needed to give a body a certain acceleration (which can also be measured).

Experiment shows that if we double the force, F, on the same body, its acceleration, a, will be twice as great; if we triple the force, the acceleration will be tripled, etc. In other words, for a given mass,

[2] This is in contrast to the gravitational mass. A balance scale (p. 137) is in equilibrium when we have equal masses on each side. The masses thus measured are called gravitational masses because the gravitational pull of the earth on each mass is the same.

$F \propto a$. Experiment also shows that if we double the mass, m, we will have to double the force to get the same acceleration. This means that $F \propto m$. It follows that if we double the mass but keep the force as before, we will get only half the acceleration. Thus, the acceleration is inversely proportional to the mass if F remains constant, i.e., $a \propto 1/m$.

NEWTON'S SECOND LAW: THE LAW OF MOTION

Newton combined these proportionalities to formulate his second law:

A force is required to accelerate a body; the magnitude of this force is directly proportional to the mass of the body, and to the acceleration produced. Mathematically,

$$F \propto ma$$

Or
$$F = Kma \qquad \text{(Eq. 7-1)}$$

Since we will define force in the same units in which we expressed m times a, the value of K in Eq. 7-1 is 1, and so may be omitted. Hence, we write

$$F = ma$$

Other forms of this proportionality are

$$a = \frac{F}{m} \quad \text{and} \quad m = \frac{F}{a}$$

The latter form shows us how to calculate the inertial mass if we know F and a.

This law tells us that if a is 0, then no force is required to keep a body moving. This is what we were saying in our discussion of the first law, which is therefore a special case of the second law. The second law reiterates our statement that if there is no friction, no counteracting force, a moving body will continue moving at constant velocity forever.

We need to clarify the concept of friction. Galileo maintained that friction between two bodies in contact was always present because perfectly smooth surfaces were impossible to make. Newton's approach was somewhat different. Since experience shows us that here on earth all moving bodies slow down and stop, there must be a force acting on them, for only a force can produce an acceleration. It follows that friction is a force, for it slows down moving bodies here on earth. It also follows that if the frictional force is 0, there will be no slowing down unless some other force is exerted.

CONCEPT OF MOMENTUM

Newton did not express his second law in terms of mass and acceleration but in terms of time rate of change of momentum. By motion Newton meant quantity of motion, which is what we call momentum today. Mathematically, it is mv (mass times velocity). Thus a 2-ton car has twice the momentum of a 1-ton car moving at the same speed, or it has the same momentum as a 1-ton car moving at twice the speed. Today we try to answer, in terms of momentum, that old pre-Galilean question, "What keeps a body in motion after the impelling force has been removed?" Consider an ice hockey puck sliding over the ice. We say that the puck has been given a quantity of motion which is gradually dissipated as it imparts motion to the atoms or molecules at the contact of the puck and the ice.

The identity of $F = ma$ and $F =$ time rate of change of momentum is shown as follows:

Force = Time rate of change of momentum. This is equivalent to

$$Force = \frac{Change\ in\ momentum}{Time\ during\ which\ change\ occurs} \qquad (Eq.\ 7\text{-}2)$$

$$Force = \frac{Final\ momentum - initial\ momentum}{Time\ during\ which\ change\ occurs}$$

$$Force = \frac{Mass \times final\ velocity\ (mv_f) - mass \times initial\ velocity\ (mv_i)}{Time\ during\ which\ change\ occurs}$$

$$Force = \frac{mv_f - mv_i}{t} = m\frac{(v_f - v_i)}{t}.$$

Since

$$\frac{v_f - v_i}{t} = Acceleration$$

we finally have

$$F = ma$$

UNITS OF FORCE

To make quantitative determinations by use of the second law, we need a unit of force. If m is expressed in grams and a in centimeters per second per second, then F is expressed in dynes. A dyne is therefore that force which can impart an acceleration of 1 cm/sec² to a mass of 1 gm. The dyne is an absolute unit; it is a very small unit, about the size of the force imparted by a mosquito lighting on your forehead.[3] By defining the dyne in terms of unit mass and unit acceleration, the value of K becomes 1.

Weight units of force, i.e., the pound in the English system, or the gram and kilogram in the metric system, are often used. These weight units, sometimes called engineering units, are "bad" units because their size varies from one place to another (see p. 137), whereas the dyne is the same everywhere in the universe. Nevertheless, we continue to use weight units because we almost always determine the gravitational masses of bodies by weighing them on scales. The force equivalent to a 1-gm mass is called a force of 1 gm. This force is really $F = ma$, or F (or W) $= mg$, so that a 1-gm force is equal to 1 gm × 980 cm/sec² or 980 dynes. Similarly, a force of 1 kg is equal to 1 kg × 9.8 m/sec² or 9.8 newtons.

NEWTON'S THIRD LAW: THE LAW OF ACTION AND REACTION

Simple as the statements of the first two laws are, we have learned they have hid-

den subtleties in them, subtleties that must be grasped if they are to be understood. The third law is still more subtle. It was these subtleties that escaped the ancients and which make force and motion so difficult to understand. Galileo took the first few steps towards understanding and Newton went the rest of the way.

To every action there is an equal and opposite reaction. The action is always on one body, the reaction always on another. This law means that there is no such thing as a single force; forces always go in pairs and act along the same straight line, but in opposite directions and on two different bodies. Neither force is the cause of the other; rather each is the cause of the other. They appear exactly simultaneously and disappear the same way.

Consider the earth in its orbit about the sun. If there were no forces operating on either, both would travel in straight lines (Newton's first law). The fact that they do not is evidence that forces are operating on them. The sun exerts a force on the earth by virtue of its gravitational attraction and the earth exerts an equal and opposite force on the sun. Note carefully that these forces operate on different bodies. $F = m_s a_s$ for the sun, and $F = m_e a_e$ for the earth. It follows that $m_s a_s = m_e a_e$. However, m_s is so vastly greater than m_e that the value of a_s is insignificant compared to that of a_e. The result is that the earth is being constantly accelerated towards the sun (p. 131) and so travels in a nearly circular path.

Let us now take the case of a man walking on a level stretch of ground. To walk he must push against the earth with his feet.[4] The earth also pushes against his

---

[3] A larger unit is commonly used by many physicists. It is that force which will impart an acceleration of 1 m/sec² to a mass of 1 kg. It is called the newton (for obvious reasons). It is equal to 100,000 dynes. We will not use the newton in this textbook.

[4] If you do not see that this is so, imagine yourself trying to walk on perfectly smooth ice, where

feet with an equal and opposite force (Fig. 7-2). The man is accelerated forward because of an unbalanced force on him; the earth is also accelerated in the opposite direction, but by a negligible amount because the reaction is on such a large mass. If you can imagine a man

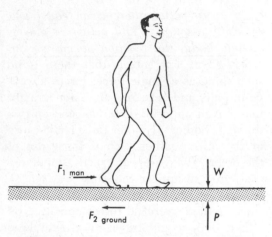

$F_{1\ man}\longrightarrow$ $\uparrow$ W

$F_{2\ ground} \longleftarrow$ $\uparrow$ P

Fig. 7-2. Forces Acting on Man Walking at Constant Velocity. If all motion were truly horizontal, the W–P pair could be eliminated from consideration. It is the F_1–F_2 pair that produces the motion.

walking on an earth that has the same mass as the man, you should be able to see that such an earth would be accelerated backwards while he is accelerated forward at the same rate.

For another example, let us assume that you are holding a book on the palm of your hand (Fig. 7-3). What are the forces acting on the book? There is a downward force, W, due to the pull of the earth on it. Another is the upward push, F_1, of your hand on the book. These two forces

your feet cannot push against the ice nor the ice against your feet.

are equal and opposite if you hold the book still but *they are not action and reaction forces.* For one thing they both operate on the same body, the book, whereas action and reaction forces never act on the same body. The reaction force to W is the upward pull, P, of the book on the earth, whereas the reaction force to F_1 is the downward force, F_2, of the book on your hand. In other words, Newton's third law says that $W = P$ and $F_1 = F_2$. It says nothing whatever about the relationship of W to either F_1 or F_2. If you hold the book still then $W = F_1$, but if you raise the book, you are accelerating it, and F_1 be-

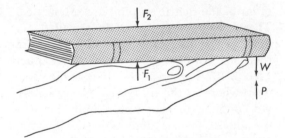

$\downarrow F_2$

$\uparrow F_1$ $\downarrow$ W

$\uparrow$ P

Fig. 7-3. Forces Acting on Book Held in Hand. There are two sets of reaction forces, W–P, and F_1–F_2. Note carefully the origin of the two forces in each action–reaction pair. If the book is at rest, the two pairs of forces are equal. If the book is being lowered or raised, they are not equal.

comes greater than W, but F_1 still remains equal and opposite to F_2. The resultant force, $F_1 - W$, accelerates the body upward, i.e., $F_1 - W = ma$. If the book is lowered, then F_1 becomes less than W but, as always, $F_1 = F_2$. The resultant force, $W - F_1$, accelerates the body downward, i.e., $W - F_1 = ma$. Throughout all of these

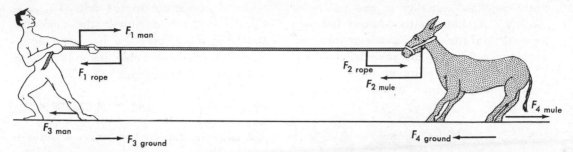

Fig. 7-4. Tug-of-war. Four pairs of forces are involved. The members of each pair are equal and opposite, but the magnitude of one pair is not *necessarily* equal to the magnitude of any other pair. The forces, $F_{1\,man}$ and $F_{3\,man}$ refer to the forces exerted *on* the man, not *by* the man; the forces, $F_{1\,rope}$ and $F_{4\,ground}$ refer to forces exerted *by* the man, and similarly for the mule. To accelerate the mule in the direction of the man the magnitude of each of the F_3 pair of forces must exceed the magnitude of each of the F_4 pair. In other words, the man must dig in his heels more effectively than does the mule.

changes the action–reaction pairs of forces remain equal and opposite.

Consider one more case, that of a man trying to lead a balky mule (Fig. 7-4) over level ground. Application of the force, $F_{1\,rope}$, by the man on the rope instantly gives rise to the reaction force, $F_{1\,man}$, by the rope on the man. Since the mule declines to be led, there arises the force $F_{2\,mule}$ of the rope on the mule and its reaction force, $F_{2\,rope}$, of the mule on the rope. In accordance with Newton's third law, $F_{1\,man}$ is equal and opposite to $F_{1\,rope}$, and $F_{2\,rope}$ is equal and opposite to $F_{2\,mule}$. This is true whether the man succeeds in pulling the mule or not. How then, you ask, can the man ever succeed in pulling the mule? To know we must analyze all of the relevant forces acting on either the mule or the man.[5] In any such analysis

we must take care to note which force acts on what body.

Since both the man and the mule are "digging in their heels" in an attempt to win the tug-of-war, each is exerting horizontal forces on the ground and the ground is exerting equal and opposite forces on them; this is true regardless of who wins the contest. Thus, $F_{3\,ground}$ is equal and opposite to $F_{3\,man}$, and $F_{4\,ground}$ is equal and opposite to $F_{4\,mule}$ at all times.

To see how it is possible for the man to win the contest, we need to compare some of these action–reaction forces with one another. Note carefully that we have emphasized that the two forces in each action–reaction pair are equal and opposite at *all* times. This is in accord with the third law. But the law says nothing what-

---

[5] There are the equal and opposite forces between the man and the earth, $F_{5\,man}$ and $F_{5\,earth}$ (not shown), due to the gravitational attractions of the earth for the man and of the man for the earth. Similarly, there are the corresponding equal and opposite forces between the mule and the earth $F_{6\,mule}$ and $F_{6\,earth}$ (not shown). Since these two pairs of forces act at right angles to any possible motion of the man and the mule, they do not contribute to any such motion, and so we may omit them from further consideration.

ever about the equality of one pair with another. As long as the contest between the mule and the man is a stalemate (or we might say, as long as the mule is winning), all action–reaction pairs are equal in magnitude. For the man to win the contest

Fig. 7-5. Newton's Proposed Jet-propelled Steam Engine. A fire built under the boiler partly filled with water created large quantities of steam which, on being ejected at high speed to the rear, drove the cart forward. Thus the principle of jet or rocket propulsion was known to Newton. (Courtesy The Bettman Archive.)

the magnitude of the force exerted by his digging in his heels ($F_{3\ ground}$) must be greater than the similar force exerted by the mule ($F_{4\ ground}$), i.e., when the F_3 pair of forces is greater than the F_4 pair of forces, there is acceleration in the direction of the man. While this acceleration is in progress, $F_{3\ man} - F_{1\ man} = m_{man} \times a$, for these are the two forces operating *on* the man, one in one direction, the other in the opposite direction. If the difference is not 0, then there is an unbalanced force, and therefore acceleration. Similarly, for the

mule to accelerate to the left,[6] $F_{2\ mule} - F_{4\ mule} = m_{mule} \times a$. Once the mule has started moving, once he has been accelerated, he will probably be pulled along reluctantly at a constant velocity, i.e.,

$$F_{1\ man} = F_{3\ man} \quad \text{and} \quad F_{2\ mule} = F_{4\ mule}$$

just as when the contest was a stalemate.

Whether at rest or moving at constant velocity there is equilibrium between all pairs of forces.[7]

Further Applications of the Third Law

What propels a propeller-type airplane forward, on the ground or in the air?[8] What propels a jet plane or a rocket? In the first, the propeller throws great quantities of air to the rear (action) and is itself "thrown" forward (reaction). In a jet plane or a rocket, great quantities of hot gases are ejected (pushed) to the rear (action) and the plane or rocket is pushed forward (reaction) (Fig. 7-5). The propeller of an outboard motor or those of a great ocean liner push water to the rear and so they are propelled forward. If you attempt to take what looks like an easy jump from a rowboat or canoe to the shore or a dock without taking into account Newton's third law, you may be in for a ducking. Many more examples could be cited, for Newton's laws are applicable to the whole field of linear motion.

---

[6] Also during acceleration, $F_{1\ rope} - F_{2\ rope} = m_{rope} \times a$, and $F_{3\ ground} - F_{4\ ground} = m_{ground} \times a$.

[7] To the man this would seem contrary to common sense, for to him it makes a world of difference—the difference between success and failure—whether the equilibrium is that of the stalemate, or that of constant velocity forward.

[8] What provides the lift is another problem.

Newton's Third Law and the Conservation of Linear Momentum

We have already seen (p. 114) how Newton used change in momentum to derive his second law. Our previous discussion of the concept dealt only with its relationship to that law. Restated in terms of momentum, the second law becomes: *The net force acting on a body is equal to the change in momentum per unit of time.*[9] We have already learned that when a net force acts on a body, that body is accelerated. Since Newton defined momentum as mv (mass times the instantaneous velocity), it is seen that the momentum of a body being accelerated is changing (since the velocity is changing). A given net force, acting on a body, A, for a given time, will produce a certain change in its momentum.[10] This same force acting for the same time on body B of twice the mass will give B only half the acceleration of A (for $F \propto ma$). Yet the same change of momentum results. Similarly the same change in momentum results if the same force acts for the same time on a body C of half the mass of A. Our conclusion is that: *a given net force will produce the same change in momentum in a given time regardless of the mass of the body.*

[9] If the role of time in the change of momentum is not clear, suppose you compare the force with which you would land if you jumped out of a second-story window onto a concrete sidewalk with that of the same jump onto a thick mattress. In either case you undergo the same change in momentum. In the first case the time in which the change takes place is extremely small and so you are stopped instantly because the concrete has no "give" to it. The mattress has "give," so the time involved is longer; hence F is smaller, i.e., the force with which you land is smaller.

[10] Throughout our discussion we must remember that momentum is a vector quantity.

This brings us to the third law. When two billiard balls, A and B (Fig. 7-6), collide head-on, the forces between them are equal and opposite. Since the time the forces act is the same for both balls, both must undergo the same change in momentum but in opposite directions. Thus, the change in mv of A equals the change in mv of B. (We are assuming the collisions are perfectly elastic, i.e., that no energy is lost during the collision). It matters not what the masses are, or what the original or final velocities are. If the mass of B were twice that of A, its instantaneous velocity would be half that of A. For two balls with equal masses rolling towards each other with the same speed (Fig. 7-6), the momentum of A before impact is $+mv_A$ and that of B is $-mv_B$ where $(+)$ means to the right and $(-)$ to the left. At the moment of impact, i.e., during the collision, the force on each ball and the time of their mutual interaction are the same but oppositely directed. Therefore the resultant force is zero, and there is no change in momentum. After impact the balls have reversed their directions, so the momentum of each has the opposite sign from that before impact. The total momentum after impact is given by $-mv_A + mv_B$. If we omit consideration of friction between the balls, and between the balls and the table, the total momentum before impact equals the total momentum after: $mv_A + (-mv_B)$ $= -mv_A + mv_B$.

Suppose that one ball stopped "dead" at the instant of collision. This "dead" ball, having 0 velocity, would have 0 momentum, whereas the other would have a momentum equal to the sum of the two masses times the velocity before impact. If three balls are involved, the same relationship holds,

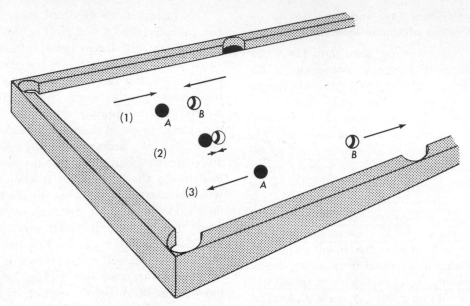

Fig. 7-6. Head-on Collision of Billiard Balls.   Since the masses of the two balls are equal in (1), $(+mv_A) + (-mv_B) = 0$ if the velocities are the same.   At the instant of impact (2) the velocity of each is 0, so that the same relationship holds.   If the collision is perfectly elastic, after collision $(-mv_A) + (+mv_B) = 0$ also.   Note that $+mv$ indicates motion to the right, $-mv$ to the left.   Thus, the total momentum of the system remains constant throughout if there is no loss of velocity due to friction.

for if no change in total momentum occurs in one collision, then no change should occur in two collisions, or three collisions, etc.   Suppose a bowling ball makes a strike, i.e., knocks all ten pins down.   Each pin would be given a certain momentum, some directly by the ball, some by other pins striking them.   If we added the individual mv's of each pin together with that of the bowling ball immediately after impact, we would find that the sum was vectorially the same as that of the bowling ball the instant before impact.   Thus, we see that *the total momentum of any system remains constant.*   For this to hold we must be careful to include all parts in the

system and exclude all that are outside the system.

To make certain that this is done, the physicist speaks of an isolated system. When a bullet is fired from a comparatively heavy rifle, Newton's third law says that the force exerted on the bullet is equal and opposite to that exerted on the rifle (Figs. 7-7 and 7-8).   The latter is referred to as kick.   In terms of momentum, the mv of the bullet is equal, but oppositely directed, to the mv of the rifle.   In primitive cannon this was also so, the cannon going backward if the ground was level and the cannon not staked down and there was no friction of the axles and the wheels.   In

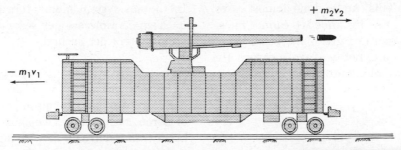

Fig. 7-7. Conservation of Momentum. Illustrated by a shell fired from a cannon mounted on railway car. Neglecting friction, the *mv* of the gun and car to the left equals the *mv* of the shell to the right, i.e., $(-m_1v_1) + (+m_2v_2) = 0$. If m_1 and m_2 are known and the velocity given to the car is measured, v_2, the muzzle velocity of the shell can be calculated.

modern artillery, there is a system of brakes and springs which are attached to the ground in some way, so that the gun and the shell no longer constitute an isolated system.

If all of the bodies of the universe were to collide, there would be no change in the total momentum.

LAW OF CONSERVATION OF MOMENTUM

We may therefore state the Law of Conservation of Momentum: *The total momentum of the universe remains constant.* If we compare this statement with Newton's third law, we find that it is simply another way of stating that forces are equal and opposite. All of the phenomena explained by action and reaction can be equally well explained by the Law of Conservation of Linear Momentum. Thus, in a jet plane or rocket, the momentum of the gases ejected from the rear is equal to the momentum given to the plane in the opposite direction.

Despite our examples illustrating action and reaction, none of them proves that the action and the reaction are equal. The

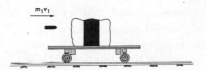

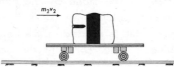

Fig. 7-8. The velocity of a bullet at any distance may be determined by firing it into a bale of cotton on a nearly frictionless cart and measuring the velocity given to the cart. The *mv* of the bullet before impact must be equal to the *mv* of the cart and the bullet after impact.

only way that they can be proved equal is by measuring the changes in the momenta of the bodies on which action and reaction take place. This can be done in most cases, but not all. For instance we cannot measure the momentum given the earth when we start to run, but we can measure the corresponding momentum given a movable

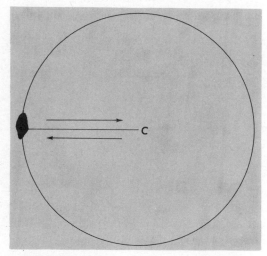

Fig. 7-9. Stone on end of string being whirled at constant speed, V, by a force exerted by a hand at C. The inward-pointing arrow is the centripetal force vector; it is the action force and is exerted on the stone by the hand. The outward-pointing arrow is the reaction force, and is exerted on the hand by the stone. Note carefully that only one force acts on the stone.

platform mounted on nearly frictionless wheels and floor as we run on it. We therefore feel that momentum is conserved wherever action and reaction take place.

UNITS OF MOMENTUM

Since mass is a scalar and velocity is a vector, momentum is also a vector. The units are those used for mass and velocity.

In the cgs system momentum is expressed in gram-centimeters per second or in kilogram-meters per second.

UNIFORM CIRCULAR MOTION

Before we leave the all-important subject of force and motion, we must investigate briefly motion in a circle with uniform speed if we wish to understand the motions of the planets and satellites of our solar system. The essential difference between linear and circular motion is that the direction of the motion in the latter is constantly changing whereas in the former it is constant. This difference is important, because, as we have already learned, (1) a body in motion will continue in motion in a straight line forever if no forces act on it, and (2) it takes a net force to change the direction of a moving body. A body moving in a circle must therefore be subject to a continuously acting net force. Since the action of a net force on any body produces an acceleration, it follows that the constant changing of the direction, even though there is no change in the speed, is an acceleration. This is obviously a different kind of acceleration than that in linear motion where the only change is in speed. Therefore, we need to express a in terms that will take into account the constant speed and the constantly changing direction of the body on which F acts. Our present problem is, then, to find what a is in uniform circular motion, i.e., motion in a circle with constant speed.

Determination of Acceleration in Uniform Circular Motion

Consider a stone of mass m being whirled in a circle of radius r with a constant speed of v cm/sec (Fig. 7-9). The stone is moving clockwise in a horizontal circle by a force provided at C by your hand. A little experimentation will show that as we vary r the minimum speed necessary to keep the stone moving in the circle will vary also. It will also show that the force necessary to maintain circular motion varies as either r or v is varied.

At the instant the stone is at A (Fig. 7-10a), the velocity is given by the vector v_{old}. When it is at a point farther on in its orbit, say at B, it has a new velocity vector which is of the same magnitude as the old. We will also call it v but will refer to it as the new v to distinguish it from the old v. We now make a vector diagram to show the change in velocity, by moving the two velocity vectors to new positions (Fig. 7-10b) so that they start from a common point O. We do not change their lengths or their directions. We now can draw the *change in velocity vector* Δv (which is normally read "delta v," but which you should read "change in velocity" until you get used to its meaning). Thus the new v is the vector sum of the old v and Δv.

Where there are changes in velocity there must also be accelerations. Thus,

$$a = \frac{v_{\text{new}} - v_{\text{old}}}{t} = \frac{\Delta v}{\Delta t} \quad \text{(Eq. 7-3)}$$

where Δt (delta t) is the change in time in going from A along the arc of the circle to B. This acceleration can be calculated only in terms of v and r, and to make it, we resort to geometry. Let us draw the chord $\overline{AB}$, and place a bar over AB to distinguish it from the arc $\widehat{AB}$.

Consider the two shaded triangles, one with sides r, r_1, AB and the other v, v, Δv. Both are obviously isosceles triangles

($r = r_1$ and $v = v$) and the apex angles C and O are equal.[11] Therefore the two

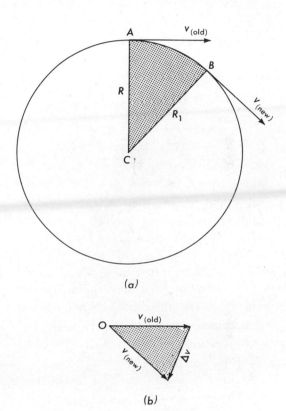

(a)

(b)

Fig. 7-10. Analysis of Uniform Circular Motion. **(a)** Derivation of $a = v_2/R$. (See text.) **(b)** The vectors, v_{old} and v_{new} are moved so that they start at a common point, O. Neither their magnitudes nor their directions have been changed. The vector, Δv, represents the change in velocity.

triangles are similar, so that the lengths of their corresponding sides are in the same proportion. Thus,

[11] v_{old} is perpendicular to r, and v_{new} is perpendicular to r_1; hence the corresponding angles formed by their intersections are equal.

$$\frac{\Delta v}{v} = \frac{\overline{AB}}{r}$$

Solving for Δv, $\Delta v = \dfrac{v \times \overline{AB}}{r}$

Dividing both sides by Δt,

$$\frac{\Delta v}{\Delta t} = \frac{\dfrac{v \times AB}{r}}{\Delta t} = \frac{v}{r} \times \frac{\overline{AB}}{\Delta t} \qquad \text{(Eq. 7-4)}$$

Now $\widehat{AB}$ divided by time will give us the average speed between A and B. If $\overline{AB}$ were equal to $\widehat{AB}$, then $\overline{AB}/\Delta t$ would be equal to $\bar{v}$ and our problem would be solved. But $\overline{AB}$ is not equal to $\widehat{AB}$.

However, if instead of taking the two points, A and B, rather far apart as we did in Fig. 7-10a, we take them quite close together, then the difference between $\overline{AB}$ and $\widehat{AB}$ becomes very small, nearly negligible. If AB were infinitely small, then $\overline{AB}$ may be said to be equal to $\widehat{AB}$.[12]

We may therefore say that in equation 7-3, $AB/\Delta t = \bar{v}$. The speed is, however, constant in the case of our stone, so $\bar{v} = v$. Substituting v for $AB/\Delta t$ in our equation 7-3 we have

$$\frac{\Delta v}{\Delta t} = \frac{v}{r} \times v = \frac{v^2}{r}$$

Since $\Delta v/\Delta t$ is the acceleration (Eq. 7-3) we have

$$a = \frac{(\text{Speed around orbit})^2}{\text{Radius of orbit}} = \frac{v^2}{r} \qquad \text{(Eq. 7-5)}$$

[12] This geometrical analysis is not as precise as that gotten by use of the calculus, but the result is exactly the same.

Since we will encounter this equation several times in this book, the student should be well acquainted with it and its meaning. It is the acceleration that a body must have to move with speed v in a circular orbit of radius r. Substituting v^2/r for a in $F = ma$, we have

$$F = \frac{mv^2}{r} \qquad \text{(Eq. 7-6)}$$

which is the force that must be applied if a body of mass m is to move in a circle. Since the force acting on the stone is acting along a line directed towards the center of the circle, it follows that the acceleration is also directed towards the center.[13] Note that here a body has an acceleration that is directed towards a center, and yet it neither goes any faster nor gets any closer to the center.

Forces in Uniform Circular Motion

This inwardly directed force is called *centripetal (center-seeking) force*. In the case of our stone revolving on the end of a string (Fig. 7-9) in a horizontal [14] circle the inward force is provided by the string acting on the stone. If the only force acting on the stone when it is moving in its orbit at uniform speed is the centripetal force, "What," you may ask, "keeps it mov-

[13] We can also see that this is so from our geometric analysis (Fig. 7-10). As B gets closer and closer to A, the angle between v_{old} and v_{new} gets smaller and smaller and Δv becomes nearly perpendicular to v. If the angle is infinitely small, we may say that to all intents and purposes Δv is perpendicular to v. Since v is tangent to the circle at all times, the vector Δv must be directed towards the center.

[14] We will confine our attention to a circle in a horizontal plane because the force supplied by the hand may be kept constant without the force of gravity complicating the situation.

ing?" The answer is, "Nothing." You should not forget that it does not take a force to keep it moving, but only to start it moving, to change its speed, or to change its direction.

Thus, the only force needed to give a body uniform circular motion is one to push it in towards the center. If we cut the string, the centripetal force instantly disappears, and the stone travels (neglecting gravity) in a straight line tangent to the circle at the point where it was when the string was cut (Newton's first law). Because of the stone's inertia, a force must be applied to it to change its direction. The instant that a force attempts to change the direction of a body's motion, a counter-force springs into being which resists that change of direction. This is the force of the stone on the string; it is the reaction force in Newton's third law. In uniform circular motion this force is properly called *centrifugal force*.[15] It is the force that the moving object (the stone) acts on whatever is holding it in its path (the string); it is the force you feel operating on your hand via the string. If we treat the string as a mere transmitter of force, then the centripetal force is the inward force that your hand exerts on the stone via the string, and the centrifugal force is the outward force exerted on your hand by the stone via the string. Note carefully that, like all action–reaction forces, these two forces are equal and opposite, and that they do not operate

on the same body. *There is no outward force exerted on the stone.*

Consider the revolution of the earth about the sun. No force is needed to keep the earth moving; one is needed to change its direction. This centripetal force is the gravitational attraction of the sun for the earth; it acts *on* the earth. But the earth also has an attraction for the sun. This is the centrifugal force; it acts *on* the sun. How the earth got started revolving about the sun, we do not know, but since it started it has needed only a force acting on it to change its direction in order to continue its revolution.

How the earth came to rotate on its axis we do not know either. But once started it has continued for a few billions of years without appreciable slowing down. The reason is that there is nothing to stop it.

ANGULAR MOMENTUM AND ITS CONSERVATION

Linear momentum is, as we have learned, a quantity of motion expressed by mv, a quantity which for any given body remains constant as long as v is constant. Since v is a vector, it cannot remain constant if its direction is constantly changing, as is the case of a body in uniform circular motion. Such a body has angular momentum as well as linear momentum. We will not attempt any rigid mathematical analysis of it here but will be content to show that the expression mv for it is eminently reasonable.

For a body that is revolving about a point or rotating on an axis at a uniform rate, it seems logical to assume that the radius of

[15] There is frequent confusion in the literature on the use of the term *centrifugal force*, confusion with the so-called *centrifugal d'Alembert force*. The latter is a fictitious quasi-gravitational force used most commonly by engineers who wish to reduce problems in dynamics to problems in statics. Because these forces are fictitious, some writers state that there are no real centrifugal forces.

the circle in which it or its center of mass is moving should play a role. Experiment shows that the force necessary to maintain a given speed varies with the radius. It also shows that the product mvr is constant for a particular mass as long as *no outside torque* ($F \times d$) is operating on the system. This is true regardless of the value of

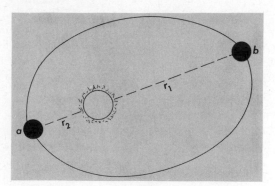

Fig. 7-11. Conservation of Angular Momentum. The earth in its orbit moves faster at *a* than at *b*, enough faster to compensate for the difference between r_1 and r_2. Thus, $mv_1r_1 = mv_2r_2$. Its angular momentum is therefore constant.

r. Newton arrived at this concept of the conservation of angular momentum by way of Kepler's law of equal areas.

Consider the earth, or any other planet, in its orbit about the sun, an orbit which deviates slightly from that of a circle. Because of this ellipticity the earth is about 3,000,000 mi closer to the sun in January that it is in July (Fig. 7-11). In January r therefore has decreased. If the quantity mvr is to remain constant, v must increase enough to compensate. Similarly, in July, r is at a maximum and so v must be at a minimum. Thus, the earth traverses a larger fraction of its orbit in January than

it does in July, as Kepler's second law states.

Another example is that of a boy on a nearly frictionless turntable (Fig. 7-12) or a figure skater who begins to pirouette with outstretched arms. After gaining as much rotational motion as she can in this way, she shifts all her weight to one skate, draws her arms very close to her body in order to reduce r. Without any further effort on her part she starts to spin faster as

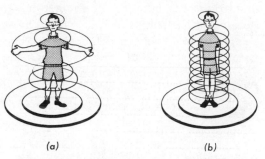

(a)   (b)

Fig. 7-12. Conservation of Angular Momentum. **(a)** The boy is spinning with his feet apart and his arms outstretched while standing on a nearly frictionless turntable. **(b)** He has moved his feet close together and pulled his arms close in to his body, thus reducing his average distance from a vertical imaginary axis passing through his body. The result is that he automatically spins faster, for his mvr in the first situation will equal his mvr in the second. Since m is constant for both, v must increase if r is decreased. Thus, angular momentum (mvr) is conserved.

she lowers her arms, reaching her fastest speed when her arms are closest. To slow down she simply increases r by raising her arms. Neglecting friction with the ice, angular momentum has been conserved.

SUMMARY

The fact that we can never on this earth free either ourselves or any other body completely from the forces of friction and air resistance makes the concepts involved in Newton's first two laws of motion difficult, since they seem contrary to experience. Both Galileo and Newton had, therefore, to generalize beyond experience. Newton went beyond Galileo by defining force, mass, and inertia precisely. The distinction between mass and weight must be carefully kept in mind. The mass of a body is the same anywhere in the universe; its weight may vary from 0, if outside any gravitational field, to many times that here on earth, since weight is determined by the magnitude of the force of gravity. In any *one* place, however, the mass of a body is proportional to its weight.

Concepts that must be clearly kept in mind when dealing with the first two laws are: No force is needed to keep a body moving in a straight line at constant speed if no friction or air resistance is involved. It does take a force to start it moving or to stop it, to increase or decrease its speed or to change its direction of motion. All of these involve acceleration, so that we include all of them when we say that it takes a force to accelerate a body, i.e., $F = ma$. Newton developed the above ideas in terms of time rate of change of momentum. The final result is the same because $ma = m(v_f - v_i/t) = $ time rate of change of momentum.

The dyne is the absolute unit of force in the cgs system. In the equation $F = ma$, F is in dynes if m is in grams and a is in centimeters per second per second. Since W (weight) is a force due to the pull of gravity, the weight of a body in the cgs system is equal to its mass multiplied by g (980 cm/sec^2).

Newton's third law introduces some new concepts:

There is no such thing as a single force, i.e., forces always go in pairs. These two forces always operate on different bodies, never on the same body; they are equal, and oppositely directed. Pairs of related forces, however, are equal only while a body is not being accelerated, as a net force acting on a body produces an acceleration. The third law may be stated in terms of momentum: The total momentum of the universe remains constant.

In uniform circular motion a body is subject to a continuously acting net force even when moving at constant speed, because it always takes a net force to change the direction of motion. The body is therefore being uniformly accelerated. The force acts along a line connecting the body with the center of the circle, and the acceleration is along the same line. Both the force and the acceleration are thus said to be centripetal. There is no centrifugal force acting on the body, for like all action–reaction forces, equal and opposite forces never act on the same body.

The acceleration in uniform circular motion is given by the equation, $a = v^2/r$. Newton's second law therefore becomes $F = mv^2/r$. Angular momentum, mvr, of a body in uniform circular motion is conserved, just as linear momentum is conserved. Thus, as the earth gets nearer the sun, as it does in our winter, r becomes less so that to conserve angular momentum, v must increase. As r becomes greater in summer, the earth's velocity is reduced.

EXERCISES

I. **TERMS AND CONCEPTS**

Mass	Equations:
Inertia	$F = ma$;
Force	$a = v^2/r$
Dyne	$F = mv^2/r$
Centripetal force	Centripetal acceleration
Centrifugal force	

Action and reaction
Newton's three laws
  of motion
Uniform circular
  motion

Linear momentum,
  mv
Angular momentum,
  mvr

II. PROBLEMS

1. State Newton's three laws of motion and give equations applicable to each of them.

2. Beyond the earth's atmosphere, what force, if any, is needed to keep a 10-ton rocket moving at a constant speed of 5000 mi/hr directly towards Alpha Centauri?

3. a. What is the relationship between mass and inertia?
   b. Does a car traveling at 30 mi/hr have more, less, or the same inertia that it has while at rest?

4. Two identical cars each travel 100 mi over the same road in the same total time. One travels at a uniform speed; the other speeds up and slows down over and over again, stopping several times. The latter car will use appreciably more gasoline. Explain why in terms of Newton's laws.

5. Use one of Newton's laws of motion to define a straight line.

6. What force does it take to give a 1-gm mass a speed of 980 cm/sec?

7. A net force of 40,000 dynes is applied to a cart having a mass of 20 kg. What acceleration is imparted to it?

8. Why does it take more force to start a heavy cart moving than it does to keep it moving at a uniform velocity? What law is involved?

9. A weight is attached to a string that is strong enough to lift the weight if one does it with a slow steady pull, but it breaks if a sudden rapid pull is exerted. Explain why the string does not break in the first case but does in the second. What law is involved?

10. A toy steam engine that really runs is placed on a circular track shaped like a bicycle wheel and which is free to turn on an axle. The engine is started. Describe the motions of the system and explain in terms of one or more of the laws of motion.

11. A shotgun (or any other gun) "kicks" when it is fired. Explain why.

12. A car is traveling along a straight level road at a uniform speed. State specifically the forces that must be overcome by the energy in the gasoline used. In other words, for what purposes is gasoline used?

13. Suppose the above car is traveling at the same uniform speed around a circular track. Would you use more or less gasoline or the same amount? Justify your answer in terms of one or more of Newton's laws.

14. Suppose that you are far out in space beyond any significant force of gravitation from any body whatsoever. How you got there is a problem that is not to be considered. You are motionless. State all answers in terms of Newton's laws of motion.

  a. You see a piano of normal size floating along at a constant speed toward you. As it passes you, you give it a kick. What happens to the piano, if anything, as a result of your kick?

  b. Since the piano is not subject to any force of gravitation, it is weightless. Would your toe feel much different than it would if you kicked a similar piano in the same way here on earth? Explain.

  c. What would happen to you, if anything, after the kick?

15. While out walking on a cold winter day you come to a pond where the ice is so smooth it might be considered frictionless. How can you get across it? (Neglect air resistance.) State the magnitude of the force needed, and explain.

16. Why is gravity referred to as a force?

17. Newton's second law states that if a net force is applied to a body it will be accelerated. Yet you can push a cart along a sidewalk at a constant velocity while exerting a steady force of, say, 40,000 dynes on it. Explain.

18. Use Newton's laws of motion to show that epicyclic motion of the planets, as assumed by the followers of Ptolemy, is not possible.

19. It is frequently said that when a car turns a sharp corner rapidly, the passengers are "thrown" towards the outside of the curve by centrifugal force. This is a fallacious viewpoint. Show why, and give the correct one.

20. Two teams are having a tug of war. What force or forces—and applied to what body—determines which team will win?

CHAPTER VIII

The Universal Law of Gravitation

Nature and Nature's laws lay hid in night;
God said, Let Newton be! And all was light.
                                        —ALEXANDER POPE

INTRODUCTION

Once Galileo's Law of Inertia (better known as Newton's first law) had been formulated and the concepts of force and mass clearly defined by Newton, it was obvious that some force must be operating on the planets and their moons to keep them in their elliptical orbits. The old belief that terrestrial laws could not be expected to apply to celestial bodies was being replaced, chiefly under the influence of Newton, by a belief that some natural laws had universal application. Galileo was probably aware of some such force; certainly a belief in the nonapplicability of terrestrial laws to celestial bodies would have left him scornful.

It is also certain, without looking at the record, that Newton formulated his first two laws of motion before he did his work on gravitation. Once laws are formulated and verified they are available for use in the study of other phenomena. Newton immediately applied the laws of motion to the astronomical problem of planetary orbits. He was especially equipped to do this, for he was a mathematical genius. While still an undergraduate at Cambridge he was doing original work in mathematics, work that shortly was to result in his discovery of the binomial theorem and the invention of the calculus. His work in the latter field was spurred by his need for certain mathematical proofs in parts of his gravitational theory.

The concept of gravity was not original with Newton. It had been used with respect to falling bodies [1] even before the time of Galileo. Members of the newly formed Royal Society of London were discussing it before Newton published his theory. They were trying to discover the force the sun exerted on planets to cause them to move according to Kepler's laws. Huygens had published his version of centripetal acceleration ($a = v^2/r$) and others were trying to apply it to the elliptical orbits of planets. They had managed to prove that an inverse-square law (p. 101) would account for circular orbits when it was combined with Kepler's third law, but they failed with elliptical orbits.

One of them, Halley (of Halley's comet fame), appealed to Newton for help, and found that Newton had solved the problem many years before,[2] using his own deriva-

---

[1] You should realize that to say that a body falls because of gravity is in no sense an explanation.

[2] This failure to publish or otherwise make known the results of his work was characteristic of Newton. His personality was the exact opposite of Galileo's. He was a shy, retiring man with no liking for controversy, even with respect to his own work. If it had not been for the urgings of some of his fellow scientists, particularly Halley, he might never have written his *Principia Mathematica*, which is very probably the greatest single book on science ever published.

tion of $a = v^2/r$. He had found that a force whose magnitude was inversely proportional to the distance between a celestial body and another revolving about it would require the revolving body to obey all three of Kepler's laws. These laws had been begging for an explanation for generations; there was as yet no "reason" for the regularities described by them. The mechanics [3] of Newton showed that the planets were simply moving according to the same laws of motion applicable to all moving bodies here on earth. It will be highly instructive to give a plausible account of the reasoning used in applying these laws, without, however, implying that our account of it is either correct in minor details or in the order followed by him.

As we have already stated in other words, Newton knew that a net force was acting continuously on the planets; otherwise they would all be moving in straight lines. In his speculations on the nature and the magnitude of this force, it has been said that he was led to the possibility of gravity as a cause by the fall of an apple from a tree while sitting in its shade. He knew that gravity operated everywhere here on earth, from the highest mountain peak to the deepest well, and even at the bottom of the ocean. If an apple released from the tree falls to the earth's surface, would not an apple released from a tree on the moon fall to the moon's surface? If an apple were released one mile, two miles, ten miles above the earth's surface, would it not also fall back to the earth because of gravity? If gravity extended that far, perhaps it extended as far as the moon, perhaps as far as the farthest planet, perhaps to infinity. Perhaps the planets were held

[3] Mechanics is the science of motion.

in their orbits by the gravitational force of the sun.[4] This was Newton's great inspiration, that the force that caused an apple to fall from a tree to the ground was the same force holding the moon in its orbit. If such is the case, then perhaps the moon is a falling body, falling with an acceleration directed towards the center of the earth. Since the moon is moving in an approximately circular path, the laws of uniform circular motion (p. 122) should apply. Its acceleration should therefore be subject to calculation from the equation, $a = v^2/r$, as follows:

$$v = \frac{d}{t} = \frac{\text{Length of orbit}}{\text{Time for one revolution}} = \frac{2\pi r}{T}$$

$$v^2 = \frac{2^2 \pi^2 r^2}{T^2}$$

Dividing both sides by r,

$$\frac{v^2}{r} = \frac{4\pi^2 r}{T^2} \qquad \text{(Eq. 8-1)}$$

Since we want our answer in our usual cgs units, r must be reduced to centimeters and T to seconds. Therefore,

$$a = \frac{v^2}{r} = \frac{\left(4 \times (3.14)^2 \times 240{,}000 \text{ mi} \times 5280 \text{ ft/mi} \times 30 \text{ cm/ft} \right)}{\left(27.3 \text{ days} \times 24 \text{ hr/day} \times 3600 \text{ sec/hr} \right)^2}$$

When the arithmetic is performed, we get

$$a = 0.273 \text{ cm/sec}^2$$

This acceleration is far smaller than the value of g on the earth's surface (980

[4] Kepler, knowing nothing about gravitation but knowing about Gilbert's work on magnetism (p. 295), speculated on the possibility of the planets being held in their orbits by magnetism emanating from the sun. Although incorrect, this was the first suggestion that the sun played the leading role in our planetary system.

cm/sec^2). To a man of Newton's ability a so much smaller value of a would suggest that the acceleration due to gravity (hence the force causing it) is also dependent on the distance between the two bodies involved. If so, how should this distance be measured—from surface to surface or from center to center? Newton used the latter distance, but being unable to show why, put aside his whole work on gravitation for some years, spending his time doing work on optics. In time he was able to show by the use of his newly invented calculus that a solid sphere attracting with inverse-square-law forces attracts as if its mass were all at the center.

To a man of Newton's genius the inverse-square-law relationship between the force of gravity and the distance between the two bodies involved presented no real problem as long as he used circular orbits as a first approximation. With the aid of his calculus he was able to derive a more precise result. He was able to prove that a body traveling in a path other than a circle, and continuously acted on by a force varying inversely with the square of the distance from a central point, must travel in an ellipse. The mathematics involved are beyond us; we will be content with an approximation by use of circular orbits. For our purposes the error is insignificant, less than that introduced by other approximations such as the distance from the center of the earth to the center of the moon, the radius and mass of the moon, the radius of the earth, etc. The method is as follows:

From Newton's second law we have $F = ma$. From the laws of uniform circular motion we get $a = v^2/r$, so that the second law becomes $F = mv^2/r$. It follows that $F \propto m$, and $F \propto v^2/r$. From Eq. 8-1 we have

$$\frac{v^2}{r} = \frac{4\pi^2 r}{T^2} \qquad \text{(Eq. 8-2)}$$

Since $4\pi^2$ is a constant,

$$\frac{v^2}{r} \propto \frac{r}{T^2}$$

Since $F \propto v^2/r$,

$$F \propto \frac{r}{T^2} \text{ also.}$$

From Kepler's third law, $T^2 \propto r^3$. Therefore,

$$F \propto \frac{r}{r^3} \propto \frac{1}{r^2}$$

or

$$F = K\frac{1}{r^2} \qquad \text{(Eq. 8-3)}$$

This equation told Newton that the gravitational force between the moon and the earth should be inversely proportional to the square of the radius of the moon's orbit, i.e., to the square of its distance from the center of the earth. If the earth and the moon were twice as far apart, the force would be one-fourth as much; if they were half as far apart, the force would be four times as much, etc.

The next problem was the role that the masses of the earth and the moon played in determining the force. Newton's second law, $F = ma$, demanded that m be as important as a in measuring or calculating any net force here on earth. We measure the force of gravity every time we weigh anything. All of us learn quite early in life that weight depends upon the amount of matter in a body, that two similar bags of potatoes weigh about twice as much as one bag. We can therefore readily accept the premise that the force of gravity in-

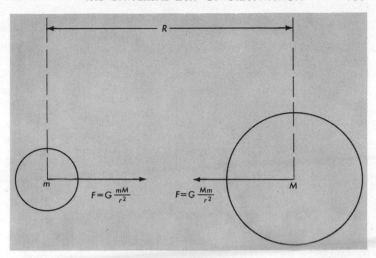

Fig. 8-1. The attraction of the earth, M, for the moon, m, is equal in magnitude to the attraction of the moon for the earth. This follows from Newton's third law. Thus, the F's in the two equations are equal but oppositely directed.

creases with an increase in the mass of a body. And if the force increases with the mass of one body, would it not increase with the mass of the other? Newton's third law says that it does. If so, $F \propto m$, and $F \propto M$, where m and M are the masses of the two bodies (Fig. 8-1). Combining these proportionalities we have $F \propto Mm$. Combining this new proportionality with the one expressed in Eq. 8-3, we have $F \propto Mm/r^2$.

Writing it as an equation,

$$F = G \frac{Mm}{r^2} \qquad \text{(Eq. 8-4)}$$

where G is a constant. G is called the gravitational constant. It should never be confused with g.

In words, Eq. 8-4 states that the force of gravitation between the earth and the moon is proportional to the product of their masses and inversely proportional to the square of the radius of the orbit of the moon. Newton used the moon in its orbit about the earth in his calculations because it is much the nearest of the celestial bodies

and because he knew its average distance and its period with satisfactory degrees of accuracy.

Newton was not quite yet ready to call Eq. 8-4 his Universal Law of Gravitation. From the standpoint of mathematical reasoning the equation was sound, but, as we have observed before, nature is not bound to follow the reasoning of man. The equation may at this point be said to be an hypothesis in mathematical form. To convert it into a law it had to be tested in various ways. The first was against the observation of the moon. We have already calculated (p. 131) what the acceleration of the moon would be if it were accelerated in circular motion. For our data we used the observed period, and its measured distance. We found a to be 0.273 cm/sec². Now if Eq. 8-4 is to hold, F must also be equal to ma, i.e., it must satisfy Newton's second law, a law that has been derived by experiment. Therefore,

$$F = G \frac{Mm}{r^2} = ma \qquad \text{(Eq. 8-5)}$$

in which M and m are the masses of the earth and the moon respectively, r is the distance between them, and a is the gravitational acceleration of the moon towards the earth. Solving for a,

$$a = G \frac{M}{r^2} \qquad \text{(Eq. 8-6)}$$

Note that m cancels out. Now r is 240,000 mi. Substituting this quantity for r,

$$a = G \frac{M}{(240,000)^2} \qquad \text{(Eq. 8-7)}$$

Newton could not solve this equation directly because he knew neither G nor M. However, Eqs. 8-5 and 8-6 should also hold if we substitute a stone on the earth's surface at a distance of 4000 mi from the earth's center, for the moon in its orbit. Using g as the acceleration of the stone,

$$g = G \frac{M}{R^2} = G \frac{M}{(4000)^2} \qquad \text{(Eq. 8-8)}$$

We have learned that a ratio is simply a fraction formed by dividing one number by another. We can therefore obtain the ratio of a to g by dividing Eq. 8-7 by Eq. 8-8. Note that we get rid of the G's and the M's, for they cancel out.

$$\frac{a}{g} = \frac{\dfrac{GM}{(240,000)^2}}{\dfrac{GM}{(4000)^2}} = \frac{(4000)^2}{(240,000)^2} = \frac{1}{3600}$$

Solving for a

$$a = \frac{1}{3600} g \qquad \text{(Eq. 8-9)}$$

Thus Eq. 8-7 tells us that the acceleration of the moon towards the earth should be $\frac{1}{3600}$ of the value of g. Therefore,

$$a = \frac{980 \text{ cm/sec}^2}{3600} = 0.272 \text{ cm/sec}^2$$

$$\text{(Eq. 8-10)}$$

Note that what has been done here is to test the validity of the inverse-square law (Eq. 8-3), for the two masses from Eq. 8-4 were eliminated (m by solving Eq. 8-5, and M by solving for a/g in deriving Eq. 8-9) before we achieved our final result. This test simply shows that the acceleration of a stone (or the moon) due to gravitational attraction of the earth, at a distance of 60 times that of the earth's radius, should be $\frac{1}{3600}$ that of a stone here on the earth's surface—and which is only *one* earth's radius away. We found that $\frac{1}{3600}$ of 980 cm/sec² is 0.272 cm/sec², almost exactly that calculated from the observed values of the moon's distance, velocity, and period (p. 131). The result of 0.273 cm/sec² from the observed values is closer than we have any right to hope for, considering the round figures we used for both the radius of the orbit of the moon and the earth's radius.

This result of 0.272 cm/sec² means that the moon is falling towards the earth with a velocity that is increasing by 0.272 cm/sec each second. Translated into miles, it means that the moon "falls" about 6300 mi in one day, and it has been doing that for some billions of years without ever getting any closer. How can this be? What do we mean when we speak of the moon as a "falling" body? Newton's first law states that if no force were acting on the moon it would follow a straight-line path (Fig. 8-2). But there is a force, the gravitational attraction of the earth acting as a true centripetal force, to cause it to deviate continuously from such a path. The "falling" of the moon is simply its deflection away from this straight-line path. In other words, the moon has to "fall" 6300 mi a day towards the earth to keep from getting farther and farther away from the earth. A careful study of Fig. 8-2 should make this clear if it is not so already. To sum up, the kind of force that holds the moon in its orbit was proved identical with that which causes objects to have weight and to fall freely here on the earth's surface. Thus, it is the force of gravity that holds the solar system together.

In order not to break the continuity of our account, we have omitted certain details. There were a number of possible variables that had to be considered, variables that had to be either eliminated, or determined and a method developed to control them. Some were temperature, density, shape, volume, composition, and speed. Did these make a difference? As we have seen they did not; only mass and distance need be considered.

The gravitational hypothesis of Newton could be taken out of the hypothetical category, and stated as a law insofar as the solar system was concerned. But did it apply to the whole universe? Newton believed it did and he boldly stated that *every particle in the universe attracts every other particle with a force that is directly proportional to the product of their masses, and inversely proportional to the square of the distance between them.* This is now what we call Newton's Universal Law of Gravitation. Its mathematical expression is $F = GMm/r^2$ (Eq. 8-5).

EXPERIMENTAL PROOF BY CAVENDISH

A little over one hundred years after Newton published his *Principia*—which in-

cluded his law of gravitation—Henry Cavendish of England actually succeeded in directly measuring the force of gravitation by experiment in the laboratory.[5]

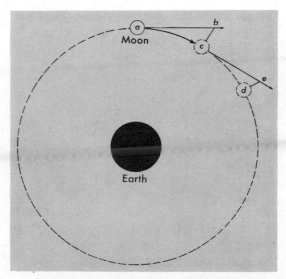

Fig. 8-2. The Moon as a Falling Body. If there were no force of gravitation, the moon would move along the line *ab* in time *t*. Instead it moves to *c* in time *t*; *ac* may be viewed as the resultant of *ab* + *bc*. In other words, the moon has "fallen" a distance equal to *bc* in moving from *a* to *c*. Similarly, it has fallen a distance equivalent to *de* in moving from *c* to *d*, etc.

The best modern value for G, called the gravitational constant, is 6.673×10^{-8} dyne-cm^2/gm^2 for all substances. This means that if two 1-gm masses are placed

[5] The principle is shown in Fig. 8-3. As you can easily see the principle is extremely simple but the execution extremely difficult, for the forces involved are incredibly small. This is the reason that Newton did not try the experiment himself. Newton had made guesses of the value of G but succeeded

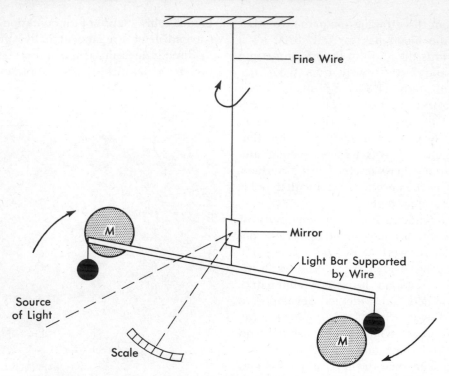

Fine Wire

Mirror

Light Bar Supported
by Wire

M

Source
of Light

Scale

M

Fig. 8-3. Cavendish "Weighs the Earth." Two small balls suspended by a light bar and wire are at rest in a closed glass cage (not shown). The two large heavy balls are brought near the small balls in such a manner that both tend to turn the bar in the same direction, twisting the wire and the mirror as it does so. See footnote 5 for more details.

so that their centers are 1 cm apart, they will attract each other with a force of about two-thirds of a ten-millionth of a dyne. Many experiments have been performed since Newton's time to see if gravitational attractions are influenced by any

only in arriving at the conclusion that no experiment that he could perform with the equipment available could give it to him. Other scientists tried to use the deflection of a pendulum by a mountain mass but succeeded only in getting very rough estimates.

Cavendish used two small lead balls and two large ones. The small ones were attached to a light metal rod, which in turn was supported by thin metal wires. This apparatus was at rest and enclosed in a glass case (not shown) so that air currents would not disturb it. The large balls (M) were then brought near in such a manner that the attractions of the heavy balls for the small ones would tend to twist the bar containing the small ones in the same direction. Since the amount of twisting is very small, a special device was needed to measure it. This device consisted of a tiny mirror attached to the twisting wire (see figure), a thin beam of light directed at the mirror, and a scale in the path of the reflected beam. By noting the positions of the reflected beam both before and after the large balls were brought in position, the amount of twisting could be determined. The farther the scale from the mirror, the greater the magnification of the twisting. Knowing by experiment the amount of force it took to twist the wire, the masses of both sets of balls, and the distances between their centers, the forces of attraction could be calculated.

conceivable factor—composition of material, shielding, temperature, crystal form, etc.—but none has so far been found. The constant is regarded as a truly universal one.

CONSEQUENCES OF GRAVITATION

The most obvious consequence is that objects here on earth have weight. When we weigh something we are literally measuring the force of gravitation between that body and the earth. If you weigh 120 lb we say that the earth attracts you with that force. The attraction is mutual, however, and so we say also that you attract the earth with a force of 120 lb. Newton's third law demands that this be so, just as much as does the law of gravitation itself. Since the force of gravitation varies with the distance from the center of the earth, it varies both with latitude and with altitude. Therefore, you should weigh a bit less at the equator than at the poles, and a bit less on the top of a mountain than at sea level. This will be evident if you weigh yourself on a spring scale (Fig. 8-4). If you weigh yourself on a balance scale, you are simply comparing the pull of the earth on you with the pull of the earth on a known mass. Since both you and the weights are attracted equally, a balance scale will give the same reading anywhere.

We see now the difference between mass and weight. If mass is defined as quantity

Fig. 8-4. Spring Scale **(a)** and Balance Scale **(b).** Objects weighed on the balance scale give the same reading anywhere because they are simply balanced against another set of weights of the same mass. In the spring scale the reading is directly dependent on the pull of gravity. Hence the reading will vary as the value of g varies.

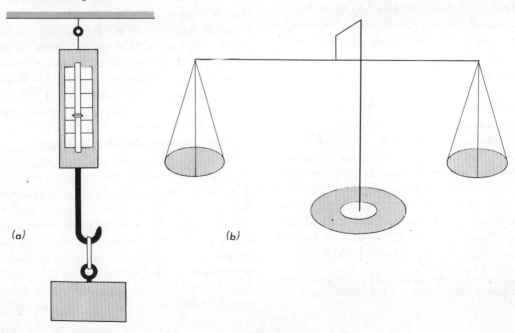

(a)   (b)

of matter, we can see that it does not change from one place to another but remains constant anywhere in the universe. On the other hand, weight is a measure of the gravitational attraction between two bodies; i.e., it is a force. On the moon you would weigh in the neighborhood of 20 lb if you

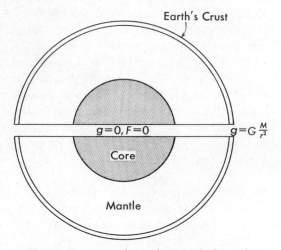

Fig. 8-5. Hypothetical Tunnel through Earth. The acceleration, g, of a ball dropped into the tunnel would decrease to 0 at the center where F is 0 because of the attraction of equal masses on all sides.

weigh 120 lb here on earth. Far out in space outside the gravitational field [6] of any celestial body, you would weigh nothing, but your mass would be the same as here on earth. However, as long as you stay here on the earth's surface, weight is both a measure of the mass of a body and of the earth's attraction for that mass. But this is not to say that weight and mass are the same thing (see pp. 113 and 155).

[6] Actually there is no such place, but you can be so far away that the force is too small to be measured.

It is interesting to consider what the situation would be if one could go deep in the earth, even to its center (Fig. 8-5). Let us consider the earth, as Newton did, as consisting of numerous concentric shells. As we descend deeper and deeper, more and more of these shells are left "behind" us and so attract us in the opposite direction. We can then conclude that at the center the force of gravitation is 0, and the value of g should be 0. Outside of the earth, the value of g varies as $1/r^2$, but inside the earth the attraction of the shells we leave behind us as we penetrate deeper, cause g to vary directly as r.

The differences in the force of gravitation with latitude and altitude are reflected in the values of g. This acceleration varies from 983 cm/sec² at the poles to 978 cm/sec² at the equator. At New York it is 980.27 cm/sec². On the top of Mt. Everest it should be slightly less than 980.

From his law of gravitation and the laws of rotational motion, Newton calculated that an earth rotating on an axis should bulge at the equator and be flattened at the poles. He figured that an equatorial radius about 14 mi greater than the polar radius should suffice. Ten years after his death such a bulge was first measured. The modern figure for the difference in the two radii is 13.35 mi.

Why, we may ask, should Newton have deduced the spheroidal shape of the earth? Why should it not be shaped like a cube, or a cylinder, or a football, or a doughnut? This same question applies equally well to all celestial bodies. Aside from comets and asteroids whose masses are too small for gravity to be significant, all celestial bodies are spherical, or if rotating rapidly, spheroidal. Since all matter is subject to gravitation, it follows no matter what the origin of any of these celestial bodies was, whether by contraction and condensation from a once gaseous state, or from a "dust" cloud or other mass of solid particles, the resulting shape would be the same. The pressure of the particles, as great size was attained, would prevent any one part of the celestial body from projecting much farther out from the center than any other part. Consider the earth, for example. As we go downward into it, the pressures quickly become enormous. At depths of 12 to 15 mi below sea level they are so great that even solid rock will flow in response to it. At these depths the pressures are everywhere equalized if the distance beneath the surface is the same. Thus, the rocks beneath the ocean basins exert the same pressure at the 12- to 15-mile depth below sea level as do the rocks beneath a high mountain range. We may therefore conclude that the rocks beneath these ranges have lesser mass per unit volume (i.e., lesser density) than do the rocks beneath the ocean basins.

Newton was also able to explain the precession of the equinoxes, unexplained since the time of Hipparchus. The sun's attraction for the earth's equatorial bulge is slightly greater than for the rest of the earth, thus tending to pull the earth's equatorial region into the plane of the ecliptic. Because the earth is rotating, it successfully resists this tendency. The pull is, however, translated into a slow motion of the axis which describes a cone about a perpendicular to the plane of the ecliptic (Fig. 2-13).

Newton was also successful in using his theory to explain the tides, another phenomenon that had been begging for an explanation ever since man began his quest for understanding. The tides correlated

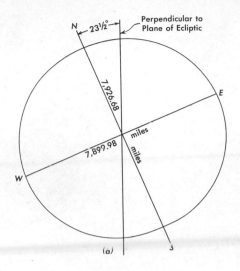

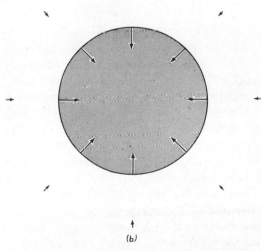

Fig. 8-6. The Spheroidal Earth. **(a)** The equatorial diameter, *E–E*, is about 26 mi greater than the polar diameter, *N–S*. **(b)** The inward pull of gravity on all points on the surface tend to make the earth spherical. Away from the earth's surface the force becomes less in accordance with the inverse-square law.

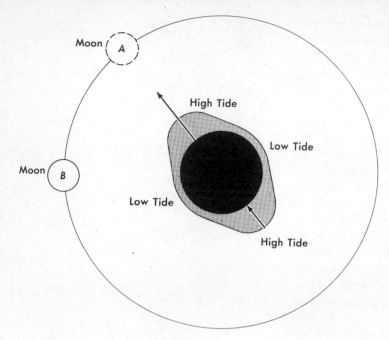

Fig. 8-7. The Tides. Tides are caused by differences of the moon's attraction. The side nearest the moon experiences an extra-large pull (as compared with that at the earth's center) so that water pulls up on that side. The side farthest away experiences an extra-low pull, and so the water flows away to produce another high tide. Because of inertia, tidal friction, and rotational effects the tides are delayed by several hours so that they are not highest opposite the moon.

with the motion of the moon, but even Galileo could see no explanation connected with it.[7] The moon does not revolve about the earth's center but about a common center of gravity (just as does the earth) 1000 mi below the surface of the earth. The sun in turn revolves about a center of gravity common to the sun-earth-moon system, a center very close to the center of the sun. Thus, we say the system is heliocentric. The pull of the earth on the moon and of the moon on the earth provides just enough mv^2/r to keep the earth (and the moon) moving around the common center of gravity once a month. Imagine the earth covered with a universal ocean with no continents to complicate matters. That part nearest the moon is pulled with a greater

force than average and so the water rises in a hump to form one tide (Fig. 8-7). The side farthest away is pulled less than average, less than enough to keep it moving with the rest of the earth in its motion about the common center of gravity. Therefore it lags behind, fails to "make the curve," so to speak, and so forms another hump opposite the first one. As the earth spins, its surface travels around, while the humps are held almost in one place by the moon and the sun. Thus, the two humps move like a wave as the oceans spin beneath them. High tide is not beneath the moon but lags behind by about six hours, due to friction and inertia. The sun also produces tides smaller than those of the moon in the same manner. Twice a month the tides of the sun and the moon coincide, giving us the high spring tides, and twice a month they are out of step, giving us the low neap tides.

[7] Actually Galileo gave a wrong explanation for the tides. Inability of some to accept his explanation played a role in their refusal to accept the heliocentric hypothesis.

Perhaps the greatest success, certainly the most astonishing to the layman, was the prediction of the existence of, and the final discovery of, the planet Neptune in 1846. Eight major members of the solar system—sun, moon, Mercury, Venus, earth, Mars, Jupiter, and Saturn—had been known for some thousands of years. To these Galileo had added four moons of Jupiter. Uranus was discovered in 1781 by William Herschel while searching the sky with his home-made telescope. Computation of its orbit began by use of Kepler's laws and the Law of Gravitation. Its period—84 years—was too long to observe in one lifetime. By 1830 it was apparent that the calculated

Fig. 8-8. Earth-satellite Orbits. A slightly modified drawing from Newton's *System of the World* showing the paths that a projectile would follow if fired at various speeds from a gun on a mountain top. It shows that Newton knew that a body would go into orbit about the earth if its speed were great enough. The first four paths were made by projectiles with too low a speed.

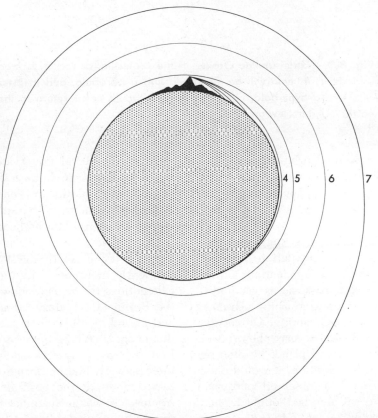

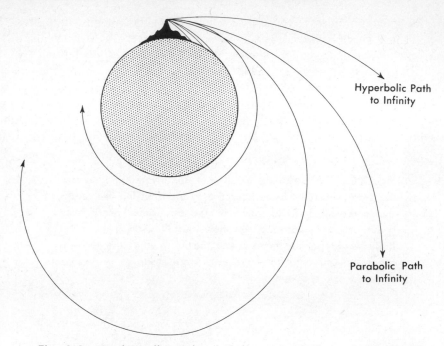

Hyperbolic Path
to Infinity

Parabolic Path
to Infinity

Fig. 8-9. Earth-satellite Orbits. If the projectile (or rocket) is fired still faster, its path will be elongated into a parabola, and if faster still, into a hyperbola. In either case, it would never return to the earth. (After Newton.)

orbit and the observed orbit did not quite match. Some of the deviations, called perturbations, could be explained by the attractions of Jupiter and Saturn. There still remained one of the order of $\frac{1}{100}$ of a degree. Some astronomers suggested that perhaps the law of gravitation was not really universal in its application; others suggested that perhaps some as yet undiscovered planet was perturbing Uranus. An undergraduate at Cambridge University, John C. Adams, began to map the orbit of this as yet undiscovered planet by plotting mathematically the positions it would need in order to cause the observed perturbations of Uranus. When he thought he had this planet located he wrote to the astrono-

mers of the Royal Observatory at Greenwich, asking them to turn their powerful telescope to a particular spot in the heavens at a specified hour. Because he was an unknown they paid him no heed.

Meanwhile a young Frenchman, Leverrier, was doing exactly the same thing independently in France. In 1846 he sent his calculations to the astronomer in charge of the Berlin Observatory. This man looked and found the planet at almost the predicted spot. When the news was flashed to London, the Royal Astronomer confirmed the discovery, finding the new planet within two degrees of the position predicted by Adams. It was a magnificent triumph for the Law of Gravitation. Pluto was discovered in 1930 in much the same way, i.e., from perturbations in the orbit of Neptune.

ARTIFICIAL SATELLITES

Newton stated that any projectile is potentially an earth satellite. Suppose we fire one at high speed with a strong horizontal component of motion. If there were no force of gravity, it would get farther and farther away from the earth as the earth's surface curved away from it. Because of gravity it falls in a curved path towards the earth. If fired fast enough this curved path would have the same curvature as the earth (Figs. 8-8 and 8-9) so that, like the moon, it would be constantly falling towards the earth without ever getting any closer. Neither artificial satellites nor rockets to the moon, Venus, or Mars would be any surprise to Newton. He worked out the principles on which they operate nearly three hundred years ago (Fig. 7-5).

One of the most important consequences of gravitation is that it makes solar and stellar systems possible. Without gravitation all bodies in the universe would be traveling in straight lines utterly independent of the movement of any other body. In such a universe life on this or any other planet would be impossible. It is gravitation that makes for order in the universe, an order that is imperative to the understanding of it. We cannot imagine a universe without gravitational attraction.

SUMMARY

The combined work of Galileo and Newton on motion made it obvious that some force had to be operating on the planets to keep them in their elliptical orbits. Eventually Newton was able to prove that the planets were all moving in accordance with the laws of motion applicable to moving bodies here on earth. He applied his concepts and methods to the moon, which he treated as a falling body. From the equations

$$v = \frac{d}{t} = \frac{2\pi r}{T} \quad \text{and} \quad a = \frac{v^2}{r}$$

he calculated a for the moon and found it to be 0.273 cm/sec^2; the moon was "falling" towards the earth with an acceleration of 0.273 cm/sec^2 without ever getting any closer.

Newton reasoned that the disparity between a for the moon and g for a stone falling here on earth was due to the much greater distance from the earth's center. Using his equations for uniform circular motion and Kepler's third law, he determined that the force of gravitation was inversely proportional to the square of the distance. By means of his newly invented calculus he was able to show that the distance should be measured from the center of the moon to the center of the earth. Reasoning next from his second and third laws of motion, he reached the conclusion that the force was proportional to the product of the masses of the earth and the moon. Combining the proportionalities of the masses with that of the distance, he had

$$F \propto \frac{Mm}{r^2} \quad \text{or} \quad F = G\frac{Mm}{r^2}$$

where G is constant, now called the gravitational constant.

The next step was to determine the value of a by use of the above equation. Since F also equals ma, $ma = G(Mm/r^2)$, from which $a = G(M/(240,000)^2)$ for the moon at the moon's distance. The equation has two unknowns. To solve he had to get rid of one. For a stone on earth, $g = G(M/(4000)^2)$. To find the ratio between a and g we divide one of the above equations by the other. Whence,

$$\frac{a}{g} = \frac{1}{3600} \quad \text{and} \quad a = 0.272 \text{ cm/sec}^2$$

which compares very nicely with the value (0.273 cm/sec^2) calculated from data obtained by observation. Newton was now ready to announce his Law of Universal Gravitation: Every particle in the universe attracts every other particle with a force that is directly proportional to the product of their masses and inversely proportional to the square of the distance between them, i.e., $F = G(Mm/r^2)$. About one hundred years later Cavendish succeeded in measuring the value of G. $G = 6.673 \times 10^{-8}$ dyne-cm^2/gm^2.

EXERCISES

I. TERMS AND CONCEPTS

Gravitational constant, G
Acceleration due to gravity, g

II. PROBLEMS

√ 1. Would the acceleration of a falling body on the moon's surface be greater or less than that on earth? Why?

2. The gravitational force between the earth and the moon at the average distance between them may be expressed as F. For the following changes in mass or distance or both, will the value of F remain constant, increase to $2F$, $3F$, $4F$, etc., or be reduced to $\frac{1}{4}F$, $\frac{1}{3}F$, $\frac{1}{2}F$, $\frac{1}{8}F$, etc.? It is understood that the factors not mentioned remain unchanged.

  a. The moon's mass is doubled.
  b. The earth's mass is doubled.
  — c. Both the mass of the earth and that of the moon are doubled.
  d. The earth's mass is doubled and that of the moon is tripled.
  — e. The distance between the centers of the two is doubled.
  f. The above distance is halved.
  g. The above distance is tripled.
  h. Both masses are doubled and the distance is halved.

  i. The mass of the moon is doubled and the distance halved.
  j. Both masses are halved and the distance is doubled.

√ 3. The moon is constantly being accelerated towards the earth but never gets any closer. Explain.

√ 4. Because of the earth's rotation, objects on the surface of the earth are, in general, subjected to a force directed inward towards the center which is called centripetal force. Is this force equal everywhere at the surface of the earth? Explain.

√ 5. Learn the difference between weighing on a spring scale and weighing on a balance. Does each measure the pull of gravity directly? Explain. If you were buying gold high in the Sierra Nevada Mountains and selling it at sea level, which scale would be most advantageous for you to use at either place?

6. Consider yourself out in space all by yourself 4000 mi from the surface of the earth. If you could weigh yourself on a spring scale, how much would you weigh if you weighed 120 lb at the earth's surface?

7. How much would a man weigh on the moon if he weighed 150 lb on earth? (Note: This, and similar problems, are best solved in two parts. On the moon you will be closer to the center of gravity since the moon's radius is only about ¼ that of the earth. First solve for this condition, assuming that the mass of the moon is equal to that of the earth. You will, of course, get a figure that is far higher than your weight on earth. Next, correct for the mass of the moon. Its mass is only about 1/80 that of the earth. Now solve the problem.)

8. The planet, Sassafrune, has a mass 16 times that of the earth and a radius 4 times that of the earth. How much would a man who weighs 150 lb on earth weigh on Sassafrune?

√ 9. The radius of Jupiter is 11 times that of the earth and its mass is about 317 times that of the earth.

a. How much would you weigh on Jupiter?

b. Suppose you landed on Jupiter in a space ship. What difficulties would arise because of this weight?

c. What difficulty would your space ship have in getting away from Jupiter? Be explicit.

10. What is the distinction between mass and weight?

11. List as many consequences of the law of gravitation as you can.

12. Describe the general method used by Cavendish to determine the gravitational constant, G. Explain precisely just what this constant represents.

CHAPTER IX

A Digression: Facts, Concepts, Laws, Theories, and Hypotheses

The value of any working theory depends upon the number of experimental facts it serves to correlate, and upon its power of suggesting new lines of work.
—LORD RUTHERFORD
(*Nobel Prize, Chemistry, 1908*)

We have delayed defining or discussing the terms in the title of this chapter until a number of them had been presented to you in enough detail to form a background for the present discussion. To have made this chapter the first in this book would, in the opinion of the author, have been largely a waste of time, somewhat like trying to understand the culture of a primitive people without having any background of information about them. Until one has had experience with scientific laws, theories, or hypotheses, and has had the opportunity to discover, think about, and describe a number of them, and until one has some knowledge of the mental climate of the time in which a theory, law, or hypothesis was de-

veloped, true understanding of them cannot be hoped for.

This is not to imply that all those using this text have to do to obtain this understanding is to read this chapter. Only a start will be made at this time, a start that will not be completed even when this course is ended. It is hoped, however, that in the end the student will have gotten rid of many mistaken notions about these terms, and that he will be able to distinguish between a law and a theory. It is also hoped that if he is somewhat disdainful of theories, as so many people are, and is prone to laud the practical over the theoretical, that he will come to the realization that man's success in his upward struggle from caveman to modern civilized man is almost wholly due to the curiosity of a relatively few individuals and their penchant for formulating theories. Some peoples even today have never lifted themselves above primitive levels, because they lacked something that other peoples possessed. That something was not just curiosity but, coupled with it, a lack of desire to understand and explain the objects of their curiosity, i.e., to formulate theories concerning them. Without theories the search for new laws of nature would be a mere fumbling in the dark.

THEORIES

For that is essentially what a scientific theory is, an explanation of some natural phenomenon. This is not a complete definition, nor is one possible.[1] If we had to

[1] The term theory is very widely misused, sometimes by people who profess to know considerable science. It is often used as a synonym for an educated guess. Sometimes a tentative answer to almost any problem, no matter how trivial, is re-

make a two- or three-word definition, we would call theories conceptual schemes: "conceptual schemes that have developed as a result of experimentation and observation and are fruitful of further experimentation and observation." Conant says that the emphasis should be on the word *fruitful*.[2]

Fruitful means that the conceptual scheme should suggest the making of new observations, new experiments, new explanations for inadequate old ones, or explanations for phenomena that have long gone without them. A good conceptual scheme will

. . . penetrate beyond the immediate and visible to the unseen, and thereby . . . place the visible into a new, larger context. For like a distant floating iceberg whose bulk is largely hidden under the sea, only the smallest part of reality impresses itself upon us directly. To help us grasp the whole picture is the supreme function of a theory. On a simple level, a theory helps us to interpret the unknown in terms of the known. It is a conceptual scheme which we invent or postulate in order to explain to ourselves, and to others, observed phenomena and the relationships between them, thereby bringing together into one structure the concepts, laws, principles, hypotheses, and observations from often widely different fields. These functions may equally well be claimed by the hypothesis. In truth, we need not lay down a precise dividing line, but might regard theory and hypothesis as differing in degree of generality only. Therefore, at one extreme we might find the *limited working hypothesis* by which we guide

our way through a specific experiment, placing at the other end of the spectrum the *general theory*, which guides the design and interpretation of all experiments in that field of study.[3]

We have emphasized the fruitfulness of a theory. Such a theory should correlate many separate, and possibly seemingly unrelated facts into a logical, easily grasped structure of thought. A fruitful theory should spark the imagination to see if paths that have heretofore been considered entirely unconnected may not connect up with the new paths. A good theory should make it possible to predict specific new observable phenomena, and it may offer a solution to some practical problems. For example, the heliocentric theory helped to determine the exact length of the year and of the lunar month.

Let us consider Newton's Theory of Gravitation, one of the most fruitful of all theories, in the light of these functions of a theory. Once the mathematics involved had been worked out, not only was an understanding of what kept the planets in their orbits possible, but it also became possible to map the orbits of undiscovered planets, to explain the tides and the precession of the equinoxes, to determine the masses of the earth, the planets, and the sun and to calculate their densities, to predict the shape of the earth and give a reason for it, to understand the variations of the value of g in different parts of the earth, to plot the paths of artificial satellites, and even to understand why the high mountains are able to stand so far above the floors of the ocean basins. A theory

ferred to as a theory. In the minds of some, a theory is something that has not been proved. Often the word *theory* is used to refer to an hypothesis or is used improperly in place of the word *speculation*.

[2] James Conant, *Science and Common Sense*, Yale University Press, New Haven, 1951, p. 25.

[3] Gerald Holton, *Concepts and Theories in Physical Science*, Addison-Wesley, Reading, Mass., 1952, p. 138.

that is not fruitful is a "bad" theory because it does not lead to further knowledge. For example, the theory that the earth was specially created as is is a "bad" theory, not because it is not true, but because it does not lead one on towards a better understanding of nature. Such a theory is barren, for it gives a final explanation to all things, that they are as they are because they were created that way. A believer in such a theory has no incentive to investigate nature except to describe it, for he already has all of the answers as to why things are as they are.

Difficult for the layman to understand is that the scientists' criterion for a "good" theory does not depend upon whether it is true or not. He measures it only by its consequences—". . . consequences in terms of other ideas and other experiments. Thus conceived, science is not a quest for certainty; it is rather a quest which is successful only to the degree that it is continuous." [4] If the viewpoint that the validity of a theory depends only upon its ability to suggest new experiments which in turn generate new ideas, and so on, seems like a form of madness, we will have to let it seem so. For to seek to justify this attitude of the scientist would take far more pages than we have available here. Suffice it to say that some theories that have been completely discarded were "good" theories at one time. They became "bad" theories only when they not only failed to suggest new experiments or to account for new facts but actually became stumbling blocks to the development of new ideas, and hence to the acquisition of new knowledge. Eric M. Rogers of Princeton says that one

[4] James Conant, *Science and Understanding*, Yale University Press, 1951, pp. 25–26.

needs to develop an educated taste for good theories just as you do for good cooking; in a sense, scientific theory is a form of intellectual cookery.

From what has been said above, one should infer that the scientist does not expect any theory to go down through the ages unchanged. Theories are always subject to change (by scientists themselves and not by others) as new facts and observations accumulate. Even Newton's theory of gravitation underwent a refining modification as a result of Einstein's general theory of relativity, a theory that predicted an extra motion for the planet Mercury. This extra motion, involving a slewing around of the long axis of the elliptical orbit by 0.00119° per century, had already been observed but not explained before Einstein. This refinement does not invalidate Newton's theory nor make Einstein's theory better than Newton's. Actually Einstein's theory still has some doubts and problems, but such doubts and problems about theories in general do not irritate scientists. They keep them in mind with hopes that the future will be more interesting to them because of the unsolved problems. For no scientist expects that the day will ever arrive when he has all the answers, for he is convinced that new knowledge begets new facts and new experiments, which in turn beget new knowledge and so on ad infinitum.

HYPOTHESES

Considerable confusion exists between the terms theory and hypothesis. In general, we might say that hypotheses are single tentative suppositions provisionally adopted for use in devising a theory or to explain a certain fact or facts, and intended to guide an experiment if one can be devised. It is thus seen that the term hypothesis is much more limited in scope than theory, and that what many people refer to as a theory is really an hypothesis.

FACTS

It is extremely difficult to state what a fact is. Since most physical scientists believe they are dealing with a real external world, they start with sense impressions as their facts of nature. In general, the facts of the physical scientist are the measurements he makes, measurements that can be checked and agreed upon by different independent observers. If an experiment reveals unexpected and perhaps startling results, the important question asked of the experimenter is, "Are your results repeatable?" Thus, science is in a sense self-correcting, for the scientist trusts only those "facts" that are the same in different laboratories, for different observers, and on different days of the week. Every scientist knows that sooner or later someone is sure to check and repeat his experiments, his observations, and his calculations and so will most likely uncover any errors and self-deceptions. In one sense facts are more important than theories, for facts are the supreme arbiters of theories. More than one beautiful theory has had to be drastically altered or abandoned because of its failure to explain one ugly fact.

SCIENTIFIC LAWS

Scientific laws, sometimes called principles, are generalizations that describe the behavior of matter under a specific set of conditions. The work of the physical scientist is based on the premise that there is order in the universe, and that this order can be expressed mathematically, that nature works according to mathematical laws, and the observations of the scientist are best explained when the mathematical law relating the observations is found. From the time of Kepler and Galileo mathematical methods have provided the best means for understanding nature. To see this we have only to recall $T^2 = Kr^3$, $d = \frac{1}{2}gt^2$, $F = ma$, and $F = GMm/r^2$.

Essential to the understanding of scientific laws is a recognition of their limitations. Thus, $d = \frac{1}{2}gt^2$ only in the absence of air resistance. We will learn that Boyle's Law does not hold at either very high pressures or at very low temperatures. Some laws are universal, or very nearly so. Such a one is Newton's Law of Gravitation. Another is Einstein's Mass–Energy Law, $E = mc^2$. Nevertheless, the most certain truth about scientific laws is that sooner or later some situation will arise in which they are found to be inaccurate or too limited. To the scientist this is no longer surprising, for matter is not compelled to obey physical laws. Unlike political laws there is never compulsion; yet the scientist expects matter to behave according to the laws, first, because the laws are an expression of the previous behavior of matter under specified conditions, and, second, because he believes that nature is orderly, not capricious. If the scientist finds that a law does not apply beyond certain limits, it does not mean that he is disappointed or that the law is a failure. Instead he tries to find out why, for beyond the limits of a law may lie new and exciting knowledge.

THE ROLE OF SPECULATIVE IDEAS

Some phases of scientific thinking fail to fit at all precisely into any part of the general picture so far presented. One of these is the role of speculative ideas. Such ideas are the product of the imagination. They may be extremely useful if we bear in mind their status; how useful will depend largely upon the background of information and the level-headedness of the man begetting them. In general, we may say that only the well informed have the right to seriously speculate on any subject. An example is space travel, now that it is, or seems to be, just around the corner. It has become common for writers and radio or television commentators to comment confidently on these matters even though they know nothing about distances or conditions on other planets. Many fields of knowledge are today only in the speculative stage, but only the experts in those fields have the right to seriously speculate. In such hands promising speculative ideas may be sorted out and some means possibly devised for investigating them further.

THE SO-CALLED SCIENTIFIC METHOD

There are few things, if any, about science that are more widely misunderstood by the nonscientist than those concerning the method or methods of science. In general, scientists are in agreement that there is no such thing as a scientific method. Few would agree that there are even a number of methods, unless you let that number equal the number of scientists. This is not to say that the methods of different scientists do not have some things in common. They do, very definitely so, but the term method implies proceeding step by step, and this is rarely done except by those who are tabulating facts.

The so-called scientific method makes little allowance for the "happy accident"—more commonly known as the role of chance. The initial observations leading to the invention of the battery, the discovery of x-rays, the vulcanization of rubber, the discovery of radioactivity, and many other things were made more or less by chance. Chance, however, favors the prepared mind, the mind ready to seize upon an unexpected observation and turn it to advantage. To one man the fogging of photographic plates kept in a room where a cathode-ray tube was operating meant (eventually) the discovery of a new kind of radiation; to another it merely meant that such a room was a poor place to keep undeveloped photographic plates.

To some scientists their solutions came "in a sudden flash of insight," but only after they had been completely immersed in their problems for some time. To most, however, if chance or inspiration enters at all, they are greatly overshadowed by hard work. In any case, once a discovery is made the good scientist subjects it to all conceivable tests, trying to ruin it, so to speak, for he knows that if he does not do so before publication, someone else will afterwards.

Someone has said that the scientific method consists simply of observing and experimenting. This is woefully insufficient for it leaves out the most important ingredients of all, those of planning and pondering, doing and pondering, and just pondering. For you do not learn simply by doing, as some educators would have us believe, but you learn by thinking about what you are doing while you are doing it.

The planning is important, for a scientist does not just search; he searches for something. Otherwise he might pass by the critical observation without recognizing it.

SCIENCE vs. NONSCIENCE

The various definitions of science and how it differs from other human endeavors would fill a moderate-sized book. Conant says that "Science is an interconnected series of concepts and conceptual schemes that have developed as a result of experimentation and observation and are fruitful of further experimentation and observations."[5] Einstein stated that, "The object of all sciences is to coordinate our experiences and to bring them into a logical system." Niels Bohr made a similar statement when he said that, "The task of science is both to extend the range of our experience and to reduce it to order."

Both of these latter "definitions" are much broader and far less specific than Conant's. Note the emphasis that Conant puts upon conceptual schemes. These schemes, theories if you like, form the flesh and blood of any science. Without them, all we would have is a bunch of dry bones. The study of science in such a course as this book is intended for is to a large and important degree the study of the development of these conceptual schemes.

One important difference between science and nonscience is that in the course of time there has been accumulated a set of basic concepts, conceptual schemes, and physical laws that have been endorsed by scientists of every country. Thus, Kepler's laws, Galileo's law of free fall and Newton's laws of motion and gravitation are

[5] *Op. cit.*

acceptable wherever scientists work. This can scarcely be said of other human endeavors.

Science, more than most disciplines, is cumulative. By this we mean that in large part one man builds on the work that his predecessors have done, i.e., he begins where the others have left off. To do this he may repeat some of the work they have done, but essentially his aim is to advance knowledge of the subject beyond that of those who went before him. Newton said that if he had seen farther than others it was because he had the shoulders of giants to stand on. In doing this, the scientist has no hesitation, if he thinks fit, in altering these predecessors' theories or laws, or even their facts and, more frequently, the interpretations placed upon them. Note how different it is in the fields of literature, art, and music. Newcomers in these fields do not begin where others left off, nor would they think of ever trying to improve their works by changing words, adding brush strokes, or changing notes of masters like Shakespeare, Leonardo da Vinci or Beethoven. Yet science is just as much a creative endeavor as are the arts, and the motivation is much the same. Some scientists have been just as willing to "Starve in a garret" as any writer, artist, or composer, provided only that they could continue their work.

Henri Poincaré, the great French mathematician, supported this view when he said,

The scientist does not study nature because it is useful; he studies it because he delights in it, and he delights in it because it is beautiful. If nature were not beautiful, it would not be worth knowing, and if nature were not worth knowing, life would not be worth living. Of course, I do not speak of that beauty which strikes the senses, the beauty of quality and appearances; not that I undervalue such beauty, far from it, but it has nothing to do with science; I mean that profounder beauty which comes from the harmonious order of the parts and which a pure intelligence can grasp. This it is which gives body, a structure so to speak, to the iridescent appearances which flatter our senses, and without this support the beauty of these fugitive dreams would be only imperfect, because it would be vague and always fleeting. On the contrary, intellectual beauty is sufficient unto itself, and it is for its sake, more perhaps than for the future good of humanity, that the scientist devotes himself to long and difficult labor.[6]

PRACTICAL SCIENCE vs. FUNDAMENTAL OR PURE SCIENCE

Many people are prone to laud the practical scientist, Thomas Edison, for example, while tending to scoff at the theoretical scientist. The practical scientist is trying to invent something that will be of some practical use, and this everyone can understand and appreciate. Far more difficult for the layman to appreciate is the work of a pure scientist on some problem that can result in nothing apparently useful at the time. Furthermore, he is amazed that the scientist considers usefulness as unimportant. The layman fails to realize that little progress in science can be made if usefulness is the sole criterion. Friends

[6] Jules Henri Poincaré, *Foundations of Science*, Science Press, New York, 1929.

of Benjamin Franklin wanted to know why he experimented with electricity. "What use is it?," they asked. Franklin's answer is supposed to have been, "Of what use is a newborn babe?"

At the time of discovery one can rarely predict where that discovery will find its uses. Because of Michael Faraday and Joseph Henry, both experimenters in the search for fundamental truth, Thomas Edison, the practical scientist was able to invent the electric light bulb. Without the work of the pure scientists, both theoretical and experimental, the practical scientists would have nothing to invent.

As an outstanding example of the inability to evaluate the full significance of a discovery at the time it is made, consider the rather casual discovery of radioactivity in the 1890's. Out of it has come a tool for extremely effective research into the structure of the atom, the treatment of certain diseases, a method for estimating the minimum age of the earth, and innumerable other uses in biology, geology, astronomy, metallurgy, archeology, and other fields. But let it not be thought that the pure scientist seeks to justify his work by citing examples like the above. To him—and to you—it should need no such justification, for knowledge for its own sake is sufficient an answer. Or, as Michelson answered when asked why he spent so much time measuring the velocity of light, "Because it's so much fun."

CHAPTER X

The Concepts
of Work and Energy

One machine can do the work of fifty ordinary men. No machine can do the work of one extraordinary man.—ELBERT HUBBARD

INTRODUCTION

These two terms, work and energy, are closely associated with each other even in the minds of people who never heard of them as scientific concepts. Both words are part of our ordinary language and of our everyday experiences. Everybody realizes that energy is something that enables us to do things, whether at play or at work. If you think briefly about how we get energy, you soon realize that it is something we pay for, directly or indirectly, when we pay our bills for electricity, gas, fuel oil or coal for our homes, or for gasoline for our cars, or even for our food. If we count food as fuel, we may almost say that energy is what we pay for when we buy fuel of one sort or another. True, the energy of the sun is free, and so is the energy of running water, and of the wind, but we usually have to pay for the machinery that enables us to use it. In fact, almost all of the energy we use had

its source in the sun. Whether our energy comes from our food, from running water, from the wind or directly from the sun to dry our clothes or heat our bodies, it is recent sunshine that we are drawing on; if it comes from fuel oil or gasoline or natural gas or coal, it is ancient sunshine that has been stored in the earth. Only when we use nuclear energy do we have a source other than that of the sun.

It is clear, then, that energy is what we need to get work done. In short, we say that *energy is the capacity to do work.* Intuitively, we realize that application of twice the energy results in twice the amount of work done.

CONCEPT OF WORK

At first the concept of work seems clear enough—until we ask, "What is work?" Serious thought shows that we must make a distinction between the colloquial and the scientific concept, for in everyday life we make a distinction between work and play that has nothing whatever to do with the amount of energy used. You may say of a friend, "He is out playing tennis, while I am sitting here quietly hard at work reading my physical science textbook." If you study long enough, you will learn that you have misstated the facts, for your friend is doing a considerable amount of work while he is "playing," whereas you who sit at your desk "working" are actually doing little or no work at all. The need to clarify the concept of work becomes clear.

It will probably be more meaningful to plunge ahead and define the modern scientific concept of work, and then proceed to its derivation from the mechanics of Newton and Galileo, than it is to reverse the presentation. From this point we will refer to work only in the scientific sense. Work, *W*, is done when a force operates through a certain distance, i.e., it is *force multiplied by the distance through which the force operates.*

$$W = F \times d$$

always with the understanding that only that part of the force which operates along, or parallel to, the direction of motion is to be used in the equation.[1] Thus, if we lift a 10-lb weight from the floor to a table 3 ft high, we do a certain number of units of work. We now see why your friend, the tennis player, does work while he is "playing," for he is applying a force to his racket as he swings it through the distance necessary to hit the ball. We also see why you are not doing any work while you are studying. Aside from the fact that a force is not operating through any distance, we cannot quantitatively measure mental work.

The scientific definition of work causes us to change some other aspects of our everyday concept of work. For example, you may get very tired holding a heavy parcel, but you are doing no work whatsoever. True, you are applying a force sufficient to overcome the gravitational force of attraction for the parcel, but this force is not operating through any distance whatsoever. If you drop the parcel to the floor, work is done (not by you), for a force (gravitational force) is operating through a distance. You will note that the usefulness of the work has nothing to do with our definition. Even if you carry the heavy parcel as you walk home along a level sidewalk, the work you do cannot be calculated simply by multiplying the weight of the parcel by the distance. This is because the force you are exerting on the parcel is directed vertically (against the force of gravitation) whereas the parcel is moving horizontally[2] along with you. If you were to carry the parcel up a stairway, you would be doing work, for you would then be exerting a force against that of gravity through a distance equal to the height of the stairway.[3]

RELATIONSHIP OF WORK AND ENERGY TO MECHANICS

The concept of work, and therefore of energy, can be obtained by an analysis of Newton's mechanics, but we will make no attempt to follow the long and difficult road that later scientists followed while clarifying these concepts. Some insight may be gotten, however, by reviewing the

---

[1] The concepts of force, energy, work, and power should not be confused. We do not need to use energy to exert a force, for a clamp can maintain a force indefinitely without any energy source. Consequently, no work is done, nor is any power involved. Power, *P*, is the time rate of doing work. Thus, $P = Fd/t$. Greater power does not necessarily mean more work done, but it always means that a given amount of work is done in less time.

[2] It is not strictly correct to say that you therefore do no work, for the parcel adds to the friction between your shoes and the ground, and there is a slight air resistance to be overcome. Also, the muscles of your body act differently than they would if you carried no parcel. The problem is too complex to solve accurately.

[3] If this restriction of the meaning of work to force times distance through which the force operates, and that distance always measured in the direction of the force, seems arbitrary, we agree that it is. The necessity for it is that we cannot otherwise develop the concepts associated with work without contradictions.

mechanical concepts that we have studied so far.

We started with three directly measurable quantities, (1) distance, (2) time, and (3) mass. These are quantities whose meanings are intuitively clear to us. From these three concepts we derived those of (4) average speed—distance divided by the time, (5) velocity—speed in a given direction, (6) acceleration—velocity divided by the time to achieve that velocity, (7) force—mass times the acceleration, and (8) momentum—mass times the velocity.

Thus, we started with three simple directly measurable quantities and from them we derived five concepts of higher and higher levels of abstraction. We are now in the process of adding two more concepts of a still higher level of abstraction, those of work—force times distance—and energy. Note that no new quantities have been introduced. The new concepts arise from a new relationship between quantities with which we are already familiar. We have not given any mathematical expression for energy simply because we can determine how much energy a body or system of bodies has only by determining how much work the expenditure of that quantity of energy can do. If you say that you are full of energy today, we can measure the amount you have only by putting you to work and measuring the amount you do. We therefore measure this energy either in terms of how much force you can exert on a body through a given distance, or of how great a distance you can move an object by exerting a definite force. If we can calculate the work, we can calculate the energy. We even use the same units for expressing both. The student should

therefore not be confused by the seeming interchangeableness of the two concepts in the following pages.

UNITS OF WORK AND ENERGY

Since work is defined as force times distance (measured in the direction the force is operating), the units used arise naturally. In the cgs system, force is expressed in dynes and distance in centimeters. The fundamental unit of work is therefore the dyne-centimeter. A special name for it is the erg, which may be formally defined as *the work done by a force of 1 dyne acting through a distance of 1 cm.* This is an extremely small unit, about equivalent to the work done in moving a mosquito 1 cm. Therefore, a larger unit, the joule (pronounced "jowl," although the incorrect "jool" is common in the United States), is more commonly used. It is equal to 10^7 ergs.

It is here in our calculations of work and energy, more than anywhere else, that we must not misinterpret the terms weight and mass. The weight of a body is a force that represents the pull of the earth on that body. Its mass represents the inertia of the body and is the property that determines how big a force is required to produce a given acceleration. Weight is always proportional to mass. There are many systems of units and thus much confusion. For example, in the cgs system, since $F = ma$, a force of 1 dyne will give a mass of 1 gm an acceleration of 1 cm/sec^2. But the weight of a 1-gm mass is sometimes called a gram or a gram force. Since $W = mg$, a gram force is g dynes, i.e., a 1-gm force is 980 dynes, and must be used in this equation. When F is in dynes, *m* is always in grams and *a* in centimeters per second per second.[4]

MECHANICAL ENERGY

Mechanical energy is used to do work (1) against the inertia of a body, (2) against gravity, (3) against friction, or (4) against any combination of them. Respectively, this work increases (1) the speed of a body, (2) the height of a body, (3) the temperature of a body, or (4) any combination of them. Thus, the work done on the body produces some change in the energy of the body. In (1) the energy of motion (kinetic energy) is increased, in (2) the energy due to position (potential energy) is increased, and in (3) the heat energy (thermal energy) of the body is

increased. In all cases, the magnitude of the energy change is equal to the work done. Two kinds of mechanical energy are recognized, potential and kinetic. They are commonly abbreviated as P.E. and K.E., respectively.

Concept of Potential Energy

If we lift a 10,000-gm weight from the floor to a table 100 cm high, we do an amount of work equal to $F \times d = 98$ joules.[5] We can say that we have accomplished that much work by expending 98 joules of energy. In a sense we have transferred this energy to the weight, for it now can do work by falling back to its original position. In doing so, it can, by use of a rope and pulley, raise another 10-kg weight an equal distance, or a 5-kg weight twice the distance, etc., if we disregard frictional losses. The only difference between the weight on the floor and the weight on the table is its position. This increased energy due to increase of height above the floor is called potential energy. If we raised the weight twice as far, its potential energy would be twice as great. If the weight were twice as heavy, and the distance it was raised remained the same, its potential energy would again be twice as great. Thus, the potential energy of any body is directly proportional to both the weight and the distance through which it is raised. This type of potential energy is, of course, a consequence of the earth's gravitational attraction for the weight, and in this chapter we will confine our discussion to this type, but, as we shall see later, there are others.

In the above example we have calculated the potential energy by using the floor as

---

[4] In the English system there is also confusion in the use of the pound as a unit of mass and as a unit of force. In $F = ma$, *m* is in pounds, *a* in feet per second per second, and *F* in poundals. (What is a poundal?) But the weight of a 1-lb mass, $W = mg$, is frequently called a pound or a pound force. A pound force is *g* poundals, and must be so used in the formula. If *F* is in poundals, *m* is always in pounds and *a* in feet per second per second. To overcome the difficulty the engineers have introduced another system. This system uses a mass of 1 slug (*g* times as large as the pound mass), which thus makes the force *g* times as large as the poundal, and this force the engineers call a pound force. To illustrate:

$$F = ma$$

and

$$1 \text{ lb} = 1 \text{ slug} \times 1 \text{ ft/sec}^2$$

Since $W = mg$, or $m = \dfrac{W}{g}$

the formula $F = ma$ may read

$$F = \frac{W}{g} a$$

or

$$\text{lb} = \frac{\text{lb}}{g} \times \text{ft/sec}^2 = \text{slug} \times \text{ft/sec}^2$$

[5] For this calculation see next page.

Level

a level of reference. In doing so we have assumed that it is 0 when the weight is on the floor. It is possible to use the surface of the earth at whatever place we happen to be, or even the surface of the earth at sea level even if we are not there, as our level of reference. This, however, is cumbersome at its best, and impossible at its worst, so we use whatever convenient level suits us best. This practice is easily justified because it is only differences in potential energy that we need to know. Thus, in the case of our 10,000-gm weight, we are concerned only with the difference in potential energy between the floor and the table. This will be unaffected by whatever potential energy it has while on the floor.

Concept of Kinetic Energy

If our 10-kg weight is dropped from the table to the floor, it will lose its potential energy, but in doing so it will gain a totally different kind of energy. This is the energy due to its motion, called kinetic energy. The energy of a falling weight is used for useful work in a pile driver, a machine in which a heavy weight (the hammer) is allowed to fall onto a pile [6] to drive it into the ground (Fig. 10-1). The engine is used to hoist the hammer to the desired height, giving it potential energy. In falling the hammer loses its potential energy, but not all at once, for when it has fallen halfway it still has half. At the instant before the hammer strikes the pile, the potential energy is 0 and the kinetic energy

[6] A pile is a long large stake or pointed timber, driven into the earth for the purpose of supporting the foundations of buildings, etc., in wet or yielding ground where the ground itself is too weak to support such structures. The four essential parts of a pile driver are the hammer (sometimes called the monkey), a hoisting engine, a tripping device, and the supporting frame.

is at a maximum. Calculation of the kinetic energy at this point shows that it is exactly equal to the potential energy at the maximum height of the hammer, if we overlook the small loss due to friction. At the halfway mark the total energy of the hammer is half potential and half kinetic energy. At the three-quarters mark one-fourth is potential and three-fourths kinetic energy, etc.

Derivation of the Mathematical Expressions for Potential and Kinetic Energy

The formulas for both can be derived from the mechanics of Newton and Galileo. That for potential energy is as follows:

$$W = F \times d \qquad \text{(Eq. 10-1)}$$

$$F = ma$$

but for a freely falling weight, a is designated by g, so,

$$F = mg$$

If we let h represent the height of the raised weight, then $h = d$, and Eq. 10-1 becomes,

$$W = \text{P.E.} = mgh \qquad \text{(Eq. 10-2)}$$

Thus, for our 10,000-gm weight raised to a height of 100 cm, the potential energy is given by 10,000 gm $\times$ 980 cm/sec^2 $\times$ 100 cm $= 98 \times 10^7$ ergs or 98 joules.

The derivation of the formula for kinetic energy is as follows:

$$W = F \times d$$

$$F = ma$$

According to Galileo's law of acceleration, $d = \frac{1}{2}at^2$. Substituting these values for F and d,

$$W = \text{K.E.} = ma \times \tfrac{1}{2}at^2 = \tfrac{1}{2}m \times a^2t^2$$

$$\text{(Eq. 10-3)}$$

But $\quad v = at,\quad$ so $\quad v^2 = a^2t^2$

Substituting v^2 for a^2t^2 in Eq. 10-3,

$$W = \text{K.E.} = \tfrac{1}{2}m \times v^2 = \tfrac{1}{2}mv^2$$

(Eq. 10-4)

Thus, the kinetic energy of our 10,000-gm weight an instant before the end of a fall of 100 cm is 10,000 gm times the square of the velocity. The velocity is given by the equation,[7] $v^2 = 2\ gd$; $2\ gd = 2 \times 980 \times 100 = 196{,}000$ cm^2/sec^2. Thus, $\tfrac{1}{2}mv^2 = 10{,}000\ gm \times 196{,}000$ cm^2/sec$^2 = 98 \times 10^7$ gm/cm^2/sec$^2 = 98 \times 10^7$ dyne-cm $= 98 \times 10^7$ ergs $= 98$ joules.

Note that the potential energy is equal to the kinetic energy. Since this is true, mgh (Eq. 10-2) must be equal to $\tfrac{1}{2}mv^2$ (Fig. 10-2). In other words, K.E. $= mgh$, and we should be able to derive $\tfrac{1}{2}mv^2$ from this equation. This we can easily do, but we will not belabor the point here.

Thus, P.E. $=$ K.E., if there are no frictional losses. Actually frictional losses are

[7] This is derived as follows:

$$d = \tfrac{1}{2}gt^2$$

Multiplying both sides by $2g$,

$$2gd = g^2t^2$$

Since $\qquad v = gt,\ v^2 = g^2t^2$

Substituting, $\qquad v^2 = 2gd$

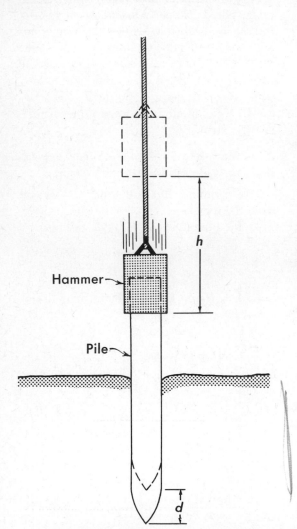

Fig. 10-1. Piledriver. The force with which the hammer strikes the pile depends on its mass and its acceleration, i.e., $F = mg$. The work done after falling distance h is given by mgh. The P.E. in the raised position is also mgh. The K.E. of the hammer after falling the distance h is given by $\tfrac{1}{2}mv^2$. Since $v^2 = 2ad = 2gh$ (see footnote 7), $\tfrac{1}{2}mv^2 = \tfrac{1}{2}m \cdot 2gh = mgh$. Thus the K.E. at the instant of impact equals the P.E. at the raised position. The striking hammer imparts K.E. to the pile. The distance d that the pile is driven into the ground is less than h, because the instant the pile starts into the ground, friction is generated between the pile and the ground. By the time the motion of the pile has stopped, all of the K.E. imparted to it has been transformed into heat.

heat losses as we might suspect from the observation that the moving parts of all machines develop heat wherever they come in contact. Therefore, to be more accurate we should write

$$P.E. = K.E. + heat$$

Heat is not mechanical energy, but it is always associated with it, so we must take it into account. If we write the above equation as

$$P.E. = K.E. + heat = constant$$

we have the Law of Conservation of Energy insofar as it can be applied to mechanical energy. We will learn more of this law later after we have studied heat. We will then find that the law will apply to all forms of energy. Still later we will have to combine this law with the Law of Conservation of Mass to give us the more accurate Law of Conservation of Mass and Energy.

Potential and kinetic energy are collectively known as mechanical energy. Other forms of energy, all of which we will study later, are heat energy, electrical energy, magnetic energy, chemical energy, radiant (electromagnetic) energy, and nuclear energy. We will also learn more about the transformation of one type of energy into other types at various places in this course.

MACHINES

Machines are devices that change either the magnitude of the force required to do work, or to change the direction of the force so that it is more conveniently applied. Among the simple machines are the inclined plane, the lever, the pulley, the wheel and axle, the wedge, the screw

and nut, the jack, the propeller, and the pump. No matter how complicated a machine may look, it is essentially a combination of simple machines. Throughout the history of man machines have been the means by which backbreaking physical

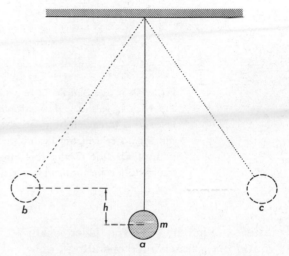

Fig. 10-2. Energy Changes in a Swinging Pendulum. At *a*, the lowest point of its swing, all energy is kinetic, and at *b* or *c*, the high points of its swing, all energy is potential. Thus $mgh = \frac{1}{2}mv_2$. Since *m* and *g* are constant the total energy depends upon the value of *h*. How does *h* govern *v*?

labor has been shifted from the shoulders of man to that of animals (horses, oxen, etc.), to steam and gasoline engines, and electric motors.

Despite the enormous advantages of machines one cannot get more work out of a machine than is put into it. Suppose you wish to raise a 100-kg mass. If you were strong enough to lift it 1 m, you would do a certain number of joules of work. It is much too heavy for you, so you use a lever

Fig. 10-3. A Simple Lever. By pressing down on the lever the rock is raised. If the force is applied at the end of the lever, less force will be needed to raise the rock a given amount but the force will act through a greater distance. If the force is applied close to the rock, the force required is greater but the distance through which it acts is less. In all cases, W = F $\times$ d.

instead (Fig. 10-3). The lever enables you to use a lesser force operating through a greater distance, but $F \times d$ will be the same in either case. The longer the lever (measured outward from the fulcrum), the less the force needed.

Actually you get less work out of a machine than the theoretical value, because there is always some friction involved. The work against friction [8] is not recoverable as is the work against gravity or the work to overcome inertia. This loss decreases the efficiency of a machine. Efficiency is defined as the ratio of the work done by the machine to the work done on the machine. It is always less than 100 per cent.

$$\text{Efficiency} = \frac{\text{Work done}}{\text{Energy supplied}}$$
$$= \frac{\text{Output of energy}}{\text{Input of energy}}$$

PERPETUAL MOTION AND THE LAW OF CONSERVATION OF ENERGY

For centuries man has been trying to make the energy output–input ratio greater than 100 per cent—the search for perpetual

[8] When two surfaces in contact move over each other, there is always some resistance to the motion. This resistance gives rise to the force that we call friction. It always opposes the motion. Friction at the start is always greater than after motion has begun. The smoother the two surfaces the less the friction. Rolling friction is less than sliding friction; hence the advantages of the wheel over a sled, and the advantage of roller bearings between a wheel and its axle. A lubricant reduces friction by changing the contact between two solids to that of two liquid films.

While man is forced to expend enormous amounts of energy to overcome friction, he cannot do without it. Belts cling to pulleys because of friction and so drive machinery. Brakes on cars operate because of friction. Screws and nails hold objects together by means of friction. Without it we could not walk.

motion. This is not a very good term, for it is misleading. It leads people to think of the problem as simply one in which all that is necessary is to eliminate friction. Nature has done this with our solar system in which all of the planets keep moving without the addition of any new energy. But even nature would fail if we succeeded in taking energy out of the system, for if we continued to do so long enough the planets would slow down and stop.

The essential problem of any perpetual-motion device is to make the output greater than the input, so that its output could supply its own input and leave something left over to do useful work. If successful, the machine would be a creator of energy without cost, thus solving all of the energy problems of the world. Thousands of devices have been tried but all have failed to deliver a continuous supply of energy without themselves using additional fuel. Professional scientists state that perpetual motion is impossible. This statement cannot be proved mathematically. In part it is based on a summary of a very large number of experimental tests, and in part it is a *statement of faith* in the Law of Conservation of Energy as applied outside the submicroscopic world of the atom.

The belief is bolstered in still another way. If we believe perpetual motion is impossible, i.e., if we believe machines cannot create energy, we might ask if they could destroy some. Only by carefully balancing the energy books in every energy transformation, paying particular attention to account for all frictional (heat) losses, have scientists come to a belief in the Law of Conservation of Energy in the macroscopic world. If energy is always conserved, i.e., if energy cannot be destroyed, it seems unlikely that it can be created. A belief in perpetual motion and a belief in the conservation of energy in the macroscopic world are inconsistent with each other.

SUMMARY

Work is defined as the product of the force acting on a body multiplied by the distance measured in the direction in which the force acts. Energy is defined as the capacity to do work. This capacity can be measured only in terms of work accomplished by the expenditure of the energy. We therefore measure work and energy in the same units. The fundamental unit is the dyne-centimeter, more commonly called the erg. It is the work done by a force of 1 dyne acting through a distance of 1 cm. A larger unit is the joule, equal to 10^7 ergs. Power, often confused with energy, is the time *rate* of doing work, i.e., the number of joules per second that can be done.

Mechanical energy involves work against inertia, against gravity, against friction, or against various combinations of them. Two kinds of mechanical energy are recognized, potential and kinetic. For a body to have potential energy, work must be done against the force of gravity or some other force to change its position. To have kinetic energy a body must be in motion. Under suitable conditions potential energy can be converted into kinetic energy, or vice versa. In falling a body loses potential energy at the same rate that it gains kinetic energy. The work that such a body does is done at the expense of its kinetic energy. In free fall the kinetic energy (at the end of the fall) equals the potential energy (at the start of the fall) if air resistance is neglected.

The mathematical expressions for gravitational potential and kinetic energy are mgh and $\frac{1}{2} mv^2$, respectively. Both are derived from the already familiar concepts of the mechanics of Newton and Galileo. If potential energy equals kinetic energy, neglecting frictional (heat) losses, then mgh must equal $\frac{1}{2} mv^2$, and each should be derivable from the other.

While machines are labor-saving devices, more energy must be put into a system than can ever be taken out because of frictional (heat) losses. Thus, perpetual-motion machines are impossible in the eyes of the scientist. They violate the well-established Law of Conservation of Energy as applied to macroscopic matter.

EXERCISES

I. TERMS AND CONCEPTS

Work	Power
Energy	Erg
Potential energy	Joule
Kinetic energy	Symbols: W, K.E.,
Mechanical energy	P.E.

II. PROBLEMS

1. Distinguish between work, force, and power.

2. Define work mathematically.

3. Give two examples of the conversion of kinetic energy into work.

4. State the equations for K.E. and P.E.

5. Why is a level of reference necessary for potential energy?

6. Define an erg; a joule.

7. Distinguish between work and energy.

8. If you are dragging a log along the ground by a long rope at a constant velocity, against what are you doing work? (Air resistance is negligible.)

9. If the log weighs 50 kg and you drag it 10 m in a straight line, how many joules of work do you do? (If your rope is long enough, it may be considered to be parallel to the ground.)

10. If you are dragging the log along the ground at a constantly increasing velocity, against what are you doing work?

11. If you are dragging the log in a circle at constant speed, against what are you doing work?

12. Where is the kinetic energy of a swinging pendulum greatest? Where is it least? Where is its potential energy greatest? Where least?

13. How much kinetic energy does a 2-gm mass moving with a speed of 1 cm/sec have? Suppose the speed to be 2 cm/sec? 3 cm/sec? 4 cm/sec? By what factor does the K.E. increase if m is constant?

14. If we neglect the small amount of friction involved, how much work do you do in "pushing" a well-oiled cart with ball-bearing wheels and weighing 20 kg across a level floor a distance of 20 m?

15. A huge rock falls from the top of a vertical cliff to the ground below. What happens to its kinetic energy when it strikes the ground?

16. A mass m slides down a frictionless inclined plane 10 ft long from a height of 6 ft above the ground. What is the difference in work done in this situation to that done by falling freely through a distance of 6 ft?

17. We have learned (p. 50) that the earth in its path about the sun travels faster when it is closer to the sun than when it is farther away. Its kinetic energy must therefore be greater when it is traveling faster. The total mechanical energy, K.E. + P.E., must be constant. Velocity-wise, where is its potential energy least? Greatest? How can you explain the earth's potential energy in this situation? (Hint: The earth, like the moon, is a "falling" body.)

18. What happens to the kinetic energy of a car when it stops?

19. What is a machine? Name some simple machines.

20. Why do scientists not believe that perpetual-motion machines are possible?

MOLECULES AND ENERGY

Starting with Galileo's studies of motion we have progressed through Newton's development of the laws known by his name, and have followed his demonstrations that linked planetary motions to motions here on earth. Newton supplied a new ingredient, that of the concept of force. The relationship of force to energy and work was slow in being clarified. When it was, new and greater insight into the understanding of matter became possible.

The phenomenon of heat was long thought to have no relationship to either motion or energy. The first theory of heat to gain any widespread acceptance (the caloric theory) considered heat an imponderable form of matter. This view persisted from the 1750's to the 1850's, even though Newton had speculatively linked heat to the motion of particles, and Daniel Bernoulli had presented a kinetic theory of heat shortly after Newton's death in 1727. The failure of these early attempts to link motion and energy to heat was in large part due to the fact that the concepts of work and energy had not yet been clearly developed.

The world-wide success of Newton's Law of Universal Gravitation, as expounded in his *Principia*, led to attempts to formulate other theories that would link together many different phenomena in an intellectually satisfying manner. Not a great deal of progress was made in developing such a theory for gases and related phenomena until Joule started his great work about 1820. Finally, with assists from predecessors like Boyle, Newton, and Bernoulli, and from contemporaries like Mayer, Clausius, Maxwell, Boltzmann, Gibbs, and others, Joule formulated the great kinetic-molecular theory, a grand conceptual scheme which correlated an unusually large number of seemingly unrelated facts, observations, and ideas, and which, in the long run, helped to prepare the way for modern atomic physics. Almost as a byproduct of this great theory came one of the three great conservation laws, the Law of Conservation of Energy. We will start our search for our understanding of the theory with an investigation of phenomena associated with heat and temperature.

CHAPTER XI

Phenomena Associated with Concepts of Heat and Temperature

Heat consists in a minute vibratory motion of the particles of bodies.—ISAAC NEWTON

INTRODUCTION

We have already stated that heat is associated with the transformation of potential energy into kinetic energy. We have implied that friction produces heat and that heat is a form of energy. That these are facts can be demonstrated in many ways. Let us refer to our pile driver again, Fig. 10-1. After it has been used, a check of the temperature of the ground next to the pile, of the top of the pile, and of the hammer itself would reveal that the temperature of all three had risen. Hammer a nail repeatedly and the nail gets hot. Pull out a nail firmly embedded in hard wood, and it will feel uncomfortably warm. Let a rope be pulled rapidly through your hands and they may even be burned. Even rubbing your hands together warms them. The list could be extended indefinitely. In all of these cases kinetic energy disappears, and heat appears as friction is produced in one way or another.

As previously stated (p. 160n), wherever two moving parts of a mechanical system are in contact, there is always friction, and a certain amount of heat develops. Furthermore, the greater the force pressing two moving parts together, the greater the friction and the greater the amount of heat produced. One of the greatest factors in producing friction is the character of the surfaces in contact. The rougher they are the greater the friction, i.e., the greater the resistance to motion. Friction is a force that arises from gravitation; it always opposes motion and never tends to move the body.

How does heat arise from such a force? Is it work that is transformed into heat? If so, and if the Law of Conservation of Energy is to hold, we should be able to reverse the process and transform heat into work. What is the relationship between heat produced by this resistance to motion and the heat produced by combustion? If we suddenly compress a gas, it gets hotter. What is the relationship between this heat and the heat of friction and the heat of combustion? These, and other questions, will have to be postponed until we have learned what heat is.

DISTINCTION BETWEEN HEAT AND TEMPERATURE

Before discussing the problems associated with the nature of heat, we find it necessary to know the relationship between heat and temperature. That scientists use the word "heat" differently from laymen is illustrated by such everyday expressions as the "heat of the day" and "blood heat." In both cases the scientist would use the word "temperature" instead. The scientist uses the word "heat" to mean that mysterious something that makes things hotter. Perhaps we can clarify the difference between the two terms by two examples.

Hot Water   Cold Water

Luke Warm Water

Fig. 11-1. Unreliability of Man's Senses as a Measure of Temperature. When the boy switches both hands to the luke-warm water, the water will feel cool to his right hand, warm to his left hand.

Suppose you have a cubic foot of ice that you wish to melt quickly. The only things you have to do it with are one tea cup of boiling water and a barrel of water at room temperature. Obviously the tea cup of boiling water would melt a small part of the block of ice very quickly but the water would soon be at the temperature of the ice and so be useless for further melting. If the ice were placed in the barrel of luke-warm water, however, it would all melt in an hour or two, and the temperature of the water would still be well above the tem-

perature of melting ice. We conclude, then, that the heat content of the barrel of lukewarm water is far greater than that of the cup of boiling water.

Let us take another case. Suppose you had to either put your hand in a gallon of water at 180° F, or to grasp a single strand of red hot wire (temperature 1500° F) with a diameter about that of a coarse human hair. Which would you choose? You would be foolish indeed if you chose the hot water, for your hand would be crippled for weeks, whereas the wire would cause only momentary discomfort. Temperature is a measure of the intensity of heat rather than the amount of heat.

If the temperature of a body is high, we say it is hot; if the temperature is low we say it is cold. The two terms, "hot" and "cold" are obviously relative, and to most of us our standard of comparison is our own body temperature. That this is an extremely unreliable standard can be shown in many ways. A convincing one is illustrated in Fig. 11-1. If the individual shown now puts both hands into the middle vessel of water, he will get two entirely different sensations of temperature. One hand will feel cold, the other warm. Obviously we need a better standard. Galileo recognized the need, and so he invented a thermometer. While the concept of the intensity of heat is derived from our sense perceptions, it is the thermometer that enables us to measure it.

THERMOMETERS

Galileo's first thermometer is shown in Fig. 11-2. The level, L, rises and falls with changes in temperature. This thermometer worked quite well as long as the pressure of the atmosphere remained constant. If the atmospheric pressure changed significantly, the level, L, would rise (if the pressure increased), or fall (if the pressure decreased), even though the temperature remained constant. How could this drawback be overcome? In time it was recognized that while the volume of a gas enclosed by a liquid

turned upside down (Fig. 11-3a), and the bulb filled with a liquid, water at first. Water, like all liquids, expands as the temperature rises; thus, the level, L, rises with

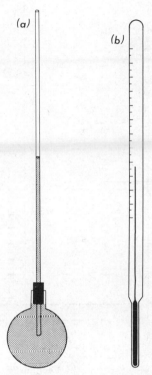

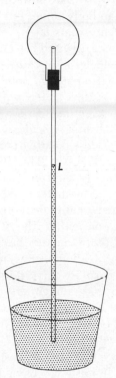

Fig. 11-2. Galileo's Thermometer. As the temperature changed, the air in the bulb expanded or contracted in volume, so the level, L, of the water in the tube rose or fell. Unfortunately, this level may change by a change in air pressure without a change in temperature.

Fig. 11-3. By turning Galileo's thermometer upside down a thermometer was made that was not affected by changes in air pressure. Water was used at first (a) and later, mercury (b). The upper ends of the tubes are sealed and the inside of each tube is a good vacuum.

as this one was, changed with the air pressure, the volume of a liquid remained practically constant at any reasonable pressure. Therefore, Galileo's thermometer was

the temperature, and is a measure of it. However, solids also expand and contract with the temperature. Fortunately, the water expanded more than the glass, so this device was useful. Further experimentation showed that mercury, the only metal liquid at room temperature, expanded far more than water relative to glass when heated, and so the common mercury-in-glass thermometer came into being.

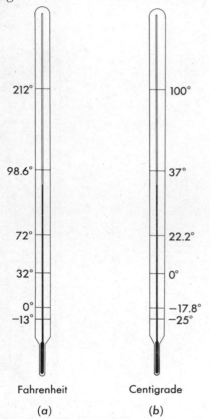

212°   100°

98.6°   37°

72°   22.2°

32°   0°

0°   −17.8°
−13°   −25°

Fahrenheit   Centigrade

(a)   (b)

Fig. 11-4. Fahrenheit and Centigrade Thermometers. Note that 0° F is colder than 0° C. Conversion equations are:

$$t° F = 9/5 \ t° C + 32°$$

and $t° C = 5/9 \ (t° F - 32).$

Fahrenheit (ca. 1715) constructed a mercury-in-glass thermometer in which the level of the mercury at the coldest temperature that he could get with an ice-water-salt mixture was marked 0°. The level of the mercury in the tube when it was at the temperature of the human body was marked 96°. The intervening space was divided

into 96 parts and the same spacing carried above the 96° mark and below the 0° mark. On this scale the freezing point of water came out about 32° and the boiling point about 212° (Fig. 11-4a). Later, to make these two points come out exactly at 32° and 212°, the size of the divisions was altered slightly, so that now the temperature of the human body comes out to be 98.6° F.

Some twenty years later Celsius, a Swedish astronomer, devised a Centigrade scale, a scale on which the freezing point of water is 0° and its boiling point 100° (Fig. 11-4b). It is thus a decimal scale, and is used in all scientific work. Still later the Kelvin (or absolute) scale was devised in which the coldest possible temperature (p. 184) was marked 0°. The divisions on the scale are exactly the same as those on the Centigrade thermometer. (See Fig. 12-11.) It should eventually be realized that the zero marks on either the Centigrade or Fahrenheit thermometers have no *absolute* significance at all; these scales are purely relative, and so we have no right to think of water at 100° on either scale as being twice as hot as water at 50° on either scale. On the other hand, 0° on the Kelvin, or absolute, scale does have absolute significance, but we will have to postpone any discussion of it until we have learned more about heat and the kinetic theory of gases.

EXPANSION AND CONTRACTION

It is common knowledge that most materials expand as the temperature rises, and contract as it drops. We have already seen that Galileo and later thermometer makers made use of this property in constructing their instruments. To allow for expansion in warm weather, the girders beneath the roadway of a long steel bridge do not quite meet at the middle, concrete roadways have small gaps at intervals filled with a tarlike substance, and the ends of steel rails of the subway or other railroad tracks do not quite touch the adjoining ones.[1]

Not so familiar is the fact that different substances have this property to different degrees. Brass expands nearly twice as much as iron per unit length per degree rise in temperature. Thus, a brass strip welded to an iron strip will bend one way as the temperature rises and the other as the temperature falls. Many thermostats are as simple as that, for as they bend one way or the other, electrical contact is made or broken. In general, liquids expand more than solids do per unit volume per degree rise in temperature. Gases will expand still more.[2]

HEAT TRANSFER

The transfer of heat from a source to other regions is what makes life possible on this earth. Transfer is accomplished by (1) radiation, as from the sun or a hot stove or fire; (2) by convection, as in the heating of buildings or the transfer of heat by the wind; and (3) by conduction, as in the transfer of heat through a piece of metal when one end of it is placed in a flame (Fig.

[1] The exceptional behavior of water should be noted here. Like other substances water contracts in volume until the temperature is about 4° C. It then begins to expand and continues to do so until frozen. Thus, ice has a lower density than water, and so floats in water. It is this property that often causes containers of water to break when the water freezes. The expansive force in a closed container full of water is sufficient to crack the cylinder head of an automobile engine.

[2] We must not confuse the property that allows a gas to fill all available space regardless of the temperature, with that which is due to temperature changes and is associated with changes in volume under constant pressure—for which see Charles' Law, p. 183.

11-5). In convection, air that is heated expands, becomes less dense, and rises, allowing colder air to move in to be warmed by the source. *If left to itself, the natural transfer is always from a warmer region to a colder one.* There are no exceptions to this rule. Nor can such transfer by one

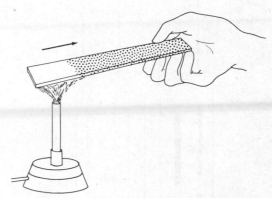

Fig. 11-5. Heat Transfer by Conduction through a Metal Bar. Heat is *conducted* in the direction of the arrow, a fact that the person holding the bar is soon aware of. Heat is also radiated through the atmosphere. This radiated heat can be detected by holding the hand a few inches from either the bar or the flame.

method or another ever be prevented. We can insulate a body to prevent some of the heat from escaping (or from entering), as in a thermos bottle, but we can never prevent it entirely. We will have more to say about heat transfer later.

HEAT UNITS

We have used the phrases "intensity of heat" and "quantity of heat." We measure the intensity of heat in degrees Centigrade, Fahrenheit, or Kelvin. Quantity of heat is measured in calories. *A calorie is defined as the quantity of heat needed to raise the temperature of 1 gm of water 1° C.* The calorie of the dieticians is the kilocalorie, equal to 1000 calories, and sometimes called the big Calorie (written with a capital C).

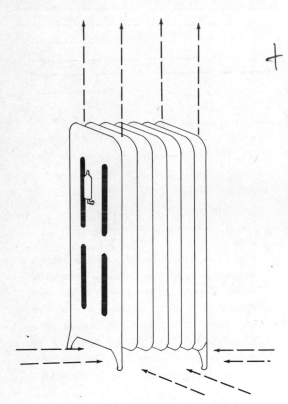

Fig. 11-6. Heat Transfer by Convection. Cold air moves in below the radiator, is heated, expands, becomes less dense and so rises and spreads through the room to heat it. The radiator also radiates some heat into the atmosphere.

SPECIFIC HEAT

It was about 1750 that Joseph Black made the clear distinction between intensity and quantity of heat, and defined what we now call specific heat. He had noted that the quantity of heat absorbed per unit mass

varied with the substance. Whereas it takes 1 calorie to raise the temperature of 1 gm of water 1° C, it takes only 0.11 calorie to raise the temperature of 1 gm of iron 1° C. If we assign a value of 1.0 as the specific heat of water, then that of iron is 0.11. *The definition of specific heat then becomes the number of calories that will raise (or lower) the temperature of 1 gm of the substance by 1° C.* Some other specific heats (at about 20° C) are: Aluminum 0.22, copper 0.09, silver 0.06, lead 0.03, magnesium 0.25, soil and rocks about 0.20.

Note that the specific heat of water is much larger than that of any of the other substances. This means that 1 lb of water contains as much heat as 4 lb of magnesium if they are both at the same temperature. If we mix 100 gm of water at 20° C with 100 gm of water at 40° C, the resulting mixture will have a temperature of 30° C. If, however, we add magnesium at 40° C to the 100 gm of water at 20° C, it will take 400 gm of it to raise the temperature of the water to 30° C.

STATES OF MATTER

We are all familiar with the fact that water can exist in three different states or phases, solid (ice), liquid, and gaseous (vapor). All substances [3] that do not decompose on being heated may also exist in these same three phases under certain conditions. Many kinds of matter, e.g., water, can exist in all three phases side by side if the conditions are right. The most important condition is the temperature. At temperatures significantly above 100° C only the vapor phase of water can exist for any length of time, and at temperatures far be-

---

[3] Helium is the only exception.

low the freezing point only the solid phase is of any significance. The state in which matter exists is therefore largely a function of temperature. Oddly enough, water is the only naturally occuring abundant liquid on the surface of the earth.[4]

Any attempt, therefore, to classify matter as solid, liquid, or gaseous is certain to run into difficulties. We think of bromine and mercury as the only two elements that exist in the liquid state at room temperature and pressure, but if we leave bromine liquid in an open dish, it quickly changes to the vapor state by evaporation. But so will water, only not so quickly. Even ice will "evaporate" without melting by a process that is more properly called *sublimation*. The state of any substance—solid, liquid, or gas—depends on the temperature and the pressure.

Gases and liquids are both fluids because both take the shape of their containers under all circumstances, whereas solids do not. Gases differ from liquids in that they completely fill their containers no matter how small the amount present. This means that they can expand indefinitely. It also means that gases are easily compressed into smaller volumes. Thus, 1 gm of oxygen will fill any size vessel you put it in. Put 1 gm of another gas in the same closed vessel with the oxygen, and it will shortly fill the whole vessel also. If someone opens a bottle of ammonia on the far side of the room, you will soon know it. The two gases have spontaneously mixed thoroughly with each other. This process is called *diffusion*. Liquids, however, maintain a fixed volume. True solids maintain not only a fixed volume but a fixed shape. A few substances, e.g., pitch, sealing wax, shoemaker's wax, etc., appear to be so hard and brittle that they will shatter like glass when a sheet of any one of them is dropped, but if thick lumps of them are allowed to stand in containers at room temperature they will gradually spread out to take the shape of the container. Such substances are said to be supercooled liquids. This ability of liquids and solids to maintain fixed volumes under ordinary conditions means that they are very nearly incompressible except at unusually high pressures.

LATENT HEATS OF FUSION AND VAPORIZATION

It had long been noted that when ice was melted by heat from a uniform source, the temperature remained at 0° C regardless of the outside temperature until the ice was all melted, if the mixture of ice and water was well stirred throughout. This heat that is added without raising the temperature is known as the *latent* [5] *heat of fusion*. For water it is 80 calories/gm. All solids that melt without decomposing behave similarly, but the heat of fusion varies with the solid. Conversely, when water is cooled to the freezing point, it will remain at that temperature until completely frozen regardless of the outside temperature.[6]

---

[4] Petroleum, a mixture of liquids, gases, and solids in mutual solution with one another, exists at relatively shallow depths (up to 3 or 4 mi) in the earth's crust. Molten rock exists in a few places at greater depth. Brought to the surface it quickly solidifies.

[5] Meaning hidden, or dormant.

[6] Under certain conditions water may be cooled a few degrees below the freezing point (supercooled) without freezing. But when it does start to freeze, it freezes so quickly that the heat liberated cannot escape as fast as it is liberated. Thus, the water actually becomes warmer as it freezes. The heat of fusion that water absorbs

A similar phenomenon is observed when liquids are boiled. In an open system they cannot be heated above the boiling point no matter how much heat is applied or how rapidly. The heat that is absorbed is used to change the water to steam without raising the temperature; this heat is called the latent heat of vaporization. For water it amounts to 540 calories/gm at atmospheric pressure. In condensing back to water, the steam must give up a like amount of heat. Therefore, 1 gm of steam at 100° C has 540 calories more heat than 1 gm of water at the same temperature; this is what makes burns by steam worse than those by water at the same temperature.

We have given you the main facts about latent heats of fusion and vaporization. However, we might very well ask where the heat is "hidden." We can say that it is stored in the water (heat of fusion) and in the steam (heat of vaporization) as potential energy. The student should realize that to say this is merely a matter of convenience of statement; it is in no way an explanation. The kinetic-molecular theory will give us a better explanation, but the electronic theory of chemical binding (Chapter XXXI) will give us a still better one.

DENSITY

We have already defined density as mass per unit volume. From the foregoing discussion it is apparent that the density of a substance must decrease as its temperature rises. In the normal temperature ranges

during the melting process is given off during the freezing process. This is also 80 calories/gm at atmospheric pressure.

these density changes are not significant in solids and liquids except in precise work, but they are important in gases. For example, the decrease in density that results from the expansion of heated air on hot summer days causes it to rise into the cooler upper regions of the atmosphere. The final result may be a thunderstorm (see Chapter XLII).

THE ROAD AHEAD

From this point on in our understanding of matter and energy, we can follow any one of several roads. No matter which we choose we will seem to be straying from the main path at times. We wish to remind you that the history of a main river cannot be complete without considering what the chief tributaries have to contribute. Just as the master river could not exist as it is without the contributions of the tributaries originating in quite different regions, so our knowledge of the constitution of matter has come from many sources, sources that give rise to several streams of scientific inquiry which ultimately must be joined together to be explained by one great integrating theory, in particular, the great kinetic-molecular theory of matter. The method used here to join these streams together is the personal preference of the author.

SUMMARY

That a rise in temperature always occurs when mechanical energy disappears shows that there is some connection between mechanics and heat. The connection appears to be via friction, but the origin of the heat is not proved in this chapter. Temperature is tentatively defined as intensity of heat, and heat as "that something" which makes things hotter.

While certain of our sense organs help us to distinguish between high and low temperatures, they are unreliable in many situations. Hence Galileo invented the first thermometer. Today thermometers with three different scales are used, the Fahrenheit, the Centigrade (or Celsius), and the Kelvin (or absolute).

All matter expands and contracts with changes in temperature, but by different amounts. This fact must be considered in many of the structures that man makes. In general, liquids expand more than solids, and gases (at constant pressure) more than liquids. Heat may be transferred from warmer regions to colder regions by radiation, conduction, and convection, or by any combination of them.

The unit of heat is the calorie. Equal masses of different substances absorb different numbers of calories per unit mass, thus giving rise to the concept of specific heat. Water is noted for having an unusually high specific heat.

The various states of matter—gaseous, liquid, or solid—are almost wholly dependent on the temperature and pressure. Therefore no classification of matter as to its state is tenable unless we state the temperature range and pressure, and even then there is considerable overlapping for, within limits, all three phases can exist side by side. Latent heats of fusion and vaporization are phenomena that can be observed whenever a change of phase takes place. A partial distinction between the three states can be made on the basis of their differing abilities to maintain fixed volumes and shapes. Density changes in normal temperature ranges of solids and liquids are not significant except in precise work, but are highly important in gases.

EXERCISES

I. TERMS AND CONCEPTS

Heat	Calorie
Temperature	Specific heat
Radiation	Sublimation
Conduction	Latent heat of fusion
Convection	Latent heat of vaporization

II. PROBLEMS

1. What property of mercury makes it particularly useful in glass thermometers?

2. In what way is water different from any other common substance with respect to its behavior on being cooled to the freezing point? Is this a desirable characteristic or not? Explain.

3. Explain the three methods by which heat is transferred.

4. Define a kilocalorie in two ways (but not in terms of calories).

5. What is the latent heat of fusion? How many calories per gram of water are involved?

6. What is the latent heat of vaporization? How many calories per gram of water are involved?

7. How much more heat is required to vaporize 500 gm of water than to melt 500 gm of ice?

8. Which has more heat, 100 gm of steam at 100° C or 100 gm of water at 100° C?

9. Define specific heat.

10. The specific heat of metal X is 0.2. If you put 100 gm of it at a temperature of 100° C in 100 gm of water at 25° C, what is the resulting temperature of the water?

11. In colonial America it was a common practice to put tubs of water in root cellars during the cold months to prevent the root vegetables and fruit from freezing. Explain.

12. If you find the above question difficult, consider the fact that as a pond freezes

the air close to and in contact with the water is slightly warmer than that in contact with the land surrounding the pond. Explain.

13. What are some of the difficulties encountered in any attempt to classify matter as gaseous, liquid, or solid?

14. Does a block of ice contain heat? Justify your answer.

15. What is the essential difference between the Centigrade and the absolute temperature scales?

16. Calculate the heat required to transform 500 gm of ice (a little over a pound) at $-10°$ C to steam at $100°$ C. The specific heat of ice is about 0.5. Note: This must be done in steps.

17. Using Fig. 11-4, determine room temperature, blood temperature, and $0°$ F on the Centigrade scale.

18. Why is a piece of ice at $32°$ F more effective in cooling a drink than the same quantity of water at $32°$ F?

19. The high specific heat of water is an aid to living organisms. Explain.

20. If 10,000 calories of heat are added to a quantity of water at $25°$ C, the new temperature is $50°$ C. What quantity of water is involved?

500×80

500

$0°C$ Water $0°C$

-10 $500 \times 0.5 \times 10$ $1L$ 500×80 500×100

CHAPTER XII

The Gaseous State of Matter

Science moves but slowly, slowly,
Creeping on from point to point.
—ALFRED TENNYSON

INTRODUCTION

It is logical to assume that we should now proceed to an accepted theory of heat that was developed about the same time as the Law of Conservation of Energy. But for reasons that will become evident later on, we instead find it necessary to develop the kinetic-molecular theory of matter first, and before we do that we find it necessary to learn more about the gaseous state of matter. This may seem odd, for most gases are invisible; our senses tell us less about them than they do about either liquids or solids.

Yet gases tell us more, far more, about the true nature of matter than do the more tangible states of matter. This is because the individual particles of a gas are separated from each other by relatively enormous distances so that the physical behavior of a single particle is more or less independent of the other particles.

Most of the properties of gases are simple, and common to all gases. They always fill any confined space offered to them. Pressure times volume always remains constant as long as the temperature remains constant. Changing the temperature changes either pressure or volume or both, depending upon whether we have an open or a closed system. Gases exert uniform pressure at every point in their containers; this is very unlike solids and liquids (Fig. 12-1). They diffuse (p. 198) through each other and through porous walls. How can all of these relatively simple properties be explained?

We need to construct a theory of gases, a kind of mechanical model,[1] that we can use to explain all of these observations, including the general gas laws, a theory that we can use to make new predictions, as any successful theory must do. In our attempt to do so we will begin by studying the pressure–volume relationships, for they are simple and easily measurable by instruments. This will eventually introduce us to Robert Boyle and the law that bears his name.

PRESSURE

Pressure (in a gas, liquid, or solid) *is defined as force per unit area*. This means that the average pressure on any plane surface is equal to the total force on that surface *acting in a direction perpendicular to that surface* divided by the area of the surface. Note carefully that pressure is not just another word for force. The pressure acting on a body should never be confused with the total force acting on it.

[1] By a model we do not mean a much reduced replica of an object, but a system of concepts, of ideas, etc., which allow us to "think describe" the things that we wish to investigate.

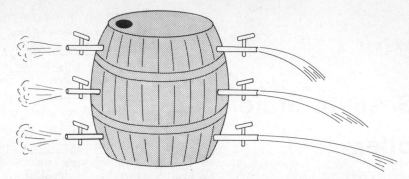

Fig. 12-1. Pressure in Liquids and Gases. If the barrel were full of water and the spigots on the right opened, the greater pressure at the lower spigot would cause the water to shoot out farther. If it were full of gas, the velocity at each spigot (on the left) would be the same.

While we will be concerned exclusively with pressure in gases, it may be instructive to compare such pressure with that in liquids (since both are fluids). In both, the pressure at any one point is the same in all directions (Fig. 12-2), up, down, or sideways. In both, any change in the pressure at any one point, is accompanied by a change in pressure at every other point if the liquid or confined gas is at rest, i.e., is not flowing.[2] In any one *liquid* the magnitude of the pressure at any point (due to the liquid only) depends only on the distance that point is below the surface. This means that in an *upright sealed container*

[2] This is known as Pascal's principle. Pascal was a younger contemporary of Galileo and an older one of Newton.

Fig. 12-2. Pascal's Principle. A number of tubes, *a, b, c, d, e*, of various sizes and shapes are all parts of the same receptacle. When water is put into the receptacle, the water rises to the same level in all of them. This means that the pressure at any point in any of them depends only on the depth below the surface.

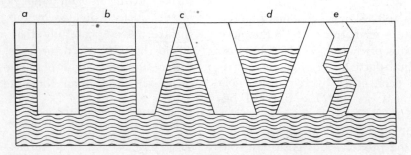

exactly full of a liquid, the pressure at the top is zero. This is not true of a gas, for the pressure against the top of any container of normal height is equal to that against its bottom. Only in open unconfined systems where the quantity of gas is very large, as in the earth's atmosphere, do the gravitational forces cause a significant difference in density, hence in pressure, of the gas at the top and the bottom of the system.

Concept of Air Pressure

The concept of gases exerting pressure is one of the things most people take for granted in this age of automobile tires, gas stoves and furnaces, balloons, etc. Likewise, we take its weight for granted, although the average student would undoubtedly be surprised to learn that the air in an average classroom weighs several hundred pounds. Yet it was not clear until about the time of Galileo's death (and Newton's birth) that air had weight, and the modern concept of gas pressure was not advanced for another two centuries. Scales sensitive enough to weigh small quantities of air had not yet been invented in Galileo's time.

It had been known since the sixteenth century that water would rise in a pipe with one end submerged if air were extracted from the other end (Fig. 12-3). Aristotle would have explained this by stating that the water rises when an attempt is made to create a vacuum by the extraction of the air because nature abhors a vacuum (see his vacuum argument on p. 76*n*). A workman had told Galileo that a suction pump [3] attached to such a pipe

[3] A suction pump sucks the air out of a pipe extending down below the surface of the water in a well. The water then rises in the pipe just as

would work only if the pipe were less than 34 ft long, i.e., if all the air were sucked out of a pipe longer than 34 ft, the water would not rise above that distance.

Fig. 12-3. Principle of Suction Pump. By sucking on it the boy removes air from the straw. Pressure of the outside air on the surface of the liquid in the glass then causes the liquid to rise in the straw. If the straw were 34 ft long and the boy could suck all of the air out of it, he could still obtain the liquid, but not if it were longer. Why not?

Galileo wondered why nature's abhorrence of a vacuum stopped at 34 ft. He therefore suggested that the rise of the water in the pipe was due to the air pushing down on the surface of the water in the well rather than to a "pulling up" of the water inside the pipe. Before the pump

it does when you suck on a straw in a glass of water (Fig. 12-3).

sucked air out of the pipe, this push was balanced by the air in the pipe pushing down with an *equal force per unit area.* Sucking the air out of the pipe eliminated this force, so that the water rose until the downward force exerted by the weight of the water in the pipe equaled the downward push of the air on the surface of the water outside the pipe. Thus, the pressure of the air in pounds per square inch should be equal to the weight of a column of water about 34 ft long and 1 in. in cross section.

However, a column of water that high is extremely difficult to work with. Torricelli, a student of Galileo's, knowing that mercury was about 13.6 times as dense as water, took a glass tube sealed at one end and longer than 30 in., filled it level with mercury, and inverted it into a dish of mercury without allowing any air to enter the tube. The level of the mercury in the tube fell until the distance between it and that of the mercury in the open dish was about 30 in. He then had a nearly perfect vacuum [4] above the mercury in the tube. The weight of this 30 in. of mercury was equal to the weight of a column of water of equal cross section and 34 ft high. If we add a scale to the mercury column so that we can read its changing level as air-pressure changes, we have the modern barometer.

Torricelli's Experiment

Torricelli thought that if the mercury was held up in the tube by the pressure of the atmosphere, then the pressure should decrease as one climbed a mountain. His reasoning was that we live on the earth's

surface at the bottom of a "sea of air," just as many organisms live on the ocean floor at the bottom of a sea of water. As we have already seen, Pascal had shown that the pressure in the water became less and less as its depth decreased. Going to the top of a mountain should therefore decrease the depth of the sea of air and the pressure should drop. This should constitute evidence in favor of the air-pressure theory. The experiment was performed, and the theory confirmed, under the direction of Pascal. He was thoughtful enough to have a man watch the level of the mercury in a second barometer at the foot of the mountain while the first was being carried to the top. Still, the evidence was not very convincing to many.

This experiment is often listed as providing direct evidence that air had weight. This is not true. It did provide direct evidence that air exerted a pressure on surfaces with which it was in contact. That air had weight could be inferred, however, unless one believed it to be a weightless material substance that could exert pressure.

It should be noted that the analogy between the sea of air and the sea of water is far from perfect. The pressure in water increases rapidly with depth with almost no change in its density; in fact the pressure would increase almost as rapidly if there were no change in the density of the water with depth. The pressure in air decreases rapidly with decreases in density. The numerical magnitude of the pressure of the atmosphere in pounds per square inch (14.7 lb/sq in. at sea level) is exactly equal to the weight of a column of air 1 in. square in cross section, extending from the earth's surface to the top of the far reaches of the atmosphere, but this is not the same

---

[4] Few of Torricelli's fellow scientists would concede that there was a vacuum above the mercury. They preferred to follow Aristotle.

as saying that the pressure of the atmosphere is *directly* due to, or is *directly* caused by, the weight of the air.[5]

Boyle's Experiments with His Vacuum Pump

The acceptance of the view that air exerted a pressure had to be postponed a few years, until Robert Boyle invented a new type of pump (Fig. 12-4) that allowed him to remove air directly from a sealed container. Boyle (1627–1691) was a teenager when Galileo died and when Newton was born. He was the precocious son of a wealthy Irish earl; he gave his life and much of his considerable wealth to scientific research and writing. His wealth enabled him to set up the finest laboratory in Europe.

His pump allowed him to make experiments that would otherwise have been impossible. This is a fine example of research of a particular type having to await technological improvements. Otto von Guericke had invented the first type of vacuum pump a few years before, and had performed his famous experiment with the Magdeburg Hemispheres (Fig. 12-5). Boyle's crucial experiment consisted of enclosing one of Torricelli's barometers in a gas-tight apparatus (Fig. 12-6) and pumping air out. As he pumped more and more air out, the level of the mercury dropped in the tube, thus proving that it was air pressure that held the mercury up in the tube. Note carefully that the weight of the air *per se* played no part in this experiment, for the total weight of the air in the gas-tight apparatus need not have been more than 5 or 6 gm, depending on its size.

[5] The more direct cause of air pressure is discussed on p. 198.

Further Clarification of the Concept of Air Pressure

If what we have stated is not clear to you, consider the following: A common gallon

Fig. 12-4. Boyle's Vacuum Pump. *A*, airtight receptacle from which air is to be evacuated. *B*, stopcock which is open while piston (*D*) is descending in the cylinder (*C*), and closed at the end of the downstroke of the piston. When the piston is raised (by the device at *E*), the air in *C* is expelled through a valve not shown. The stopcock (*B*) is opened as the piston descends, allowing air from *A* to enter *C* again.

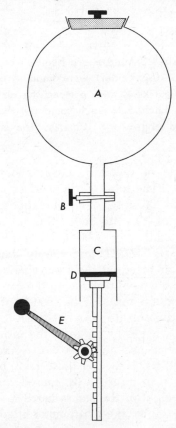

Fig. 12-5. Magdeburg Hemispheres. The edges of two large hollow copper hemispheres (left of top center) were smoothly polished until they fitted together nicely. Otto von Guerike (1654) then pumped the air out with his newly invented vacuum pump. Fifteen horses hitched to each could not then pull them apart until air was readmitted. (From an old engraving. Courtesy The Bettman Archive.)

can made of metal measures about $4 \times 6 \times 8$ in. The total outside surface area is a bit over 200 sq in. The total atmospheric pressure of 14.7 lbs/in.² acting on all six sides is a bit over 3000 lb. Consider the can *tightly sealed* and empty but for enough air to equal the atmospheric pressure. This amount of air (in the can) will weigh about 5 gm. Yet the 3000 lb. of pressure on the outside does not crush it. Remove this 5 gm of air from the inside by a vacuum pump and the can is crushed (Fig. 12-7). How can these facts be explained if air pressure is caused *directly* by the weight of the atmosphere?

Or we might take a barometer fitted with a gas-tight bell jar such as that shown in Fig. 12-6. Let the pressure inside equal the pressure outside. If we increase the temperature of the air inside the bell jar, we will find that the pressure inside will increase. In fact if the original temperature was 0° C, and we increase the temperature by 273° C, we will find that the pressure has doubled. Let us now cool it far below zero by packing dry ice about the bell jar. We will find that the pressure inside the bell jar will decrease well below that outside, and if we cool the system by immersing it in liquid air (about −185° C) the pressure would be reduced to less than half that at room temperature.

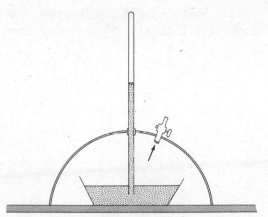

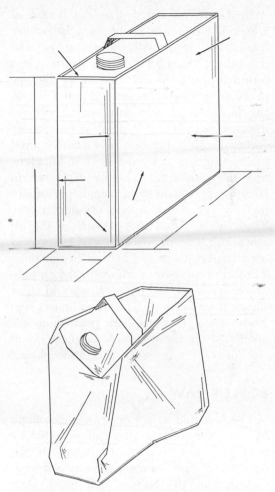

Fig. 12-6. Mercury Barometer in Gas-tight Bell Jar. The air pressure inside and out is the same so that the barometer reads the same as it would outside the bell jar. Note that the weight of the atmosphere above but outside the bell jar can have no effect on supporting the column of mercury. If a vacuum pump is attached to the stopcock and most of the few ounces of air inside the bell jar removed, the mercury level in the tube drops nearly to the level of that in the dish, proving that the mercury is forced up in the tube by the pressure of the air, but not by the weight of the air in the bell jar.

Fig. 12-7. Can Crushed by Atmospheric Pressure. A bit of water was boiled to create steam, which displaced air in the can. The can was then sealed. When the steam condensed the can was crushed.

Yet the weight of the air in the bell jar has not changed one bit. Clearly there is more to air pressure than just the weight of the atmosphere.[6]

[6] Nothing that we have said so far should be taken to mean that the weight of air (gravitational attraction of the earth for air molecules) has nothing to do with its pressure. It is gravitational attraction that permits the earth to have an atmosphere in the first place. If the force of gravity were reduced to that of the moon, the earth would soon lose its air by diffusion into space, just as has happened to the moon (if it ever had an atmosphere). It is this gravitational attraction that is responsible for the decreased density, hence the decreased pressure, at high altitudes. But this is *not* to say that air pressure is *directly* caused by its weight. It does say that we cannot have air pressure in an open system without gravitational attraction to prevent the atmosphere from diffusing into outer space. In a closed system, say a

It should be noted that the height at which the mercury stands in a barometer has nothing to do with the size or shape of the tube (Fig. 12-2). Since mercury is a liquid it obeys the law that states that the pressure at any point in a liquid (due to the liquid) depends only on the *vertical* distance between that point and its upper surface. This distance may be measured in either inches, centimeters, or millimeters, and the pressure is usually expressed in these units instead of in pounds per square inch or grams per square centimeter, etc. Thus, we say that the pressure of the atmosphere is 30 in., or 76 cm, or 760 mm at a particular place and at a particular time. The actual pressure varies with the altitude above sea level, the temperature, and other physical conditions. The above figures represent average atmospheric pressure at sea level and are the pressures we mean when we speak of a pressure of 1 atmosphere.[7]

BOYLE'S LAW

The fact that as we decrease the volume of a gas the pressure rises can be tested by squeezing a sealed toy balloon. If we squeeze it hard enough, thereby reducing the volume, the balloon will burst. We need more complicated apparatus to show the quantitative relationship.

---

gas-tight container at a pressure of 14.7 lb/sq in. and constant temperature, in an environment completely free from gravitational forces, the air pressure would be only slightly less than in our normal environment. Lack of space forbids further discussion of this subject.

[7] Boyle performed many other experiments. Among them was the demonstration that a coin and a feather fall together in a near vacuum. Another was that which showed that a bell ringing in a vacuum cannot be heard. More important were those that led to the relations between pressure and volume at a constant temperature.

Boyle used a tube of glass bent into the shape of a J (Fig. 12-8) with the short

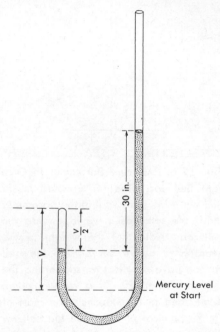

Fig. 12-8. Boyle's J-Tube. When the mercury was at the same level in both arms of the tube, the air pressure in the enclosed end of the tube was equal to that outside. Let the volume of the air trapped in the closed end be V and the pressure be P. Boyle now added mercury to the other arm until the volume of the trapped air was $V/2$. The difference in the new levels of mercury was then about 30 in. The pressure on this air was now $2P$. How much more mercury would he have to add to reduce the volume to $V/4$? What would the pressure on it then be?

end graduated and sealed. The tube was carefully made so that the graduated part was as nearly uniform as was possible with the techniques of the time. A small quantity of air was trapped in the short end by mercury as shown in the figure. When the mercury stood at the same level in both parts of the tube, the air pressure in the trapped end equaled the outside air pressure. Adding more mercury to the longer tube increased the pressure on the trapped air, and raised the level of the mercury in the longer part. When the volume of air was half the original, the difference in the heights of the mercury in the two parts of the tube was about 30 in. (760 mm). We have already seen that this is a pressure of 1 atmosphere. Since Boyle started out with 1 atmosphere of pressure and has added another, the pressure on the trapped air has been doubled, whereas the volume has been halved. To reduce this new volume to half again, he had to add about 60 in. more of mercury (2 atmospheres), etc. (Table 12-1).

TABLE 12-1

Volume (cu in.)	Pressure (atmospheres)	Pressure (in. Hg)
48	1	30
24	2	60
12	4	120
6	8	240

Thus, we see that there is an inverse proportion between the pressure and the volume. Mathematically,

$$P \propto \frac{1}{V} \quad \text{or} \quad P = \frac{K}{V} \quad \text{(Eq. 12-1)}$$

Transposing $\quad PV = K \quad$ (Eq. 12-2)

This is now known as Boyle's Law. The value of the constant, K, depends only upon the quantity (weight) of the gas and the units used. Boyle was careful to keep the temperature of the gas constant. In words, Boyle's Law states that *the volume of a fixed quantity of gas varies inversely with the pressure if the temperature is constant.*

Experiment shows that the PV relations begin to break down as the pressure becomes high. This problem is discussed again in the next chapter.

We can write the equation in another form,

$$P_1V_1 = P_2V_2 \quad \text{(Eq. 12-3)}$$

where P_1 and V_1 represent one pressure and volume of a given amount of gas, and P_2 and V_2 represent its pressure and volume after expansion or compression of the same gas without change of temperature. For example, suppose 22.4 liters of a gas at 1 atmosphere pressure is compressed to a final volume of 5.6 liters. What is its new pressure?

Substituting in Eq. 12-3,

$$1 \times 22.4 = 5.6 \times P_2$$

$$P_2 = 4 \text{ atmospheres}$$

CHARLES' LAW

Boyle knew that the pressure of a gas varied with the temperature if the volume was kept constant, but he did not investigate the problem. For one thing, adequate thermometers had not yet been invented.[8] Later experimenters encountered the same problem. About one hundred years after Boyle's death, Jacques Charles of France proved that the pressure of all gases changes by the same amount per degree change in temperature if the volume is kept constant. Also, the volume changes by the

[8] See problem 12, p. 186.

same amount per degree change in temperature if the pressure is kept constant. These two statements mean that the product, *PV*, changes uniformly with temperature.

Suppose we start with a gas at 0° C whose *PV* product is arbitrarily chosen as 1. We cool it 1° C and find our *PV* product has decreased by $\frac{1}{273}$ of its original value. With 2° C of cooling the value decreases by $\frac{2}{273}$ of the original value. At −20° C it is $\frac{20}{273}$ less, etc. Presumably if we cool it to −273° C, the *PV* product has decreased to where it is $\frac{273}{273}$ less than the original value, i.e., the new value of *PV* is zero! No one of you would be so foolish as to believe that the particles composing a gas could be destroyed simply by cooling them. It does suggest, however, that something, some property of the gas, has declined to zero (see p. 203). It also suggests why there is a temperature below which no lower temperature is possible, a temperature that we call absolute

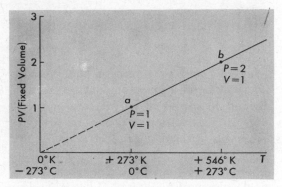

Fig. 12-9. Graphic Representation of Absolute Zero via Charles' Law. *PV* for a definite weight of a gas is plotted against temperature. Extension of the graph downward to the left gives us the lowest theoretical temperature possible.

zero. It also suggests a reason for this temperature being −273° on the Centigrade scale, or 0° on the Kelvin or absolute scale.

Suppose we make a graph (Fig. 12-9) plotting temperature on the horizontal axis and *PV* on the vertical axis. First we plot the value of *PV* at 0° C, which we will arbitrarily designate as 1. This gives us point *a*. Now we will raise the temperature until our *PV* value is 2.[9] We find this temperature to be 273° C. We now plot this point, *b*. The heavy part of the graph connects these two points.

We can determine other points if we wish; if we do our work carefully they will all fall on the same straight line, which slopes downward to the left. Let us extend this line until it intersects the horizontal axis, the axis on which we plotted temperature. We find that the intersection will be at a temperature of −273° C. It matters not what scale we use for the graph, nor what points we start with, nor what gas we use. It follows that there must be something special about this particular temperature. No lower temperature is possible, hence we have a natural zero point for a new kind of thermometer, the absolute (or Kelvin). The capital letter *T* from now on in this book will always refer to temperature measured on the absolute scale. The capital letters A or K following a temperature reading indicate absolute or Kelvin temperatures, respectively, just as F and C indicate Fahrenheit and Centigrade temperatures, respectively.

We may now state Charles' Law, as follows: *The volume of a definite quantity of confined gas varies directly with its abso-*

[9] We do this by keeping the volume constant, i.e., at its original value of 1. At 273° C the pressure will have doubled, giving a *PV* value of 2.

lute temperature if the pressure is kept constant. Mathematically,

$$V \propto T \quad \text{or} \quad V = KT \quad \text{(Eq. 12-4)}$$

Transposing, $\quad \dfrac{V}{T} = K \quad\quad$ (Eq. 12-5)

The value of K here is dependent upon the quantity (weight) of gas and the units used. Note, however, that the value of K here is different from the K in Boyle's Law because the units are different. Here the units are those of V and T, whereas in Boyle's Law the units are those of P and V.

As in the case of Boyle's Law, it follows that

$$\frac{V_1}{T_1} = \frac{V_2}{T_2} \quad \text{or} \quad V_1 T_2 = V_2 T_1 \quad \text{(Eq. 12-6)}$$

IDEAL (GENERAL) GAS LAW

We now have two gas laws, Boyle's Law, in which the volume is inversely proportional to the pressure, i.e., $V \propto 1/P$, and Charles' Law, in which the volume is directly proportional to the absolute temperature, i.e., $V \propto T$. We can combine them into a single law, called the Ideal (or General) Gas Law.[10] Thus,

$$V \propto \frac{T}{P} \quad \text{or} \quad V = \frac{KT}{P} \quad \text{(Eq. 12-7)}$$

Transposing, $\quad PV = KT \quad\quad$ (Eq. 12-8)

The constant K is a number whose magnitude depends upon the mass of the sample of gas and upon the units chosen for P, V, and T. Note that we have still an-

---

[10] A well-known law of proportionality states that (at constant T) if V is proportional to $1/P$, and V is proportional to T (at constant P), then V will be proportional to the product of $1/P$ and T.

other K in Eq. 12-8, different from both the K in Boyle's Law and the K in Charles' Law, for here there are three sets of units.

We prefer to refer to the law as the Ideal Gas Law to help us remember that gases do not obey the law precisely. The deviations are negligible if the pressures are low and the temperatures high. The causes of these deviations will be discussed later (p. 204).

Despite the deviations, the Ideal Gas Law has helped in the organization of our knowledge about gases. However, we still have no overall theory that will explain all of our observations. For example, what is the mechanism by which gases exert pressure? Why does the Ideal Gas Law hold at some temperatures and pressures but not at others? Why are specific heats of all monatomic gases the same? Why are they less than those of the diatomic gases? Etc. A theory seems called for, but not quite yet. For curiously enough, the development of our knowledge of the constitution of matter, as may be inferred from the preceding questions, was intimately associated with the development of our knowledge of heat. We will therefore consider the early theories of heat first.

SUMMARY

Our present understanding of the constitution of matter began with the study of the behavior of gases, rather than with liquids and solids. For one thing, the pressure–volume–temperature relationships are simple and easily measurable by instruments. The analogy between pressures in a liquid and pressure of a gas cannot be carried very far, even though both are fluids. Galileo was the first to guess at the cause of air pressure. Further work by Pascal and Torricelli, both younger contemporaries of Galileo, helped to clarify the concept, but the modern concept came two centuries later. More precise knowledge came with Boyle's improved vacuum pump and his use of Torricelli's barometer. Eventually, Boyle arrived at the law known by his name, which may mathematically be expressed as $PV = K$ at constant temperature, from which it follows that $P_1V_1 = P_2V_2$. A century or so later Charles investigated the temperature–volume relationships at constant pressures. The mathematical expression for his law is $V/T = K$, from which it follows that $V_1T_2 = V_2T_1$. Combining the two laws gives us the Ideal Gas Law, $PV = KT$. This law is called the Ideal Gas Law to remind us that there are no ideal gases. However, the deviations from it are negligible as long as we keep the pressures low and the temperatures well above the liquefaction temperatures of gases.

EXERCISES

I. TERMS AND CONCEPTS

Pressure	Boyle's Law
Barometer	Charles' Law
Equations:	Ideal Gas Law

$$PV = K$$

$$\frac{V}{T} = K$$

$$PV = KT$$

II. PROBLEMS

1. Are the K's in the above equations the same, or are they different? Explain.

2. Distinguish between the force acting on a body and the pressure exerted on it.

3. Describe, and state the significance of, von Guericke's Magdeburg hemisphere experiment.

4. Suppose that your classroom measures 50 ft × 30 ft × 12 ft. If the density of air is 0.08 lb/cu ft, how much does the air in the room weigh?

5. In the experiment to check Torricelli's air-pressure theory, Pascal had a man keep constant watch on a barometer at the foot of the mountain. Why was this necessary?

6. Why is mercury used in a barometer? Would some other liquid not do equally well, e.g., water?

7. Suppose that you put a thin hollow tube of glass with the hole in it the same diameter as a straw into a dish of mercury. Mercury has a density of 13.6. Would you have to suck on it harder to make the mercury rise in the tube than you would if you were sucking up milk? Explain your answer.

8. State Boyle's Law. What are its limitations?

9. Show that the following data concerning the pressure and volume of a gas demonstrate Boyle's Law (without drawing a graph). Then do the same by drawing a graph.

P (cm Hg)	V (cm³)
76	283
150	140.3
40	537.5
210	102.4
30	707.1

10. A cubic inch of mercury weighs 0.491 lb. What is the weight of the mercury in a barometer with a cross section of 1 sq in. and 30 in. high? How does this compare with normal atmospheric pressure?

11. In Fig. 12-9 we plotted temperature against PV to obtain absolute zero. We can also plot temperature against V (at constant P) and reach the same result. Do so.

12. If $PV = K$ at constant T, then changes in the product PV can be used to construct a temperature scale. Take a sample of gas and measure its volume and pressure at the temperatures of melting ice and boiling

water. A device which makes this sort of measurement is called a gas thermometer. Such an instrument is not graduated to read temperature directly. Instead V and P are read and the product PV determined from a graph. Other kinds of thermometers may agree with one another at 0° and at 100° but not in between, because their scales depend upon the properties of particular substances. All gas thermometers agree no matter what gas is used in them. Why?

13. State Charles' Law. What are its limitations?

14. If 32 gm of oxygen occupies 22.4 liters at 0° C and 760 mm pressure, what volume will it occupy at 100° C at the same pressure? [11]

15. A quantity of a gas occupies 25 liters at 25° C and 760 mm pressure. What will be its volume at 298° C and 1520 mm pressure?

16. State the Ideal Gas Law. What are its limitations?

17. Under what conditions may matter absorb heat without increasing its temperature?

18. Gases here on earth expand to fill any container regardless of size. Could you explain this by the continuous concept of matter? By the discrete molecular concept?

19. Suppose all matter existed only in the solid state. Would this have made our understanding of the fundamental nature of matter easier? More difficult? Or would it not have mattered? Justify your answer.

20. What conclusions can you reach about the nature of a gas *solely* from the laws of Boyle and Charles?

---

[11] In problems like 14 and 15 equations 12-3 and 12-6 may be used. Solve first for the change in V due to the change in P, and then, if asked, for the change in V due to change in T. Remember that T must be expressed in the absolute scale.

CHAPTER XIII

Early Theories of Heat

False facts are highly injurious to the progress of science, for they often endure long; but false views, if supported by some evidence, do little harm, for everyone takes a salutary pleasure in proving their falseness; and when this is done, one path towards error is closed and the road to truth is often at the same time opened.—CHARLES DARWIN

INTRODUCTION

No serious theory of heat was advocated until the latter half of the eighteenth century. Some historians of science have flatly stated that the reason for this delay was Aristotle's rejection of the atomic views of Democritus because they were in disagreement with some of his philosophical ideas about nature. At any rate, the atomic concept of matter lay dormant until about 1700, when it was slowly revived. Newton speculated on heat as being a kind of "atomic" motion, but the atomic concept was still vague—Dalton's theory was a hundred years in the future—and the association of heat with "atomic" motion was still vaguer. Moreover, the concepts of work and energy had not yet been clarified when Newton died in 1727.

PHENOMENA TO BE EXPLAINED BY ANY THEORY OF HEAT

About 1750 Joseph Black, a Scotsman, made clear the distinction between heat and temperature and defined specific heat. In the course of his investigations into the phenomenon of heat he developed what came to be known as the caloric theory of heat. Before stating the assumptions of this theory, let us list the facts a satisfactory theory of heat had to explain (in light of the knowledge of the time, not in light of what is known now).

1. Why things get hotter when a flame is applied to them, and why they cool off when the flame is removed.

2. Why heat always moves from the warmer to the cooler body.

3. The differences in the specific heats of different substances.

4. Why solids turn to liquids and liquids to gases when sufficient heat is added, i.e., why substances change their state.

5. The phenomena of latent heat.

6. Why friction produces heat.

7. Why most liquids and solids expand when the temperature rises. The few exceptions must also be explained.

8. Why the pressure of a gas multiplied by its volume is proportional to the absolute temperature provided the pressure is not too high.

9. Why the compression of a gas produces heat, and, conversely, why expansion produces cooling.

10. Why the evaporation of a liquid is a cooling process.

11. Why denser substances are better conductors of heat than less dense ones.

CALORIC THEORY OF HEAT

The assumptions of the caloric theory were essentially as follows:

1. Caloric is an invisible self-repulsive weightless substance that is attracted by the corpuscles of all matter, forming a kind of shell about them.

2. Caloric can be added to or subtracted from a body, whose temperature depends upon the amount of free caloric present.

3. Different substances have different capacities for holding caloric. For any one substance the gaseous phase can hold the most caloric and the solid phase the least.

4. As more and more caloric is added, the corpuscles are forced farther and farther apart as the amount of self-repulsion increases.

5. Chemical reactions change the capacities of substances for holding caloric.

6. Stresses reduce the ability of substances to hold caloric.

The theory could explain most of the observed facts. By 1780 it was firmly entrenched. Among its staunch supporters were many of the renowned men of science of the times. Yet by 1850 it had been largely discredited by Joule and Helmholtz, who showed it to be about as wrong as it is possible for a theory to be. In large part it was slow in being rejected because its only rival was so slow in developing; you cannot replace something with nothing.

There were a number of objections; we will content ourselves with citing three. The first is not an objection if you can "swallow" the existence of a weightless substance, i.e., a substance without mass, crowding the corpuscles of matter apart as the temperature was increased. The second is that of an apparent contradiction. If adding caloric to a substance caused it to get hotter, how could "squeezing it out" as in friction also cause a rise in temperature? The third was the lack of a relationship between the specific heats and the melting points.[1]

THE CANNON-BORING EXPERIMENTS OF COUNT RUMFORD

During the late 1700's and early 1800's more and more scientists were suggesting that heat was a form of motion (equivalent to saying that it was a form of energy) but none produced any evidence until a traitor to the American Revolution, born Benjamin Thompson, gained everlasting fame under the title of Count Rumford by presenting a paper to the Royal Society of London in 1798. Rumford was one of the most fantastically colorful men that ever lived. He led

a life of unswerving honesty in science and unconscionable duplicity in politics. . . . George III hated him but used him; the Elector of Bavaria ennobled him and made him his prime minister; Napoleon considered him one of the great minds of the day. . . . He was unsurpassed in arrogance; he had few peers in science.[2]

While Rumford was Minister of War in Bavaria, he became interested in the boring of cannon made of brass. A horse in a

[1] Lead, gold, and platinum have specific heats of 0.0306, 0.0312, and 0.0324 respectively, but their melting points are 327° C, 1063° C, and 1773° C.

[2] Mitchell Wilson, Count Rumford, *Scientific American,* Vol. 203, No. 4, p. 158, October, 1960.

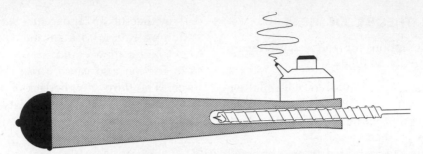

Fig. 13-1. Rumford's Cannon-boring Experiment. He used horses as his source of energy. The heat developed by friction boiled the water in a receptacle placed on the cannon.

treadmill furnished the force to turn the boring instrument. He noted that a great deal of heat seemed to be endlessly produced, a phenomenon that he could not explain by the caloric theory.

Perhaps friction could drive caloric out of a substance, but that a *material* substance could be present in unlimited amounts in a piece of brass was too much for Rumford's imagination. His doubts about caloric as a material substance rose when he found that the ice formed from a given weight of water weighed the same as the water despite the fact that great quantities of heat were given up during the freezing process. Other weighings showed that the temperature of a substance did not affect its weight in the slightest. Nor could he explain by the theory why water contracted as it cooled to 4° C and then began to expand. True scientist that he was, he became curious about this inexhaustible supply of heat produced in the cannon boring and decided to investigate further. He placed kettles of water on the cannon (Fig. 13-1) and found that in about 2½ hours of continuous boring enough heat was generated to boil about

26 lb of water.[3] He could keep the water boiling as long as his horse could keep his boring instrument turning. The caloricists tried to explain the endless supply of heat by assuming that the chips of brass produced by the boring instrument had a higher specific heat than the cannon itself. Rumford measured it and found it to be exactly the same as for the rest of the cannon. He further confounded them by changing from a sharp boring tool to a very dull one, one which produced a lot of friction but few chips for the amount of work done. This produced more heat with fewer chips. Thus, he discovered that heat was something that could be manufactured *in unlimited amounts at the expense of mechanical energy.* In his own words, ". . . heat is nothing but a vibratory motion taking place among the particles of a body."

THE FAILURE OF RUMFORD

Rumford was unable to devise a good working theory of heat as a form of motion,

[3] Later he immersed the whole cannon in water as he continued the boring.

so he had few converts during his lifetime. Even the evidence produced by Sir Humphry Davy [4] failed to dislodge the caloric theory, thus emphasizing again that scientists in general prefer a wrong theory that explains many things to no theory at all. Davy devised an apparatus in which two pieces of ice were rubbed against each other in as good a vacuum as he could produce. The ice melted despite the fact that there was no source for the heat other than that produced by the motion of the blocks of ice against each other.

The failure to develop a working theory of heat as "the motions of atoms and molecules" at this time (1800–1810) was quite likely in large part due to the lack of quantitativeness in Rumford's work, i.e., it failed to answer the question, "Does the same amount of heat always arise from the expenditure of the same amount of mechanical energy?" In other words, proof that heat was a form of energy was still lacking. In part, the delay was due to the very human characteristic that people are unwilling to give up a long-held belief that explains many of the observed facts. As in other fields of endeavor, a new idea often supplants an older one by the dying of the defenders of the older belief, leaving the world to the upholders of the new idea.[5]

The caloric theory is probably the finest example we have of a scientific theory being able to explain most of the facts, while at the same time being completely false. No matter how beautifully a theory can seem to explain most of the facts, it can fatally flounder by the failure to explain one recalcitrant fact.

THE WORK OF JOULE AND THE SUCCESS OF RUMFORD

It was left for an English physicist, James P. Joule, son of an English brewer and an amateur scientist, to do the quantitative work necessary to establish the fact that heat is a form of energy. In doing this he not only established that Rumford was right, but he also established the Law of Conservation of Energy and laid much of the groundwork for the kinetic theory of gases. Joule's first work was in the field of electricity and magnetism but he soon became interested in heat; it might truly be said that he devoted his life to proving that heat was a form of energy.[6] He developed great enthusiasm, great skill, and great perseverance in this project, one which extended over forty years of his life. Much of his most important work in this field was done between 1840 and 1850.

One of the things that Joule did was to heat water by pushing it around. His

---

[4] Davy was the first director of the Royal Institution of London, a scientific laboratory set up and financed by Rumford out of his own pocket. It was shortly to become one of the great research institutions of the world—and still is.

[5] One should not reach the conclusion that this reluctance to discard the old for the new is necessarily bad. A certain skepticism towards a new idea is a healthy attitude. In science it forces the advocates of the new to obtain all the evidence they can, to develop their theories carefully, and to subject them to further experiment. If the evi-

dence is overwhelmingly in favor of the new, only a few "die-hards" will stick to the old.

[6] When Joule went to the Alps on his honeymoon he took along not only his bride but a very sensitive thermometer for the purpose of measuring a suspected difference in temperature between the water at the top of waterfalls (of which there are many in the Alps) and that at the bottom. He found as much as 2° F difference.

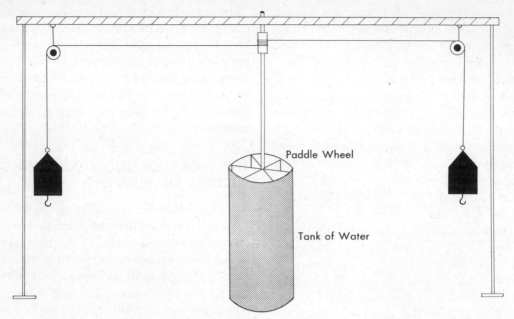

Paddle Wheel

Tank of Water

Fig. 13-2. Joule's Paddlewheel Experiment. Weights could be shifted from the hook on one side to that on the other to turn the paddles in the tank. The potential energy of the weights when elevated could be calculated, and the rise in temperature of the known mass of the water measured.

problem was to compare the amount of heat produced to the amount of mechanical energy used to do the pushing. One of the greatest difficulties—and this is always a difficulty when working with heat—is to prevent the escape of heat insofar as that is possible, and to measure or make a reliable estimate of the heat that cannot be prevented from escaping. The devices that he used were many and varied; his most famous one consisted of a system of paddles turned in a vessel of water by falling weights (Fig. 13-2) whose potential energy could easily be measured. He could read his thermometers to $\frac{1}{200}$ of a degree. He repeated each experiment over and over again, one of them 34 times. He used other liquids besides water, e.g., mer-

cury and whale oil. He also heated water by means of an electric current in experiments in which he could measure both the current and the heat produced by a measured amount of mechanical energy. In these electrical experiments he used both batteries and the newly developed electric dynamo to generate the current. (In the battery, chemical energy is used as the source of the current; in the dynamo mechanical energy is used.)

Ultimately he was able to announce that the expenditure of a certain number of units of work always gave rise to a certain number of calories of heat. This ratio is called the *mechanical equivalent of heat*. Here we will express it in cgs units rather than in the English system that Joule used, and we will use the more precise modern figure.

$$J = 4.18 \text{ joules/calorie} \quad (\text{Eq. 13-1})$$

where J is the mechanical equivalent of heat. It is, of course, a constant. By means of it we can convert joules to calories and vice versa. This means that for every 4.18 joules of mechanical energy expended, 1 calorie of heat is produced. Other scientists working during the same years performed many other relevant experiments, some of a similar character and some quite different. Their results tallied within reasonable limits of experimental error. Since 1 calorie of heat is produced for each 4.18 joules of mechanical energy expended regardless of the mechanism involved, it follows that heat must be a form of energy.

LAW OF CONSERVATION OF ENERGY

Heat and mechanical energy are interchangeable at the fixed rate of exchange of 4.18 joules/calorie. This is the First Law of Thermodynamics, originally known as the Law of Conservation of Mechanical Energy and originally announced by Joule. Further experiments by Joule and many others on the conversion of electrical, magnetic, chemical, and radiant energy into heat and back again, always without loss if careful accounting procedures are followed, resulted in a broadening of this generalization to include all forms of energy. The broader generalization is known as the Principle (or Law) of Conservation of Energy.

Energy, though interconvertible, is indestructible. It may be the only indestructible thing in the universe. In the myriads of experiments that have been performed since Joule first started his work, in the enormously varied operations and processes of modern industry, even in the complexities of biological processes, the energy books have always been found to balance. No matter how small an amount of energy with which we start, no matter in what form or in what disguise, if we keep track so that none of it slips away unnoticed between our fingers, we will always wind up with the same amount in one form or another. Inherent in this principle is our previous statement that perpetual motion-machines are impossible.

In the years just preceding, during, and just following World War II, it was shown that tiny amounts of some kinds of mass could be turned into energy (see Chap. XLVI). Einstein had made the prediction back in 1905. This discovery in no way makes invalid all that we have said. It merely means that to include the processes of conversion of matter into energy, processes that are limited to those going on in the stars, in atomic bombs, and in substances subject to radioactive decay, we need to combine the great laws of conservation of mass (p. 227) and energy into one: *The total mass and energy in the universe is constant.*

The Law of Conservation of Energy was one of the great concepts of the nineteenth century, probably the greatest, for it helped to integrate all of the other great concepts that developed during that tremendous scientific century. Modified as above, it states that the only thing that is taking place in this world of matter is a transformation of matter into energy and of energy from one form to another. The scientist believes this applies not only here on earth, not only in the motions of the solar system, not only to all of the stars of our galaxy, the Milky Way, but also he does not doubt that it applies to all of those other millions of galaxies whose distances are far beyond our imaginations. We can never test this statement, of course; our belief must therefore rest on faith. It is not so much faith in the validity of the principle of conservation of energy as it is in the principle of uniformity of nature and her laws, the faith of every scientist that there is law and order in the universe.

his famous paddle-wheel experiments, and later by other experiments, he showed that mechanical energy could be converted into heat at the rate of 4.18 joules/calorie. This figure is known as the mechanical equivalent of heat. Other experiments by Joule and others showed that any kind of energy could be converted to other forms of energy. From these experiments came the great integrating Law of Conservation of Energy: *Energy though interconvertible is indestructible*. Inherent in this law is the concept that perpetual-motion machines are impossible.

SUMMARY

The suggestion that heat might be a form of motion dates back at least as far as Galileo but no theory incorporating that suggestion was developed until more than two hundred years after his death. This was in part because the concepts of work and energy had not yet been clarified, and in part because no acceptable theory concerning the constitution of matter had yet been formulated. In the meantime Joseph Black (*ca.* 1760) formulated the caloric theory of heat which reigned with only token opposition from 1780 to about 1850. Highly successful though it was in explaining many of the phenomena of heat, it turned out to be about as wrong as a theory can be. Count Rumford, a renegade American, obtained compelling evidence against it by turning mechanical energy into heat in his cannon-boring experiments. He failed, largely because he was unable to do the quantitative work necessary, to develop an adequate theory, a theory that could incorporate in it his ideas of heat as a vibratory motion of particles.

Joule, an Englishman who devoted most of his life to establish heat as a form of energy, finally succeeded where Rumford failed. In

EXERCISES

I. TERMS AND CONCEPTS
Caloric
Mechanical equivalent of heat
Law of Conservation of Energy

II. PROBLEMS

1. Why did so many prominent scientists in the last half of the eighteenth and first half of the nineteenth centuries believe in the caloric theory of heat?

2. Who was Benjamin Thompson and for what (in science) is he particularly remembered?

3. What were the essential points in Count Rumford's cannon-boring experiments that were detrimental to the caloric theory of heat?

4. Why could Rumford not make his cannon-boring experiment quantitative?

5. State Rumford's final conclusion.

6. What did Joule do that Rumford did not that made him successful in overthrowing the caloric theory?

7. Describe and state the significance of Joule's most famous experiment.

8. What is the proof that heat is a form of energy?

9. Specifically, what is heat according to Joule? (To say that it is a form of energy is entirely inadequate as an answer.)

10. In the discussion of the pile driver on p. 158 we failed to state what happened to the kinetic energy of the hammer when it was stopped by the pile. When the hammer struck, the pile was driven into the ground a few inches, ground that resisted the movement of the pile. State precisely and completely what happened to the kinetic energy of the hammer.

11. Did the caloric theory recognize heat as a form of energy? Explain.

12. What is meant by the mechanical equivalent of heat? What is J?

13. How did the caloricists explain:

   a. Why heat always moves from warmer to cooler bodies?

   b. Why friction makes a substance hotter?

   c. Why substances change their state?

   d. Why hammering a substance makes its temperature rise?

   e. Why things get hotter when put in a flame?

14. Is there any contradiction between your answers to *b* and *d* on the one hand and to *e* on the other (assuming you gave the correct answers to all three)?

15. Upon what foundation does the Law of Conservation of Energy rest?

16. A man weighing 75 kg climbs a vertical ladder a distance of 8 m. How many calories of heat are expended? (Hint: The mechanical energy expended must first be determined.)

CHAPTER XIV

The Kinetic-Molecular Theory of Gases

Believing, as I do, in the [regularity] of nature, I cannot stop abruptly where our microscopes cease to be of use. Here the vision of the mind authoritatively supplements the vision of the eye.
—JOHN TYNDALL

We now have sufficient background concerning the nature of heat, temperature, and energy, and of the behavior of gases to formulate a theory that will explain and integrate most of the phenomena noted in this section. We could go on citing the results of more experiments and thus accumulate more evidence, but such a procedure would tend to make this account unnecessarily tedious, for it would tax our memories to remember all of the evidence, and increase the difficulty of keeping track of all of the interrelationships. We will proceed to the development of a theory and will begin, as usual, to list its assumptions, citing a few of the more obvious observations we may have mentioned previously but not discussed.

We must remember that the assumptions are not simply the products of man's imagination, but are really clues that have been obtained through observations and experiments. Perhaps it is better to say that they are *inferences,* reasonable ones in all cases if proper attention is paid to the observations and experiments; they cannot be classified as facts because they have not been "proved" beyond all doubt. In the kinetic-molecular theory all but the last assumption are especially readily seen to be reasonable inferences derived from observation and experiment.

We cannot ever observe a lone molecule directly, even by a high-powered optical microscope. We can, however, under certain circumstances, observe the behavior of masses of them. This is most difficult to do in the solid state, somewhat less difficult in the liquid state, and relatively easy when molecules are in the gaseous state. This is true despite the fact that our senses give us more *direct* information about liquids and solids, and relatively little about gases. Yet it is through a study of gases that we have learned what liquids and solids really are like. In large part this is because each molecule of gas acts almost independently of all of the other molecules around it, and in part because gases exert pressure, occupy volume, and their behavior changes as the temperature changes, all of which can be measured by instruments. We can even make some direct observations on gases if they are colored, as are bromine and chlorine, or if they possess characteristic odors or tastes, e.g., ammonia. For these reasons we began our investigation into the fundamental nature of matter by a study of gases rather than of liquids or solids.

KINETIC-MOLECULAR THEORY OF IDEAL GASES

1. Gases consist of tiny discrete [1] particles called molecules.

2. Gas molecules are in constant *random* motion.

3. Gas molecules are, on the average, far apart relative to their size so that they exert no forces on each other except at the instant of collision.

4. Gas molecules collide with one another and with the walls of their container without loss of kinetic energy, i.e., all collisions are perfectly elastic.

CONTINUITY OF MATTER

Only two possibilities exist with respect to the fundamental nature of matter; it is either continuous or discontinuous. If continuous, it is theoretically possible to subdivide it endlessly, without ever reaching a particle too small to be divided again. If discontinuous, subdividing would eventually end with some fundamental discrete (separate) particle. Democritus (*ca.* 400 B.C.) advanced this latter view, and gave us the word "atom" as the name of that particle.[2] Aristotle rejected this view, and his great influence caused it to be forgotten

for two thousand years. The atomistic concept was revived in the sixteenth century but it was not developed into a theory until the beginning of the nineteenth century, when Dalton advanced his atomic theory. Others before him, among them Boyle, Newton, and Lavoisier, the great French chemist, believed in the atomicity of matter, but none of them defined the properties of the atoms.

We will adopt the discrete-particle concept here—leaving the development of the atomic theory until later—but we will omit the distinction between atoms and molecules at this time. We will use the term molecule to mean the smallest discrete particle of any kind of matter that can exist independently *when that matter is in the gaseous state*. In almost all cases this use will be consistent with its modern meaning. On occasion we will carry over the same general concept of the word to liquids and solids in order to prevent confusion—which certainly would result otherwise. Later on we will give a more rigorous definition of a molecule. Our first assumption therefore seems well justified.

Break a small vial of bromine (brown in color) in the bottom of a glass cylinder and it can be seen to diffuse throughout the whole cylinder in a matter of minutes (Fig. 14-1). If we evacuate the cylinder first, the diffusion is almost instantaneous. Or if someone opens a bottle of ammonia in the far corner of a room, our noses soon know it. We are also all aware of the fact that gases can leak through the tiniest of openings, in automobile tires, e.g.; we already know that gases expand without limit to fill their containers no matter what the size or shape. The above observations merely confirm this knowledge, and so jus-

---

[1] Meaning separate or discontinuous; composed of distinct parts.

[2] Democritus reasoned from the differing densities of matter. If substance *A* is denser than *B*, it is because there are open spaces in *B*, and if *C* is denser than *A*, then *A* must also have open spaces. Extending this argument to all known kinds of matter (except the densest), he came to the conclusion that matter was made of "pieces." How could matter be continuous if it contained open spaces? Today we can use the great expansive capacities of gases to support the atomistic view of Democritus.

tify our second assumption. By random motion we mean that just as many molecules move in one direction as in any other. When molecules of gases are violently aroused, as in hurricanes, tornadoes, explo-

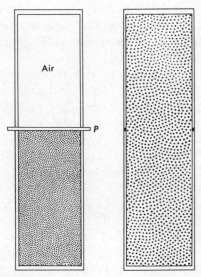

Fig. 14-1. Diffusion of One Gas through Another. Bromine, a reddish-brown gas fills the lower half of the container on the left. After the dividing plate, *P*, is removed, the bromine quickly diffuses through the air in the upper part to form a uniform mixture of bromine and air. If the space above the dividing plate were a vacuum, diffusion would be almost instantaneous on removal of the plate.

sions of all kinds, there is little that withstand the forces they collectively exert. It is not this type of motion, however, that we are discussing. The random motion that we refer to is that of gases at rest, e.g., the air in this room. We should realize, however, that even in those masses of air that move in one direction (as in steady winds), sometimes at high speeds, these

random motions of the molecules are still taking place.

We also know that gases are easily compressible, that we can walk through the air, pushing it aside as we do so. Thus, our third assumption seems reasonable.

We have already seen that gases exert a pressure on every surface with which they are in contact. Assumption 2 gives us a logical explanation, for we should expect that rapidly moving molecules would exert a force on the walls of the container as they bump into them. If the impacts were frequent enough and made by an enormous number of molecules per unit area, a continuous force would result. Using the laws of mechanics we should be able to calculate the value of this force. We also reason that if the molecules collide with the walls of the container, they should also collide with one another. Furthermore, these collisions should all be perfectly elastic, i.e., there should be no loss of energy during the collisions. If this were not so, the molecules of the gas would gradually slow down, losing their kinetic energy, and finally settle to form a layer on the bottom of the container. That they do not do this is obvious, so we conclude that all collisions are elastic. Since the molecules rebound elastically, there is no friction.

What we have said above is true only of large numbers of molecules, for in every collision between molecules one will gain kinetic energy, the other lose it. The average, however, remains the same. A conclusion from this assumption is that the molecules of a gas remain eternally in motion.

By means of these four assumptions all of the readily observable phenomena with respect to gases seem perfectly reasonable. The same is true for Boyle's Law, for if gas pressure is due to the impact of enormous numbers of molecules upon the walls of the container or other surfaces, then compressing these molecules into half the space should cause twice as many impacts per unit time and so double the pressure. However, the relationship between P and V on the one hand and T on the other is not at all evident from our assumptions. Perhaps a mechanical model will help. It was Lord Kelvin who said, "If I can make a mechanical model then I can understand; if I cannot make one, I do not understand." But first we will review the history of the development of the kinetic theory.

The first to devise a theory of gases was Daniel Bernoulli, a member of one of the most illustrious families in the annals of science. He began his career a few years before the death of Newton, and advanced his theory in 1738, over one hundred years before Joule put the finishing touches to the concept of heat as a form of energy. He explained gas pressure as due to the impact on the walls of a container. By mathematical analysis he deduced Boyle's Law—which Boyle had established by experiment some eighty years earlier. Bernoulli believed that heat was "an internal motion of the particles." This conclusion was a logical outcome of his theory of gas pressure, for if heat is a form of motion, then heat must be associated with gas particles that are in motion; gas particles had to be in motion if they were to exert pressure upward as well as downward. His views were too advanced for the time, and so his theory fell by the wayside, not because of any contrary evidence but simply for want of attention. This is a common happenstance for those in any field who are

too far in advance of the mental climate of the time.

It was Joule,[3] convinced from his many experiments that Rumford was right in his concept of heat as the motion of particles, who revived Bernoulli's theory. Joule incorporated many of Bernoulli's ideas in his own work. By the application of the assumptions listed above, he devised a theoretical, idealized mechanical model. This, combined with Newton's laws of mechanics, enabled him to develop a quantitative kinetic theory of gases. Although the calculation is a bit long, it is not at all difficult except at one point. A little earnest concentration should suffice for that small hurdle.

DERIVATION OF THE IDEAL GAS LAW BY HYPOTHESIS

Suppose we have a cubical box as our container of a gas, a box whose three dimensions, a, b, and c, are each equal to a length that we will call L (Fig. 14-2). Its volume is therefore L^3. Myriads of molecules are in *random* motion in this box (Fig. 14-3). We will assume that all are moving with the same *average* speed, v. At any one instant as many are moving parallel to one dimension as to either of the other two. That is, if the total number of molecules in the box is N, then $N/3$ are moving parallel to ee, $N/3$ are moving parallel to ff, and $N/3$ parallel to gg.[4] According to our as-

[3] Besides Joule, other (and later) contributors to the kinetic theory were James Clerk Maxwell, Stefan Boltzmann, Heinrich Helmholtz, and others.

[4] Actually the shape of the container makes no difference—our model would be very unsatisfactory if it did. We use the cubical box to make the geometry simpler. The same is true of the assumptions regarding speeds and directions of motion. However, when we carry out all calculations

sumption each impact involves a rebound perpendicular to the wall without loss of speed.[5] The average time, t, that it takes one of them to move across the box and

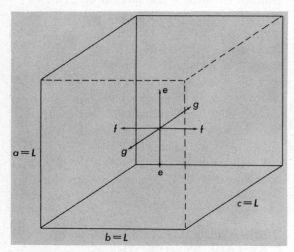

Fig. 14-2. Kinetic Theory Diagram. A cubical box contains a definite weight of a gas. Equal numbers of molecules are assumed to be traveling back and forth parallel to each of the three dimensions of the box.

back again (a distance of $2L$) is $2L/v$, where v is the average speed. Mathematically,

$$t = \frac{2L}{v} \qquad \text{(Eq. 14-1)}$$

We need now to calculate the force exerted by a single molecule. According to

for any shape container and *without* the assumptions regarding average speeds and directions of motion, exactly the same result is obtained, provided that $mv^2/2$ is interpreted as the *average* kinetic energy of the gas molecules.

[5] This assumption is obviously not true of individual molecules except in the *statistical* sense. It is justifiable because it represents a correct *average* behavior of an enormous number of molecules.

Newton's second law, $F = ma$. This law in this form does not help us for we do not know a and have no way of calculating it. Neither are we sure of m, but we really do not need to know that, for Newton gave us his second law in another form (Eq. 7-2, p. 114):

$$F = \frac{\text{Change in momentum}}{\text{Time}}$$

or

$$F = \frac{\text{Change in } mv}{t}$$

Force here is thus defined as the total momentum transfer per second. Now we learned (p. 122) that momentum is a vector quantity, i.e., it has direction as well as magnitude. A molecule moving perpendicular to one of the walls has a certain momentum, mv. Since it is going to make a perfectly elastic collision (assumption 4) with the wall, it is going to rebound with a momentum equal in magnitude to the forward momentum but opposite in direction. To distinguish these two momenta we will call the forward one $+mv$ and the rebounding one $-mv$. The difference between $+mv$ and $-mv$ is $2mv$, i.e., $mv - (-mv) = 2mv$; the change in momentum is $2mv$. Therefore, the force exerted by a single molecule against the wall of the container is given by

$$F_{\text{per molecule}} = \frac{\text{Change in } mv}{t} = \frac{2mv}{2L/v}$$

$$= \frac{2mv^2}{2L} \qquad \text{(Eq. 14-2)}$$

(We deliberately do not cancel out the 2's.)

Now the total force exerted by all of the molecules on one face of our box is the

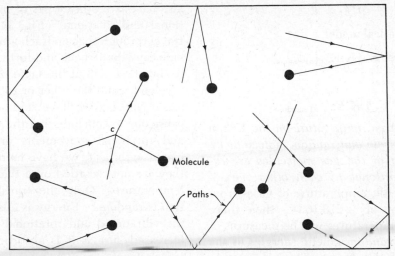

Fig. 14-3. Actual Paths of Molecules in Box. The actual paths are random, colliding with the walls at various angles and with one another (as at c) and rebounding. The net effect of all these random collisions with the walls is the same as if one-third of them moved parallel to *ee*, one-third parallel to *ff*, and one-third parallel to *gg*.

force per molecule, $2mv^2/2L$, multiplied by the number striking that face per second; this number is $N/3$. Mathematically,

$$F_{\text{total on one face}} = \frac{N}{3} \times \frac{2mv^2}{2L} \quad \text{(Eq. 14-3)}$$

Since

$$F_{\left(\substack{\text{total on} \\ \text{one face}}\right)} = P_{\left(\substack{\text{force per} \\ \text{unit area}}\right)} \times A_{\left(\substack{\text{area of} \\ \text{one face}}\right)}, \text{ and}$$

$A = L^2$, then $F = PL^2$

Substituting in Eq. 14-3,

$$PL^2 = \frac{N}{3} \times \frac{2mv^2}{2L} \quad \text{(Eq. 14-4)}$$

Multiplying both sides by L,

$$PL^3 = \frac{N}{3} \times \frac{2mv^2}{2} \quad \text{(Eq. 14-5)}$$

Since L^3 is the volume (V) of the cubical box,

$$PV = \tfrac{2}{3}N \times \frac{mv^2}{2} \quad \text{(Eq. 14-6)}$$

You should recognize $mv^2/2$ as the formula for kinetic energy. Here it represents the average random kinetic energy of the molecules of the gas in the box. This means that for any given number of molecules, N, the PV relationship depends on the average random kinetic energy of the molecules, i.e., PV equals two-thirds of the total *random* kinetic energy if our hypothesis is correct.

Now if we go back to the last chapter, we find that both Boyle and Charles derived laws experimentally, laws that could be combined into one Ideal or General Gas Law,

$$PV \propto T$$

By the theoretical model,

$$PV \propto \tfrac{2}{3} K.E._{\text{total random}}$$

Therefore,

$$T \propto \tfrac{2}{3} K.E._{\text{total random}}$$

This means that *temperature on the Kelvin or absolute scale and random molecular kinetic energy of the gas molecules are directly proportional to each other,* i.e., if we measure all temperatures of gases from a zero point of $-273.16°$ C, then those measured temperatures will be measures of the average *random* kinetic energies of the molecules of the gases. This relationship between temperature and kinetic energy can mean only that heat is a form of energy. Note that in explaining the Ideal Gas Law, the theory has also explained Boyle's and Charles' laws.

TYPES OF MOLECULAR MOTION

You are undoubtedly wondering why the word random is italicized so many times. This is done because all atoms and molecules have kinetic energies that are not random, and these never decline to zero. Consider the molecules of oxygen and nitrogen in the atmosphere. They exist as double atoms, i.e., two atoms to a molecule. The motions that they have along a path, the motion that allows them to fill all empty space, is the random motion we have mentioned so many times. It is often called translational motion. Only this motion of translation of the molecule as a whole will be registered as pressure on the walls of a container or recorded by a thermometer as temperature. The molecules also have two other types of motion, vibrational and rotational (Fig. 14-4), as they travel through space. Each atom in a molecule can vibrate back and forth with respect to the other, and at the same time each can revolve around the other or rotate about an axis. Nothing we have said so far should cause one to conclude that these vibrational and rotational movements are not associated with heat; we have merely said that they are not recorded on a thermometer as temperature. Only the translational motion is random.[6] Energy is absorbed when the vibrational and rotational motions are increased, just as it is absorbed when the translational (random) motions are increased. Hence the *total heat content of a gas* (or of a liquid or a solid) *is the sum of the energies of the three kinds of molecular motion—translational, vibrational, and rotational.* The orderly vibrational and rotational motions, we repeat, have no effect on a thermometer, whereas the disorderly translational motions do.

Evidence for these conclusions come from an investigation of the specific heats of gases. The inert gases, helium, neon, argon, krypton, xenon, radon, and certain vapors such as mercury all have simple molecules,[7] one atom each. It is reasonable to suppose that these *monatomic* molecules cannot have rotational movements as other molecules do, hence their specific heats should be less than those of other gases or vapors. It would also be expected that the specific heats for all monatomic gases should be the same—and they are. *Di-*

[6] Note that in our mechanical model we dealt only with random motion. The vibrational and rotational motions were ignored.

[7] Note our definition of molecule on p. 202n.

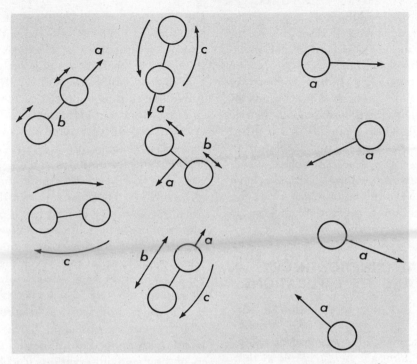

Fig. 14-4. Types of Molecular Motion. **(a)** Translational. **(b)** Vibrational. **(c)** Rotational. The latter two types are denied single-atom molecules (inert gases). Multiple-atom molecules have all three types. All three types are heat, but only that of translation is registered on a thermometer.

atomic gases—oxygen, hydrogen, nitrogen, chlorine, fluorine, hydrogen chloride, carbon monoxide—all have specific heats that are the same; they are two-thirds as large again as those of the monatomic gases. Gases that consist of three atoms—water vapor, carbon dioxide, sulfur dioxide, etc. —have still greater specific heats; they can vibrate in ways denied monatomic and diatomic gases. Heat must be absorbed to increase these motions but this heat does not make the substance absorbing it any hotter, i.e., give it a higher temperature.

SIGNIFICANCE OF THE ABSOLUTE (KELVIN) SCALE

Note carefully the differences between the Centigrade, Fahrenheit, and absolute (Kelvin) scales. The first two were purely arbitrary; some other point could just as well have been chosen as the 0° point on either. But there is nothing arbitrary in the zero point on the absolute scale. *It is the point reached when all random molecular motion of molecules has ceased.* This is the property that has declined to zero rather than the volume of a gas. Obviously, no gas can exist at absolute zero, for a gas by definition consists of "flying" molecules which must have random kinetic energy in order to fly. Before reaching absolute zero, all gases become liquids or solids, which in turn lose random kinetic energy as the absolute temperature drops still further. Before reaching absolute zero these liquefied gases become solids—which still have a definite volume. All gases have been solidified in the laboratory. However, to solidify helium a pressure of at least 25 atmospheres is required.

DYNAMICAL (KINETIC) THEORY OF HEAT AND ITS IMPLICATIONS

We now have a new definition of temperature: *Temperature on the absolute scale is a measure of (or proportional to) the average kinetic energy of molecules.*[8] The emphasis is on the word *average*. This definition shows that it is meaningless to speak of the temperature of a single molecule, for at the instant of a collision its velocity, hence its kinetic energy, may be zero. Another molecule strikes it in the next instant, and is traveling at high speed. Moreover, we can never isolate a molecule, or even a few thousands of them. In a thimbleful of air the number of molecules is more than 100,000 times the population of the earth.

We also begin to understand why the collisions between molecules are elastic, i.e., why there is no friction involved, why they do not lose energy as a bouncing ball does, and so finally come to rest. If we accept

the evidence for our definition of temperature above, and if we also accept the concept of temperature as a measure of the intensity of heat, it automatically follows that heat is molecular motion. Note carefully that it is not molecular motion that produces heat, for *heat is molecular motion.*

Bear in mind that Joule did not set out to explain temperature. There is nothing in our four assumptions which, by itself, indicates that heat and temperature are at all involved. He *did* set out to develop a quantitative theory of heat based on molecular motions because his experiments would not let him think otherwise. But to convince other people, to forever destroy the caloric theory of heat, a theory had to be formulated that could not only explain all of the facts but that could also explain other seemingly unrelated facts, and that could by prediction, followed by experimentation and observation, lead us on to new knowledge. We will turn our attention to some of the seemingly unrelated facts that the kinetic-molecular theory can explain.

VERIFICATION AND EXTENSIONS OF THE KINETIC THEORY

1. Deviations from the Ideal Gas Law

Our reference to the gas laws as *ideal* laws that real gases do not always obey merits special comment. Since Galileo's time the scientist has invented, in his imagination only, frictionless pulleys and wheels, blocks sliding down frictionless inclined planes, air with no air resistance, weightless weights, and unstretchable ropes and strings. After analysis he then adds the real conditions and so modifies the ideal situations that exist only in his imagination

---

[8] Some authors list this as an additional assumption of the kinetic theory. It is more properly treated as a consequence of the theory and of the experimental facts.

to fit those actually encountered in nature. Thus, the gas laws have been formulated to apply to ideal gases that do not exist. Most gases are very nearly ideal when the temperature is high and the pressure low; they become less and less so as lower and lower temperatures and higher and higher pressures are attained. If our kinetic theory is valid, it should reveal a reason for such deviations, for a fruitful theory should not only account for the phenomena that it was designed to explain but should also be applicable to other phenomena in the same field that heretofore have been unexplainable.

We have already stated that Boyle's Law ($PV = K$) does not hold at low temperatures and high pressures. We idealized the concept of gas pressure in the assumption of the kinetic theory that states that gas molecules have no attractive forces for one another except at the instant of collision. This assumption holds for ideal gases—but there are no ideal gases. We feel justified in applying this assumption to real gases because gases free to expand do so without limit. This means that in such gases the attractive forces are ineffective. However, if we compress gases, we force the molecules closer together. Since the attractive forces are intermolecular in character, it follows that the closer the molecules are, the greater these forces should be. As they are forced closer and closer together, especially at low temperatures where their average velocity is relatively low, the attractive forces begin to produce detectable effects. When these forces become large enough the gas begins to liquefy or solidify. Well before this stage is reached, the departure of the real gas from Boyle's Law becomes considerable.

Since gases vary enormously in the temperatures and pressures at which they can be liquefied and solidified, the range of temperatures and pressures in which the deviation is slight varies enormously also. For nitrogen, which cannot be liquefied at a temperature above $-147°$ C, no matter how great the pressure, this range is far greater than for carbon dioxide, which can be liquefied at $31°$ C and 73 atmospheres.[9]   Under any circumstances gases obey Boyle's Law far more closely at high temperatures than at low because the molecules have a higher average kinetic energy. Their more rapid motions decrease the length of time the forces have to act as the molecules collide or move past one another.   These mutual attractions of molecules for one another are called van der Waals forces, after the man who first used them to explain the behavior of real gases.[10] Thus, the deviations from the ideal gas laws are explained.

2. Changes of Temperature upon Expansion and Compression of Gases

Our refrigerators attest to the fact that the expansion of a gas is a cooling process. Again we call upon the van der Waals intermolecular forces and the kinetic theory

[9] If the temperature is low enough any gas can be liquefied at atmospheric pressure except helium. This temperature varies from $100°$ C for steam to $-259°$ C for hydrogen. All can be liquefied at somewhat higher temperatures if pressure is applied, but for each there is a definite critical temperature above which the gas cannot be liquefied no matter what the pressure is. At room temperatures all of the common gases are above their critical temperatures, and all liquids below theirs. A substance in the gaseous state, but below its critical temperature, is called a vapor.

[10] Van der Waals formulated an improved gas law to apply to real gases by taking into consideration the fact that gas molecules occupy space and that they are not entirely free from each other's attractive forces.

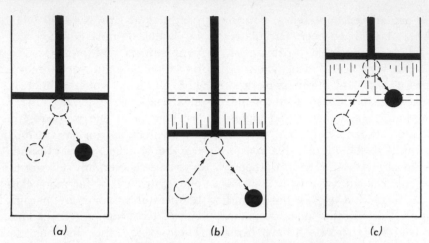

(a)   (b)   (c)

Fig. 14-5. Compression of a Gas as a Heating Process, and Its Expansion as a Cooling Process. Cross-sectional views of a piston in a cylinder are shown. In **(a)** the piston is motionless; gas molecules are rebounding without loss or gain of kinetic energy. The temperature is constant. In **(b)** the piston is descending, compressing the gas. The piston and the gas molecules are moving towards one another when they collide. The piston contributes kinetic energy to the molecules, thus increasing their average kinetic energy; the temperature rises. In **(c)** the piston is ascending, allowing the gas to expand. The gas molecules and the piston are moving in the same direction when they collide. Thus the colliding molecules impart some of their kinetic energy to the piston. Their average kinetic energy is decreased; the temperature drops.

for an explanation. A fixed quantity of gas expands by occupying more space, space commonly occupied by other gas molecules. In the process of expansion the distances between the molecules are increased. Thus, during expansion of a gas its molecules have to "push" other gas molecules out of the way, or perhaps a piston, as in Fig. 14-5.[11] In any case, energy has to be expended, energy that

comes from the gas molecules themselves. In doing the necessary work to expand, their average speeds, and hence their average kinetic energy, are reduced. Reduced kinetic energy means reduced temperature. Heat energy has been transformed into mechanical energy. Carrying our reasoning a bit further we might be led to believe that if a gas were allowed to expand into a vacuum, where there would be nothing to push out of the way, there would be no change in temperature. Experiment shows our reasoning to be wrong. For our explanation we turn to the van der Waals

[11] Note that all the piston has done when it descends is to make the molecules move faster, and that when it ascends it makes them move more slowly.

forces. Small as these intermolecular attractions are, some work must be done to overcome them, and the energy can come only from the molecules themselves; the resulting energy decrease shows up in reduced average velocity, hence in reduced average kinetic energy and lower temperature.[12]

It is an easily observed fact that compressing a gas heats it up; anyone who pumps up a bicycle tire by hand can observe it. What is the source of the heat? Obviously one has to do work to pump up the tire, i.e., energy has to be expended. If the Law of Conservation of Energy is valid, we should expect this energy to be transformed into some other energy. This is merely a case of transformation of mechanical energy into heat energy.

We can also explain this phenomenon in terms of temperature, i.e., in terms of average kinetic energies. From our kinetic-theory definition of temperature, we see that anything that increases the average kinetic energy will increase the temperature. Consider a bicycle pump (Fig. 14-5) before the piston is made to descend. Molecules are striking the piston and the walls of the cylinder with a certain average force, rebounding from them with a certain average speed. Now when the piston descends, its downward motion has the effect of increasing the speed of rebound, just as a baseball squarely striking a bat that is moving rapidly towards it rebounds from it with considerably greater

velocity than it will from a motionless bat. Thus, the average kinetic energy is increased—which means that the temperature is increased.

3. Evidence for Molecules: Brownian Movement

Despite the apparent success of our theory, we still might very well ask the questions, "Are molecules real? Is there any other evidence of molecular motion, evidence of a very different character?" A Scottish botanist, Robert Brown, an older contemporary of Joule, looking through a microscope at plant pollen in water, saw the tiny specks of pollen *incessantly* jiggling about. The smaller the specks the faster their seemingly random motion. The higher the temperature the faster the "dance." Put a drop of India ink in a dish of water and the black soot particles in the ink may be observed to "dance" if viewed with a high-power microscope. By means of a special device, smoke particles may be observed to do the same with a low-power microscope.

We are now sure that this irregular unceasing jiggling is due to chance bombardment of the tiny solid specks by water (or air in the case of smoke) molecules. The molecules cannot be anywhere near the size of the quivering solid particles or the latter would jump more violently. They cannot be infinitely small and infinitely numerous, for if they were the bombardment would be exactly equal on all sides, and we would see no movement. To jiggle, more must hit one side of a speck than the other—in the manner we visualize molecules with random motion would do. The paths of a single particle have been mapped (Fig. 14-6) by spotting its position every

[12] The thoughtful student will wonder how temperatures colder than any produced by natural processes are obtained, how temperatures close to absolute zero are produced. In general, they are obtained by allowing gases like hydrogen and helium to expand again and again and again, each expansion lowering the temperature somewhat.

two or three minutes, much as you may map the approximate path of a football player by spotting his position on the field at brief intervals.

Fig. 14-6. Brownian Movement. Map (enormously magnified) of the path of a tiny particle in water as it was buffeted first one way and then another by the molecules of water. Starting at A, it first moved to B and finally wound up at C. Positions were determined at intervals of two minutes by observations made with a high-powered microscope.

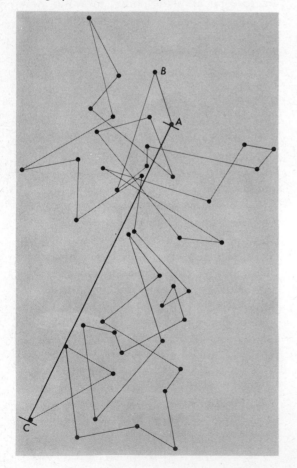

4. Explanation of Avogadro's Hypothesis

About 1813, Avogadro, an Italian chemist, attempted to explain Gay-Lussac's Law of Combining Volumes (p. 236) by assuming that equal volumes of gases under the same conditions of temperature and pressure contain the same number of particles.[13] Why should this be?

Consider equal volumes of two different gases, say hydrogen and oxygen, both at the same temperature and pressure. Boyle's Law states that

$$P_1V_1 = P_2V_2$$

if T is constant. Since $PV = \frac{2}{3}N \left(\frac{1}{2}mv^2\right)$ for both hydrogen and oxygen (Eq. 14-6),

$$\frac{2}{3}N_H\left(\frac{1}{2}mv^2\right)_H = \frac{2}{3}N_O\left(\frac{1}{2}mv^2\right)_O \quad \text{(Eq. 14-7)}$$

N_H and N_O are, respectively, the number of hydrogen and oxygen molecules in the given volumes. Canceling out the quantities that appear on both sides of the equation, $N_H = N_O$, i.e., the number of molecules in the two volumes is the same. Thus, Avogadro's hypothesis, originally presented as an educated guess, turns out to be correct according to kinetic theory; it is now called Avogadro's Law, a law that we will meet several times during the remainder of this book. The law, of course, applies to all gases, not just to hydrogen and oxygen.

5. The Speeds of Gases

From Eq. 14-7, if the temperatures of the two gases are the same, we get

$$\left(\frac{1}{2}mv^2\right)_H = \left(\frac{1}{2}mv^2\right)_O$$

[13] Particle is here meant to mean atom for the monatomic gases (the inert elemental gases) and molecule for the diatomic elemental gases and all gaseous compounds.

Canceling out the ½ and transposing,

$$\frac{v_H{}^2}{v_O{}^2} = \frac{m_O}{m_H}.$$

If we assign a value of 1 for $v_O{}^2$, and substitute the mass *ratios* for m_O and m_H (which are 16 to 1), we have

$$\frac{v_H{}^2}{1} = \frac{16}{1}$$

Whence

$$v_H{}^2 = 16, \quad \text{or} \quad v_H = \sqrt{16} = 4.$$

This means that for the average kinetic energies to be the same for the gases at the same temperature, the hydrogen molecules must be moving four times as fast as the oxygen molecules. If we are good at seeing relationships between numbers, we can see directly from Eq. 14-7 that the squares of the speeds of the molecules of any two gases are inversely proportional to the masses of the individual molecules. There are various ways of checking this. One is to time the rate of diffusion of two gases at the same temperature and pressure through the walls of a porous membrane, or to time the rate of escape of two gases through a single small opening.

The average speeds of gas molecules may be calculated from the equation, $PV = \frac{2}{3}N\left(\frac{mv^2}{2}\right)$. Solving for v^2, we have

$$V^2 = \frac{3PV}{Nm}.$$ For N we will use the number of molecules in 32 gm of oxygen. Thirty-two grams of oxygen will occupy 22,400 cm³ (22.4 liters) at 0° C and a pressure of one atmosphere, i.e., the mass of all of the molecules of oxygen in 22,400 cm³ is 32 gm. In the above equation Nm represents the total mass of the gas in the container (number of molecules, N, times the mass of one molecule). We can therefore set $Nm = 32$ in the case of oxygen. Since we must use cgs units, P must be stated in dynes. One atmosphere-10^6 dynes/cm².

Hence

$$V^2 = \frac{3PV}{Nm} = \frac{3 \times 10^6 \times 22,400}{32}$$

$$= 21.0 \times 10^8 \text{ cm}^2/\text{sec}^2.$$

$$V = \sqrt{21.0 \times 10^8 \text{ cm}^2/\text{sec}^2}$$

$$= 4.6 \times 10^4 \text{ cm/sec}$$

$$= 46,000 \text{ cm/sec}$$

$$= \text{a little over } \tfrac{1}{4} \text{ mile per second}$$

6. Changes of State

Evaporation of a liquid results in a change from the liquid to the vapor (see footnote 9). It is an easily observed fact that evaporation is a cooling process, for a breeze on a hot summer day always feels cool to us if we stand in it while we are perspiring. Kinetic theory gives us an explanation.

The molecules of the liquid, e.g., water, are in continuous motion. The temperature of the water is a measure of the average kinetic energy of its molecules. The term average presupposes that some of the molecules have less than average and some more than average kinetic energy. To evaporate, molecules must escape from the liquid, and to escape they must break through the barrier formed by the surface of the liquid.[14] To "crash" this barrier

[14] This barrier is created by a greater attractive downward than upward force (van der Waals force) on a molecule at the barrier. The molecule at the surface (Fig. 14-7) is attracted downward by the other molecules but there are none close enough above them to balance the downward forces. Thus the necessity for a greater than average velocity to "crash" the barrier.

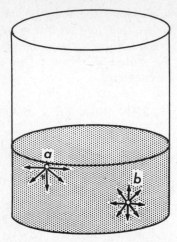

Fig. 14-7. Attraction by van der Waals forces on a molecule of water at the surface (as at *a*) are greater downward than upward, whereas deeper in the liquid (as at *b*) they are equal. Therefore, molecules approaching the surface must have greater than average kinetic energy to escape.

they must have more than average kinetic energy. Only the fastest moving molecules have enough. When they escape, the average kinetic energy is lowered, hence the temperature is lowered. Therefore, evapo-ration is a cooling process. Adding heat increases the average kinetic energy of the molecules so that more have the necessary energy to escape. These escaped molecules form the vapor of the liquid. In any system some of the escaped molecules are returned to the liquid as they are "bounced" back into the liquid through collision with air molecules.

If they escape into a confined space above the liquid, as in a well-corked bottle, the density of the escaped molecules in the region between the surface of the liquid and the cork will gradually increase until the saturation point is reached (Fig. 14-8). At this stage the number of molecules escaping equals the number returning to the liquid. A dynamic equilibrium has been reached. The vapor of a liquid exerts a pressure in the manner of any gas. *Its pressure at the equilibrium stage is called the vapor pressure of the liquid;* its value for a given liquid depends only on the temperature. For water vapor at room temperature it is about 24 mm of mercury.

Thus, if we heat water, its vapor pressure rises until, in an open system (Fig. 14-8*b*), it becomes equal to the atmospheric

Air Saturated with Vapor

(a)

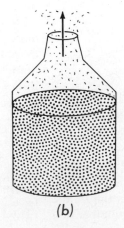

(b)

Fig. 14-8. Vapor Pressure. **(a)** In a confined system a dynamic equilibrium has been reached, i.e., as many molecules return as escape.

(b) In an open system some of the vapor escapes so that an equilibrium can never be established.

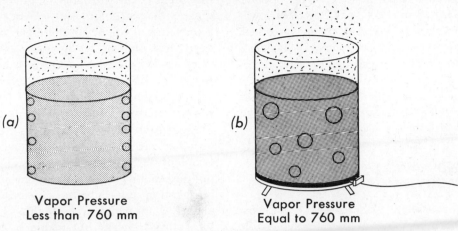

(a)

(b)

Vapor Pressure
Less than 760 mm

Vapor Pressure
Equal to 760 mm

Fig. 14-9. Boiling. (**a**) Blow the boiling point air bubbles rise along sides as the temperature rises and water evaporates only from surface.

(**b**) At boiling point water evaporates *also* from inside surfaces of bubbles of steam, thus increasing the size of the bubbles as they rise.

pressure, 760 mm on the average. Before the boiling point is reached, evaporation takes place only from the surface.[15] When the boiling point is reached, evaporation takes place *in growing vapor bubbles* as well, bubbles that rise to escape (Fig. 14-9b) and break when they reach the surface. When the boiling point is reached, the liquid can be heated to no higher temperature. More heat simply means more evaporation (see p. 209). The rate of evaporation increases with the temperature because energy is supplied to break the van der Waals forces (or other forces, in some cases) holding the molecules together. All of the molecules have sufficient energy to overcome the forces that tend to

hold them together in the liquid state. Thus, the molecules get farther and farther apart, up to a maximum which depends upon the density of the vapor or gas.

On the other hand, as the pressure of a gas is increased, the molecules get closer and closer together. Obviously the intermolecular forces are increased, thus tending to "pull" the molecules closer together. (This "pull" makes gases at high pressures more compressible than Boyle's Law predicts.) As the temperature of a gas is decreased, the average kinetic energy of its molecules is decreased; the pressure drops. When the temperature has dropped below its critical value, the gas will liquefy if the pressure is sufficiently great. This is the stage at which the average kinetic energy of the molecules has been so reduced by lowering the temperature that the van der Waals forces are able to hold the molecules in the quivering shapeless

[15] The formation of air bubbles on the bottom and sides of the container should not be mistaken for vapor bubbles (Fig. 14-9a). These are air bubbles coming out of solution as the temperature rises. Air, like all gases, becomes less soluble as the temperature rises.

mass that we call a liquid, except for some of the faster moving ones. At still lower temperatures the freezing point is reached, i.e., the average kinetic energy becomes low enough for the van der Waals [16] forces to be able to hold the molecules into a rigid mass in which molecular movements are confined to a very tiny region about each molecule.

SECOND LAW OF THERMODYNAMICS

We have seen (Chapter XIII) that heat and mechanical energy are interchangeable at a fixed rate of exchange, 4.18 joules/calorie. This is the First Law of Thermodynamics; its extension to include other types of energy transfer is known as the Law of Conservation of Energy. An intensive study of heat engines, e.g., steam engines and gasoline engines, has produced a Second Law of Thermodynamics: *Heat does not of its own accord flow from cold regions to hot regions.* This simple statement, at first glance, might not seem to warrant being called a law, but combined with the first law it provides the basic theory of heat engines, including modern steam turbines and rocket motors, of heat pumps, of refrigeration, and is useful in understanding many other phenomena, even in dealing with heat energy of the human body.

It means that no *net* mechanical energy can be obtained from a medium by cooling it below the temperature of its sur-

roundings. Any substance at a temperature greater than absolute zero possesses heat. The waters of the ocean therefore contain a great deal of heat. Why can we not use this heat for useful mechanical work? Assume for the moment that someone invented a device that could do just that. If heat energy were extracted from a part of the ocean waters, the temperature would drop, i.e., it would be cooled below the temperature of its surroundings. We can do the cooling all right, by means of a refrigerator, but only *by expending* more energy than we would obtain. There is thus no *net* energy obtainable by any device. During the nineteenth century as many people worked as hard trying to develop such a machine as worked on perpetual-motion machines. In fact, they have been called perpetual-motion machines of the second order.

In stating that heat never flows of its own accord from a cold body to a hot one, the Second Law of Thermodynamics implies that it will flow from a hot region to a cold one. This is perfectly obvious to everyone. However, it is not so obvious that it does this spontaneously without our being able to do anything about it. True, we can slow it down, by insulation of various kinds, including the clothing we wear. But we cannot stop it. In running any motor, steam, gasoline, rocket, or electric, considerable heat is dissipated to their surroundings. Our automobiles, e.g., must have a cooling system to carry away the heat produced. This energy is wasted, for ultimately it passes off into the atmosphere. Thus, heat energy can never be completely converted into any other type of energy, for in every conversion some heat is transferred from a hotter region to a colder one. Mechanical energy can, however, be com-

[16] The molecules of most solids other than those formed by the solidification of the true gases and the natural common liquids (water and the liquids contained in petroleum) are held together by interionic and interatomic forces rather than by van der Waals forces.

pletely transformed into heat by way of friction, e.g., in our pile-driver example (p. 158). In fact we might say that friction is heat, for the only thing that frictional forces, operating between two bodies in motion relative to each other, do is to increase molecular motions at the points of contact between the two bodies.

DEGRADATION OF ENERGY

We have learned that heat is the *random* motions of molecules. If in every transformation of energy some heat is produced and dissipated to its surroundings it follows that some ordered motion has been transformed into random disordered motion. Consider the ordered motions in a pile driver, or of a bullet striking a target, or of the pistons in the cylinders of an automobile. In all, a part of the order at least is transformed into disorder. It is apparent to us that all we have to do to produce disorder in our daily lives is to sit and do nothing, whereas it takes work to keep our homes in order. Order is thus an unnatural state in many respects and it takes work to maintain it. In the molecular world the natural tendency is to go from a state of order into a state of disorder. Thus, we explain the natural way for heat to flow, from hotter to cooler bodies. The hotter a body is, the higher the state of commotion among its molecules. This commotion is passed on from molecule to molecule. Thus, heat is conducted away from its source.

The result of all this is that all processes in nature proceed in the direction of increasing molecular disorder, i.e., in all of them some random molecular motion is produced. Thus, energy is being continuously degraded to heat energy, a portion of which

can never be converted back to any other form. Consider the sun and the stars, and the dissipation of their heat energies throughout space. The natural conclusion is that in time all matter in the universe will be at a uniform temperature. In such a universe there can be no transfer of heat from one body to another; no life would be possible. Our natural conclusion, as stated above, may not be the correct one; certainly we do not mean to prophesy a "heat death" for the universe as a whole. Our knowledge is nowhere near complete enough to make such a prophecy. At any rate, if such a "death" is to come, it is many billions of years in the future.

SUMMARY

Of the three states of matter gases are the easiest to study if we wish to learn about the nature of the ultimate particles of matter, for in them the molecules are separate, move about independently, and in large groups exhibit characteristics that can be observed and measured. From these observations and measurements a molecular-kinetic theory, or simply a kinetic theory, of gases has been formulated. Each of the assumptions explains a number of observations, and various combinations of them explain still more observations.

The theory was initiated by Bernoulli, a considerably younger contemporary of Newton. Additions and revisions were made by Joule, Clausius, Maxwell, Boltzmann, and others more than a century later. To enable the gas laws to be derived from the theory, a mechanical model which made use of Newton's laws of mechanics was conceived, a model in which the completely random motion of the molecules was emphasized. From it the equation $PV = \frac{2}{3}N \times (mv^2/2)$ was derived. Since $\frac{2}{3}N$ is a constant for any fixed quantity of gas at the same temperature and pressure, we may write $PV = (Kmv^2/2)$. From the General Gas Law (Eq. 12-8), and derived from experiment, we have $PV = KT$. Thus, T must be related to $mv^2/2$. Theory and experiment are shown to be in accord if we conclude that T (on the Kelvin scale) is proportional to the average kinetic energy of the molecules of a gas.

Various anomalies vanish if we assume that molecules composed of two or more atoms may have motions denied single-atom molecules (like the inert gases), and that only one of them, that of translation, is recorded on the thermometer—because only it is random, only it has been considered in the mechanical model. From the above analysis we see that it is the average kinetic energy that declines towards zero as $0°$ K is approached. Thus, meaning is given to the term *absolute zero;* we see why there has to be a fixed lower limit for temperature.

It now becomes clear that random molecular motion is heat—or we might say that this form of heat is the disorderly motions of molecules, never the orderly motions such as the vibrational and rotational. However, a theory of heat, if it is to be widely accepted, must be fruitful, i.e., it must be able to explain other observations some of which, superficially at least, may seem to be unrelated, which in turn must lead to new concepts, etc. Some of the fruits of the theory are explanations for:

1. Deviations from the ideal gas laws.
2. The changes in temperature due to expansion and compression of gases, i.e., why expansion of a gas is a cooling process and compression a heating process.
3. The Brownian movement.
4. Avogadro's Law.
5. The varying speeds of different gases at the same temperature and their rates of diffusion.
6. Evaporation as a cooling process.

7. The relationship of vapor pressure to boiling point.
8. The reason for latent heats of fusion and vaporization.
9. The Second Law of Thermodynamics.
10. The relationship between friction and heat.
11. The concept of the degradation of energy.

Consideration of the last three items leads to the conclusion that all processes in nature proceed in the direction of increasing molecular disorder. The logical, but by no means certain, conclusion is that ultimately the whole universe will be at a uniform temperature with no heat transfer possible.

EXERCISES

I. TERMS AND CONCEPTS

Molecule	Kinetic theory of heat
Elastic collision	Assumptions of the
Vapor pressure	kinetic-molecular
Boiling point	theory
Molecular motion	Van der Waals forces
translational	Second Law of Thermodynamics
vibrational	Degradation of
rotational	energy
Critical temperature	

II. PROBLEMS

1. If matter were continuous, could it have structure?

2. State the assumptions of the kinetic theory and cite at least one item of evidence from everyday experience to support each.

3. What is meant by an elastic collision? Why *must* we assume that collisions between individual molecules of gases are perfectly elastic?

4. Who advanced the first kinetic theory of gases? About when?

5. How does kinetic theory explain the fact that gases exert pressure on every surface with which they come in contact?

6. What happens when heat is added to a gas in a closed container? In an open system like our atmosphere? How is its rise in temperature explained? What happens when a gas is cooled?

7. What distinction can you make between a gas and a vapor?

8. How do you explain the fact that clothes will dry eventually even while frozen?

9. What type of molecular motion did the mechanical model of the kinetic theory take into account? Explain what is meant by it.

10. What three types of motion may polyatomic molecules have? Which is recorded as temperature on a thermometer? How do we know this?

11. How have we defined a molecule in this section?

12. What conclusion is reached from the two proportionalities, $PV \propto T$ (derived from the experimental work of Boyle and Charles), and $PV \propto mv^2/2$, where $mv^2/2$ is taken as the average kinetic energy of gas molecules (derived from the theoretical mechanical model)?

13. What is heat according to our kinetic theory? What is temperature?

14. What meaning is given to $0°$ on the absolute or Kelvin scale by the kinetic theory?

15. What is meant by the critical temperature of a gas? What gas is most difficult to liquefy? Can you suggest a reason?

16. Helium can be liquefied only at temperatures below $-272°$ C and at 25 atmospheres of pressure. What inference can you make about the attractive forces between its molecules?

17. What is meant by the vapor pressure of a liquid? What is the vapor pressure of water at $100°$ C?

18. How is the boiling point of a liquid defined?

19. On a mountain top 12,000 ft high it is impossible to cook dried beans in an open container no matter how long you boil them. Why?

20. Why does the use of a pressure cooker reduce the cooking time?

21. Why can you not heat a pan of water on the stove higher than the boiling point?

22. At a temperature a bit above $0°$ C, water can be made to freeze while it is boiling. This is done by evacuating the container to a very low pressure, and pumping the vapor away as fast as it forms. Explain.

23. Explain why evaporation is a cooling process.

24. Why does water evaporate faster in a warm room than in a cold one?

25. Why do you feel cooler sitting in the breeze from an electric fan than elsewhere on a hot summer day?

26. Why does alcohol at room temperature feel cooler to the touch than does water at the same temperature?

27. If you put a very shallow dish of water in a pan of ether and blow air over it by means of an electric fan, the water will freeze. Explain.

28. You have samples of nitrogen, chlorine, fluorine, and oxygen, all at the same temperature. Are the molecules in each sample moving with the same average speeds, or are their average speeds different? Explain.

29. The mass ratio of SO_2 (sulfur dioxide) and H_2 (hydrogen) molecules is 64 to 2. Samples of both gases are at the same temperature. What are the numerical relative average speeds of the molecules of the two gases?

30. Explain why expansion of a gas is a cooling process. Do the same for compression of a gas as a heating process.

31. How can you eliminate the possibility that the heat produced in pumping up a bicycle tire (p. 207) is not due to friction within the pump itself?

32. Students commonly ascribe the heating effect due to compression of a gas to the increased collision rate between molecules. This violates one of the assumptions of the kinetic theory. Which? Prove by experiment that the heating effect cannot be produced this way by using two containers of gas on a table, one with a pressure P, the other with a pressure $2P$.

33. By what means does an electric refrigerator produce its low temperature?

34. From what you know of ether, would you say the magnitude of the van der Waals forces operating to hold its molecules together were less or greater than those of water? Justify your answer.

35. The meniscus of some liquids, e.g., water, in a narrow glass tube is concave, and in others, e.g., mercury, it is convex. Explain both cases.

36. Explain the Brownian movement and state its significance.

37. On a sweltering summer day you decide to try to keep cool by closing the doors and windows of your kitchen and leaving the refrigerator door open. Would this be effective in reducing the average temperature in your kitchen, assuming, of course, that you are doing no cooking? Explain why or why not.

38. The molecules of a gas are, statistically speaking, in perpetual motion. Can this fact be reconciled with the statement that perpetual-motion machines are impossible? Explain.

39. The Second Law of Thermodynamics results from a common observation that we all have made at one time or another. What is it?

40. Why can heat energy not be completely converted to mechanical energy?

41. Mechanical energy can be completely converted to heat energy under certain circumstances? Give an example.

42. In some gambling houses a group of friends may play poker all by themselves, the proprietor taking a specified amount out of every pot (called his cut) for allowing them to play in his establishment. Suppose the players all start with a specified amount of money. If they play *long enough*, the proprietor will have all the money, provided no new money comes into the game. In a similar way we may start with a specified quantity of mechanical energy which we put through a series of transformations from one type to another. If we do this long enough, what will have happened to our energy, and why?

43. Arrange the following men in proper order with respect to time. State one thing for which each is remembered with respect to heat or temperature or kinetic theory: Newton, Joule, Boyle, Black, Kelvin, Charles, Rumford.

CHAPTER XV

From Alchemy to Chemistry

I would . . . establish the conviction that Chemistry, as an independent science, offers one of the most powerful means towards the attainment of a higher mental cultivation; that the study of Chemistry is profitable, not only inasmuch as it promotes the material interests of mankind, but also because it furnishes us with insight into those wonders of creation which immediately surround us, and with which our existence, life and development, are most closely connected.

—JUSTUS VON LIEBIG (*1851*)

INTRODUCTION

In the preceding chapter we have seen that all matter, whether gaseous, liquid, or solid, consists of enormous numbers of molecules. So far our attention has been focused only on the general characteristics of the molecules. We paid particular attention to the gaseous state of matter, because in this state the molecules are separated by comparatively large distances so that the physical behavior of a single molecule is more or less completely independent of the great mass of the other molecules. This is, of course, not the case in liquids and solids, and is less true in solids than in liquids. We have seen that the degree of independence of the molecules is a func-

tion of the temperature, which in turn is a measure of the average kinetic energy of the molecules. The phenomena of melting and boiling give rise to changes in the arrangements of the molecules with respect to one another as their average kinetic energy increases. Throughout these changes the molecules remain intact.

In our endeavor to understand more about the nature and the properties of the various kinds of matter which make up our solar system in general, and our earth in particular, we now turn to another avenue of investigation. This investigation will result in our delving into the composition of the molecules themselves. In a general way we already know that these molecules consist of smaller units called atoms. We shall learn something of the evidence for the existence of these atoms, some of their physical characteristics, and something about the way they combine to form molecules.

VIEWS OF THE ANCIENT GREEKS

We have seen that Pythagoras, and later Aristotle, believed that all matter consisted of four elements—earth, water, air, and fire—a solid, a liquid, a gas, and an element more intangible than the gases. Empedocles (*ca.* 450 B.C.) believed that by uniting these four elements in various proportions he could explain all of the endless kinds of substances known to man.

Along with the composition of matter the Greeks were concerned about its structure. Their concern was limited largely to its continuity. Is matter continuous, i.e., can it be subdivided endlessly without limit as can a line, or is it discontinuous, i.e., composed of particles too small to be discernible with the eye, and incapable of further subdivision? The latter view was held by Democritus, who gave us the word "atom." The atoms of Democritus were eternal, all composed of the same substance, and all in constant motion. The differences in properties were due to differences in size, shape, and position with respect to one another. Aristotle, on the other hand, rejecting the views of Democritus, believed that matter was continuous, capable of infinite subdivision.

RISE OF THE ALCHEMISTS

From the views of Democritus came the conviction that some forms of matter could be turned into other forms by altering the proportions of these four elements. Thus arose the science of alchemy, a science that was in the beginning no different from chemistry. Alchemy seems to have originated among the Greeks in Alexandria about the beginning of the Christian era. Its purposes seem to have been twofold, one scientific, i.e., an investigation into the nature of matter, and one practical, i.e., to supply cheap imitations of expensive materials such as jewelry and fine dyes. During the Dark Ages and continuing into the Renaissance, alchemy consisted in large part of a search for the "philosopher's stone," an elixir or quintessence (a fifth element) which was supposed to be capable of turning the baser metals into gold, and of curing all human ills, thus imparting everlasting life. It was supposed to be the stuff of which the heavenly bodies were made.

In the sixteenth century Paracelsus, a Swiss doctor, attempted to give a new direction—and a new respectability—to alchemy by declaring that its true purpose should be the preparation of medicines. The term chemistry gradually came to be applied, in part at least, to lend respectability to a newly developing science whose objectives were quite different from those of the alchemy of the time.

The practice of alchemy persisted into the early 1700's—and even later by charlatans. Although alchemy had started off as a legitimate investigation into the properties of matter, and had been continued in part as such by a few of the alchemists for nearly two thousands of years, it had contributed comparatively little to the understanding of matter. Nevertheless, what it had to contribute was important, for it advanced the science of chemistry by the better part of a century. Among its contributions were the development and refinement of many experimental techniques, several new elements (phosphorus, antimony, bismuth, zinc), several acids, alcohol, and a large number of salts.

The paucity of these contributions, considering the length of time and the great numbers of practitioners involved, is unquestionably due to the falseness of their basic underlying assumptions. Matter does not consist of four material elements plus a fifth mysterious, imponderable one. Thus, their conceptual scheme was not fruitful; it could lead them only to a dead end. This acceptance of, and adherence to, a wrong hypothesis acted as a stifling influence to further development of their science. Not until this wrong hypothesis was discarded was further progress into the understanding of the nature of matter possible.

BOYLE AND THE TRANSITION FROM ALCHEMY TO CHEMISTRY

The transition from the old alchemist view to that of modern chemistry was begun (but not completed) by Robert Boyle. Boyle, an older contemporary of Newton, was the first truly great chemist, although he is better known for some of his work in physics, notably with respect to the law that bears his name (p. 182).

He started out as an alchemist, and he never did rid himself of the belief that the baser metals could be turned into gold. Nevertheless he soon rejected the Aristotelian concept of four elements, and eventually arrived at a definition of an element that is still usable, even if not in accord with modern knowledge of the nuclei of atoms. His definition, the first ever made, was that *elements are simple bodies of matter which cannot be resolved into other bodies of matter, and of which all other bodies of matter are composed.* The trouble with this definition is that it is not operational, for Boyle had no way of knowing which substances satisfied his definition and which did not. To be operational a definition of an element should describe some operation for detecting the element. Boyle recognized the difficulty but there was little that could be done about it at the time.

It was not until about a hundred years later that Lavoisier (*ca.* 1776), the great Frenchman who has been called the father of modern chemistry, defined an element as *any substance not known to be decomposable.* This caused the list of elements to be revised from time to time as new knowledge was obtained. Nevertheless, within a century after Lavoisier the list became much the same as it is today. Today we substitute "cannot be by chemical means" for Lavoisier's "not known to be" because of a far greater confidence in our modern operations.

Boyle was one of that group of illustrious men which was responsible for the seventeenth century being called the century of genius. Others were Kepler, Galileo, Huygens, Newton, Pascal, Descartes, and Leibnitz. These men helped to emancipate natural science from philosophy; they did not believe that because a phenomenon could be expressed quantitatively in mathematical terms, it could be explained philosophically as well. By believing this they became free to accept facts as facts even if they could not be incorporated into a general scheme of knowledge. They came to regard the acquisition of knowledge as an end in itself. It is not to be supposed, however, that all of these men were equally free from the symbol-seeking mysticism that had pervaded Western Europe for centuries. Beginning with Kepler, however, the tendency to formulate physical laws first and to look for the symbolism afterwards became more and more dominant, until late in the eighteenth century we see little or no tendency for philosophical speculation to precede factual analysis.

MODERN CLASSIFICATION OF MATTER

Most matter with which we are in everyday contact is complex, far more complex than most of us realize. The air we breathe is a mixture of at least five gases, the water we drink is pure only in the health sense, the food we eat is unbelievably complex. Steel, largely composed of iron, is different from iron because of the various other substances that have been added during its manufacture to give it special qualities. Gasoline and milk are both mixtures of up to a dozen different substances. Pure substances in nature are almost nonexistent. Even artificially made ones are rare; familiar ones are distilled water, cane sugar, and the copper used in electric wires. It is not surprising that chemistry as a true science remained so long in the embryonic state.

The concept of a pure substance is an important one. Pure substances exhibit constant composition, i.e., they are so homogenous that any small part of each has the same composition as does every other part, *even down to molecular size.* Some mixtures exhibit constant composition down to particles of microscopic size but fail when the division is carried down to particles of molecular size. Such homogeneous mixtures are called solutions. Air is a mixture of several gases in mutual solution with one another, gasoline is a mixture of about a dozen liquids in mutual solution with one another, brass is a solution of copper and zinc, brine is a solution of salt (a solid) in water (a liquid), and soda pop is a solution of a gas (CO_2) in water. None of these solutions can be called pure substances because their compositions are not constant; each has a wide range of possible compositions. Examples of heterogeneous mixtures are rocks,[1] soil, whole milk, blood, and smoke.

Pure substances are divided into elements (if they cannot be further subdivided[2]) and compounds (if they can be further subdivided). Sugar, e.g., is a compound, for it can be separated into carbon and water if it is heated to a high enough temperature. Carbon cannot be further subdivided and so it is an element. By the

process of electrolysis the water can be broken down into hydrogen and oxygen, and so is a compound. Hydrogen and oxygen cannot be further subdivided, and so are elements.

We may summarize the classification of the various kinds of matter as follows:

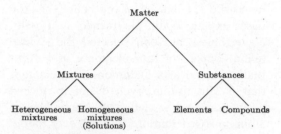

PROPERTIES OF MATTER

In general, any discussion of properties at this stage of your knowledge is largely confined to those of elements and compounds. The properties of matter pertinent to our discussion are either physical or chemical, and if we limit the meaning of these terms to those ordinarily given to them by the chemist, we find that it is usually not meaningful to talk of the physical and chemical properties of heterogeneous mixtures. Solutions do have significant properties but they are beyond the scope of the present discussion.

The physical properties, in contrast to the chemical properties, are those we can detect with our senses in one way or another. They are color, luster, smell, taste, feel, shape of the particles of which it is made, hardness, density, cleavage or fracture (how a specimen breaks), melting points, boiling points, etc. They are properties that do not change while being observed. Not all are meaningful with every substance. Chemical properties are those that describe the capacity of a sub-

---

[1] Rocks containing only one mineral and therefore homogeneous exist in small pieces, but rocks in the mass as those found in nature are always heterogeneous to some degree. Most are completely so.

[2] In this section whenever we say that a substance cannot be further subdivided we always mean by chemical means.

stance for reacting with other substances. They are properties that do change while being observed.[3] They cannot be determined by a physical examination of a substance or by a simple experiment that any student can perform.

Associated with physical and chemical properties are the terms *physical change* and *chemical change*. A change from a liquid to a solid or a gas, or a change in shape due to a deforming force of some kind are physical changes. Chemical change involves chemical reaction, during which elements or compounds combine to form other compounds with totally different sets of physical properties, or the original compounds are broken up into elements or other compounds. The substances that react are called the *reactants* and those produced are called the *products*. The burning of any substance is the most obvious example. The transformation of the food we eat to the flesh, blood, and bone of your bodies is another. The distinctions between physical change and chemical change are not always clear cut.

The separation of heterogeneous mixtures into components can usually be accomplished fairly easily by some mechanical process, such as by sifting if the component particles differ consistently in size or shape; by solution if only one component is soluble, e.g., sand and sugar; by a magnet if only one component is attracted by a magnet; by flotation if their densities are appreciably different; by melting if their melting points are far enough apart, etc. Other methods applicable to solutions are evaporation of the solvent if one of the

components is a solid, distillation if two or more liquids are present, boiling in the case of a gas dissolved in a liquid, taking advantage in the difference of rate of diffusion in cases of gases dissolved in gases, or in the differences in temperature and pressure at which gases may be liquefied. None of the above are effective in separating the elements that make up a compound from one another. Chemical changes must take place in order to do that.

BEGINNINGS OF CHEMISTRY

Some have called Robert Boyle the father of chemistry. Certainly he was the first to break away from the four-element concept [4] of Aristotle, and the first to base his concepts of the fundamental nature of matter on the experimental rather than on the metaphysical. However, he never became emancipated from all of the ways of thinking of the alchemist, and so is another example of the observation that a man can advance only a limited distance ahead of the mental climate of the time in which he lives. The great Newton appears to have spent more time on alchemy and chemistry than he did on the researches for which he will forever be remembered. He wrote no book concerning his chemical researches, so the record of his work is incomplete. It is known, however, that he accepted the atomistic view of Democritus and that he

---

[3] An example is the measurement of the temperature at which oxygen will unite with hydrogen to form water.

[4] A Belgian, van Helmont (*ca.* 1600), coined the word "gas," and reduced the four elements to one. This conclusion was based on the fact that he weighed a willow tree, planted it in a weighed amount of soil in a tub. For five years he carefully watered it. At the end of that time he carefully separated it from the soil and weighed both again. The soil weighed only 2 oz less, but the tree had gained 164 lb—just by adding water alone. His one element was therefore water.

rejected the four-element concept of Aristotle. It is also clear that he showed greater insight into the nature of matter than did other chemists of the time (with the possible exception of Boyle). He made no striking discoveries, however.

Others have called Antoine Lavoisier the father of modern chemistry, an appellation that, viewed from many angles, he justly deserves. He did most of his work between the American and the French revolutions. Lavoisier's contribution was that he changed chemistry from a qualitative science to a quantitative science, thus enabling progress to be made in understanding the fundamental nature of matter.

In the hundred years between Boyle and Lavoisier probably the most important development was the formulation of the phlogiston theory (the principle of fire) by Stahl of Germany from ideas advanced by Beccher.[5] Man's interest in the process of burning probably dates back to his discovery of fire. His failure to understand it persisted until near the end of the eighteenth century. This failure undoubtedly presented an insurmountable obstacle to real progress in the science, for no concept of what a chemical reaction consisted of could prevail unless it explained the process of burning. The phlogiston theory was a first step in this direction.

The formation of ashes from the burning of wood and paper, the soft powders that resulted when metals were long heated to high temperatures in air, the fact that these powders became metals again when heated with charcoal, and other similar phenomena could not be imagined to take place by Stahl and Beccher without the addition or subtraction of some substance.

[5] Johann Joachim Beccher, or Becher.

Therefore they postulated the existence of an invisible substance that all combustible substances possessed. They named it phlogiston, supposing it to be an element. Their theory was very simple: During combustion phlogiston escapes; air must be present to absorb phlogiston but its capacity to absorb phlogiston is limited.

While this theory dominated the world of chemistry for about fifty years, no one ever obtained any experimental or observational evidence of its physical properties. It came to be known as an *imponderable*, i.e., a substance whose physical properties are incapable of being detected by man's senses, and which can have apparently contradictory properties at the same time. Thus, on some occasions it exhibited weight, on others it appeared to be weightless, and on still others it was supposed to have negative weight. Looking backward we may wonder how such a concept could survive among intelligent men. We must not forget the mental climate of the time; the significance of quantitative measurements had not been impressed upon the chemists, although the work of Galileo and Newton had impressed it upon the physicists. Moreover, it explained many phenomena that had long gone without explanation. It was better than no theory of combustion, and is an example of the observation that truth is more likely to come out of error than it is out of a void.

The theory could explain: Why most combustibles lose weight on burning (they lose phlogiston); why a flame goes out in an enclosed space (the air becomes saturated with phlogiston); why charcoal leaves so little residue on burning (it is nearly pure phlogiston); why a mouse dies in an enclosed space (mouse saturates the air with phlogiston from his lungs); why some calxes (metallic oxides) turn to metal when heated with charcoal (phlogiston from charcoal is restored to calx).

The theory foundered eventually over the changes in weight that occur when certain metals are heated or burned in air to form calxes. The calx-forming process is called calcination. It differs from combustion in that no gas is given off in the process as it is in combustion. The modern term for calx is *oxide*. The phlogistonists believed that the calx was the element, and the metal the compound, a compound of calx and phlogiston. This belief was essential to the theory, for when a metal burned, the calx was observed to form. Consider magnesium, a metal not known at the time. It will burn with an intensely white light, forming the white powder, magnesium oxide (a calx). The disconcerting thing to a would-be phlogistonist is that the magnesium calx weighs more than the metal. The theory had to explain such observations if it was to survive, and so a new postulate was put forth.

Phlogiston that escapes from metals has negative weight, whereas that which escapes in normal combustion has positive weight. The addition of a special postulate to a theory to explain one lone troublesome fact is usually an indication that the theory is not going to be fruitful. This is particularly true if the postulate strains the credulity of some of its supporters. Eventually Lavoisier was able to prove that the products of combustion always weighed more than what was burned, but he was unable to identify the substance that caused the added weight.[6]

Lavoisier early in his career became interested in the quantitative aspects of chemistry. His great intellect would not allow him to accept the phlogiston theory. He knew that condemnation of it would do no good; he had to have a better theory to replace it. He quickly realized that the best attack was by means of weighing both the reactants and the products of chemical reactions. To this end he had more accurate balances made than had ever been made before.[7] His best could detect changes in weight as small as 0.0005 gm, roughly $\frac{1}{100}$ the weight of a drop of water.

Most notable of the experiments that Lavoisier did were three using tin. The first consisted of simply heating a weighed quantity of tin in the open air for a time and then reweighing it. He found that the tin gained weight, thus verifying the results obtained by others. This was not truly quantitative, however.

In the second he carefully weighed a quantity of tin, placed it on a block of wood which he floated in a shallow pan of water. He then placed a bell jar over the block, allowing the jar to rest almost on the bottom of the pan of water (Fig. 15-1). This trapped a specific quantity of air in the bell jar and prevented more air from entering. Next he heated the tin by focusing the sun's rays on it by a lens. As the calx formed, the water rose in the jar. He con-

---

[6] Antoine Lavoisier (1743–1794) carried on his scientific work as an avocation. The scope of his interests both in fundamental and applied science staggers the imagination. He carried on his work in chemistry at the same time that he worked for the local and national governments, often combining them to the advantage of France. He often used his own money to advance the public interests. Nevertheless he was beheaded in 1794 (about one hundred years after the death of Boyle) during the excesses of the Revolution, because he had once been a collector of the royal taxes. An appeal for clemency was denied with the comment, "The Republic has no need of savants."

[7] See Proust-Berthollet controversy, p. 229.

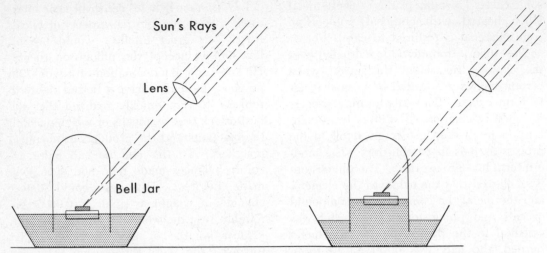

Fig. 15-1. Lavoisier's Experiment with Tin. The tin, heated by focusing the rays of the sun on it, combined with oxygen in the bell jar, thus decreasing the air pressure in the jar. As a result water rose in it until the air pressure outside and inside were equal. This proved that something from the air combined with tin.

tinued to heat it until the water stopped rising. He carefully noted how far the water had risen so that he could calculate how much the volume of air had decreased. This decrease turned out to be about one-fifth of the original volume. He then weighed the calx to get the increase in weight.

In his third experiment he placed a quantity of tin in a flask, tightly sealed it and then weighed it. He then heated it strongly until no more tin changed to calx. He weighed the still sealed flask again, and found no change. Then he carefully removed the seal, and observed that air rushed in. Using the same seal he now sealed the flask again and once more weighed it. He found that the flask had increased in weight. He concluded that the increase was due to the weight of the air that had rushed in when he first

broke the seal, and was equal to the weight of air used to form the calx. Lavoisier had now established that some "atmospheric principle" had been removed from the atmosphere during combustion and calcination but he had not identified the "principle."

Meanwhile Joseph Priestley of England had been experimenting with various kinds of "airs," the name then used for gases. Investigation of airs was begun by van Helmont and Boyle but there was little understanding of them until the time of Lavoisier.[8] Priestley had discovered a new

[8] Stephan Hales of England had investigated hydrogen, carbon monoxide, carbon dioxide, marsh gas, sulfur dioxide, and others but had concluded that they were all air that had been contaminated. He prepared oxygen in 1729. Borch had prepared it as early as 1678. Van Helmont had discovered carbon dioxide in 1640. All of these observations and discoveries were forgotten; they

gas by strongly heating the red calx of mercury (mercuric oxide) and collecting the released gas under water (Fig. 15-2). He found that it supported combustion far better than ordinary air. He thought this was due to the fact that it was completely devoid of phlogiston, and so he named it "dephlogisticated air." He found, also, that a mouse lived in it in an enclosed space longer than in ordinary air. Lavoisier, on hearing of the properties of the new air, immediately suspected that it was the atmospheric principle that he was searching for. As soon as he learned how Priestley obtained it, he hastened to repeat the experiment. Now mercury can be heated in air at moderate temperatures to form a calx, the red oxide of mercury. If the calx

had to be made over again and their significances reinterpreted. Air was still believed to be the only gaseous element up to and beyond the time that Joseph Black discovered what he called "fixed air," and which we now call carbon dioxide.

is now more strongly heated, it breaks down to give us the metal again:

Mercury metal + air + heat

→ Red calx of mercury

Red calx + strong heat

+ dephlogisticated air → Mercury metal

Lavoisier now made the truly quantitative experiment that spelled doom for the phlogiston theory. Using a set-up such as that in Fig. 15-3, he heated 4 oz of mercury to near the boiling point with 50 cu in. of air in a glass retort for 12 days. As the red calx was formed, the volume of air became less and less, allowing the water to rise in the cylinder. When the water ceased to rise, presumably because no more calx was forming, the heating was stopped.[9] The remaining mercury and the calx were

[9] Note that *so far* this experiment is a repetition of his second experiment with tin.

Fig. 15-2. Priestley's Discovery of Oxygen (called dephlogisticated air by him). He collected the gas under water. As the gas evolves, water is displaced in the cylinder. Note that this was not a quantitative experiment as were those of Lavoisier.

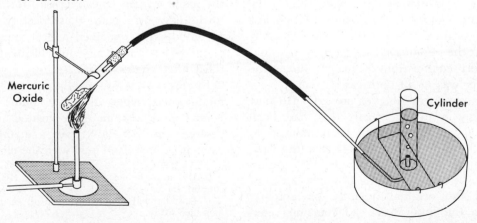

Mercuric Oxide

Cylinder

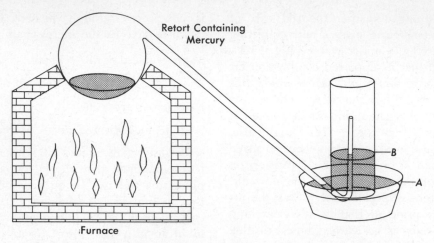

Fig. 15-3. Lavoisier's 12-day Experiment. Mercury was heated in contact with 50 cc of air. Part of the air combined with the mercury to form a calx. At the start the water level was at A, after heating it was at B. The volume of air above the water was reduced by 42 cu in.

weighed and compared with the weight of the mercury originally put in the retort. The increase was 3.5 grains. (There are about 156 grains in a gram.) Next he determined the loss in weight of the air in his apparatus. He found it to be also 3.5 grains. The loss of weight of the air equaled the increase of weight due to the formation of calx; thus, there was no loss of mass during the experiment. He now tested the remaining "air" to see if it would support combustion or sustain life. The answer was *no* in both cases.

His case was not yet proved. He now strongly heated the calx that had been formed until it had all been reduced to metallic mercury. He collected the "air" given off and found it to weigh $3\frac{1}{2}$ grains. Thus, he recovered the original "air" lost —and the original quantity of mercury. Again the total mass had remained con-

stant. He now tested this recovered "air" and found that it supported combustion and sustained life much more effectively than ordinary air. Thus Priestley's new "air" was proved to be the atmospheric principle responsible for combustion, calcination, and respiration. Lavoisier gave the name *oxygen* (meaning acid-former) [10] to the new air, a name that Priestley never accepted. He remained a firm supporter of the phlogiston theory until his death (in the United States).

In this way it was finally proved that a metal plus oxygen give rise to an oxide (calx), and that an oxide heated in the presence of charcoal [11] gave a metal plus oxygen (which combined with the charcoal

[10] Also a misnomer, for some acids, HCl, e.g., contain no oxygen.
[11] The charcoal is not needed in all cases, e.g., mercuric oxide.

to form carbon monoxide or carbon dioxide). Lavoisier continued his experiments which eventually led him to the conclusion that combustion and respiration were essentially alike, the difference being essentially in their rates.

LAW OF CONSERVATION OF MASS

Lavoisier's genius lay not only in his ability to plan and execute experiments, but also in his ability to grasp the all-important significance of them. Here we have two men, Priestley and Lavoisier, performing the same experiment but drawing different conclusions. Those of Priestley led only to a dead end, while those of Lavoisier led (to quote Galileo) to "wonderful new knowledge." Fortified by his conclusions from the above experiment, he went on to experiment with other reactions, always carefully weighing the reactants and the products. By the unanswerable evidence of the balance he showed that the total weight of all of the reaction products is exactly equal to the total weight of all of the reactants from which the reaction products were formed.

Newton's success in mechanics was based on his assumption that mass remained constant, and he proved that weight, while a different conception than mass, was always proportional to mass. Here we have Lavoisier showing *there is no loss of mass during chemical change.* This principle, now firmly established insofar as normal chemical reactions are concerned, is called the *Law of Conservation of Mass.* This is one of the great fundamental laws of nature. It is the bulwark of every analytical chemist, who it may be said, are testing it

almost every day in chemical laboratories all over the world.[12]

| | SUMMARY | |

With this chapter we start an investigation of a different sort into the nature of matter. In order to understand better our present views, the views of the ancients are presented. Most influential was Aristotle's concept of all matter consisting of earth, air, fire, and water. Democritus believed that matter was composed of atoms but Aristotle believed it to be continuous. Alchemy arose because of a legitimate interest in the nature of matter, and, in the hands of a few, remained that way until it was replaced by the science of chemistry. More generally, alchemy was practiced by charlatans whose chief interests were in finding cheap imitations of expensive materials, and in the discovery of the philosopher's stone, an imagined fifth element supposed to be capable of changing base metals into gold, and of imparting everlasting life.

With the passing of the belief in Aristotle's elements, and with Boyle's new definition of an element, the classification of matter could begin. The distinctions between physical and chemical properties, and between physical and chemical changes acquired a significance that had heretofore been lacking. Theories to explain chemical phenomena were now possible, the first of which was the phlogiston theory to explain ordinary combustion and calcination. It succeeded for a time, but its inability to account for calcination when subjected to the unanswerable evidence of Lavoisier's balance

[12] Let it not be said that atomic fission and fusion have invalidated this law so far as the usual chemical reactions are concerned. Almost every law has its limits; the limits of this one stop short of reactions involving the nuclei of atoms.

eventually spelled its death, its place being taken by the oxygen theory. Further investigation into combustion in which all reactants and products were carefully collected and weighed, and extended to include other types of reactions led to the Law of Conservation of Mass. Burning and respiration were shown to be essentially alike, the difference being in their rates.

EXERCISES

I. TERMS AND CONCEPTS

Alchemy	Physical change
Element	Chemical change
Compound	Reactant
Substance	Product
Mixture	Phlogiston theory of com-
Solution	bustion
Calx	Oxygen theory of combus-
"Air"	tion
Physical property	Law of Conservation of
Chemical property	Mass

II. PROBLEMS

1. Distinguish between physical change and chemical change by citing the differences between the reactants and the product when sodium and chlorine unite to form sodium chloride (common table salt).

2. What was phlogiston supposed to be? What was a calx supposed to be?

3. Explain each of the following by means of the phlogiston theory:

 a. Wood burns.

 b. Candle goes out when confined to an enclosed space.

 c. Charcoal leaves little residue when burned.

 d. Mouse dies in an enclosed space.

 e. Metals form calxes when heated in air.

 f. Metals gain weight when heated in air.

 g. Wood, paper, etc., lose weight on burning.

4. What were the fatal flaws in the phlogiston theory?

5. How did Boyle's definition of an element differ from Lavoisier's? From that of the chemists of about 1900?

6. What is an operational definition?

7. What is the difference between a substance and a mixture? Between an element and a compound?

8. Describe the essentials of an experiment that provides evidence for the oxygen theory of combustion.

9. How did Lavoisier establish the Law of Conservation of Mass?

10. What is the essential difference between combustion and respiration?

CHAPTER XVI

Basic Laws and Theories in Chemistry

The chemists are a strange class of mortals impelled by an almost insane impulse to seek their pleasure among smoke and vapour, soot and flame, poisons and poverty; yet among all these evils I seem to live so sweetly that I may die if I would change places with the Persian king.
—JOHANN JOACHIM BECHER (*1669*)

Lavoisier's success using the balance led others to its use, so that by 1800 the science of chemistry was well on its way to being put on a quantitative basis. Just as Galileo, Newton, and others had been able to establish their laws—and later, their theories—by experiments in which quantitative measurements played the leading role, so the chemists were able to establish the laws of chemical change—and later, their theories—by means of the balance and the measuring glass. A qualitative chemical theory based on little more than philosophical speculation either had to meet the challenge of these measuring tools or face rejection. From this time on, the chemists had to do what the physicists had been doing for a hundred years, i.e., they had, as

Newton stated, ". . . first to inquire diligently into the properties of things, and of establishing these properties by experiment, and then to proceed more slowly to hypotheses for the explanation of them."

LAW OF DEFINITE PROPORTIONS

The second famous controversy that the balance was called on to settle was one centered about two French chemists, Claude Berthollet (1748–1822) and Joseph Proust (1754–1826). About 1800 Proust announced that when elements combine to form compounds they do so in a fixed proportion by weight. About the same time Berthollet announced that elements combine to form compounds in ratios that are variable. When he heated copper and tin in air (in separate experiments) he got what seemed to him to be a continuous series of "compounds" of varying composition. Other evidence cited by Berthollet included solutions, alloys, and glasses—which are unquestionably variable in composition, but which can today easily be shown not to be true compounds—which was stated by Proust at the time. Berthollet cited many other examples, but Proust was able to show that in most of them Berthollet (and his followers) had been analyzing impure compounds.

The refutation of the copper and the tin oxides proved a very different matter, but by a brilliant series of analyses of metallic oxides (and sulfides) Proust was able to prove that some metals form two oxides, or two sulfides, each with a definite composition. Berthollet's continuous series of copper oxides turned out to be mixtures in varying proportions of two of these oxides. Without a good balance Proust could never have won the controversy, could never

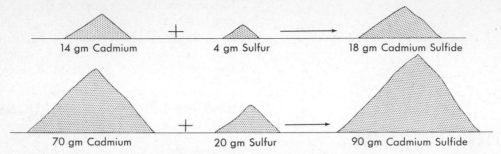

Fig. 16-1. Law of Definite Proportions. No matter how much cadmium sulfide we make, the proportion of cadmium to sulfur is always 7 to 2 by weight.

have established the Law of Definite Proportions (sometimes called the Law of Constant Composition): *When two pure substances combine to form a given compound, they do so in a definite proportion by weight* (Fig. 16-1). From this we derive a present definition of a compound: A compound is a substance formed by the combination of two or more elements in definite proportions by weight.

To the uninitiated the Law of Definite Proportions may seem to be only of passing importance. Actually it was fundamental to the development of the pure science of chemistry and it is one of the fundamental clues to the existence of atoms. It is of great importance to applied chemistry in industry and to all research laboratories, for it allows the use of just the right quantities of materials without waste in the synthesis of any compound. Or, if we speak of analysis instead of synthesis, we can say that the Law of Definite Proportions is the foundation stone of all chemical analysis.

LAW OF MULTIPLE PROPORTIONS

This law was established by John Dalton about the same time as the Law of Definite Proportions, which Dalton had been among the first to accept, for it fitted in perfectly with other ideas of his. It had been known for some time that some elements combined to form more than one compound, e.g., carbon and oxygen to form carbon monoxide and carbon dioxide. We saw that Berthollet's doubt of the validity of the Law of Definite Proportions arose from the fact that he failed to recognize that when one heated tin or copper in the open air for an insufficient length of time or in an enclosed vessel with insufficient air, two oxides are formed.[1] Consider the two oxides of copper, one red, the other black. Suppose we analyze 100 g of each, obtaining the following results:

Wt. of oxide	Wt. of Cu	Wt. of O
100 gm red oxide	89 gm	11 gm
100 gm black oxide	80 gm	20 gm

[1] The two compounds of tin are SnO and SnO_2. For a given number of atoms of tin and the same number of atoms of oxygen there will be one atom of oxygen for each of tin. Only SnO will be formed. If we double the number of atoms of oxygen present, there will be two atoms of oxygen for each atom of tin. Only SnO_2 will be formed. For any intermediate number of atoms of oxygen present some atoms of tin will get two atoms of oxygen and some one. Thus, both SnO and SnO_2 will be formed.

There is nothing in these figures by themselves that even remotely suggests a Law of Multiple Proportions. However, if we are checking the existence of such a law, we would certainly look farther to see if a hidden relationship existed. You will note that in a 100 gm of our two compounds there are different masses of copper present. Suppose we increase the amount of black oxide so that when we analyze it we have 89 gm of copper, the same as for the red oxide. How much oxygen would be combined with this 89 gm to give the black oxide? For 80 gm of copper the table shows that it is 20 of oxygen, so for 89 of copper we have a simple proportion:

$$\frac{x}{89} = \frac{20}{80}$$

Whence $\quad x = \dfrac{89}{4} = 22 + \text{gm}$

Now if we compare the amount of oxygen (22 gm) that combined with 89 gm of copper to form the black oxide with the amount of oxygen (11 gm) that combined with 89 gm of copper to form the red oxide, we see that the ratio is 22 to 11, i.e., 2 to 1. If we had used tin and its two oxides, we would have arrived at the same ratio.

By analyses of these and other pairs of compounds Dalton reached the conclusion that *a simple ratio must exist between the two weights of one element that can combine with a given weight of another element.* Note carefully that in this Law of Multiple Proportions, the simple ratio is between the two weights of one element; it is not between the weights of two elements. Note that in the example given the element with the given weight is copper (89 gm), and the simple ratio is between the two weights of oxygen that combine with this given weight.[2]

DALTON'S ATOMIC THEORY

Dalton's atomic theory was developed some forty to fifty years before the kinetic-molecular theory. In fact, Dalton's atomic theory helped to develop the kinetic theory. We learned that gases played a prominent role in the development of the kinetic theory because of their obvious particulate[3] nature. It was Priestley's discovery of the gas oxygen that led to the overthrow of the phlogiston theory, and it was prob-

[2] As another example we can take the oxides of nitrogen listed in Table 16-1. If we analyzed each, we would find that the weights of oxygen combined with 100 gm of nitrogen (this is the fixed weight) to form each of the five compounds, they would be 57 gm, 114 gm, 171 gm, 228 gm, and 286 gm, respectively. Now if we divide each of the above by the smallest weight of oxygen (i.e., by 57), we get the simple ratios between the weights of oxygen (1 to 1, 1 to 2, 1 to 3, 1 to 4, and 1 to 5) that are demanded by the Law of Multiple Proportions.

We have used approximate weights so that the arithmetic would be easy. In an actual analysis the oxides might first have to be purified, weighed, decomposed, purified and weighed again. At every step errors can creep in, due to faulty techniques, imperfect equipment, etc., all of which will cause more or less discrepancy between the final results as calculated from experimental data and the expected results as deduced from theory. These discrepancies in Dalton's time were understandably greater than those of today. How great can the above discrepancy be before it may be said that the experimental data invalidates the theory? To help him make this decision the scientist learns to estimate the limits of error for each particular experiment. How he does this need not concern us here. Suffice it to say that absolute accuracy is experimentally unobtainable, so that this problem is always with the experimental scientist.

[3] Of the nature of discrete particles. The student should familiarize himself with this word for it will be used many times later on in this book.

TABLE 16-1

Compound	Wt. Ratio N–O	Packet Ratio	Formula* of Compound
A	14:8 or (28:16)	2:1	N_2O
B	14:16 or (14:16)	1:1	NO
C	14:24 or (28:48)	2:3	N_2O_3
D	14:32 or (14:32)	1:2	NO_2
E	14:40 or (28:80)	2:5	N_2O_5

* The actual numbers of atoms per molecule as shown here cannot be deduced without additional information.

ably no accident that the atomic theory was developed by a man who began his career in chemistry by studying gases, the atmospheric gases, in particular. Dalton [4] saw that the properties of gases are best explained by a theory of atoms. From the fact that under suitable conditions of temperature and pressure gases can be converted first to liquids and then to solids, it follows that they, too, should be composed of atoms. Dalton was probably the first to associate a theoretical atomic concept with the Law of Definite Proportions. He saw that the law had meaning only if each element consisted of discrete particles, all of which had the same weight.[5] For example, if some oxygen atoms had one weight and others some other weight, how could you explain that the weight ratio of oxygen to

hydrogen in water was always 8 to 1, no matter how many samples you analyzed? Or how could it happen that in the five oxides of nitrogen the weight ratios should be as shown in Table 16-1? This table shows that if 14 gm of nitrogen are combined with oxygen to form the five compounds, the weight of the oxygen used is always some multiple of 8. Let us use the term *packet* for the smallest unit of nitrogen or oxygen that can exist. Then, if we assign a relative weight of 14 to each packet of nitrogen and a relative weight of 16 to each packet of oxygen,[6] we have, for compound A, two packets of nitrogen to one of oxygen; for B, one of nitrogen to one of oxygen; for C, two of nitrogen to three of oxygen; for D, one of nitrogen to two of oxygen; and for E, two of nitrogen to five of oxygen.

This "packet" concept is the strongest possible evidence for the existence of atoms, for we see that never is there any indication of half a packet, a third of a packet, or any other fraction of a packet,

[4] John Dalton (1766–1844) was an elementary school teacher who was very largely self-taught. He used all of his scanty leisure—he was a bachelor—in scientific investigation. Some have claimed that he was dull and somewhat stupid, but if he was he did extremely well for himself as far as the annals of science are concerned. One of his pupils was a man named Joule, of whom you already have heard.

[5] Actually wherever the term weight is used in the following discussion, we mean mass. Dalton used the term weight and chemists to this day have commonly followed him.

[6] The thoughtful student may well ask why we do not assign a value of 8 to each packet of oxygen. The reason is that it can be shown that one packet of oxygen weighs a bit more than one packet of nitrogen.

no matter what compound or series of compounds we use. Always the quantities of oxygen and nitrogen are multiples of 16 or 14, respectively.

This is such an important concept that we will use an analogy so that there will be no lingering doubts in your mind. Sugar, as you know, comes in small granules or in cubes, cubes that are pretty much the same size and weight. For our purposes let us assume that each weighs exactly the same as any other. Suppose now that you take a number of glasses of water and dissolve varying amounts of sugar in each. In some you dissolve lumps of sugar, one, two, three, etc. In others you dissolve granulated sugar, half a teaspoonful, a teaspoonful, etc., making no effort to measure exactly. We now mix the glasses up so that you do not know which received the cubes, which the granules. Is there a method of finding out? Suppose we now evaporate the water from each glass and weigh the sugar that is left behind. Our results are shown in Table 16-2.

TABLE 16-2

Glass	Wt. of Sugar (gm)	Glass	Wt. of Sugar (gm)
1	4.2	6	6.3
2	3.9	7	4.2
3	2.1	8	5.2
4	2.7	9	6.8
5	4.6	10	8.4

We can see that the weights of sugar in glasses 1, 3, 6, 7, and 10 are all even multiples of 2.1, a circumstance that would make it almost infinitely improbable that these could be other than the glasses in which 2, 1, 3, 2, and 4 lumps, respectively, had been

dissolved. We also come to the conclusion that each cube probably weighs 2.1 gms. There is no such relation among the amounts put in the other five cups.

We can put this another way, as follows: Suppose that you did not know whether sugar came in cubes or in a "continuous" form like loose granulated sugar. If sugar had been put in ten cups of water, and you now evaporated the water, weighed the precipitated sugar and found that all weights were either 2.1 or some integral multiple of 2.1, then you would undoubtedly conclude that sugar came in discrete lumps or packets, each having the same weight as every other packet.

It is difficult for us to present the actual way in which Dalton arrived at his theory, or even give the exact date, for he gave his contemporaries different accounts of his methods of reasoning, all of which are inconsistent with his notebooks. Even his notebooks lead to contradictory conclusions. The time that he presented his theory was somewhere between 1805 and 1810. The assumptions of his theory, somewhat modernized as to wording, are as follows:

1. Elements consist of tiny discrete particles called atoms which cannot be divided, destroyed, or created.[7]

2. Atoms of the same element are all alike; in particular they are all alike in weight.[8] Atoms of different elements are

[7] The recent discoveries that show that some kinds of atoms are divisible, and that not all of the same element have exactly the same mass have no bearing on normal chemical reactions.

[8] For the present we are going to continue to use the word molecule to mean the smallest particle of a compound, or of any gaseous element or compound, that can exist in nature and still retain the characteristic properties of the compound.

unlike; in particular they are unlike in weight.

3. Atoms combine with other atoms to form molecules of compounds, and always in fixed simple ratios.

4. Atoms of different elements may combine in more than one ratio.

5. When they combine in more than one ratio, the simplest compound will contain the atoms of the elements in a one-to-one ratio, the next simplest in a two-to-one ratio, etc.

The first assumption accounts for the Law of Conservation of Mass, and the second and third integrate the Law of Definite Proportions with the Law of Conservation of Mass. If neither of these laws had not already been derived by experiment, both would have been deduced from these first three assumptions. The third has been revised somewhat, for we have found that the ratios are not always as simple as Dalton thought; for example, consider the compound, $C_{34}H_{39}I_3N_2O_6$. The fourth assumption accounts for the Law of Multiple Proportions (p. 230), which had been established by Dalton himself as a part of his work on the atomic theory. This law helped mightily to convince many of his skeptical opponents.

The fifth is invalid and has long since been discarded. It was stubbornly defended by Dalton right up until his death, although he had no substantial evidence for it. Its inclusion in the theory caused no end of trouble for the next fifty years. The reason for the trouble can be illustrated by the formula for water. It is the simplest compound that we know that consists of hydrogen and oxygen only. Applying Dalton's fifth assumption, its formula should be HO, i.e., one atom of hydrogen unites with one atom of oxygen,

and this is what Dalton insisted it was. Since it was known by chemical analysis [9] that the weight *ratio* of oxygen to hydrogen was 8 to 1, Dalton's fifth assumption demanded that the oxygen atom weigh eight times as much as the hydrogen atom. On the other hand, there is nothing in the 8 to 1 weight ratio that demands this. For example, suppose that the oxygen atom weighs 16 times as much as the hydrogen atom. Then if we assume that the atomic ratio is one oxygen atom to two hydrogen atoms, our weight ratio is 16 to 2, or again 8 to 1. The formula for water would then be H_2O. If we make the assumption that the oxygen atom weighs 24 times as much as the hydrogen atom, we can also assume that the atomic ratio is three hydrogen atoms to one oxygen atom, and still have our weight ratio 24 to 3, or again 8 to 1, etc. The formula for water would then be H_3O.

Which of these atomic ratios is correct, or which of these relative weights is correct, cannot be determined without obtaining additional and *independent* information. However, if we can determine one of the weights, we then can determine the other, for these two quantities depend upon one another. There are several ways of determining one or the other of the above quantities. We will use one that is relatively easy to understand, and that involves a principle mentioned in the last chapter. It is not the method that Dalton used, for it was not developed until about 1860, some fifteen years after his death. However, before we do this, we need to consider some other developments.

[9] Water had been decomposed into hydrogen and oxygen by Humphry Davy by the process of electrolysis about this time.

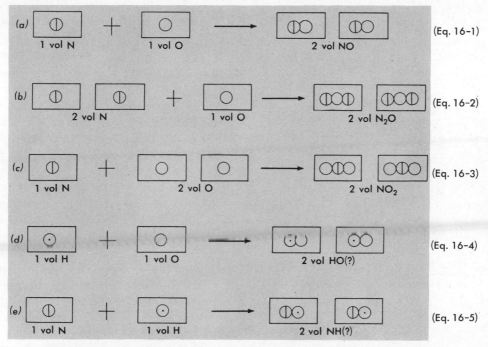

Fig. 16-2. The diagram illustrates the conflict of Dalton's atomic theory with the Law of Combining Volumes. That there is a conflict is shown by the fact that the numbers of molecules on both sides of each equation are different, whereas the number of volumes on each side is the same. This cannot be. The conflict stems from the concept of elemental gases being composed of monatomic molecules, and, for **(d)** and **(e)** Dalton's insistence on his fifth assumption.

GAY-LUSSAC'S LAW OF COMBINING VOLUMES

Refined techniques for handling gases developed early in the science of chemistry (beginning with Boyle in the late 1600's), probably because of the reasons stated on pp. 175, 196. At this point we must digress to remind the student that since the volume of a gas varies with its pressure and its temperature, when comparing volumes of gases we must always do so at the same pressure and temperature. For this purpose we reduce the volumes of all gases to the volumes they would occupy at 0° C and 760 mm of mercury, called the standard temperature and pressure, and abbreviated STP. It is to be understood that the reduction has been made even though not specifically stated.[10]

[10] The equation for the reduction is as follows:

Measured volume

$$\times \frac{\text{Measured pressure}}{273° \text{ C} + \text{measured temperature}}$$

$$\times \frac{273° \text{ C}}{760 \text{ mm}} = \text{Corrected volume}$$

About the time that Dalton was promoting his atomic theory (1808) Gay-Lussac was analyzing and synthesizing various gases. Some of the typical volume

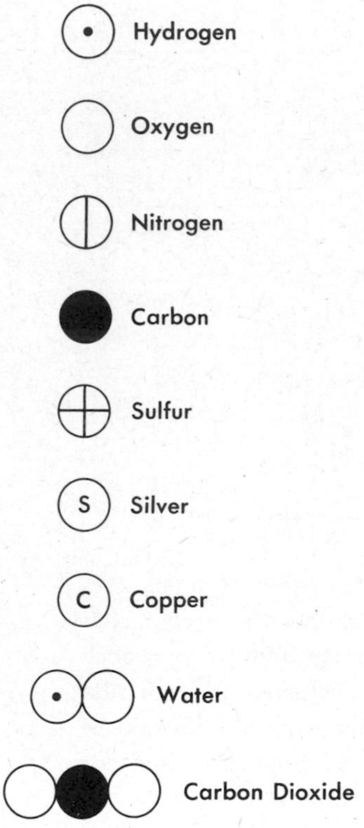

Fig. 16-3. Chemical Symbols of Dalton.

relations that he found among both the reactant gases and the products (when they were also gases) are shown in Fig. 16-2.[11]

[11] The chemical symbols used here are those used by Dalton to represent various elements, $\bigodot$ for oxygen, $\odot$ for hydrogen, $\bigcirc\!\!\!\mid$ for nitrogen (Fig. 16-3). The equations are written to show Gay-Lussac's simple ratios, not as Dalton would have written them. Note that in Eq. 16-4 one must assume that in 1 volume of oxygen there are as many atoms as there are in 2 volumes of hydrogen if Dalton's formula for water, HO, is correct. Compare this with Avogadro's Hypothesis (later Avogadro's Law) on next page.

Note first only the left sides of the equations. Here we see that the volume ratios of the *reactants* in the reactions are 1:1, 2:1, 1:2, 2:1 and 3:1, respectively. From these relationships Gay-Lussac arrived at the Law of Combining Volumes: *When two or more gases combine, the volumes of these combining gases are in the ratio of small whole numbers.* Note that in no case are the ratios fractional, i.e., 1½ to 1, 2¾ to 1, etc. Note that this applies to the reactant gases.

Now let us look at the products on the right sides of the equations. Note that in each case 2 volumes of the gas are formed, regardless of the number of volumes of reactants. Again, there are simple ratios, this time between the reactant gases and the product gases.[12] This was a wholly unexpected experimental result, one which Gay-Lussac did not explain.

In 1845 Joule stated that, "The discovery of Gay-Lussac, that gaseous bodies combine in equal or multiple volumes, and that the resulting compounds stand in a simple relation to their constituents, is one of the most important discoveries ever made in physical science."

THE CONTROVERSY BETWEEN DALTON AND GAY-LUSSAC

Dalton, however, refused to accept the Law of Combining Volumes. He was so opposed to it that he accused Gay-Lussac of careless experimental work, despite the fact that Gay-Lussac was known as a fine experimenter whereas his own work was that of a "coarse" experimenter. What

[12] These ratios occur even if one of the reactants is a solid, provided the product is a gas, e.g., 1 volume of carbon dioxide plus charcoal (carbon) gives 2 volumes of carbon monoxide.

bothered Dalton was that he had worked on these same gases, had applied his atomic theory to the weight (not volume) relations among them, had deduced the relative weights of the individual atoms in the elemental gases (hydrogen, oxygen, nitrogen), and had assumed that they existed in the gas as single atoms.

The chief trouble lay in the impossibility of reconciling this single-atom state with the fact that in each reaction 2 volumes of the product were obtained. For example, 1 volume of nitrogen plus 1 volume of oxygen should form 1 volume of NO (nitric oxide) instead of 2, according to Dalton. In the case of hydrogen combining with oxygen, Dalton insisted also on the 1:1 ratio, and so held that the formula of water was HO.

Dalton's mental picture of a gas helped confuse the issue. A believer in the caloric theory, he held that gas molecules had shells of caloric about them, and that these shells were in contact. From this view it followed that if the sizes of the atoms were different, the number of atoms in a given volume would vary from gas to gas. Dalton insisted on the size difference because it was obvious from experimental data that for given volumes there were pronounced weight differences, an 8 to 1 difference in the case of hydrogen and oxygen at STP. This controversy was not resolved for fifty years, some ten to fifteen years after the death of both men, even though the key to the whole puzzle had been published in the most prominent journal of science in continental Europe by Amadeo Avogadro [13] in 1813.

[13] Avogadro (1776–1857), an Italian of noble birth, was educated for the law, which he practiced for a time. His love of mathematics and

AVOGADRO'S HYPOTHESIS

As soon as Avogadro learned of Gay-Lussac's Law of Combining Volumes, he accepted it, for he saw how it could be reconciled with Dalton's atomic theory. If Dalton had not been so much in love with his own theory, especially with that disastrous fifth assumption, he probably would also have seen that Gay-Lussac's data showed that *equal volumes of gases at the same temperature and pressure contain the same number of particles.*[14] This we have already learned (p. 208) as Avogadro's hypothesis. When first advanced it was no more than a brilliant guess, supported only by its possibility of explaining Gay-Lussac's law. The simple ratios must exist if we accept the hypothesis. Nevertheless, the hypothesis will not of itself explain why two volumes (rather than one) of product gases are always formed. He therefore added a second brilliant guess to his hypothesis: *Each particle of the reactant gases consisted of at least two atoms.* Again there was no evidence for it except the fact that it completed the reconciliation of Gay-Lussac's and Dalton's Laws.[15]

To see how controversy is resolved, we will rewrite Eqs. 16-1 to 16-5 (Fig. 16-2) in terms of this second guess; one must, however, bear in mind the first guess—that each volume contains the same number of

physics led him to desert law to teach physics at the University of Turin.

[14] By particles he meant the smallest units of gases that had an independent existence. Today we use the word molecule but in those days the distinction between a molecule and an atom was not clear. Furthermore, the word particle, in today's usage, may mean either an atom, which it is in some cases, or a molecule, which it is in others.

[15] Provided also that Dalton's fifth assumption was rejected. Eq. 16-9 cannot be written unless we discard it.

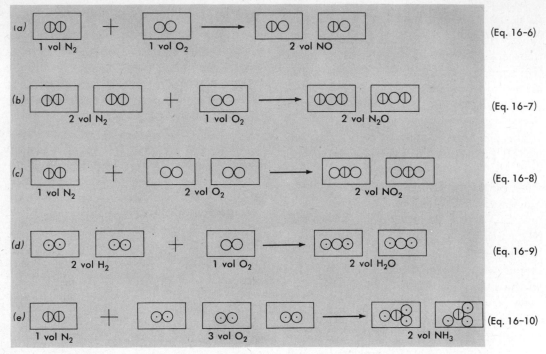

Fig. 16-4. Law of Combining Volumes. Compare with Fig. 16-2. The data on the left are consistent with those on the right if we accept Avogadro's educated guess that elemental gases consist of two atoms per molecule. (The inert gases were not known at the time.) For **(d)** and **(e)** we discarded Dalton's false fifth assumption. Note the Law of Conservation of Mass holds, for there are the same numbers of each kind of atom on both sides of the equations. Note that the ratios of the reactant gases are those of small whole numbers in all cases.

particles. The rewritten equations are shown in Fig. 16-4.

Note that the atoms on both sides of each equation now balance, i.e., there are the same number of atoms of each kind on both sides, as demanded by the Law of Conservation of Mass (compare with the corresponding Eqs. 16-1 to 16-5). One should also note that we can assume that each particle of each gas can consist of four atoms, or six atoms, etc., without affecting our result, for at this time it was

not known how many atoms *actually* were present in a molecule of any of the products. The formula[16] NO at that time merely meant that the atomic ratio was 1:1; a molecule of NO could consist of any number of atoms as long as the ratio of N atoms to O atoms was 1:1. We now know that the number of atoms in any particle of

[16] Henceforth we will use present-day symbols, invented by Berzelius (1777–1848), a Swedish chemist whose painstaking analytical work did much to establish the validity of the atomic theory.

these or other elemental gases (except the inert gases, none of which were known at the time) is rarely more than two.[17]   How this knowledge was obtained is, in part, the subject of the next chapter.

THE REFUSAL TO ACCEPT AVOGADRO'S HYPOTHESIS

As we have stated, Avogadro presented his hypothesis to the scientific world in a journal where it could be read by any interested scientist.   Yet he had few, if any, converts.   It is instructive to see why.[18]

For one thing Dalton's was the greater name, and the trend of opinion even in science leans towards the views of the greater "authority."   For another, the kinetic theory of gases had not yet been developed; a static theory prevailed which did not jibe with Avogadro's theory as a kinetic one would have.[19]   Then, too, it was difficult to see how two atoms of an elemental gas could join to form a molecule.   It was generally agreed at the time that atoms of the same gas repelled one another.   The modern concept of the cause of air pressure had not yet been developed, so the fact that it took a force to compress a gas was best explained by the repulsion of one atom of a gas for another of its own kind.   Moreover, the general view that gas atoms were surrounded by thick shells of caloric, sup-

posedly self-repulsive, was supported by the experimental evidence from compression.   Conversely, if two like atoms attract one another, why should a gas resist compression?

This is a fine example of a man being too far ahead of his time.   Avogadro had no experimental evidence to support his views and to answer the objections.   The result was that Avogadro's hypothesis was forgotten as the years passed, even though the difficulties of the atomic theory increased.   In time others showed that the Law of Combining Volumes was valid, but none could reconcile it with the atomic theory.   In fact, the theory came under a cloud; some chemists were talking of rejecting the whole atomic concept.

Such was the status of the atomic theory when another Italian chemist, Stanislao Cannizzaro, resurrected Avogadro's hypothesis about the time of the beginning of the War between the States.   By use of the hypothesis, it became possible to determine easily the relative weights of atoms, and with these known, it was but a short step to the determination of the number of atoms in a molecule.   These determinations involve the "weighing" and "counting" of atoms, which is the title of our next chapter.

[17] Avogadro argued for two, using the argument presented by Newton, Ptolemy, and many others (p. 15) that the rule of simplicity should apply.

[18] No significance is to be attached to the order in which these reasons are listed.

[19] The static theory pictured atoms or molecules of gases as in contact with one another, like fluffy balls of wool packed loosely in a crate.   For equal volumes of gases to have equal numbers of molecules, a theory was demanded in which the molecules are widely separated, which in turn suggests motion.

SUMMARY

The first ten years of the nineteenth century were notable in the science of chemistry, for in those years the Law of Definite Proportions, the Law of Multiple Proportions, Dalton's atomic theory, the Law of Combining Volumes for gases, and Avogadro's hypothesis were all formulated.   All were fundamental to the chemist, so much so that we might reasonably expect his science to progress by leaps and bounds rather than at the snail's pace with which it had been developing. Unfortunately it did not, for Dalton refused to accept Gay-Lussac's Law of Combining Volumes, because it did not jibe with one of the assumptions of his atomic theory. Avogadro's hypothesis would have reconciled the theory and the law (if Dalton had given up this erroneous assumption) but the hypothesis conflicted with other erroneous conceptions of the nature of gases, and so it was rejected and forgotten. Some fifty years later, after these erroneous ideas concerning gases had been straightened out by the kinetic-molecular theory, Cannizzaro resurrected Avogadro's hypothesis, and by doing so, firmly established Dalton's atomic theory.

EXERCISES

I. TERMS AND CONCEPTS

Law of Definite   Law of Combining
Proportions   Volumes
Law of Multiple   Avogadro's hypothe-
Proportions   sis
Dalton's atomic
theory

II. PROBLEMS

1. State the Law of Definite Proportions.

2. What argument accompanied the establishment of the Law of Definite Proportions and who were the chief people involved?

3. Different chemists analyzed three samples of pure table salt (sodium chloride, NaCl) from different sources. They obtained the following data for the relative weights:

Chemist A: Na 16.5 gm   Cl 25.4 gm
Chemist B: Na 5.2 gm   Cl 8.0 gm
Chemist C: Na 32.3 gm   Cl 49.7 gm

Show that the above data support the Law of Definite Proportions. (To do this all you have to do is show that the ratio of Na to Cl is the same.)

4. The most common ore of iron is the red oxide, hematite. Its composition is Fe_2O_3, which means that two atoms of iron and three atoms of oxygen combine to form one molecule of hematite. The weight ratio is 7 gm of iron to every 3 gm of oxygen. How much iron can be obtained from 100 kg of hematite? From 50 tons?

5. Ammonia gas (NH_3) is composed of nitrogen and hydrogen in the ratio of 3 atoms of hydrogen to 1 of nitrogen. The weight ratio is 3 gm of hydrogen to 14 gm of nitrogen. A sample of ammonia gas contains 21 gm of hydrogen. What weight of nitrogen will it contain? How many grams of nitrogen does 68 gm of ammonia contain? How many grams of ammonia can be obtained from 100 lb of hydrogen?

6. State the Law of Multiple Proportions. Note carefully what is related to what in this law.

7. It is found that 100 gm of tin will combine with 13.4 gm of oxygen to form the oxide, SnO; 100 gm of tin are also found to combine with 26.8 gm of oxygen to form the oxide, SnO_2. Show that these facts are consistent with the Law of Multiple Proportions.

8. By analysis it is shown that 100 gm of CO (carbon monoxide) contains 43 gm of carbon and 57 gm of oxygen. It is also found that 112.5 gm of carbon will unite with 301 gm of oxygen to form CO_2 (carbon dioxide). Show that these data are consistent with the Law of Multiple Proportions.

9. State Gay-Lussac's Law of Combining Volumes.

10. Two volumes of hydrogen combine with 1 volume of oxygen to form 2 volumes of water vapor. Show that this conforms to the Law of Combining Volumes.

11. One volume of nitrogen combines

with 3 volumes of hydrogen to form 2 volumes of ammonia (NH_3). Show that this conforms to the Law of Combining Volumes.

12. What is there in question 10 that Dalton could not accept?

13. Give the assumptions of Dalton's atomic theory.

14. If Proust had not already established the Law of Definite Proportions, it would have been deduced from the atomic theory. Show how or why.

15. If the Law of Conservation of Mass had not already been established, it too would have been deduced from the atomic theory. Show how or why.

16. State both parts of Avogadro's hypothesis.

17. Why was it not accepted at the time?

18. If there are 2.7×10^{22} molecules of chlorine in a liter at STP, how many molecules of hydrogen are there in a liter (at STP)?

19. What is meant by STP? With what substances is it important?

20. A sample of gas has a volume of 100 liters at 25° C and 750 mm pressure. What will be its volume at STP?

CHAPTER XVII

Weighing and Counting Atoms and Molecules

Want of time prevents me from saying anything at present respecting other points on which we differ. Those which are purely speculative will long afford room for discussion. Respecting a matter of fact, which can easily come under the test of experiment, we cannot long be at variance.
—A FELLOW SCIENTIST IN A LETTER TO DALTON
(1804)

In 1857 Clausius published the first version of the kinetic-molecular theory in something anywhere near its modern form. The concepts of energy, of gas pressure, and of molecules and their motions were clarified. Gone were Dalton's static model of a gas, the caloric theory of heat, the concept that gases resisted compression because of their self-repulsion for molecules of their own kind. Had Avogadro presented his hypothesis at this time it unquestionably would have won almost immediate acceptance, for the atomic theory was in a sad state, on the verge, in the opinion of some writers, of being abandoned. But Avogadro was dead, and so it was Canniz-

zaro who revived the forgotten hypothesis by presenting it to an international conference of chemists in 1860. The response was immediate; in the words of one, "It was as though scales fell from my eyes; doubt vanished, and was replaced by the feeling of calm assurance." Not long afterwards Avogadro's hypothesis (equal volumes of gases at the same temperature and pressure contain the same number of molecules) was deduced from the kinetic-molecular theory (p. 208). Avogadro's hypothesis thus gained status as a law, one of the utmost importance to the science of chemistry.

ATOMS vs. MOLECULES

If we are going to count and weigh atoms and molecules, it is fitting that we understand the difference between them. Avogadro's service to science included his making the distinction between atoms and molecules. In general, *atoms are the smallest units in which an element enters into chemical combination; molecules are the smallest particles in which a compound or element can exist as an independent substance.* Thus, in a gas the individual particles are called molecules even though in all the inert gases [1] and in mercury vapor, these particles are atoms. The inert gases are therefore commonly said to consist of monatomic molecules, and so are called the monatomic gases. When vaporized, most of the metals exist as monatomic molecules. All of the other elemental gases exist in the independent state as molecules consisting (almost always) of two atoms

[1] See the column on the far right in the chart on the inside of the front cover.

per molecule. They are the diatomic elemental gases. There are a large number of gases that are compounds, e.g., carbon monoxide, carbon dioxide, sulfur dioxide, the various oxides of nitrogen listed in Table 16-1, and scores of others. Their molecules consist of at least two atoms each, most of them of more than two. They might be called polyatomic molecules. It should be kept in mind that the terminology we employ with gases is not *necessarily* the same as that which we employ with liquids and solids.

DETERMINATION OF MOLECULAR WEIGHTS OF GASES

Neither molecular nor atomic weights refer to weights in the absolute sense. For example, to say that the molecular weight of an oxygen molecule is 32 tells us exactly nothing about its actual weight. If we say *also* that the molecular weight of hydrogen is 2, then we know that the weight of the oxygen molecule is 16 times greater than that of the hydrogen molecule. But we still do not know the actual weight or mass of either molecule. If we know that a molecule of either of these two gases consists of two atoms, then from the molecular weights, we know that the atomic weight of oxygen is 16 and that of hydrogen is 1. But still we do not know the actual weight or mass of either atom. We know today that the mass of a hydrogen atom, the lightest of all atoms, is 0.00000000000000000000000166 gm (1.66×10^{-24}). While this to the scientist is an interesting piece of information, and very important to modern physicists, to most chemists it is not very helpful. What we are trying to say here is that it is the *rela-tive weights* of atoms and molecules that concern us here. Since only relative weights are involved, there are obviously no units. When we say that the atomic weight of nitrogen is 14, we mean that a molecule of nitrogen weighs $14/16$ as much as an atom of oxygen—just that and nothing more.

Avogadro's Law gives us an extremely simple method of determining the relative weights of the molecules of any gas. Since equal volumes of all gases at STP contain the same number of molecules, all we have to do is to compare the measured weights of equal volumes of gases. For example, we weigh a liter of oxygen and a liter of hydrogen, both at STP. The liter of oxygen weighs 1.43 gm and the liter of hydrogen 0.09 gm. The ratio of the weight of the oxygen to that of the hydrogen is $1.43/0.09 = 16$ (within the limits of experimental error). Since there are the same number of molecules in both volumes, this tells us that a molecule of oxygen weighs 16 times as much as a molecule of hydrogen. If we assign a value of 2 for the molecular weight of hydrogen, that of oxygen is 32.

A liter of nitrogen at STP weighs 1.26 gm. Therefore, its molecular weight is $1.26/0.09 = 14$ times that of the molecular weight of hydrogen, i.e., its molecular weight is 28. A liter of water vapor at STP weighs 0.81 gm. Its molecular weight is $0.81/0.09 = 9$ times that of the molecular weight of hydrogen, i.e., it is 18.

Thus, the molecular weight of any gas can be determined by simply comparing the weight of a liter of it with that of a liter of hydrogen, both at STP. We could, of course, use oxygen instead of hydrogen, but the arithmetic would not be quite so simple. The actual formula, derived from Avogadro's Law, using oxygen as a standard rather than hydrogen is: [2]

Molecular weight of gas $X =$

$$32 \times \frac{\text{Weight of liter of gas } X}{\text{Weight of liter of oxygen}}$$

It should be carefully noted that as yet we do not know the number of atoms in a molecule of any of the gases. Avogadro *guessed* that for the elemental gases known at the time, the number was two.

DETERMINATION OF ATOMIC WEIGHTS

Dalton was greatly interested in the relative weights of different kinds of atoms. Because of his blind adherence to the fifth assumption of his atomic theory, his conclusions about relative weights were not valid. Not having accepted Avogadro's hypothesis, he had no easy method. There was no absolute certainty in his method even if he had not insisted that his fifth assumption held in all cases. It is not worth the time to analyze his method in detail. Suffice it to say that it involved the Law of Multiple Proportions, the Law of Definite Proportions, and a guess as to the number of atoms of each element per molecule. In his guessing he followed the rule of greatest simplicity: [3] When only

[2] Any other volume besides a liter could be used on the right, as long as the same volume of oxygen is used. A liter is slightly more than a quart, 1.06 quarts to be exact.
[3] All scientists follow the rule of simplicity, first stated by Ptolemy (p. 15) and reiterated by many since, but not blindly. Actually the rule states that one should not introduce *unnecessary* assumptions; it does not insist that the assumptions be the simplest possible.

one compound of an element was known, he assumed its molecules to be linked together in a 1:1 ratio. This may be recognized as his fifth assumption (p. 234). Sometimes it was right; it gave him the correct formulas for carbon monoxide (CO) and carbon dioxide (CO_2), but led him astray on water (HO instead of H_2O) and ammonia (NH instead of NH_3), etc.

CANNIZZARO'S METHOD OF DETERMINING ATOMIC WEIGHTS

It is now possible to go from the relative weights of gaseous molecules to the relative weights of atoms by use of a method developed by Cannizzaro and based on Avogadro's Law. We will make no attempt to reproduce the method exactly as he did, but will be content to outline the principles involved.

We will start with pure hydrogen. We have already seen that 1 liter of it weighs 0.09 gm. For reasons that will be apparent later we will use 22.4 liters instead of 1 liter for our volume, although any volume can be used, just so long as the same volume is used for each gas. This volume of hydrogen gas weighs 2.016 gm. We assume that we do not yet know whether these molecules of hydrogen are composed of one atom or two atoms, or even more. How do we find out?

Next let us take 22.4 liters of steam (water vapor) at STP and analyze it. The steam weighs 18 gm. We find that the hydrogen in it weighs 2.0 gm. We take another hydrogen compound, hydrogen chloride gas, weigh it and analyze it to determine the weight of hydrogen in it. Since we are going to do the same thing for a number of gaseous hydrogen com-

TABLE 17-1

	1	2	3	4
				Col. 3 ÷ least weight, 1.01 (gives number of atoms per molecule)
Compound	Volume	Wt. of 22.4 liters at STP (gm)	Wt. of H in a Compound (gm)	
Hydrogen	22.4	2.02	2.02	2
Steam	22.4	18.02	2.02	2
Hydrogen chloride	22.4	36.45	1.01	1
Methane	22.4	16.03	4.03	4
Ammonia	22.4	17.03	3.02	3
Any other hydrogen gaseous compound	22.4	———	$n \times 1.01$	n

pounds, let us put the data in the form of a table, Table 17-1.

There are many thousands of compounds of hydrogen; a large number are gaseous at room temperatures. No matter how many are analyzed, we would find that the weight of hydrogen contained in 22.4 liters of the compound was never less than that found in hydrogen chloride, i.e., 1.01 gm. This is just *half* the weight of hydrogen contained in 22.4 liters of pure hydrogen. Avogadro's Law says that the number of molecules in each volume is the same. This means that there is just half as much hydrogen in one molecule of hydrogen chloride as there is in one molecule of pure hydrogen. Thus, there must be at least two atoms in a hydrogen molecule. If we analyze enough gaseous hydrogen compounds, and find no molecule that contains a package of hydrogen smaller than that in a hydrogen chloride molecule, we should feel reasonably confident that the package of hydrogen in a hydrogen chloride molecule is the atom. Our confidence seems justified when we find that the

weights of hydrogen in 22.4 liters of every one of these gaseous compounds is an even multiple of the weight found in hydrogen chloride. Looking at the last two columns in Table 17-1, we see that water must contain two atoms of hydrogen per molecule, ammonia must contain three per molecule and methane (cooking gas) four per molecule.

We can prepare a similar table for oxygen, Table 17-2. We make the same assumption as before, that our group of oxygen compounds (if it is big enough) will include at least one compound whose molecules contain only one atom of oxygen. This assumption has turned out to be correct, not only for oxygen, and hydrogen, but for any other gaseous element whose numbers of atoms per molecule we wish to determine.

Following the same reasoning as for hydrogen, we find that there is just half as much oxygen in one molecule of water as there is in one molecule of pure oxygen, and so reach the conclusion that this quantity is one atom per molecule. Fortified

TABLE 17-2

	1	2	3	4
Compound	Volume (liters)	Wt. of 22.4 liters at STP (gm)	Wt. of Oxygen in Compound (gm)	Col. 3 ÷ least weight, i.e., by 16
Oxygen	22.4	32.0	32.0	2
Steam	22.4	18.02	16.0	1
Carbon dioxide	22.4	44.0	32.0	2
Carbon monoxide	22.4	28.0	16.0	1
Nitrogen trioxide	22.4	76.0	48.0	3
Nitrogen pentoxide	22.4	108.0	80.0	5

with our conclusion that there are two atoms of hydrogen per molecule of steam, we may now write the formula of water as H_2O. This has been the accepted formula ever since Cannizzaro showed how to determine it.

We can also set up a table like 17-1 or 17-2 for solid elements,[4] e.g., carbon. In those two tables we have already listed three compounds of carbon, the two oxides and methane; Table 17-3 adds three more compounds.

[4] All solid and liquid elements become gases if the temperature is high enough.

Analyzing a large number of gaseous carbon compounds shows that there is never less than 12 gm of carbon in 22.4 liters of any such compound, and that where there is more, it is always an even multiple of this amount.

We have not yet completed our atomic weight determinations. From Tables 17-1 and 17-2 we see that the least weight (column 4) of hydrogen in 22.4 liters of any of the compounds listed is 1 gm (rounded off), and that of oxygen is 16 gm. Leaving off the units, the ratio of the weight of a hydrogen atom to the weight of an

TABLE 17-3

	1	2	3	4
Gaseous Compound	Volume	Wt. of 22.4 liters of compound (gm)	Wt. of carbon in compound (gm)	Col. 3 ÷ by least weight, 12
Carbon monoxide	22.4	28.0	12	1
Carbon dioxide	22.4	44.0	12	1
Methane	22.4	16.0	12	1
Acetylene	22.4	26.0	24	2
Propane	22.4	44.0	36	3
Ether	22.4	74.0	48	4

oxygen atom is 1:16. The above method of determining the number of atoms of any particular element in a molecule of one of its compounds, and the reasoning involved is confined to gaseous compounds. However, if we search among the possible compounds of any element, we can usually find one, or synthesize one, which is gaseous at workable temperatures. If we analyze them and tabulate the least weight (column 4 in the tables above) in 22.4 liters of *each* of the elements, we see that the smallest weight of any element in 22.4 liters of the gaseous compound is that of hydrogen. Since we are here dealing with equal volumes of gases, we are dealing with the same number of molecules. We also know the number of atoms per molecule (column 4). It follows that the lightest element must be hydrogen, i.e., analysis shows there is always more than 1 gm of any other element in 22.4 liters of that element when in the gaseous state, or in **any** of its *gaseous* compounds.

ATOMIC WEIGHT SCALE

We are now ready to set up a *relative* weight scale for atoms. Since the hydrogen atom is the lightest, we will assign it a value of 1. Since the oxygen atom is 16 times as heavy, its value on this scale is 16. That of carbon is 12. And so it goes. Nitrogen becomes 14, chlorine 35.5, copper 63.5 and uranium, the heaviest of the naturally occurring elements, 238; one atom of it weighs as much as 238 atoms of hydrogen. The whole list of elements is given alphabetically in the table on the inside of the front cover. *Note carefully that this table does not tell you what the weight of any atom is.*

MOLECULAR WEIGHTS

We have seen that the number of atoms in a molecule of pure hydrogen is two (Column 4, Table 17-1). Its molecular weight is therefore 2. Similarly, the molecular weight of all the diatomic elemental gases is just twice their atomic weights, 28 for nitrogen, 32 for oxygen, 71 for chlorine, and 38 for fluorine. For the monatomic gases (the inert gases, helium, neon, argon, krypton, xenon, and radon) the molecular weight may be considered to be the same as the atomic weight. For the two elements that are normally considered liquids and so have an important vapor phase, bromine forms diatomic and mercury monatomic molecules when in the vapor state. All of the elements that are solids at room temperature have unimportant vapor phases in the normal temperature range, and so we consider them to consist of discrete atoms rather than as molecules. They are therefore considered to have atomic weights only.

Compounds, since they are always composed of more than one atom (by definition), have molecular weights only. These molecular weights are always equal to the sum of the atomic weights of the atoms composing them. Thus, the molecular weight of carbon monoxide (CO) is $12 + 16 = 28$, that of carbon dioxide (CO_2) is $12 + 16 + 16 = 44$, that of sulfuric acid (H_2SO_4) is $1 + 1 + 32 + (4 \times 16) = 98$, etc.

SOME USES OF ATOMIC AND MOLECULAR WEIGHTS

Aside from the importance of the concepts of atomic and molecular weights to the research chemist (who could not possibly do much research without them), they are of great importance to the industrial chemist. Knowledge of atomic weights gave new impetus to the making of compounds, for the atomic weight combined with knowledge of the number of each kind of atom in a molecule, made it possible to manufacture compounds without waste. Ammonia, e.g., is synthesized from hydrogen and nitrogen. What proportions of these two gases should a manufacturer use? Since there are three atoms of hydrogen and one atom of nitrogen per molecule of ammonia (NH_3), and since the atomic weights are 1 and 14 respectively, he knows that the *weight ratio* of hydrogen to nitrogen must be 3 to 14. This means that for every 3 gm, lb, or tons of hydrogen, he must use 14 gm, lb, or tons of nitrogen. Such knowledge has helped to reveal certain regularities in the way atoms combine, which in turn has been largely responsible for the synthesizing of substances that are rare or even nonexistent in nature. Thus, our vast chemical industry owes a debt to Dalton, Avogadro, Cannizzaro, and others who were curious about the relative weights of atoms at a time when it seemed that such information was useless.

ATOMIC WEIGHTS IN TERMS OF THE OXYGEN ATOM

When the atomic weight scale was first developed, the relative weight of the hydrogen atom was chosen as the base, i.e., it was assigned a value of 1 and the weights of all other atoms were expressed in terms of it. In order to determine the atomic weight of a new solid element, it is necessary to find a compound of that element that is a gas. It turned out that such compounds were more likely to contain oxygen than hydrogen. Furthermore, it was noted that if the atomic weights of the elements were expressed in terms of the weight of the oxygen atom rather than in terms of the hydrogen atom, more of the elements would have relative weights closer to whole numbers. For example, the atomic weights of 50 of the 90 naturally occurring elements known today deviate from a whole number by not more than 0.1. It was felt that this was too much of a coincidence to be accidental, although the meaning of it, if any, was not apparent at the time. The change was therefore made; the weight of the oxygen was symbolized by the figure 16.0000, and the weights of all of the other elements are expressed in numbers *relative* to it. The weight of the hydrogen atom is then 1.008, close enough to unity for most purposes, so that we will call it 1 except where precision demands that it be 1.008.

NEW ATOMIC WEIGHT SCALE (1961)

In 1959 the International Union of Chemistry voted to formally introduce an atomic weight scale based on a particular isotope of carbon called ^{12}C (to be read carbon 12) at its meeting in 1961. The International Union of Physics endorsed the proposal in 1960, and the chemists fulfilled their part of the bargain in 1961. ^{12}C therefore now has an atomic weight of 12 exactly. This will make little difference for ordinary operations in chemistry, since the value for oxygen will be changed but slightly, from 16.0000 to 15.9999.

One possible fruit of the change may be the dropping of the term atomic weight, for atomic weight certainly does not mean the weight of an atom. Perhaps the new scale will be called the relative atomic mass scale.

Another fruit of the change will be the tidying up of the definition of a mole: *The mole is the amount of substance containing the same number of molecules (or atoms, or radicals, or ions, or electrons, as the case may be) as there are atoms in 12 gm of ^{12}C.*

GRAM ATOMIC AND GRAM MOLECULAR WEIGHTS

These must not be confused with either atomic weights or molecular weights, which are relative weights; when we speak of them we are *never* thinking of a definite quantity of the element or compound. On the other hand, when we speak of a gram atomic or a gram molecular weight of a substance, we are speaking of as definite a quantity as we are when we speak of 5.01 lb of sugar.

A gram atomic weight of an element is that quantity of the element whose weight in grams is numerically equal to its atomic weight. Thus, a gram atomic weight of oxygen is 16 gm, of carbon is 12 gm, of uranium is 238 g. Similarly, *a gram molecular weight is that actually weighable quantity of a compound or of an elemental diatomic gas that is numerically equal to its molecular weight.* Thus, a gram molecular weight of oxygen is 32 gm of it, of hydrogen is 2 gm, of carbon dioxide is 44 gm, of water is 18 gm, and of sulfuric acid is 98 gm. The distinction between atomic weight and gram atomic weight, between molecular weight and gram molecular weight, is of great importance in understanding the elements of chemistry. The terms *gram atom* or *gram molecule* are sometimes used as substitute terms.

Much better is the term *mole*. It has been used up to the present to refer to either a gram atomic weight of an element or to a gram molecular weight of a compound or of a diatomic elemental gas. There is rarely any confusion as to which we mean. For example, a mole of carbon is 12 gm, a mole of oxygen is 32 gm, and a mole of carbon dioxide is 44 gm. If we remember that the diatomic elemental gases exist in nature as "double atoms" and that a mole of any of them means, for them, a gram molecular weight, there should never be any confusion. We can, of course, speak of a gram atomic weight of oxygen, but if we do, we do not mean a mole of oxygen.

However, in this text we are going to use the new definition (1961) of a mole not yet formally endorsed by the physicists. We will repeat it here: The mole is the amount of substance containing the same number of molecules (or atoms, or radicals, or ions, or electrons, as the case may be) as there are atoms in 12 grams of ^{12}C. This number is still Avogadro's number, 6×10^{23}.

GRAM MOLECULAR VOLUME

For some time we have been using gram molecular volumes without using the term. You may recall that on p. 244 when we began our investigation into Cannizzaro's method of determining atomic weights, we switched from the use of 1 liter of a gas to 22.4 liters for reasons that would become apparent later. If we check columns 1 and 2 in Tables 17-1, 17-2, and 17-3, we will see that the weights given in column 2 for each of the compounds, are equal to the molecular weights of each of the gases listed. This means that a gram molecular volume of a gas is that volume which will be occupied by a gram molecular weight of any gas at STP. This volume is 22.4 liters. Thus 32 gm of oxygen, 2 gm of hydrogen, 36.5 gm of hydrogen chloride, and 76 gm of nitrogen trioxide will each, when at STP, just fill a container of 22.4 liters in volume. It follows that to obtain the molecular weight of any gas, all we have to do is to weigh 22.4 liters of it at STP. This will, of course, for the diatomic elemental gases give us their atomic weights, too, by simply dividing by 2. Once these are determined, and once we know the number of different kinds of atoms per molecule, it is easy to determine the atomic weights of any elements that combine with any of the diatomic elemental gases.

AVOGADRO'S NUMBER

To make the last statement clear we must again remind you of Avogadro's Law: Equal volumes of gases contain the same number of molecules at STP. This means that in 22.4 liters of every gas at STP there are the same number of molecules (molecules, we repeat, not atoms). This number is commonly designated by the letter N and is called Avogadro's number [5]—in

---

[5] The actual value, 6×10^{23}, is a number so large that it is impossible for anyone to visualize it. We can try, however. Suppose you had an ordinary 100-watt light bulb that was a complete vacuum—not a single molecule of air in it. Now suppose you made a tiny hole in it, a hole just large enough to admit one million molecules per second. How long will it take for enough molecules of air to stream into the bulb at that rate before the density of the air on the inside would be equal to that on the outside at STP? The answer is 100,000,000 years. Let's try another way. Suppose that the maximum age of the solar system is 5 billion years. Now let us reduce this to seconds. There are approximately 31,500,000 seconds in a year. The number 6×10^{23} is 4,000,000 times the number of seconds in 5 bil-

honor of him, and not because he determined it. In fact, he never heard of it. Its value is 6×10^{23}. How this number is determined we will learn later. There are several quite different ways of determining it, all of which agree within reasonable limits of error.

Let us further consider the meaning and the consequences of Avogadro's number, N. We have already stated that there are N numbers of molecules in a gram molecular volume (22.4 liters) of any gas. Since a gram molecular volume (abbreviated GMV) of hydrogen weighs 2 gm and a GMV of oxygen weighs 32 gm, it follows that there are the same number of molecules in a mole of hydrogen as there are in a mole of oxygen. Following the same line of reasoning, the number of molecules in a GMV of any gas is the same—6×10^{23}. If there are 6×10^{23} molecules of carbon monoxide in 1 GMV, it follows that there must be 6×10^{23} atoms of oxygen and 6×10^{23} atoms of carbon in that volume of CO. From column 3 in Table 17-3 we see that the *weight* of carbon in 1 GMV of CO is 12 gm. Therefore, 6×10^{23} atoms of carbon weigh 12 gm. But we have already learned that the atomic weight of carbon is 12. Therefore, there are 6×10^{23} atoms in 1 gm atomic weight of carbon. Following the same line of reasoning for all other solid elements, we finally reach the conclusion:

There are 6×10^{23} atoms in a gram atomic weight of any element, and 6×10^{23} molecules in a gram molecular weight of any compound or diatomic elemental gas.

The fact that there are the same number

---

lion years. Avogadro's number is now known to a precision of 1 part in 60,000. The percentage error is about 0.006 per cent.

of atoms in a gram atomic weight of any element is apparent from the atomic weight scale alone. (The actual number, however, is not apparent.) If an oxygen atom weighs 16 times as much as a hydrogen atom, then there must be the same number of atoms in 16 gm of oxygen as there are in 1 gm of hydrogen, and this is the same number as in 14 gm of nitrogen, 12 gm of carbon or 238 gm of uranium.[6]

Let us now go back and recapitulate what we have said directly or indirectly about Avogadro's number:

1. It is the number of molecules in 22.4 liters of any *gas* at STP.

2. It is the number of atoms in a gram atomic weight of any *element*, gas, liquid, or solid.

3. It is the number of molecules in a gram molecular weight of any *compound*, gas, liquid, or solid.

4. It is the number referred to in the 1961 definition of a mole on p. 249.

5. For any element in any compound in which there is not more than one atom of that element per molecule, it is the number of atoms of that element in an Avogadro's number of molecules of that compound. That is, in 6×10^{23} molecules of hydrogen chloride, there are 6×10^{23} atoms of hydrogen and 6×10^{23} atoms of chlorine. In

[6] If you have trouble seeing this, consider apples all of the same weight, and oranges all of the same weight, but let an apple weigh half as much as an orange. Suppose you have a 10-lb bag of each. You may not know how many you have of each but you can be certain that you have twice as many apples as you have oranges. You also know that to have the same number of oranges as you have apples you would have to have a 20-lb bag of them. You might assign an atomic weight of 1 to apples, and 2 to oranges. It follows that there are as many oranges in 2 tons of them as there are apples in 1 ton.

6×10^{23} molecules of NaOH (sodium hydroxide) there are 6×10^{23} atoms of Na, 6×10^{23} atoms of oxygen and 6×10^{23} atoms of hydrogen. It follows that if there are 2, 3, or 4 atoms of an element per molecule of a compound then there will be 2, 3, or 4 times 6×10^{23} atoms of that element in a gram molecular weight of the compound. Thus, in 6×10^{23} molecules of H_2SO_4 (sulfuric acid) there are $2 \times 6 \times 10^{23}$ atoms of hydrogen, $1 \times 6 \times 10^{23}$ atoms of sulfur, and $4 \times 6 \times 10^{23}$ atoms of oxygen. If these concepts are not clear to you, solving the problems at the end of the chapter should make them so.

DETERMINATION OF FORMULAS

Once the atomic weight of an element had been determined, it was easy enough to determine the number of atoms of that element in any of its gaseous compounds. For example, 22.4 liters of gaseous ether (the kind used as an anesthetic) weighs 74 gm. By actual analysis this amount of ether contains 48 gm of carbon, 10 gm of hydrogen, and 16 gm of oxygen. Dividing each of these quantities by the respective atomic weights of carbon, hydrogen, and oxygen, shows that there are 4 atoms of carbon, 10 atoms of hydrogen and 1 atom of oxygen per molecule of ether. The chemical formula of ether is then $C_4H_{10}O$.

CHEMICAL SYMBOLISM

We have, of course, been using chemical symbols for some time. You should already be familiar with them. Dalton used pictorial symbols, a few of which are illustrated in Fig. 16-4. Berzelius, the great Swedish analytical chemist, dropped the pictorial symbols for the first letter of the name of the element, or, if two elements began with the same letter, he added one of the other letters in the name, e.g., C for carbon, Cl for chlorine, Ca for calcium, Cr for chromium, etc. What, you may ask, about Na for sodium, K for potassium, Fe for iron, Cu for copper, Au for gold, and a few others? These were first given Latin names, for almost up to 1800 Latin was the language of the scholars. Na stands for natrium, the Latin name for sodium, Fe for ferron, Au for aurum, Ag for argentum (silver), etc.

These symbols always represent one atom, and one only, of the element. In conjunction with its atomic weight, the symbol for an element signifies one atom of the element and gives us (1) an abbreviation of the name of the element, (2) the weight of one atom relative to that of the ^{12}C atom, (3) the weight in grams of 6×10^{23} atoms of the element, (4) the least weight (in grams) of the element found in 22.4 liters of any of its gaseous compounds.

In order to write the chemical formula of a compound we need to know two things, the elements composing it and the number of atoms of each element per molecule. Chemical analysis gives us the first, and the method discussed in the preceding section gives us the second. For the elemental diatomic gases the formulas are H_2, O_2, N_2, Cl_2 and F_2, for all occur in the free state as double atoms. You have already seen how formulas in general are written, H_2O, CO_2, N_2O_3, HCl, H_2SO_4, $C_4H_{10}O$, etc. The formula of a compound gives us a shorthand method of writing the compound, it tells us the kinds of atoms composing the compound and the number of each kind of atom present. In conjunction with the atomic weights of the various atoms in the compound, we can determine

how many grams of the compound make a mole (gram molecular weight), the weight of 6×10^{23} molecules of it, and the percentage composition by weight of the various elements composing it. Thus, from the formula, H_2O and the atomic weights of 1 and 16 for H and O, respectively, we see that the molecular weight is 18, and that $\frac{2}{18}$ of any given weight of water is hydrogen and $\frac{16}{18}$ of it is oxygen.

CHEMICAL EQUATIONS

Chemical symbolism helps us to write chemical reactions. Such reactions are written in the form of equations, with an arrow taking the place of an equal sign. Thus,

$$Iron + sulfur \rightarrow Iron\ sulfide$$

becomes

$$Fe + S \rightarrow FeS$$

Other examples are

$$Zn + Cl_2 \rightarrow ZnCl_2$$

and

$$C + O_2 \rightarrow CO_2$$

These equations tell us that one atom of zinc combines with one molecule of chlorine to form one molecule of zinc chloride, and one atom of carbon combines with one molecule of oxygen to form one molecule of carbon dioxide.

$$2H_2 + O_2 \rightarrow 2H_2O$$

Here two molecules of hydrogen combine with one of oxygen to form two molecules of water vapor. A formula represents a molecular unit, often called a formula unit, and the number in front of it (called a coefficient) applies to the whole unit. On the other hand, the number placed as a subscript applies only to that particular kind of atom.

To write an equation one must know whether or not the substances involved will react, and, if they do, one must know what products will be formed. Furthermore, the Law of Conservation of Mass applies, so that there must be the same number of the same kinds of atoms on both sides of the equation. Seeing that there are is called balancing an equation. Thus, the equation

$$H_2 + O_2 \rightarrow H_2O$$

is not balanced. However,

$$2H_2 + O_2 \rightarrow 2H_2O$$

is balanced. Similarly,

$$Na + O_2 \rightarrow Na_2O$$

and

$$Al + O_2 \rightarrow Al_2O_3$$

are not balanced. In balancing equations, it is always assumed that the formulas for the compounds formed are correctly written. Knowledge of the combining power of atoms (valence) is necessary in the balancing of any but the simplest equations.

From the formulas H_2O and Na_2O we see that hydrogen and sodium have the same combining power. If that of hydrogen is 1, then that of sodium must be 1, and that of oxygen must be 2. Therefore, just as it took 4 hydrogen atoms to combine with 2 oxygen atoms to form 2 molecules of water, it takes 4 sodium atoms to combine with 2 atoms of oxygen to form Na_2O. Hence, to balance the above equation we write,

$$4Na + O_2 \rightarrow 2Na_2O$$

Following the same general line of reasoning we balance the other equation by writing

$$2Al + 3O_2 \rightarrow 2Al_2O_3$$

Carefully examine the following equations to see how they are balanced.[7]

$$Zn + 2HCl \rightarrow ZnCl_2 + H_2 \uparrow$$

$$AgNO_3 + NaCl \rightarrow AgCl \downarrow + NaNO_3$$

RADICALS

Radicals are groups of atoms that have strong tendencies to maintain their identity as a group in chemical reactions, e.g.,

$$H_2SO_4 + Zn \rightarrow ZnSO_4 + H_2 \uparrow$$

$$2HNO_3 + Mg \rightarrow Mg(NO_3)_2 + H_2 \uparrow$$

$$CaCl_2 + Na_2CO_3 \rightarrow CaCO_3 + 2NaCl$$

Here the radicals are $-SO_4$, $-NO_3$ and $-CO_3$. Note that they have valences of 2, 1, and 2. They are called the sulfate, nitrate, and carbonate radicals, respectively. Some other common radicals are $-OH$ (hydroxide), $-PO_4$ (phosphate), $-NO_2$ (nitrite), $-SO_3$ (sulfite), NH_4- (ammonium), $-ClO$ (chlorate). Note that the -ate radical contains more oxygen than the corresponding -ite radical.

NAMING OF COMPOUNDS

The naming of compounds is for the most part systematic, i.e., the name tells us something about the composition. Of greatest importance is the suffix. Thus, any compound composed of two elements

[7] The arrow pointing upward indicates that the hydrogen is given off as a gas, whereas the arrow pointing downward indicates that a solid has been "thrown down," i.e., precipitated from solution (because it is insoluble in the solvent).

has the suffix *-ide* for the second element. Examples are hydrogen chloride, sodium chloride, carbon dioxide, hydrogen oxide (water), hydrogen sulfide, sodium hydride, potassium iodide, calcium carbide.

Other suffixes are those of the radicals already listed. Thus NaOH is sodium hydroxide, $Ca_3(PO_4)_2$ is calcium phosphate, KNO_2 is potassium nitrite, $MgSO_3$ is magnesium sulfite, and NH_4OH is ammonium hydroxide.

Where two elements form more than one compound, the suffixes *-ous* and *-ic* occur in the name of the first element. Examples are mercurous oxide (Hg_2O) and mercuric oxide (HgO), ferrous oxide (FeO) and ferric oxide (Fe_2O_3), and cuprous sulfide (Cu_2S) and cupric sulfide (CuS). Note that the compound in each pair that has the largest proportion of the metal per oxygen atom is the -ous compound; the others are -ic compounds. Note also that acids are -ic compounds, e.g., nitric acid, hydrochloric acid, sulfuric acid, etc. Prefixes such as mono-, di-, tri-, tetra-, penta-, etc., are also given to the second element in a compound to indicate the number of atoms of that kind present per molecule of the compound, e.g., carbon monoxide, carbon dioxide, sulfur trioxide, carbon tetrachloride, phosphorus pentachloride, etc.

These examples form only a small part of the system, a system made necessary by the tens of thousands of inorganic compounds, let alone the hundreds of thousands of organic compounds. The naming of the organic compounds can become singularly complex. For example, the compound, $C_6H_4COOCH_3COOH$ is acetylsalicylic acid, a name that tells the organic chemist a great deal about its composition, whereas its common name, aspirin, tells him nothing.

SUMMARY

About 1860 Cannizzaro resurrected Avogadro's hypothesis of fifty years before, and thus cleared away the confusion in the science of chemistry that had resulted from the failure to reconcile Dalton's atomic theory with Gay-Lussac's Law of Combining Volumes. As soon as it was recognized that equal volumes of all gases at STP contained the same number of molecules and that the chemically reactive elemental gases consisted of two atoms per molecule, a very simple method of determining the relative weights of atoms was devised. This method consisted of comparing (at STP) the weights of a liter of a gaseous element or compound with a liter of hydrogen, the lightest of all gases, which was assigned a relative molecular weight of 2 (atomic weight of 1). If oxygen is used as the standard of comparison, then

Molecular weight of gas $X =$

$$32 \times \frac{\text{Weight of liter of gas } X}{\text{Weight of liter of oxygen}}$$

Dalton had begun an investigation into the relative weights of atoms by a method that involved the Law of Multiple Proportions, the Law of Definite Proportions, and a guess at the number of atoms per molecule. His insistence on the correctness of the fifth assumption of his atomic theory made most of his atomic weights invalid. Cannizzaro's method was accurate and simple. It consisted of weighing 22.4 liters of various gaseous compounds (at STP) *containing the element under consideration*, and assuming that if you used a large enough number of such compounds, one of them would contain only one atom of the element per molecule. The molecules of such a gaseous compound contain the smallest "packet" of the element possible in any of that element's gaseous compounds. By comparing the weight of the element in 22.4 liters of that compound with the weight of the ^{12}C in 22.4 liters of a gaseous carbon compound at STP, the molecular weight of the element is determined.

The adoption of ^{12}C as the standard for atomic weights makes it possible to redefine a mole in a simpler and more meaningful manner: *The mole is the quantity of substance containing the same number of molecules (or atoms, or radicals, or ions or electrons, as the case may be) as there are in 12 grams of ^{12}C.* This number is 6×10^{23}, now known as Avogadro's number. It is also the number of molecules in a gram molecular volume (22.4 liters) of any gas at STP. These concepts make the determination of chemical formulas possible.

In the early investigations into relative atomic weights, the comparison was made with hydrogen. Later it was switched to oxygen, which was assigned a relative weight of 16.0000. In 1961 the chemists, at the insistence of the physicists, have agreed to change over to a specific isotope of carbon, ^{12}C, as the standard of comparison.

EXERCISES

I. TERMS AND CONCEPTS

Atomic weight
Molecular
  weight
Gram atomic
  weight
Gram molec-
  ular weight

Gram molecular
  volume
Avogadro's
  number
Mole
Formula
Chemical symbol
Chemical equation

II. PROBLEMS

1. How are atoms and molecules defined in this chapter?

2. What is meant by atomic weights?

From what assumption does the concept of atomic weights arise?

3. The oxygen in a quart container weighs 1.39 gm. How much would a quart of hydrogen weigh at STP? A quart of nitrogen?

4. Let us assign a value of 2 for the molecular weight of hydrogen. How do we determine the atomic weight of oxygen?

5. At STP 22.4 liters of butane (bottled gas, formula, C_4H_{10}) weighs how much? How much does the hydrogen in it weigh? How many molecules of propane are there in 22.4 liters? How many atoms of hydrogen are there in 22.4 liters of butane? How many atoms of carbon?

6. How much will 6×10^{23} atoms of gold (Au) weigh? Of lead (Pb)? Of sodium (Na)? Of helium (He)?

7. How many atoms are there in a mole of gold? Of lead? Of sodium? Of helium?

8. One liter of a gas X weighs 0.715 gm at STP. Under the same conditions a liter of oxygen weighs 1.430 gm. Calculate the molecular weight of gas X.

9. How many grams are there in a mole of NaCl? Of H_2SO_4? Of $C_{12}H_{22}O_{11}$ (cane sugar)? Of a compound whose formula is $Fe_3Al_2(SiO_4)_3$?

10. Refer to Table 17-1. At the end of it add the data for butane (question 5 above).

11. A liter of an oxide of sulfur weighs 2.81 gm at STP, and by analysis is found to consist of 50 per cent S and 50 per cent O_2 by weight. Calculate its formula by the method used in Table 17-2.

12. Refer to question 5. What is the percentage by weight of hydrogen in butane?

13. From the following data calculate the atomic weight of chlorine:

Compound	Molecular Wt.	% Chlorine
Hydrogen chloride	36.5	97.3
Chlorine	71.0	100.0
Carbon tetrachloride	154.0	92.2
Chloroform	119.5	89.0

14. How many moles are there in 140 gm of nitrogen? In 69 gm of sodium? In 256 gm of SO_2?

15. Learn the symbols for hydrogen, helium, oxygen, nitrogen, fluorine, chlorine, bromine, carbon, sulfur, phosphorus, sodium, potassium, calcium, magnesium, aluminum, iron, copper, zinc, lead, mercury, silver.

16. Write the names of the following compounds: HCl, HNO_3, H_2SO_4, $NaCl$, NH_3, $NaOH$, KOH, CO, CO_2, SO_2, FeO, Fe_2O_3, HgO, Hg_2O, Cu_2O, CuO, KCl, $MgCl_2$, $AlCl_3$, $FeCl_2$, $FeCl_3$, Na_2SO_4, $CaCO_3$, H_2S.

17. Write the formulas for the following compounds: sodium nitrate, magnesium sulfate, silver chloride, sodium oxide, magnesium oxide, carbon tetrachloride, potassium sulfide, sodium carbonate, calcium sulfate, sodium nitrite.

18. Balance the following equations if they are unbalanced:

$$Na_2O + H_2O \rightarrow 2NaOH$$
$$CaO + H_2O \rightarrow Ca(OH)_2$$
$$K + Cl_2 \rightarrow 2KCl$$
$$Al + HCl \rightarrow AlCl_3 + H_2$$
$$Na + H_2O \rightarrow NaOH + H_2$$

19. Learn the radicals: $-OH$, $-SO_4$, $-CO_3$, $-NO_3$, NH_4-.

20. Write chemical equations for each of the following:

a. One molecule of nitrogen combines with three molecules of hydrogen to form two molecules of ammonia.

b. One atom of lead combines with two atoms of chlorine to form one molecule of lead chloride.

c. Two atoms of lithium combine with one atom of sulfuric acid to form one molecule of lithium sulfate plus free hydrogen.

CHAPTER XVIII

Evolution of the Periodic Table

The classification of the elements has not only a pedagogical importance, as a means for more readily learning assorted facts that are systematically arranged and correlated, but it also has a scientific importance, since it discloses new analogies and hence opens up new routes for the exploration of the elements.

—DIMITRI MENDELYEEV (*1871*)

Classification is a very important kind of scientific activity. It is the first step that man must take in order to reduce chaos to order. No one can talk intelligently and for long about any large group of items, be they chemical elements or compounds, kinds of life, cloth, or even people without using some system of classification. Furthermore, to be of much use a classification system must be one that is widely used by other people; otherwise confusion results. In science, the systems used are world wide, so that scientists can intelligently communicate with one another. In the classification of life, for example, the names of the various classes, orders, families, genera, and species are the same in all languages. Not until some classifying has been done is it possible to see relationships, to speculate, devise hypotheses, formulate laws, and develop theories about the various kinds of matter.

It should be realized, however, that all classification systems are man made, that they are made for particular purposes, and that if better systems are invented, the old ones are usually discarded. Just as the pathways of science are strewn with discarded hypotheses and theories, they are also strewn with discarded classification systems. The making of a classification system involves definitions of the various categories of materials with which we are working. As our knowledge increases, differences that appeared important earlier may turn out to be trivial, and vice versa. Our definitions may turn out to be inadequate, or even invalid, and so new ones have to be made that are in accordance with new facts.

THE PROBLEM OF CLASSIFICATION OF THE ELEMENTS

So it has been with the chemical elements. No progress was made, in fact no progress could be made, in the classification of matter as long as it was believed that there were only four elements—earth, fire, water, and air. We have seen (p. 219) how Robert Boyle started the science of chemistry by attempting to classify matter into elements and compounds. His trouble was his lack of an operational definition of an element, i.e., his definition did not include some operation for detecting an element. This could only come with time, and, needless to say, the list of elements had to be revised from time to time as it continued to grow. In a list published in 1789 Lavoisier included 26 that have stood the test of time. Once a proper theory of combustion and an acceptable atomic theory had been formulated, the science of chemistry developed at a faster rate. More and more elements were added, some because of new developments in other fields. For example, the invention of the battery led to the discovery of sodium and potassium via electrolysis, and, later, the developing science of spectroscopy added rubidium and cesium to the list. By 1869 about sixty elements were definitely known, with a few more in the doubtful column.

Ever since it was realized that the elements held the key to the understanding of all matter, chemists have been largely concerned with the study of their physical and chemical properties, and with investigations that would reveal which elements react with which, and under what conditions, what compounds were formed from them, and the nature of these compounds. The knowledge accumulated for a time at an ever increasing rate, but as more elements were discovered and the number of known compounds increased prodigiously, this knowledge became burdensome; the need for a basis of classification grew.

There had to be some system; there could not be a never-ending number of elements, for this would be a denial of law and order in the universe. The belief that the number of elements was limited grew as it became increasingly difficult to add to the list. The common elements were known early; the new ones were rare elements. Today the list has increased to 90 for the naturally occurring elements; a dozen more artificially made elements have been created.

The long quest for simplicity in nature has been at least partially fulfilled, for the chemist is now certain that there are no more new naturally occurring elements to be discovered *anywhere in the universe.* This sounds like a very dogmatic statement, which probably will be viewed with scorn by the nonscientists. But every chemist and every physicist in the whole world believes that it is as definitely established as the law of gravitation; he has to, or else admit that the enormous body of evidence we have concerning the structure of the atom is completely false. Before you reach the end of this course this evidence will be presented to you.

Under the stimulus of Dalton's atomic theory with its emphasis on the relative weights of atoms, the atomic weights of many elements had been determined. As early as 1815 the Englishman, William Prout, had noticed that the atomic weights, as then determined, were close to even multiples of the weight of the hydrogen atom. He therefore suggested that hydrogen was the primordial stuff of which all other matter is made. However, as more accurate determinations of atomic weights became available, the deviations from exact multiples of that of hydrogen became greater. The popularity of his hypothesis declined and was forgotten, only to be revived again in our own century, albeit in somewhat different form.

VALENCE

The fact that elements combine to form compounds indicates that they have a "combining capacity." One of the assumptions of Dalton's atomic theory states that chemical combination consists of the union of atoms of different elements in fixed ratios. This union, together with whatever determines the fixed ratio, i.e., the number of atoms of one element that will combine with one atom of another element, is the combining capacity. We call it *valence*, a term coined by an English chemist in 1850. As he defined it, it expresses the relative capacities of atoms for combination with one another. In Chapter XXXI we will see that valence today is a far more complicated concept than the simple one of a hundred years ago. We prefer the simple concept at this stage of our knowledge, and so will use it just as the professional chemists did for nearly seventy-five years. Moreover, the designation of valence as positive or negative, common in high school texts, is incorrect, for how can there be a negative combining capacity?

Two elements with the lowest combining capacities were selected and assigned a valence of 1. These elements were hydrogen and chlorine. They themselves combine in a one-to-one ratio to form HCl (hydrogen chloride). One or the other of them will combine with every other naturally-occurring element (except for the inert gases, which will not combine with any element and so have a valence of zero). By determining the atomic ratios in a compound containing an element combined with either hydrogen or chlorine, we learn its valence. Thus, the valence of oxygen is 2, for from the method of determining atomic ratios (see pp. 245–246), we see that its combining capacity is twice that of hydrogen. For example, one oxygen atom will combine with two hydrogen atoms to form H_2O. Using the same method we find that three hydrogen atoms will combine with one nitrogen atom to form NH_3 (ammonia). The valence of nitrogen is thus 3 in ammonia. In methane (cooking gas) we find (Table 17-1) that one atom of carbon will combine with four atoms of hydrogen. Thus, carbon has a valence of 4. Higher principal valences are unknown

(see below). Once the atomic ratios (formulas) have been determined experimentally by the methods described on pp. 245–247, the valence can be determined by simple inspection of the formula as long as we stick to simple compounds. The situation is complicated by a few elements that have multiple valences, e.g., iron, phosphorus, nitrogen. Such elements, as a general rule, have one valence that occurs more often than the other (or others), which is called the principal valence.

METALS AND NONMETALS

The division of the elements into these two groups is the simplest and the oldest of all classifications. It is an obvious one, for metals have a characteristic way of reflecting light, a metallic sheen that we call luster, which makes them look different from the nonmetals, even to the layman. They also conduct both heat and electricity far better than the nonmetals, most have high density, and most can be flattened by hammering without breaking, or can be made into wires. Not all have these properties to the same degree; they range from a degree that borders on perfection to almost not at all. Some are semimetallic in character, i.e., their properties are, in part at least, nonmetallic.

Nonmetallic elements that are solids lack the luster, the conductivity, the malleability of metals. Many nonmetals are gases at room temperature. Actually there is a gradation both ways, from the metallic into the nonmetallic and from the nonmetallic to the metallic, not only in physical properties, but also in chemical properties. The result is a number of borderline elements, e.g., silicon, arsenic, boron, germanium. These are sometimes called metalloids. In general, metals have no great tendency to combine with other metals to form simple compounds, but show considerable tendency—sometimes a violent tendency—to combine with nonmetals. Nonmetals, on the other hand, show considerable tendency to combine with one another, although rarely with the readiness with which they combine with metals.

One group of elements, the inert gases (none known before the 1890's), while definitely nonmetallic in their physical properties have none of the chemical properties of the other nonmetals. About 70 of the 90 naturally occurring elements are metals, leaving only 20 for the nonmetallic group. Moreover, all of the artificially made elements are metallic. This classification into metals and nonmetals is an extremely useful one, so useful in fact that we will be using it constantly, despite the lack of a clear-cut boundary between the two groups.

The search for regularities among these two groups continued. Gradation of properties existed no matter what property was considered. For example, among the metals, the melting points ranged from below 0° C (mercury) to more than 3300° C (tungsten). The hardnesses paralleled the

melting points, i.e., those with the highest melting points had the greatest hardnesses. On the other hand, as the intensities of some properties increased, those of others decreased, e.g., the densities of some subgroups increased as the melting points dropped. The most active metals formed the strongest bases, the least active the weakest (if at all). These were all general trends only; exceptions among them made the task more difficult. More detailed investigation led to the grouping of elements into families, the members of which had for the most part similar properties, or properties that changed systematically. Progress along this line was handicapped at first by too few of the possible members of a family being known, but as time went on, more and more elements were added to the list, and confidence in the family grouping as a valid concept increased.

ALKALI METALS

The members of this family are lithium, sodium, potassium, ribidium, and cesium. All are highly active chemically; all combine with chlorine with varying degrees of violence to form salts with similar properties. They all react more or less vio-

TABLE 18-1

THE ALKALI METALS

	Li	Na	K	Rb	Cs
Chemical activity	High—increasing $\longrightarrow$				
Strength of base	Very strong—increasing $\longrightarrow$				
Density	Low—increasing $\longrightarrow$				
Melting point	Low—decreasing $\longrightarrow$				
Atomic weight	Low to moderate—increasing $\longrightarrow$				
Valence	All are 1				
Formula of chloride	LiCl	NaCl	KCl	RbCl	CsCl

TABLE 18-2

THE ALKALINE EARTH METALS

	Be	Mg	Ca	Sr	Ba	Ra
Chemical activity	Moderately high—increasing $\longrightarrow$					
Strength of base	Moderately strong—increasing $\longrightarrow$					
Density	Moderate					
Melting point	Moderately high*					
Atomic weight	Low to high—increasing $\longrightarrow$					
Valence	All are 2.					
Formula of chloride	$BeCl_2$	$MgCl_2$	$CaCl_2$	$SrCl_2$	$BaCl_2$	$RaCl_2$

* The melting points do not grade systematically as in the alkali metals.

lently with water, releasing hydrogen gas and forming strong bases [1] (hydroxides). The trend of some of the properties of the members of this family are shown in Table 18-1.

ALKALINE EARTH METALS

The members of this family are beryllium, magnesium, calcium, strontium, barium, and radium. They are all active metals but not so active as the alkali metals.

[1] The bases formed from the union of potassium and sodium with water are commercially sold as lye.

They all react vigorously with chlorine to form salts with similar properties; they all form bases but of more moderate strength than those of the alkali metals. They are also harder, denser, and have higher melting points. Above all, they all have a valence of 2. Their properties are shown in Table 18-2.

HALOGENS

The halogens—fluorine, chlorine, bromine, and iodine—are a familiar family of nonmetals. At room temperature the first two are gases, bromine is a liquid, and

TABLE 18-3

THE HALOGENS

	F	Cl	Br	I
Chemical activity	Extremely high	Very high	High	Moderately high
Strength of acid	Strong	Very strong	Very strong	Very strong
Melting point, C	-223	-103	-7.2	114
Valence	1	1	1	1
Atomic weight	19	35.5	80	127
State	Gas	Gas	Liquid	Solid
Odor	Strong	Strong	Strong	Strong
Molecular formula	F_2	Cl_2	Br_2	I_2

iodine a solid. They all react with hydrogen to form the very strong acids. They are all highly active, fluorine being the most active of all the nonmetals. The trends of their properties are shown in Table 18-3.

INERT GASES

Another family, completely unknown before the 1890's, is that of the inert gases—helium, neon, argon, krypton, xenon, and radon. Their density and the atomic weight increase in the order given. They are completely unreactive, i.e., they form no compounds whatever. They are obviously not metals, but it is scarcely fair to call them nonmetals either, for they have none of the chemical properties of the nonmetals, but there is no other place to put them. The reasons for their lack of chemical properties must await a later chapter.

MENDELYEEV'S PERIODIC LAW HISTORICAL DEVELOPMENT

For many years chemists in their search for order among the elements attempted to arrange them in some kind of order. One of the difficulties in the 1860's was that only about two-thirds of the elements known today were known then; where the gaps were, no one knew. The chemists working on the problem then had an advantage over their predecessors, for it was in 1860 that Cannizzaro presented his method of determining atomic weights based on Avogadro's Law. More accurate atomic weights (or should we be up to the minute and say, more accurate relative atomic masses) became available.

It was Dmitri Mendelyeev (1834–1907), a brilliant Russian chemist, who was the first to clearly recognize the fundamental importance of both atomic weights and valence, and to suspect that these two properties probably played the chief role in determining the other physical and chemical properties of the elements. After many false starts he hit upon the method of arranging the elements in horizontal and vertical rows according to atomic weights, taking care to place those with the same valence, *and with similar physical and chemical properties* in the same vertical column.[2]

This puts elements with similar properties in the same family. Gaps appeared in the rows in places. Two of these gaps appeared between zinc and arsenic. Arsenic could not be put next to zinc and below aluminum for it had none of the properties of aluminum. Nor did it have any of the properties of silicon, but it does have some of the properties of phosphorus. Mendelyeev predicted that two elements would some day be discovered that would have atomic weights between those of zinc and arsenic, and that one would have properties similar to those of aluminum, the other similar to those of silicon. Not long afterwards these were discovered; one was called gallium, the other germanium.[3] Mendelyeev had predicted its properties. How close he came is shown in Table 18-4.

Mendelyeev did nearly as well on two other missing elements. The prediction was based on the properties of the elements before it, after it, above it, and below it in

[2] While his initial chart had elements in horizontal and vertical rows, its appearance was very different from a modern chart. It is the technique of representing the elements that makes the difference. Mendelyeev himself revised the chart many times.

[3] Germanium was long held to be a useless element, annoying to the metallurgist because it was commonly an impurity in other ores that was difficult to get rid of. It has recently become highly valued because it makes transistors possible.

TABLE 18-4

PROPERTIES OF GERMANIUM

	Predicted	Measured
Atomic weight	72.0	72.6
Valence	4	4
Specific heat	0.073	0.076
Specific gravity	5.5	5.47
Specific gravity of its tetrachloride	1.9	1.887
Boiling point of its tetrachloride	under 100° C	83° C

the table. He even questioned the atomic weight assigned to thorium at that time because it placed thorium in the wrong place in his table. He was later proved right. He felt justified in announcing what we today call his Periodic Law: *When the elements are arranged in the order of their atomic weights, elements with similar properties are repeated periodically.* In the words of Mendelyeev, "the properties of the elements are a periodic function of their atomic weights."

A period represents a stepwise change from elements strongly metallic to weakly metallic to weakly nonmetallic to strongly nonmetallic, and then, at the end, an abrupt cessation of all chemical properties, i.e., the inert gases. In the next period, the same sequence is repeated all over again although not exactly in the same way. For example, the boundary line between the metals and the nonmetals, indefinite though it may be, shifts to the right from period to period.

The system is far more complicated than it may appear from this brief description, as can be seen by a glance at the periodic chart on the inside of the front cover of this text.[4] The horizontal rows are called

periods, the vertical rows families. None of the inert gases were known at the time, so this family was missing completely. Mendelyeev had to deviate from the order of atomic weights when he came to iodine and tellurium, for to put them in regular sequence would have meant taking iodine out of the halogen family. Later two other such reversals, nickel and cobalt, and potassium and argon, had to be made for similar reasons.

Chemists were slow to accept it at first despite the brilliance of Mendelyeev's predictions. By 1900, however, the periodic chart, greatly improved, was a tool of every chemist in the land. In the modern form, serial numbers are assigned each element for easy reference, just as are house numbers on a street.[5] Thus, number 17 is chlorine, number 92 is uranium, etc.

The chart contains a great wealth of information for those who know how to read it. Thus, all the elements in the first vertical row on the left have a valence of 1, those in the second vertical row a valence of 2, etc. The transition series offer complications that we will not attempt to unravel here. In later chapters we will

[4] The chart is placed here so that you can quickly locate it with no effort. You will have abundant use for it. There is also a table of ele-

ments arranged alphabetically on the inside of the front cover.

[5] Later on we will find that these numbers have far greater significance than mere serial numbers.

return to this, when we will be better able to understand it. The chart lists all the kinds of naturally occurring atoms in the universe. From these atoms are made all of the different kinds of matter that we know. Therefore, if we can completely understand everything the chart has to tell us, including above all the basic reasons for the periodicity, the basic reasons for the gradually changing properties in each period, and in each family, we will have progressed a very long way towards understanding matter. Not all the way, however, for the fact that these regularities and interrelations exist suggests that atoms may not be the fundamental building of the universe after all. If atoms do not consist of parts, i.e., have no structure, and the atoms of different elements are different, then it is hard to see how the similarities and the gradational aspects of the physical and chemical properties could exist.

Be that as it may, the periodic chart was a tremendous step forward. The next step is to find out the reasons behind it, what makes it "tick," so to speak. But before we can do this we must investigate another aspect of matter, its electrical nature. This electrical aspect is so fundamental to the understanding of matter that we will now turn our attention to the study of electricity and magnetism.

SUMMARY

The fundamental belief of scientists that there is order in the universe caused them to look for an orderly arrangement of the elements. All attempts were either unsatisfactory or failures until about two-thirds of the naturally occurring elements had been discovered. This was expectable, for if there are too many holes in a pattern, they may prevent you from seeing the pattern. The search for regularities revealed that the properties of the elements were not separate and distinct, entirely unrelated to the properties of all other elements. Instead, most could be arranged in sequences of one sort or another in which the properties graded from one to the other more or less systematically. Certain families were recognized, e.g., the alkali metals, the alkaline earth metals, and the halogens (among the nonmetals).

Finally, Mendelyeev, in 1869, arranged the known elements in a series of vertical rows arranged in order of their atomic weights (as generally accepted at that time). The horizontal rows emphasized a certain periodicity of elements with similar properties. There is little point in further describing Mendelyeev's original table. In the course of time his vertical rows became the horizontal rows that we call periods, and his horizontal rows, such as they were, became our vertical columns, which we now call groups (or families). From his table he formulated the periodic law: *When the elements are arranged in the order of their atomic weights, elements with similar properties are repeated periodically.* Most important among these similar properties was their valence. Mendelyeev left blank spaces for undiscovered elements and described their probable properties on the basis of the properties of the known elements above and below, to the right and the left, of the blank space. His success at prediction helped greatly in getting his Periodic Law accepted. The chart was a great step forward in the understanding of matter.

EXERCISES

I. TERMS AND CONCEPTS

Valence	Periods
Metals	Groups
Nonmetals	Families
Alkali metals	Periodic Law
Alkaline earth metals	Periodic chart
Halogens	Periodic table
Inert gases	

II. PROBLEMS

1. On the inside of the front cover of this book is a modern version of the periodic table. On the inside of the front cover is an alphabetical list of the elements which can be used to quickly ascertain the symbol, the atomic weight, and the atomic number of any element. Knowing the atomic number and the symbol, you can quickly locate any element in the periodic table. Study both until you learn how to use them.

2. Which of the following are metals, which nonmetals?

Cesium	Silicon
Strontium	Bismuth
Manganese	Radon
Argon	Radium
Arsenic	Phosphorus

3. In the periodic table there are a few pairs of elements that are reversed with respect to the order of their atomic weights. Pick them out.

4. If the valence of sodium is 1, what is the valence of potassium? Of cesium? How do you know? (Do not refer to any tables in the text.)

5. If the valence of sodium is 1, what is the valence of calcium? Of barium? How do you know?

6. Would you expect copper to have properties more similar to those of silver or more similar to those of zinc? Why?

7. What is a period? A family? A group?

8. What family was entirely unknown when Mendelyeev first formulated his table?

9. Why could the periodic chart not have been formulated in the early 1800's?

10. Given a sample of an element in a finely powdered form, describe a way in which you could establish it as a metal or a nonmetal with reasonable certainty.

11. Sodium and potassium (among many other elements) are never found free, or native, i.e., as the pure element in nature, whereas gold and platinum are almost always found free. Why?

12. a. Which may be said to be more metallic, sodium or aluminum? Sodium or silicon? Justify your answer.

b. Would you expect iodine to be more, or less, metallic than fluorine? Justify your answer.

13. Name three elements that are metalloids, i.e., like metals in some respects but yet not true metals.

14. In what fundamental respects are helium and radon alike?

15. Note that hydrogen occurs on both sides of the periodic chart. Suggest reasons for placing it on both sides.

PART

IV

THE ELECTRICAL NATURE OF MATTER

In Part III we studied two great theories, the kinetic-molecular theory and the atomic theory. Together they give us a picture of matter as consisting of tiny moving particles whose freedom of motion determines the state of that matter in bulk, i.e., whether it will be gaseous, liquid, or solid. The two theories supplement one another. The kinetic theory is a purely mechanical one—as was Newton's planetary theory—which explains a large number of diverse physical phenomena in terms of the moving particles and the forces due to or on them. The atomic theory, also essentially mechanical in nature, was more concerned with the chemical properties of matter, i.e., the properties that are based on a change in matter while those properties are being observed, than with the physical. Neither theory gives us much fundamental information about the nature of atoms or molecules. Both allowed for attractive forces between the particles, but neither provided any explanation of the origin or the nature of these forces.

The first suggestion that these forces were electrical in nature was made about 1817. Berzelius, the great Swedish analytical chemist, was probably the strongest early advocate of this view. Experiments involving the electrolysis of certain solutions added to the evidence without offering a fruitful explanation of these electrical forces. In fact all early attempts to explain them were entirely mechanical; they were based on the properties of a supposed imponderable fluid, reminiscent of caloric and phlogiston. Up to about the beginning of the present century all fruitful physical theories were mechanical in nature; there was no compelling reason to believe that all phenomena in nature could not be interpreted in terms of other mechanical theories.

In the closing years of the last century and the beginning years of the present one, the realization grew that the electrical nature of matter could not be explained in terms of a mechanical model. The phenomena of electricity (and magnetism) depend on a new fundamental property of matter itself, the electric charge, and not on an external imponderable fluid. The concept of charge cannot be defined in terms of more elementary concepts; it has to be intuitively arrived at just as are the concepts of mass, length, and time. In the final analysis, this means that we cannot state in so many words what charge really is. However, we must understand the concept if we are to learn about the fundamental nature of atoms and molecules. We can do this only by studying the behavior of charges, by measuring their magnitude, by learning the laws that govern their behavior, etc. We therefore turn to a study of the more important aspects of electricity and magnetism.

CHAPTER XIX

Electrostatics

Like charges repel, and unlike charges attract each other, with a force that varies inversely with the square of the distance between them . . . in all of atomic and molecular physics, in all solids, liquids and gases, and in all things that involve our relationship with our environment, the only force law, besides gravity, is some manifestation of this simple law. Frictional forces, wind forces, chemical bonds, viscosity, magnetism, the forces that make the wheels of industry go round—all these are nothing but Coulomb's law. . . .

—J. R. ZACHARAIS

HISTORICAL DEVELOPMENT

As far back as the time of Thales or before, man knew of four phenomena that we now know to be electrical in origin. These are (1) the power of amber (fossil resin), which had been rubbed against one's garments, to attract bits of straw or other light objects, (2) lightning, (3) the phenomenon of St. Elmo's fire,[1] and (4) the ability of the torpedo fish and electric eel to stun their prey by contact. The ancients saw no connection between these phenomena. Little new knowledge was added from the time of Thales to the time of Queen Eliza-

beth I, over two thousand years later. It was then that William Gilbert, best known for his work on magnetism, added many other substances, all of them of nonmetallic composition, to the list of those that had this power of attraction. Somehow he failed to discover that electrified bodies sometimes repelled one another, even though he must have observed repulsion many times.[2] A number of later experimenters observed this power of repulsion, among them Otto von Guericke, best known for his Magdeberg hemisphere experiment. In the early eighteenth century an English experimenter, Stephen Gray, was able to conduct a charge over a distance of more than 650 ft by means of a damp twine. Gray also showed that the power of attraction could be transferred from one metallic object to another.

About the same time, Charles Dufay of France was able to demonstrate that there were two, and only two, kinds of electricity. One, which he called the vitreous kind, was produced on glass by rubbing it with silk; the other, which he called the resinous kind, was produced on amber by rubbing it with wool or fur. He also discovered that the two kinds had an attraction for the other, but that both were *self-repulsive*. In more modern language, *like charges repel one another and unlike charges attract.*

EARLY THEORIES OF ELECTRICITY

Dufay's work led to the first theory of electricity that was capable of explaining the facts. The theory was that each kind was a subtle fluid present in all uncharged

---

[1] The pale glow sometimes seen on the tips of pointed objects such as ships' masts, aircraft propellers, wings, or other projecting parts, etc., especially during thunderstorms.

[2] This is undoubtedly a case of the mind seeing only what it is prepared to see. There was no place for repulsion in Gilbert's theory of electricity. He therefore missed seeing the repulsion entirely.

matter in equal amounts. Each could be transferred to other objects by rubbing. Thus, rubbing an amber rod with fur transferred some of the resinous fluid to the amber, leaving the fur with an excess of vitreous fluid, the amber with an excess of resinous fluid. Both amber and fur were electrified, or charged. The rubbing created nothing; it simply redistributed some of the resinous fluid. Rubbing a glass rod with silk redistributed some of the vitreous fluid.

Another way of viewing the phenomenon is to state that charges can only be separated, positive charges from negative charges or vice versa. It should be remembered that it takes energy to make the separation. Benjamin Franklin [3] (1706–1790) reasoned that there was no need to assume two fluids to explain the facts. He thought that perhaps neutral matter contained a "normal" amount of a single fluid.[4] More than this normal quota would give one kind of electrification (or charge), less than normal the other kind.

Franklin used the term *positive charge* to refer to the kind on a glass rod rubbed with silk, and *negative charge* to the kind on an amber rod rubbed with fur. These designations are purely arbitrary, for he had no way of knowing which kind was associated with the excess fluid and which the deficiency; he could only guess. He could have hoped that the glass rod actually contained the excess fluid and that the amber rod had a deficiency, for the term positive suggests the former and the term negative suggests the latter. If so, his hopes were dashed, for we now know that he guessed wrong.

CONDUCTORS AND INSULATORS

We have already noted that the list of substances which can be charged by rubbing *as you hold them in the bare hand* consists entirely of nonmetals. The fact that charges can be rubbed off glass by silk suggests that the glass holds some of its charges less tightly than does silk. Similarly, fur must hold some of its charges less tightly than does amber, for amber removes them from the fur. The fact that metal rods held in our bare hands cannot be charged no matter what we rub them with is due either to the tightness with which metals hold their charges, or it is due to looseness with which they are held. If held too loosely, they may escape through our bodies. The problem is easily solved; we wear rubber gloves—and find that we can charge any metal because the charges can no longer escape through our bodies. Furthermore, we find that we can charge metals either positively or negatively, something that we could not do with nonmetals—some of which can be charged positively only, others negatively only.

This discussion suggests that various substances have different abilities to hold their charges. This is true, but more significant is the ease with which charges may move about through various substances. Those materials through which charges move easily are called *conductors;* others

---

[3] In the middle of the eighteenth century electricity became a popular rage which was exploited by many popular lecturers. Spectacular experiments were devised to entertain the public and to enrich the lecturers. One such lecturer got Franklin interested in electric phenomena. As a result Franklin would have been remembered as a scientist even if never as a statesman.

[4] Electricians to this day refer to electricity as "juice."

are called *insulators*. The metals are all good conductors, although there is great variability among them. The best are silver, gold, aluminum, and copper; they are far better than iron, mercury, lead, or zinc. Carbon is an indifferent conductor. The other nonmetals are insulators, some better than others, the best being sulfur. Other excellent insulators are glass, amber, bakelite, mica and air. The human body, fortunately, is a rather poor conductor, but it, like many other things, is a better conductor when it is wet than when dry. That rare commodity, pure water, is an excellent insulator, whereas ordinary water is a relatively good conductor because of the dissolved materials in it. The poorer conductor a substance is, the better insulator it is. There is no perfect conductor and no perfect insulator.

We can now understand why insulators held in the bare hand may be charged by friction whereas conductors cannot—not because charges cannot be transferred from or to them but because they "run off" to the ground [5] as fast as they are transferred. If a person holding a conductor in his bare hand is insulated from the ground or floor, both he and the conductor may be given a heavy charge (as can be done with the Van de Graaff machine).

FRANKLIN'S EXPLANATIONS OF EARLY EXPERIMENTS

Let us now return to some of the early experiments of Gilbert, Gray, Dufay, and

[5] A ground in this context is anything that has great capacity to hold both positive and negative charges. The earth is the best of all, hence the name. To dispose of an electric charge, we simply ground it. The human body acts as a good ground for small amounts of charge.

Franklin, and see if we can explain them in terms of the one-fluid theory. Pith balls,[6] or toy balloons coated with aluminum paint, or even metallic spheres if they are suspended from a support of some kind by an insulating thread, preferably a thread of pure silk, will serve. Since the charge collects only on the outside of a conductor (p. 275), any insulator covered with a metallic paint acts as a conductor just as efficiently as if it were made entirely of metal. Fig. 19-1a shows the distribution of charges in an uncharged pith ball. Note carefully that the assumption is made throughout this discussion that a positive charge represents a deficiency of the electric fluid.

Charging by Contact

In Fig. 19-1b, a positively charged glass rod is brought near. Note the redistribution of charge on the outside of the ball because of the attraction of unlike charges and the repulsion of like charges. Note the corresponding effect in c when a negatively charged amber rod is brought near. In either case there is a net force of attraction on the ball, for the attractions between charges of opposite sign are greater than the repulsions between charges of the same sign because of the differences in the distances. (See Coulomb's Law, p. 277.) In Fig. 19-2a the glass rod is allowed to touch the pith ball. Instantly some (not all) of the excess positive charges leave the rod for the ball. This is called charging by contact. The ball now has an excess of positive charges, too, and so the rod and the ball now repel each other. We now

[6] Pith balls are commonly made from a piece of thoroughly dried raw potato.

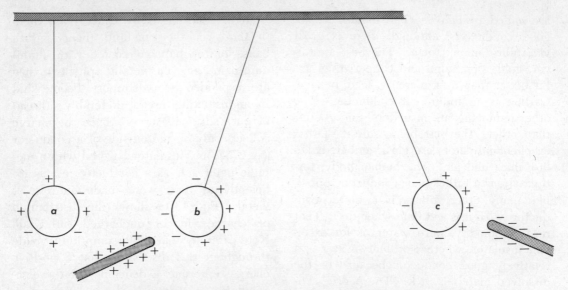

Fig. 19-1. Charging a Pith Ball. **(a)** An uncharged pith ball. Note the distribution of the charges. **(b)** A pith ball attracted by a positively charged glass rod and **(c)** by a negatively charged amber rod. Note the redistribution of the charges on the pith balls in both cases.

Fig. 19-2. **(a)** The pith ball is attracted to position (1) by the glass rod, where it is allowed to touch the rod. It becomes positively charged and so is repelled to position (2). **(b)** The glass rod has been removed (1) and a negatively charged amber rod brought near (2).

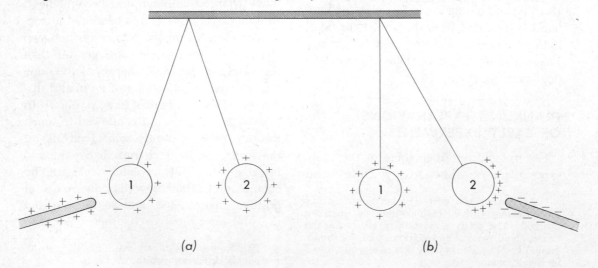

(a)   *(b)*

remove the glass rod and bring the charged amber rod near. Attraction results, as in Fig. 19-2b.

Anyone can verify the above experiments if he has the patience; it will take more patience in summer than in winter, and more patience on a humid day than on a dry day. In fact, if the humidity is really high, you may find your patience will do you no good, for you may be unable to charge a glass rod because of the affinity of glass for water. In any case there is a tendency for the charges to leak off the ball or the rod. Given time enough this always happens, and so we always have to keep recharging. Moisture in the atmosphere helps the leakage, so that on a really humid day, we may have to suspend our experiments to await a drier day.

The Electroscope

We will be able to perform a greater variety of experiments if we have an instrument that will not only detect a charge, but, if the sign on the instrument is known, will detect the sign of any other charge. Gilbert invented the precursor of the electroscope when he made a wooden arrow delicately balanced, as shown in Fig. 19-3. A charged body brought near would cause the arrow to swing, whereas an uncharged one would not. Later experimenters used a metallic needle suspended by an insulating thread. Either kind of charge could be placed on it, and so the sign of another charge could be determined by bringing it near.

Today we use a bottle or a flask with a rubber stopper, through which a metal rod projects (Fig. 19-4). Inside the bottle the rod is bent at a right angle so that a gold

leaf [7] can be bent double and hung over it. The outside end of the rod is a metal knob. The bottle or flask shuts out air drafts. We can now substitute the far more sensitive gold-leaf electroscope for the pith balls.

Charging by Induction

If we bring a charged glass or amber rod close to, but not in contact with, the knob of the electroscope, the gold leaves will

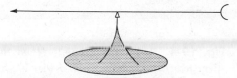

Fig. 19-3. Gilbert's "Electroscope." He called it a versorium. It consisted of a wooden arrow delicately balanced so that a charged body brought near would cause it to swing one way or the other.

separate, indicating like charges on both leaves. The divergence of the leaves is due to the repulsive effect of these like charges. The charge is said to be *induced* since no contact with the knob is made. They are also temporary, since they exist only as long as the charged rod is held close to the knob. Charging by induction refers to the production of electric charges by the mere presence of other charges. Originally, charging by induction was called charging by influence. A "permanent" charge by induction can be given if we ground the electroscope (Fig. 19-4b) while holding, e.g., a positively charged rod near the knob, and *then removing the*

---

[7] A gold leaf is used because gold can be hammered to an unbelievable thinness without breaking, and so a leaf of it is extremely light in weight. Aluminum foil is often used at present.

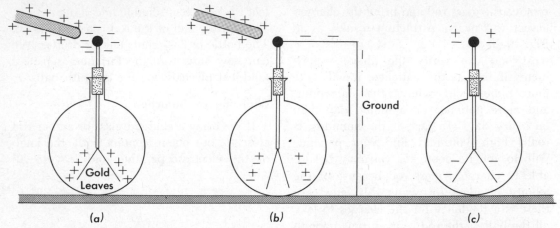

Fig. 19-4. **(a)** Electroscope. When the charged glass rod is brought near, the leaves diverge. **(b)** Same, but with a wire leading from the knob to the ground. Negative charges are attracted up to the knob and enough go down to the leaves to neutralize the charge there, causing the leaves to collapse. **(c)** The ground is broken while the glass rod is still near the knob. Some of the negative charges brought up from the ground are now trapped in the knob. Removal of the glass rod allows these charges to redistribute themselves but there are now more negative charges than positive ones. Hence the leaves diverge again.

ground while still holding the charged rod near the knob. When the ground was connected, some of the earth's vast reservoir of negative charges were attracted up to the knob, just enough to compensate for those pulled up to the knob from the gold leaves. When the ground is broken, and then the positively charged rod removed, the charges redistribute themselves. Since there is an excess of negative charges, the leaves diverge (Fig. 19-4c). Essentially the same situation would prevail if a negatively charged rod were used except that then the negative charges would move down into the earth, leaving the electroscope positively charged.

Distribution of a Charge on a Conductor

With an electroscope we can also prove that electrical charges distribute them-

selves only over the outer surfaces of conductors. Suppose we take an uncharged electroscope into a well-grounded metal cage (Fig. 19-5) [8]—or a solid metal box. No matter how violent or what kind of an electrical disturbance is taking place on the outside of the cage, the electroscope on the inside would show no evidence of it. Lightning could strike the cage but the electroscope, no matter how sensitive, would never show it. This is explained by the repulsion of like charges for one another. If our cage is negatively charged, as it would be if a positively charged thundercloud were above it, the excess negative charges can get farther away from one another if they remain on the outside of the

[8] Such cages are called Faraday's cages, after the great scientist who discovered their properties.

cage than they could if they were on the inside. This makes such cages excellent places to be during a thunderstorm. It explains why people inside buildings with a steel framework are never hurt by lightning, nor is the interior of the building ever damaged.

Distribution of Charge vs. Shape of Conductor

An electroscope can also be used to prove that on a spherical insulated conductor the charge is evenly distributed over the outside surface, whereas on a pear-shaped conductor it is not (Fig. 19-6). All we need to do is to charge two such conductors and bring them near an electroscope. It matters not how we rotate the spherical one, the electroscope will behave in the same manner as long as we keep the distance from the knob constant. With the

pear-shaped one, however, the electroscope clearly shows a greater charge on the end with the smallest radius of curvature. The more pointed this end is the greater the concentration of charge. There is no easy explanation of this phenomenon in terms which we have developed so far and so we will not attempt any.

Lightning as Electricity

Probably Franklin's most important work was that in which he positively identified lightning as electricity. The idea was not new with him, but it took his famous kite experiment to prove it.[9] He showed that

[9] He flew a kite during a thunderstorm. Some of a cloud's charge traveled down the twine. Franklin was able to prove that this electricity had exactly the same properties as that produced by an ordinary electrical machine, which "generated" charge by friction. Franklin was extremely fortunate that he received no injuries while per-

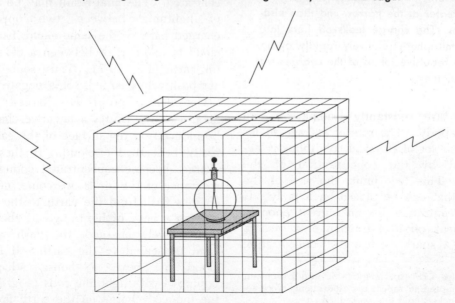

Fig. 19-5. A Faraday Cage. Note that the electroscope is entirely unaffected by the lightning outside, even though it may strike the cage.

the charge which traveled down through his kite string had the same properties as charges produced by friction.

It was Franklin's knowledge of the peculiarity of pointed conductors that led him to the invention of the lightning rod.

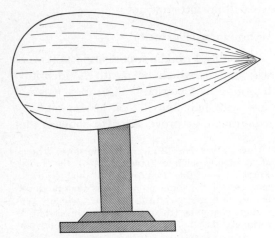

Fig. 19-6. Distribution of Charge on a Charged Insulated Pear-shaped Conductor. Note that the density of charge is far greater at the narrow end than elsewhere. The charge leaks off here into the atmosphere relatively rapidly owing to the repulsive forces of the charges for one another.

Charges are constantly leaking off any charged body. The rate of leakage under any given set of physical conditions is determined by the concentration of the charge. This fact limits the size of the charge that can be placed on a body. If the concentration becomes great enough, it will leak off in a fraction of a second, causing a spark. Since the concentration

is greatest at points or edges (if any) of conductors, the leakage is greatest there. In fact, the leakage is so rapid that a charge of spark proportions never builds up on a conductor with sufficient points or edges. The escape of the charges from points or edges of conductors during a thunderstorm at night accounts for the phenomenon called St. Elmo's fire.

Lightning rods are pointed metallic rods, connected together and well grounded, placed on the high parts of buildings. In a thundercloud considerable friction is developed between the condensing water droplets falling through the cloud and the upward-rushing air currents. In the process the water droplets are broken up. The lighter spray particles of the broken droplets gain a positive charge and are carried upward by the rising air currents. The heavier parts gain an equal negative charge as they resume their downward journey, increasing in size as they do so. Thus, the charges are separated, and possibly concentrated. The final result may be a flash of lightning between two oppositely charged parts of the same cloud, from one cloud to another, or between a cloud and the earth (Fig. 19-7). Thus, some clouds are positively charged, some negatively.

Consider a positively charged cloud. Such a charge causes a negative charge to be induced on the surface of the earth directly beneath the cloud. If these two charges become concentrated enough, the resistance of the air is overcome; negative charges flash from the earth to the cloud, causing a flash of lightning. If the cloud is negatively charged, the flash will be from the cloud to the earth. If such a cloud is above a house adequately equipped with lightning rods (Fig. 19-7c), the induced charge on the earth flows up

forming his kite experiments. Several Europeans who attempted to repeat his experiments were severely shocked, and one was killed.

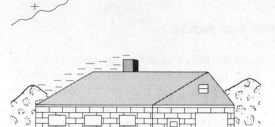

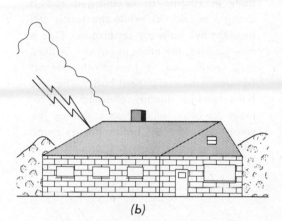

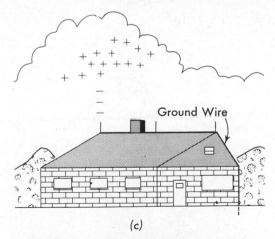

Fig. 19-7. **(a)** Positive charges on a cloud induce a negative charge on the house, particularly if it is wet.

(b) The concentrations of the charges

the ground wire and leaks rapidly off the points into the atmosphere where they rise to neutralize the charge on the cloud.

In general, we may state that the charges on the cloud, in flashing to or from the earth, follow paths of least resistance. Hence, any place indoors is normally safer than outdoors, low places are safer than hills, low trees are safer than high trees, no trees are better than one tree, and land is safer than water. Wire fences, lone trees, and wide open spaces, or bodies of water should be avoided. One hundred per cent safe, or nearly so, are houses properly equipped with lightning rods, buildings or towers with steel frames sunk into the ground, steel bridges with steel supports, and the inside of automobiles, all of which are, in a sense, Faraday cages.

COULOMB'S LAW

Apparatus like that used by Cavendish to measure the force of gravitation (Fig. 8-3) may be used to measure the magnitude of the force between two charges. The principle is exactly the same (Fig. 19-8), and the law that resulted is in the same form, i.e., it is an inverse-square law.

This law, known as Coulomb's Law, states that *the force between two small charged bodies is proportional to the product of the charges carried by each and is inversely proportional to the square of the distance between them.* Mathematically,

have become great enough so that a flash from the house to the cloud occurs. The charges are now neutralized.

(c) House protected by lightning rods. Charges leak off the points of the rods so that no accumulation occurs.

$$F \propto \frac{q_1 q_2}{d^2}$$

where q_1 and q_2 represent the two charges.[10] Writing this proportionality as an equation, we have

$$F = \frac{K q_1 q_2}{d^2}$$

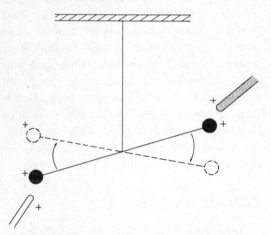

Fig. 19-8. Principle of Coulomb's Experiment. The delicately suspended bar with two positively charged balls on the two ends turns away from positively charged glass rods.

Coulomb did the experimental work leading to the law two or three years after Cavendish measured the gravitational constant, G. Coulomb's apparatus did not

[10] Coulomb had no way of knowing the absolute magnitude of the charges carried by the two bodies. He could, however, easily obtain equal charges on two spheres. First he charged one sphere, then he brought another sphere (uncharged) of the same size in contact with the first. The charge on the first instantly spread itself evenly over the surfaces of the two spheres. On separating them he had two spheres similarly and equally charged (Fig. 19-9).

need to be as sensitive as that of Cavendish, for electrical forces are far greater than gravitational forces. Compare, however, the form of the law with that of gravitation. These are two of several inverse-

Fig. 19-9. Method of Charging Two Identical Metal Balls Equally. (a) Two balls in contact as a charged rod is brought near. (b) While the rod is still near the two balls are separated. One is now positive, the other negative. A third ball, uncharged, is brought in contact (c) with either charged ball. The two balls become equally charged and remain so after separation. During the whole process the balls, being metal, must be insulated from any ground.

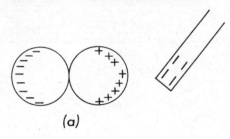

(a)

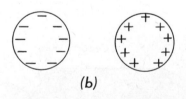

(b)

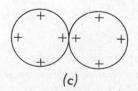

(c)

square laws; we will encounter at least two more in this course.

Note that the force of gravitation is one of attraction only, whereas that between charges may be one of either attraction or repulsion. There is one other difference between the forces. If any substance, a piece of glass, e.g., is placed between two charges, the force is somewhat reduced. The amount of reduction is a characteristic of the shielding medium. It follows that the force is greatest in a vacuum. There is no such shielding effect in gravitation. This is shown by the fact that the attraction between the moon and the sun is the same when the earth is squarely between the two (as in a total lunar eclipse) as it is at other times. If this were not so, the moon would follow a somewhat different curve after the eclipse from that before.

UNITS OF CHARGE

Coulomb's Law is used to define the unit of charge. If two equal charges are of such magnitude that when they are placed 1 cm apart in a vacuum, they exert a force of 1 dyne on each other, then each charge is defined as 1 electrostatic unit (abbreviated to esu). Since the dyne is a very small unit, an esu is very small. A larger unit, the coulomb, consists of 3×10^9 electrostatic units.

In our equation for Coulomb's Law, if q_1 and q_2 are each 1 esu and d is 1 cm, then $K = 1$. But if q_1 and q_2 are in coulombs, then K becomes 9×10^{18} (3×10^9 multiplied by 3×10^9) if F is expressed in dynes.[11] This means that if 1 coulomb of negative charge could be placed 1 cm

[11] Because there are 3×10^9 esu in 1 coulomb.

from another coulomb of negative charge, the repulsive force would be given by

$$F = K\frac{q_1 q_2}{d^2} = (9 \times 10^{18})\frac{1 \times 1}{1^2}$$

$$= 9 \times 10^{18} \text{ dynes}$$

This force is equal to about 10,000,000,000 tons—which means, of course, that they could never be brought that close together. It should be emphasized that both the esu and the coulomb represent definite quantities of charge, i.e., definite quantities of electricity. Approximately 1 coulomb of negative electricity flows through a 100-watt electric light bulb per second.

MODERN THEORY OF ELECTRICITY

Small as the esu is, it is not by any means the smallest possible unit. At the time the esu and the coulomb were defined, it was not known if there was a smallest bit of electricity. Perhaps charges could be endlessly divided, just as Aristotle thought matter could be. We now know that the smallest bit of negative electricity is that which we call the electron. We also know that in neutral atoms there are positive charges, equal in number to the negative charges, and which are actual physical entities. (In this one respect the modern theory resembles the two-fluid theory.) However, *these positive charges are nontransferable in bulk solid matter*, so they are entirely irrelevant to the present discussion. Only a few of the total number of negative charges (electrons) present in atoms are transferable, and in our modern theory positive and negative charges are explained in terms of excesses and deficiencies of these transferable electrons, in much the same manner as does Franklin's one-fluid theory. We continue to use Franklin's designation of positive and negative, even though it is not in entire agreement with the literal interpretation of our modern theory.[12]

We have used the term *electron* before we have "discovered" it. This premature use of it is justified, partly on the grounds that most students have some familiarity with the word, and partly because we believe that doing so is desirable in the discussion of current electricity that is shortly to follow.

ELECTROSTATIC DISCHARGE

The charge that can be developed on a glass or amber rod by rubbing it with silk or fur is small, and only a small fraction of it is transferred to another body by con-

[12] In our modern theory ordinary electricity in wires is considered to consist solely of the movement of negative charges (electrons). The flow is always from a region of excess electrons to a region of fewer electrons. This current of electrons, hereafter called the electron current, is then from negative to positive. In the Franklin terminology, hereafter called the conventional current, the current is considered to be from positive to negative. We do not change because of two difficulties. One is the problem of the re-education of a host of practical electricians, the other has to do with scientists reading the earlier literature. More significantly, the point involved here is what we expect of a theory. If it is useful, adequate, and consistent with all of the known observations, must it also be true? If you insist upon "truth," then you are insisting upon more than the scientist demands in his theories, for he knows that it is frequently impossible to decide what truth really is in this context. He does insist, however, upon truth in his observations. Thus, the scientist continues to use Franklin's designations of positive and negative until he meets some observations that cannot be explained by them. In these cases he uses the term "electron current" instead of the conventional current.

tact, for charges do not move freely on or from an insulator. The small amounts of charge that are transferred give no visible sign of such transfer. However, if we put a moderate amount of charge on an insulated metal conductor, and then bring it close to a grounded conductor, a visible spark may be seen—and heard. Such a spark gives off light and heat energy. Remembering our Law of Conservation of Energy, we might well ask where this energy comes from. It took work to put the charge on the insulated metal conductor, i.e., mechanical energy was expended in rubbing the conductor with fur. It is this energy that reappears in the spark as light and heat.

There are several types of machines, some operated by hand, some by motors, that can separate large quantities of charge, quantities large enough to cause sparks from a few inches to several feet long. One such device is the Van de Graaff generator (Fig. 19-10), which comes in several sizes and designs. In all of them a charge is built up on an insulated metal ball of a size appropriate to the charge-separating capacity of the machine. It is the mechanical energy expended in separating the charges that reappear in the sparks produced. The larger the charge that is developed on such a conductor, the greater the rate at which they leak off into the atmosphere. Hence, there is a limit to the amount of charge that can be placed on any conductor.

POTENTIAL DIFFERENCE

The concept of potential difference is as important to static electricity as it is to current electricity—which is why we de-

Fig. 19-10. Van de Graaff Generator. A motor turns a belt made of insulating material which is charged by rubbing against a device that removes charges from a source. The charges are carried upward by the belt where they are removed by a brush, which transfers them to the metal sphere. The sphere is insulated from other parts of the generator, allowing a difference of potential of some thousands or even millions of volts to develop between it and the ground. The total charge is, however, comparatively small. (Courtesy Central Scientific Company.)

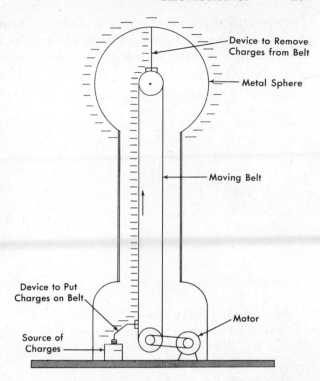

Device to Remove Charges from Belt

Metal Sphere

Moving Belt

Device to Put Charges on Belt

Motor

Source of Charges

velop it here. The term is a short way of referring to a difference in electrical potential energy per unit charge, and is often abbreviated P.D. The analogy with gravitational potential energy is nearly perfect. Just as work must be done on a body to give it gravitational potential energy, so must work be done on a charge to give it electrical potential energy.

Consider a positively charged body, A, in Fig. 19-11. A positive charge at C will experience a force of repulsion by A. (Consider B to be absent.) The magnitude of this force can be calculated from Coulomb's Law. If we now move the charge from C to B, we are moving it against this repulsive force, and so we are doing work. The energy that we expend in doing this work is stored up in the charge as electrical potential energy. The

amount of work that it can now do in returning to C is a measure of the difference in electrical potential energy of the charge at B and at C. Furthermore, since the charge has more potential energy at B than at C, we say that B is at a higher potential than C. If free to do so, a positive charge will spontaneously move from B to C because of the mutual repulsion of like charges.

Remembering that we can measure energy only in terms of work that is or can be done by that energy, we can define *potential difference as the quantity of work done during the transfer of 1 unit of positive charge from one point to another.* The practical unit of potential difference is the volt (V). *If we do 1 joule of work while transferring 1 coulomb of charge from one point to another, say, from C to B, then* *the potential difference between C and B is 1 volt.* If we do 2 joules of work while transferring 1 coulomb of charge, then the

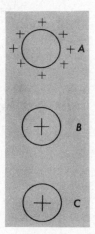

Fig. 19-11. Difference of Potential. Charge B has more electric potential energy with respect to A than does charge C because it experiences a greater force of repulsion. It therefore can do more work in moving away (spontaneously) from A than can charge C. We therefore say that B is at a higher potential than C.

potential difference is two volts, etc. Mathematically,

$$\text{volts} = \frac{\text{joules}}{\text{coulombs}}$$

In symbols, $V = \dfrac{W}{Q}$ (Eq. 19-1)

Thus, the voltage of any electrical system represents the energy transfer per coulomb. In charging a 12-volt automobile storage battery [13] 12 joules of work must be done

to transfer 1 coulomb of positive electricity from an outside source to the positive terminal of the battery. The battery can then do 12 joules of work for each coulomb of charge transferred from the positive terminal to the negative terminal via the electrical system (starter, lights, horn, radio) of the car. Ordinary households in the United States are provided by the electric power company with a difference of potential of 110 or 120 volts. This means that *for each coulomb of charge* that passes from one wire in an outlet to the other wire of that same outlet, 110 (or 120) joules of work can be done (or 26.3 calories of heat can be produced) [14] by any appliance connected between the two wires.

SUMMARY

Knowledge of static electricity goes back at least as far as Thales (*ca.* 600 B.C.). William Gilbert (1540–1603), physician to Queen Elizabeth I, started the investigations that were eventually to lead to our modern theory of electricity (about 1900). Two-fluid theories were first developed, followed by Franklin's one-fluid theory. Both could account for vitreous (positive) and resinous (negative) electricity, but the one-fluid theory is simpler. Positive electricity (charge) is defined as that kind produced by rubbing a glass rod with silk, negative electricity (charge) as that produced by rubbing an amber rod with fur. In the process charges are not created; they are only separated, for uncharged matter is conceived of as consisting of like and unlike

---

[13] A storage battery generates charge just as in any chemical cell or voltaic pile (p. 286) but it differs from the cell or the pile in that the chem-

ical action can be reversed by the application of external energy and so become recharged.

[14] See Eq. 13-1.

charges in equal amounts. The mechanical energy used to separate them reappears as electrical energy, made evident in the attraction of unlike charges and the repulsion of like charges. Pith balls can be used to detect charged bodies but electroscopes are much more sensitive. Electroscopes were used to prove that the charge distributes itself only over the outer surfaces of conductors, and that the density of charges is greater on the points or edges of conductors, from which they leak off comparatively rapidly. Franklin's kite experiments proved the identity of lightning and static electricity. Combining this knowledge with that of the fast leakage of charge from points, he invented the lightning rod.

Coulomb derived an inverse-square law for the forces of attraction and repulsion similar in form to that for the force of gravitation: $F = Kq_1q_2/d^2$. The unit of charge in the cgs system is the esu (electrostatic unit). The practical unit of charge, the coulomb, consists of 3×10^9 esu. The smallest possible unit of charge, the electron, was not discovered until about 1900. It takes 6×10^{18} electrons to equal 1 coulomb. About 1 coulomb flows through a 100-watt light bulb per second. Large amounts of charge can be developed on insulated metal conductors by mechanical means.

The greater the charge on an insulated conductor, the greater the difference in electrical potential energy between such a conductor and another uncharged one nearby. The amount of work done in charging the first one is a measure of the difference in the amount of electrical potential energy possessed by each. If the two bodies are now brought close together, an electrostatic discharge occurs, during which this electrical energy is converted into heat energy and light energy. Charge has been transferred and work has been done in the process. The amount is given by the equation $V = W/Q$.

EXERCISES

I. TERMS AND CONCEPTS

Electrostatics	Two-fluid theory
Positive charge	One-fluid theory
Negative charge	Coulomb's Law
Electroscope	Electrostatic unit
Conductor	Coulomb
Insulator	Electron
Induced charges	Potential difference
	Volt

II. PROBLEMS

1. A glass rod is rubbed with silk. What charge appears on the silk?

2. A hard rubber rod is rubbed with fur. What charge appears on the fur?

3. In terms of electrons explain what happened during the rubbing in problems 1 and 2 above.

4. In terms of electrons explain what happens when the charged glass rod is brought near an uncharged electroscope.

5. Do the same for the charged hard rubber rod.

6. The charged glass rod is made to stroke the metal rod of the uncharged electroscope, giving it a charge. What is the sign (positive or negative) of the charge?

7. If the rubber rod is used in place of the glass rod, what is the sign of the charge?

8. From your answers to problems 6 and 7, we may generalize as follows: When an object is charged by contact with a charged body, the sign of the transferred charge will always be (the same as) (different from) that of the original charge. Cross out the wrong choice.

9. An electroscope is given a "permanent" charge by being grounded while a charged glass rod is close by. What is the sign of the charge?

10. Suppose a rubber rod is used in

place of the glass rod. What is the sign of the charge?

11. From your answers to problems 9 and 10 we may generalize as follows: When an object is given a "permanent" charge by induction, the sign of the induced charge is always (the same as) (different from) that of the inducing charge. Cross out one.

12. Why should television and radio sets with outside aerials be grounded?

13. In giving an object a "permanent" charge by induction, does it matter if the finger (or other ground) is removed from the object before or after the charging body is removed? Explain.

14. Suppose the temporary induced charge given to the electroscope was large. What would happen as you attempted to touch the electroscope to ground it? Explain in terms of electrons.

15. Why cannot a metal rod be given a charge while holding it in the bare hand?

16. Why may it be dangerous to turn on an electrical appliance while in the bath tub or standing on wet ground?

17. A person inside a building with a steel frame is safe from lightning. Explain.

18. Why are lightning rods made with sharp points?

19. A positively charged cloud drifts over a building protected by lightning rods which are well grounded in damp earth. No flash occurs although one would have if there were no lightning rods. Explain how the rods protected the building.

20. From what you have already learned about electric charges, criticize the old adage, "Lightning never strikes twice in the same place."

21. Two unlike charges 6 cm apart attract each other with a force X. If they are moved so that they are 3 cm apart, they will now attract each other with what force? If they are placed 12 cm apart, what will the attracting force be?

22. Two charges of 10 esu each are placed 10 cm apart. The force (of attraction, or repulsion) will be how many dynes?

23. Two negative charges of 1 coulomb each are placed 1 cm apart. Calculate the force in dynes.

24. How does an electrical potential difference arise?

25. What is the relationship between electrical potential difference (P.D.) and work?

26. What is a volt? What is the mathematical relationship between potential difference, work done, and charge transferred?

27. If 550 joules of work are done in moving 5 coulombs of charge from point A to point B, what is the potential difference between these two points?

CHAPTER XX

Current Electricity

Electricity, carrier of light and power, devourer of time and space, bearer of human speech over land and sea, greatest servant of man.—CHARLES ELIOT

INTRODUCTION

No American needs to be convinced of the role that electricity plays in his life. Few of us ever go more than a few hours without making use of it in one way or another. No one discovery has made so great a direct impact on our way of life as that which made possible the power and the heat and the light generated by electric charges in motion. Man has been relieved of countless tedious or back-breaking jobs by the marvels performed by current electricity.

Most people are considerably more familiar with the various ways in which electricity is used than they are with how it is generated. Actually this is a gross understatement, for very few people have any concept at all of how it is generated, either in a battery or by a dynamo at a power station. As master or mistress of a house you should know more about electricity than how to plug in an appliance, replace a burned-out bulb, or change a fuse. You should understand the relationships among current, voltage, power, and resistance. You should know how alternating current differs from direct, the advantages of the former, and something of its generation and transmission. In the following pages we hope to teach you these essentials of electricity.

We need first to realize the differences between static and current electricity. We have already referred to the latter as the time rate of flow of charges through a conductor, most commonly a wire. Of course, static electric charges move also whenever they are transferred. In lightning or other spark discharges they move suddenly, noisily, riotously, and instantaneously from a negatively charged body to a positively charged one. In current electricity the negative charges (electrons) move continuously and quietly in an orderly manner most commonly through a conducting wire, usually for an appreciable time, and sometimes indefinitely.[1]

INVENTION OF THE ELECTRIC (CHEMICAL) BATTERY

The generation of current electricity had its inception in a chance observation made near the end of the eighteenth century by an Italian medical professor, Luigi Galvani.

[1] If electric current flowed only through wires, the problem of direction with respect to the flow of charges would be simplified. In electrolytic solutions (p. 499), in various types of gas discharge tubes, in radio tubes, and in X-ray tubes the current is not entirely confined to wires. Since we are going to be concerned during this and the following chapter (except briefly in discussing the voltaic cell) entirely with current flowing through wires, we will omit the other cases from consideration. We will drop the Franklin terminology and speak of the direction of the flow as that of the electrons; this flow is sometimes referred to as the electron current.

He noticed that a frog's leg spontaneously contracted when near a machine for generating electricity. Investigating further, he found that if two dissimilar metals were in contact while one was touching a nerve of the frog's leg and the other a muscle, the

more effective than others), each separated by paper moistened with water or brine. This was originally known as a Voltaic pile. Actually it was the first crude electrical cell or battery. Now for the first time, a steady continuous flow of electric charge could be maintained.

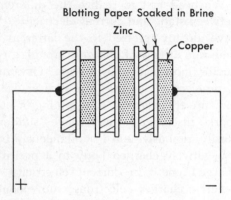

Fig. 20-1. A Voltaic Cell. Alternating discs of copper and zinc separated by blotting paper soaked in brine. A difference of potential develops between the zinc and the copper. If the two open ends of the wires are connected, a current will flow. The brine-soaked blotting paper takes the place of the frog's leg of Galvani.

same contraction of the muscle was observed. He attributed this (falsely) to "animal electricity."

Another Italian, Alessandro Volta, carrying these researches further, discovered that the frog's leg was not necessary to produce the electricity. All that was needed were two dissimilar metals, e.g., copper and zinc, connected by a conducting wire and separated by moistened paper. A greater current was obtained by making a pile of alternating copper and zinc plates (or any two dissimilar metals, although some are

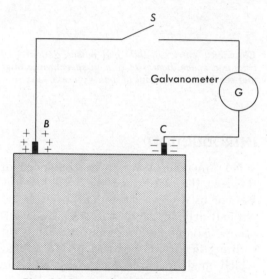

Fig. 20-2. Modern Battery. Because of chemical action within, the cell maintains an excess of positive and negative charges on the two terminals, B and C. Mutual repulsion of like charges on each terminal limits the potential difference between B and C. If the two terminals are connected by a wire and the switch, S, is closed, a current, which can be detected and measured by the galvanometer, G, will flow. The direction of the conventional current is from B to C (through the wire).

The principle may be at least partially understood if we consider two plates, one zinc and one copper (Fig. 20-1) partially

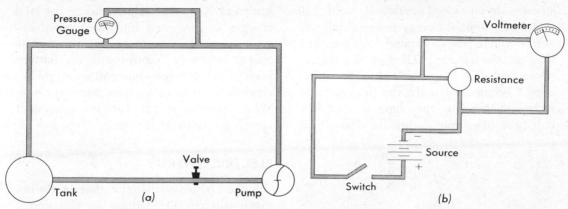

Fig. 20-3. Analogy between Water and Electrical Systems. **(a)** The pump is necessary to keep the water circulating. The valve must be open. **(b)** In an electrical system the source is analogous to the pump, the voltmeter to the pressure gauge, and the switch to the valve. The resistance may be any electrical appliance, a motor or a light bulb, etc.

immersed in a salt solution. The salt makes the water a good conductor. For a reason that we need not concern ourselves with here, positive charges collect on the copper plate and negative ones on the zinc plate. This means that a difference of potential develops between the plates. Hence if the two plates are connected by a conducting wire, a current will flow through the wire from one plate to the other. It will continue to flow until the difference in potential is eliminated.

ELECTRIC CIRCUIT

In all circuits a difference in potential must exist between two points, and these two points must be connected by a conductor if the current is to flow. To flow continuously, some means must exist to maintain the difference in potential. Only an electric generator, of which the battery (Fig. 20-2) is one type, can do that.

Consider a *closed system* of water pipes. The water will not flow continuously un-

less a pump inserted in the line somewhere operates continuously (Fig. 20-3a). The battery or electric generator (dynamo), a common source, is analogous to the pump (Fig. 20-3b). An electric system comparable to that of the system of water pipes and pump is called a *circuit*. For an electric current to flow, the circuit must be closed. Minimum essentials for a practical circuit (Fig. 20-4) are a source, S, a resistance, R (appliance, motor, light bulb, or just the connecting wires), a switch to open or close the circuit, all connected by conducting wires. These symbols for the source and the resistance are conventional ones which will be used frequently hereafter.

Suppose we follow the charges through a complete circuit, a circuit somewhat more complex than the simple one in Fig. 20-4. The source will consist of a series of dry cells, enough to give us 110 volts. Instead of one resistance we will put in two, e.g., an electric iron and a motor. Hordes of negative charges leave the source in a steady stream, well endowed with 110 joules of potential energy per coulomb, energy which they expend in traveling through the circuit. Through the thicker wires they can move with little loss of energy. When they reach the thinner wires of the electric iron they have a more difficult time—the same number of charges are

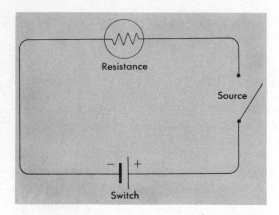

Fig. 20-4. Simple Practical Electric Circuit. The switch is needed only to make it practical. Even the resistance is not necessary if the current is weak, for the wire has some resistance by itself.

trying to get through a smaller passageway. The result is greatly increased friction between the atoms in the wire and the moving charges. Friction, as we well know by this time, is associated with heat. Some of the kinetic energy of the moving charges is turned into heat, heat which causes the wires of the eletcric iron to glow and heat the iron.

When the charges encounter the motor, a different phenomenon appears, one which will be described later (p. 303). At this time we will merely say that the effect is as if the charges had to push uphill against a contrary force. In the process

some of the remaining energy of the charges is converted into mechanical energy, causing the motor to turn. The charges move on, returning to the battery bereft of their original potential energy because of the work they have done en route. What happens in the battery we cannot completely state at this time.

ELECTRIC ENERGY

Suffice it to say that the charges do not move through the battery in the simple manner that they moved through the wires, but that they receive a fresh supply of energy to make the round trip again. Thus, we can visualize quantities of charge, coulombs of electricity if you will, moving from resistance to resistance, delivering energy as they do so, energy obtained from the battery.

Whence comes this energy? Joule discovered that the same amount of energy was released through chemical changes just by throwing the same ingredients into a beaker—only in the beaker the energy is released as heat instead of as electric energy.[2] Thus, the electric energy released from a battery is transformed chemical energy, energy that in turn is ultimately transformed via electric energy, into heat energy, light energy, mechanical energy, or some combination of them, depending upon the kind of resistance that the charges pass through.

How much energy does each coulomb deliver? We have already seen that this energy transfer per coulomb is expressed in volts. Instruments called voltmeters measure the number of volts. Voltmeters

[2] This was one of the things that Joule did in determining the mechanical equivalent of heat, 4.18 joules per calorie.

are best thought of as electrical pressure gauges (Fig. 20-3*b*), since they measure the potential energy delivered by each coulomb in some chosen part of the circuit, just as a water-pressure gauge measures the potential energy per unit volume of the water at a particular point in a pipe or tank. Compare Figs. 20-3*a* and 20-3*b*.

We have already seen (Eq. 19-1) that $V = W/Q$, where V is expressed in volts, W in joules, and Q in coulombs of charge. To calculate the total energy delivered in time t, we need to know first the number of coulombs flowing through a circuit per second. This information is provided by the equation,

$$\frac{\text{Total charge}}{\text{Time}} = \text{Current}$$

In symbols $\qquad \dfrac{Q}{t} = I \qquad$ (Eq. 20-1)

If Q is in coulombs and t is in seconds, then I is in coulombs per second, or, as more commonly stated, in amperes. *An ampere is defined as 1 coulomb per second.* Thus, if 20 coulombs pass through a conductor in 4 sec, the current, I, is calculated as follows:

$$I = \frac{Q}{t} = \frac{20}{4} = 5\,\text{amperes}$$

An ammeter inserted in the circuit will indicate the number of coulombs flowing through the circuit per second. Note that an ampere is a measure of the *rate* of flow; it is not a measure of the total flow. The principle on which the ammeter works is described on pp. 304–305.

The second thing we need to know is voltage. To date we have defined voltage, V, in terms of energy transfer per coulomb, and we have defined the rate of transfer,

i.e., current, in terms of coulombs per second. It follows that the total transfer of energy per second is given by the energy transfer per coulomb multiplied by the number of coulombs flowing per second. In other words it is given by volts times amperes, as follows:

$$\text{Volts} \times \text{amperes} = \frac{\text{Joules}}{\text{Coulombs}} \times \frac{\text{Coulombs}}{\text{Seconds}}$$

$$= \frac{\text{Joules}}{\text{Seconds}} \qquad \text{(Eq. 20-2)}$$

Joules per second is the rate of doing work, i.e., it is (by definition) power (symbolized by the letter P). In symbols equation 20-2 is:

$$VI = \frac{W}{Q} \times \frac{Q}{t} = \frac{W}{t} \qquad \text{(Eq. 20-3)}$$

Therefore, $\quad P = VI = \dfrac{W}{t} \qquad$ (Eq. 20-4)

The unit of power is the *watt*. By definition it is 1 joule per second. A 100-watt light bulb uses 100 joules of energy for every second it is lighted. If we burn it for 1 hour, it consumes 100 watt-hours (360,000 joules) of energy. If we burn it for 10 hours, it consumes 1000 watt-hours or 1 kilowatt-hour of energy. This is what the power company bills us for—kilowatt-hours of energy, not the amount of electricity (charge) that we use.

HEATING EFFECT OF CURRENT

Joule, in his work on the mechanical equivalent of heat, investigated the relationship between the heating effect and the current, keeping all other factors constant. He found that if he doubled the current the amount of heat produced was increased

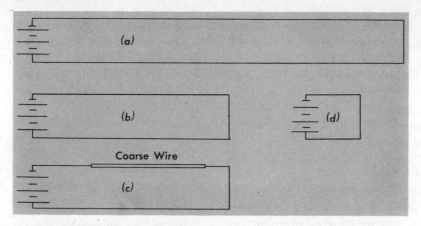

Fig. 20-5. "Long" Circuits vs. Short Circuits. In a "long" circuit the resistance of the wire is an appreciable amount if it is of copper and of normal size. The current rises as the resistance decreases at constant voltage. The current can flow more easily through a coarse wire than through a finer one. Thus, the resistance decreases from a to b to c to d (which is really a *short circuit*).

by a factor of 4, that if he tripled the current, by a factor of 9. Thus, the amount of heat produced is proportional to the square of the current. It is also, of course, proportional to the time the current flows. Hence,

$$W \propto I^2 t \qquad \text{(Eq. 20-5)}$$

Introducing a proportionality constant, R, we can write

$$W = RI^2 t \qquad \text{(Eq. 20-6)}$$

This is sometimes referred to as Joule's Law.[3]

The proportionality constant, R, is called the resistance of the conductor. Every conductor offers some opposition to the

[3] If you are confused by the fact that we use W for heat produced as well as for work expressed in joules, remember that the exchange rate for mechanical energy to heat is 4.18 joules/calorie.

flow of electrons through it because the moving electrons which constitute the current collide with the "fixed" atoms composing the conductor. This opposition to flow is *electric resistance*. Its value depends upon the length of the conductor, the cross-sectional area of that path, and the material of which the conductor is made. For a copper wire the resistance is directly proportional to length and inversely proportional to the square of the diameter, i.e., to area, at constant temperature (Fig. 20-5). If we think of the friction of water flowing through pipes of varying lengths and diameters, we should be able to see the reasonableness of this, except for the temperature factor. Temperature increases the resistance of a wire, for the more rapid motions of the atoms makes more collisions per unit time, hence increases the friction. The resistance varies with the material of which the conductor is made, for we have already seen that some substances are better conductors than others. The better the conductor, the less the resistance.

OHM'S LAW

The relationship between voltage and current in different conductors was first studied in the 1820's by George Ohm, a German schoolmaster. The ratio of the potential difference across the ends of a wire to the current is called the resistance of the wire. Ohm made wires (by hand) of different sizes and lengths, and of different metals, varying only one factor at a time in the manner of any good scientist. Batteries and thermocouples [4] were still the only means of obtaining an electric current. Despite these handicaps he finally established the law justly named in his honor.[5]

Ohm's Law states that for a given conductor the current is proportional to the voltage across the ends of that conductor. In symbols, $I \propto V$. With the proportionality constant R, we can write

$$V = RI \qquad \text{(Eq. 20-7)}$$

If V is in volts and I in amperes, then R is expressed in ohms. *An ohm*, our unit of

[4] Two wires of dissimilar metals joined together to form a circuit and heated at their junctions. The heating causes a small current to flow through the wires. The principle will not be discussed here.

[5] He published his work in 1826, and promptly lost his teaching job, for the Minister of Education viewed his findings with scorn. For six years he lived in dire poverty and bitter disappointment. Finally his great work received recognition, at first from abroad, and then, more slowly, in Germany. Eventually he received a professorial appointment at the University of Munich, where he happily finished the last five years of his life.

resistance, is defined as *that resistance which will allow a current of one ampere to flow through a conductor under a P.D. of one volt.*

Ohm's Law may be deduced from Joule's Law (Eq. 20-6), as follows: [6] From Eq. 20-3, we get,

$$W = VIt$$

Hence, $$VIt = RI^2t$$

Whence $$V = RI$$

Let us see if we can gain a better understanding of the significances of this law, for it plays an important part in the life of every householder who uses electricity. We see from the law that as V is increased in a conductor of constant resistance, I is increased proportionately. Thus, a potential difference of 220 volts will cause twice as many coulombs to flow through an appliance per unit time as does a potential difference of 110 volts. Since $W \propto I^2t$, and Q/t is doubled, the heating effect is increased 4 times, a desirable effect in electric stoves and clothes dryers, but highly undesirable in most other appliances made to withstand a lesser temperature.

A short circuit means just that (Fig. 20-5). Commonly, it is a circuit made short by a defect that allows the current to bypass a resistance. This reduces R almost to zero in that circuit, and since V is about 110 volts in our homes at all times, I must become enormous, for the product of RI must equal 110. The heating effect therefore may be increased a hundred- or even a thousandfold, so that if the circuit is not protected by a fuse, the heat developed

[6] Ohm completed his experimental derivation of this law some twenty years before Joule's Law was established.

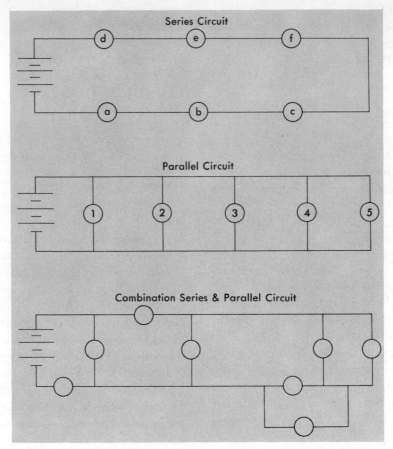

Fig. 20-6. Series, Parallel, and Combination Series-parallel Circuits. The latter indicate which appliances are in series, which are in parallel circuits.

will melt or burn the insulation off the wires and start a fire if the wire is in contact with anything inflammable.

A fuse is a short piece of wire of low melting point inserted in the circuit at an appropriate place to prevent a fire if a short circuit occurs. Melting it has the same effect as "pulling the switch." Too heavy a load, caused by plugging too many lights or appliances into the same parallel circuit (discussed in the next section) will also cause a fuse to blow. With a house current of 110 volts appliances using not more than 1650 watts (110×15) should be connected in a circuit protected by a 15-ampere fuse. Substituting a fuse with a capacity of 20 or 30 amperes to prevent the protecting fuse from melting is dangerous if the circuit was designed for a capacity of 15 amperes. By-passing a burned-out fuse —by inserting a penny, e.g.—is not only folly but well-nigh criminal.

SERIES AND PARALLEL CIRCUITS

Fig. 20-6 shows a series circuit, a simple parallel circuit, and a combination of the two. The words series and parallel are essentially self-explanatory. Most of the circuits we encounter today are either parallel or combination types. In a series circuit, if one light or appliance fails, the whole series fails. This is because there is only one path for the current to follow in such a circuit. How many paths may the current follow in the parallel and combination circuits shown in Figs. 20-6b and 20-6c?

SUMMARY

A continuous flow of electric charges was not possible before the invention of the chemical cell (battery) about 1800. For a continuous current to flow there must be a closed circuit which includes an electric generator of some sort to maintain a potential difference between two points in the circuit. If the generator is a battery, the two points are the terminals of the battery. In moving through the circuit the charges can do work en route, i.e., they lose energy as their electric potential energy is transformed into heat, light, or mechanical energy. They return to the battery where they receive a fresh supply of energy to start the circuit again. The source of this supply is in the battery itself where chemical energy is being transformed into electrical energy (and heat). In time their chemical energy is all transformed and the cell goes dead.

From $I = Q/t$ and $V = W/Q$, we get $VI = (W/Q)(Q/t) = W/t = P$ (in watts), which is the rate of doing work, i.e., it is the power supplied by a given current flowing through a circuit under a specified potential difference.

This power multiplied by the time gives the total energy delivered; it is commonly expressed in kilowatt-hours.

The heating effect of a current is given by $W = RI^2t$ (Joule's Law), in which R is the resistance to the flow of electrons through the circuit. For any given circuit, it is a constant. From this equation Ohm's Law, $V = RI$, may be derived. Ohm, however, had determined the law experimentally some twenty years before Joule's Law was established. Ohm's Law gives the relationship between V and I in a circuit; for a given circuit, i.e., if R is constant, $V = RI$. Since V is a function of the source (generator) and does not normally vary significantly for a given source, I will increase rapidly if R is reduced (as in a short circuit). Since Joule's Law also applies, the increase in I increases the heating effect as the square of I; a fire may result if the circuit is not properly protected by a fuse.

EXERCISES

I. TERMS AND CONCEPTS

Coulomb	Equations:
Current	$V = \dfrac{W}{Q}$
Ampere	
Volt	$I = \dfrac{Q}{t}$
Resistance	
Ohm	$P = VI$
Power	$V = RI$
Watt	$W = RI^2t$
Electric energy	
Joule's Law	
Ohm's Law	

II. PROBLEMS

1. What is the difference between a static discharge and an electric current?

2. What is the relationship between the current in a wire and the potential difference between the ends of the wire?

3. Since $V = RI$, what happens to I if R drops to zero?

4. If 480 coulombs of charge pass through a resistance in 2 min, what current flows through it?

5. If 550 joules of work are done in moving 5 coulombs of charge from point A to point B, what is the difference of potential between these two points?

6. How is the heating effect of a current related to the resistance when I remains constant?

7. Approximately how many electrons move past a point in a wire per second when a current of 10 amperes flows through the wire?

8. An electric lamp carries a current of 2 amperes under a potential difference of 110 volts for 30 sec.

    a. How much energy is supplied to the lamp?

    b. In what form, or forms, is this energy delivered?

9. How many amperes does a 100-watt lamp draw on a 110-volt circuit?

10. An electric iron takes 6 amperes when operating on 120 volts.

    a. What is the resistance of the heating element in the iron?

    b. How much energy is supplied to the iron in two minutes?

    c. How many calories is this? (Suggestion: What is the mechanical equivalent of heat?)

11. The wire of the heating element in an electric stove, toaster, or iron gets red hot, but the wire running from the outlet to the stove, toaster, or iron does not. Explain.

12. The resistance of a circuit remains constant.

    a. How will doubling the voltage affect the current?

    b. How will halving it affect the power?

13. By mistake you plug a radio into a 220-volt outlet and find that it burns out all the tubes. Explain precisely why.

14. Which of the following combinations of electric devices could be plugged in the same 110-volt outlet and all turned on at the same time without burning out a 15-ampere fuse in a parallel circuit?

    a. A 1000-watt toaster and a 400-watt coffee percolator.

    b. A 140-watt electric blanket, a 60-watt radio, three 100-watt lamps, and a 2-watt electric clock.

    c. A waffle iron having a resistance of 15 ohms, an electric refrigerator with a 1/5-horsepower (150-watt) motor, a 750-watt electric iron, and a 50-watt radio.

15. State two reasons why tungsten is used as the filament in electric lamps rather than copper.

16. Which has the greatest resistance?

    a. The filament in a 25-watt bulb or that in a 100-watt bulb?

    b. The filament in a 100-watt bulb or the heating element in your toaster?

    c. Two 50-watt bulbs or one 100-watt bulb?

17. A 100-watt bulb is a more efficient light giver than two 50-watt bulbs. Why?

18. A 100-watt lamp burns steadily for 24 hours. At a rate of 5 cents per kilowatt-hour, what is the cost?

19. In a certain experiment 96,500 coulombs are sent through the apparatus. If the current is a steady 5 amperes, how long must it remain turned on?

20. a. Draw a series circuit to include a source, switch, 2 lamps, a radio, and an electric iron.

    b. Draw a parallel circuit to include the same resistances.

CHAPTER XXI

Electricity and Magnetism

If there is no other use discovered of electricity, this, however, is something considerable, that it may help to make a vain man humble.
—BENJAMIN FRANKLIN (1747)

MAGNETISM

The relationship of magnetism to electricity is an entirely unexpected one. Only two observational facts even suggested any relationship at all. One was that lightning discharges had been noted to have occasionally magnetized pieces of steel, or to have demagnetized a magnetic needle. The other was the observed similarity in the behavior of static electric charges and magnetic poles. Without this observation it is unlikely that the relationship would have been discovered as soon as it was (1820). Even with it, no one suspected how fundamental the relationship is.

HISTORICAL BACKGROUND

The discovery of magnetism in certain specimens of an iron ore mineral (magnetite) [1] was made by many peoples in dif-

ferent lands at unknown times in the early history of modern man. The Chinese made the discovery that an elongated specimen suspended by a thread, so that it was free to turn, always oriented itself in an approximately north–south direction. Another Chinese (*ca.* A.D. 1100) hit upon the idea that such specimens could be used for direction finding, and so the magnetic compass was born. Still later it was discovered that pieces of soft iron rubbed against specimens of the mineral acquired the same property of acting like a magnet. In time these discoveries were to lead man to exploration of the Old World, and to the discovery and exploration of the New. Without compasses ships could not sail freely over the oceans. The sun and the stars were useful, but could not inspire the confidence a compass could, since the latter could be checked at any time of day or night and in any kind of weather.

The first comprehensive study of magnetism was made by William Gilbert to whom we have already referred in our discussion of electric charges (p. 269).[2] His greatest contribution was his conclusion that the earth acts as a huge magnet. The reason for this is still being investigated.

SOME EXPERIMENTAL FACTS CONCERNING MAGNETISM

One end (pole) of a magnet points approximately north. This is the north-seeking pole, and by definition it is called the north pole. In the proximity of Cincinnati,

---

[1] Magnetite (Fe_3O_4) from most localities does

not itself act as a magnet. All magnetite is magnetic, however, for by magnetic we mean the ability to be attracted by a magnet.

[2] His chief incentive was to see if magnetism could account for the forces to keep the planets in their orbits as pictured by the Copernican theory —in which he was a firm believer.

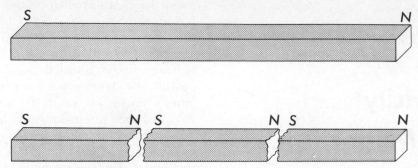

Fig. 21-1. A broken magnet develops new poles instantaneously at the broken ends.

Ohio, a compass points directly to the true geographic pole (point of emergence of the imaginary axis of the earth), whereas in New York City it points nearly 12° to the west of true north and in Denver it points somewhat over 12° to the east of north. Correlation of a large number of such determinations from points all around the earth locates the magnetic pole in the north as lying north of Hudson Bay some fourteen hundred miles from the geographic pole.

From a *practical* viewpoint only a few metals can be magnetized. Chief among them are iron and steel. Others are nickel, cobalt, and certain alloys—some of which make the finest of permanent magnets. All "permanent" magnets eventually lose their magnetism.

The forces of repulsion and attraction found between like and unlike poles, respectively, are exactly similar to those between like and unlike electric charges. That is, *like magnetic poles repel and unlike poles attract*. Coulomb found that these forces of repulsion and attraction between two poles obeyed the same general inverse-square law as did electric charges:

Force of attraction or repulsion

$$= \frac{\left(\begin{array}{l}\text{Strength of 1st pole } (P_1)\\ \times \text{ strength of 2nd pole } (P_2)\end{array}\right)}{(\text{Distance apart})^2}$$

In symbols $F = K\dfrac{P_1 P_2}{d^2}$ (Eq. 21-1)

As usual, we need to define a unit magnetic pole in order to have some basis for measuring P_1 and P_2. This unit of pole strength is defined as follows: If two like poles of equal strength are placed in a vacuum 1 cm apart and the force of repulsion between them is 1 dyne, then each pole is defined as a unit pole. Thus, in the above equation, if P_1 and P_2 are both unit poles, and d is 1 cm, then F is 1 dyne, and K becomes 1.

Magnetic poles occur only in pairs. This is proved by breaking magnets into any number of parts (Fig. 21-1). Each part, no matter how small, will have a north pole and a south pole.

THEORY OF MAGNETIZATION

This suggests that the cause of magnetism is associated with atoms or their arrangements, or more probably with both. Each atom and each electron can be considered a small magnet in itself. If enough of these tiny magnets are lined up the same way (Fig. 21-2), north-seeking poles pointing one way, south-seeking poles the other, then the magnetic behavior of the material as a whole would be accounted for. Thus, nothing has been added during the magnetization process except orientation. Methods of checking this theory are included in the problems at the end of this chapter. Note, however, that there is nothing in the theory that ultimately explains magnetism.

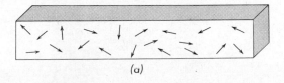

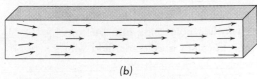

Fig. 21-2. (a) Molecular magnets in an unmagnetized steel bar are randomly oriented.

(b) During the process of magnetization the molecular magnets line up parallel to the external field, producing poles at the ends.

MAGNETIC LINES OF FORCE

Suppose we place a sheet of glass on a bar magnet, and sprinkle iron filings lightly on the glass.[3] If we now tap the glass

[3] The glass is to prevent the filings from sticking to the magnet.

lightly, we will see the filings arrange themselves in a pattern like that in Fig. 21-3. If we use two unlike poles, as shown in Fig. 21-3, the patterns will be as indicated.

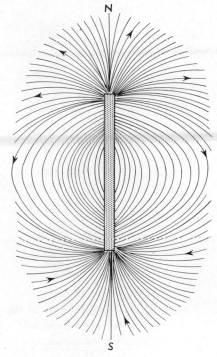

Fig. 21-3. Magnetic Field. The orientation of the field is as indicated by the arrows on the lines of force. Note that they are directed outward from the north pole and inward towards the south pole.

Note that the directions of the arrows in the drawings are outward from the north poles and inward towards the south poles. This is a matter of convention. The magnetic needles of tiny compasses placed on any of the lines orient themselves with the field (Fig. 21-4). The lines—which, of course, are imaginary—are referred to as lines of force. The complete pattern of

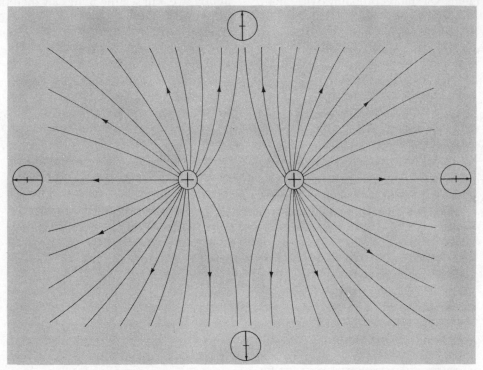

Fig. 21-4.   Lines of Force about Two Like Poles.   Small compasses are used to indicate the orientation of the field.   The two like poles may also be considered as like electric charges.   The field then becomes an electric field with the orientation as shown.

lines is three-dimensional (Fig. 21-5), i.e., patterns similar to that in Fig. 21-3 are obtained in all planes passing through the axis of the magnet.   The density of the lines is an indication of the force exerted. Thus, the lines are denser near the poles, because experiment shows the magnetic forces are greatest there.

MAGNETIC FIELDS

If we place a magnetic pole in a certain space, that space about the pole appears to have been altered from what it was before.   It is altered because any piece of

iron brought into it will now experience a force that it will not experience if the magnet is removed.   This altered space is called a *magnetic field*.   The field is considered to exert a force on any magnetic body.   If the magnetic body is another small bar magnet or a magnetic needle, the magnetic field will be found to have direction (Fig. 21-4).   By definition the direction of this field at any point is given by the direction of the force exerted on a small unit north pole.   In Figs. 21-3 and 21-4, the directions of the field are shown by the arrows.   Note that they are from the north pole to the south pole (by definition).

ELECTRIC FIELDS

The field concept originated with Michael Faraday, one of the greatest experimenters in electric and magnetic phenomena that ever lived.[4] Faraday applied the field concept to electric charges as well as to magnetic poles.

Place an electric charge in the vicinity of another charge and it experiences a force, either of attraction or repulsion, just as does a magnetic pole in the presence of another magnetic pole. This altered space is an electric field (Fig. 21-4). More formally, *an electric field is a region of space in which a stationary charge is acted upon by an electric force of attraction or repulsion.* Of course, every charge has its own field, and whether the force experienced by two adjacent charges is one of attraction or one of repulsion depends upon the interaction of the two fields, just as in the case of adjacent poles. By definition, the direction of an electric field at any point is given by the direction of the force exerted

on a small unit positive charge in that field (Fig. 21-6).

ON FIELDS IN GENERAL

The field concept can be applied equally well to any region of space where forces at a distance interact. It has been applied

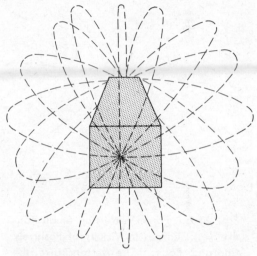

Fig. 21-5. Three-dimensional Field about a Bar Magnet.

successfully to the force of gravitation. Thus, we speak of the gravitational field surrounding every material body. In all fields the forces obey an inverse-square law. Curiously, too, the same space can be a gravitational field, an electric field, and a magnetic field at one and the same time without the fields interfering with one another.

Gravitational fields are of one kind only, so the only forces acting are those of attraction. No material body in the whole universe can exist without a gravitational field surrounding it. In the normal state

[4] Faraday was apprenticed to a London bookbinder for seven years. He became interested in physics and chemistry by reading some of the books that he bound. He had little formal education. In 1813 he became assistant to Sir Humphry Davy, director of the Royal Institution of Great Britain (founded by Count Rumford), where he started out as little more than a bottle-washer. His experimental genius quickly showed itself, so much so that when Sir Humphry Davy, who among other successes discovered sodium and potassium, was asked what his greatest discovery was, he replied, "Michael Faraday." Twelve years later (1825) Faraday became director of the Institution, a position he occupied until his death in 1867. For a few years he acted as an industrial consultant, earning fees many times his salary for work in applied science. He gave this up in order to devote his full attention to pure science. This was a fortunate circumstance for industry, for not long afterwards he discovered the principles that made possible the development of our present electrical industry.

material bodies are electrically neutral, but an electric field can be created about any material body under the proper circumstances. From the practical viewpoint magnetic fields can be created about only

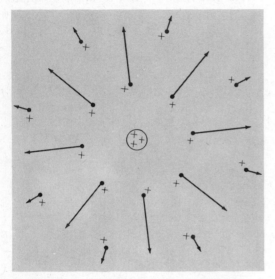

Fig. 21-6. Force Vectors on Small Positive Test Charges in Vicinity of Positively Charged Body. The vectors give the magnitude and direction of the force acting on the charges at the points indicated. If the central body were negatively charged, the vectors would point inward.

a few metals or metallic alloys. The strength of the gravitational field is extremely weak compared to electric and magnetic fields. Gravitational attraction becomes enormous only as the size of the bodies becomes enormous. The gravitational field cannot be destroyed or neutralized, nor can an object be shielded from its effects, whereas electric fields are easily neutralized, magnetic fields can be either

created or destroyed [5] by various means, and both can be shielded from their surroundings in various ways.

While magnetic and electric fields are similar in ways that have been already mentioned, their differences are significant also. If free to move, magnets align themselves in a north–south direction, whereas there is no tendency for any sort of alignment among charges. Positive charges may be isolated from negative ones and vice versa, but north poles cannot be isolated from south poles. Charges move readily from one body to another along conductors; there is no corresponding movement of magnetism. Insulated charged conductors will share their charges with neutral insulated conductors, with the result that their electric fields become weaker. A magnetized piece of steel will magnetize any number of other pieces of steel without itself losing any of its magnetic field strength.

MAGNETISM FROM ELECTRICITY: OERSTED'S EXPERIMENT

It was Hans Christian Oersted, a Danish professor of physics, who discovered that magnetic fields could exist where there were no magnets. In a series of experiments in which he was using an unusually large Voltaic pile (battery) so as to produce a large current, he happened to note that a compass in the near vicinity was behaving oddly. Further investigation showed that the compass needle always oriented itself at right angles to the current-carrying wire (Fig. 21-7a), and that it re-

[5] Except, of course, for huge fields like that of the earth.

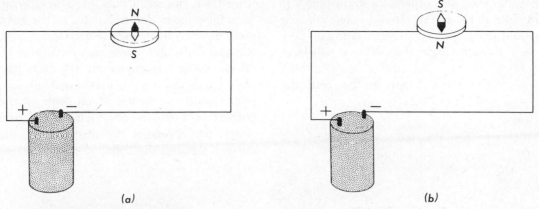

Fig. 21-7. Oersted's Experiment. **(a)** The compass is below the wire. The needle will turn when a current is flowing through the coil, to orient itself at right angles to the direction of the current. Reversal of the current causes the needle to reverse its direction.

(b) The direction of the compass needle is also reversed as the compass is moved from a position below the wire to one above.

versed its direction if either the direction of the current was reversed, or the compass was changed from a position below the wire to one above (Fig. 21-7*b*).

This was an important discovery, for many experiments by many investigators had shown that stationary charges and magnets had no effect on each other. This experiment meant that moving charges did have an effect on magnets. The problem now was to find out how and why. We have already learned that one magnetic field will interact with another. It seems reasonable therefore to suspect that the current passing through the wire has set up a magnetic field about the wire. To check we orient a current-carrying wire vertically through a horizontal board and sprinkle iron filings about it; we find that the filings form concentric circles about the wire (Fig. 21-8). A number of tiny

compasses placed alongside the wire orient themselves at right angles to the radii of these concentric circles. Therefore, the lines of force are circular about the wire— since compass needles always line up with the lines of force. If the current is reversed, the compass needles reverse their directions.

PRACTICAL RESULTS OF OERSTED'S DISCOVERY: ELECTROMAGNETS

If instead of a straight wire, we use a loose coil of wire [called a helix (Fig. 21-9) if no current is passing through, and a solenoid if a current is passing through] sprinkling iron filings as before, we see that the filings take much the same form as they do around a bar magnet. Moreover, if we check with a compass, we will find that one end of the solenoid acts as a north pole, the other as a south pole. If mounted to swing freely, the solenoid would orient itself as does a compass needle. Even a single loop of wire will have a north-seeking side and a south-seeking side. The more loops in the coil, the

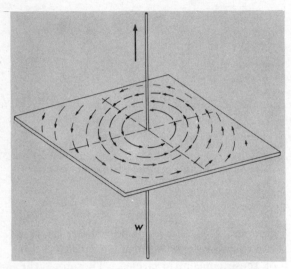

Fig. 21-8. Current-carrying wire (w) has a magnetic field in which the lines of force are concentric about the wire. If the current stops, the field disappears. If the current is reversed, the field is reversed. Would a compass needle point towards the wire?

greater the strength of the field. This makes electromagnets possible.

Electromagnets more powerful than any permanent magnet of the same size are made by inserting soft iron cores inside closely-wound coils. The core greatly strengthens the magnetic field, for the core itself becomes magnetized, and the lines of force which pass through the coil are gathered into a smaller volume within the core. Electromagnets today have countless

uses, from the small ones used in hearing aids, telephones, doorbells, etc., to the giant ones used to load and unload scrap iron, railroad rails, and other heavy equipment. Of enormous importance are the facts that electromagnets can be demagnetized simply by pulling a switch which shuts off the current, and that the poles can be reversed simply by reversing the direction of the current through the coils.

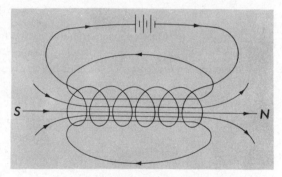

Fig. 21-9. Solenoid. A solenoid is a coil of wire with an electric current passing through it. One end of the coil is a north pole, the other a south pole. Thus, it is an electromagnet. To be a practical electromagnet, the solenoid must have a soft iron core, i.e., a bar or rod of soft iron about which the coil is wound. The core greatly strengthens the magnetic field, as will also the number of turns of wire about the core.

DISCOVERY OF THE MOTOR EFFECT

As soon as Oersted's discovery was announced, experimenters everywhere went to work to exploit it. It was that great electrical genius, Michael Faraday,[6] who

---

[6] Faraday may not have been the first to do so.

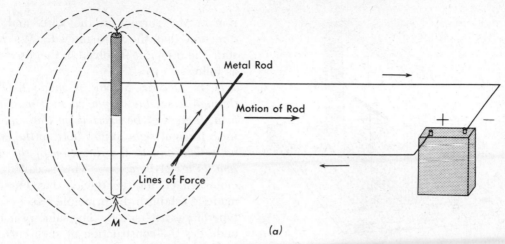

Metal Rod

Motion of Rod

Lines of Force

M

(a)

Fig. 21-10. The Motor Effect. **(a)** Two bare rigid horizontal wires are connected to a battery. A metal rod laid across the wires completes the circuit. Note that the rod is free to move. If a magnet, M, is now brought near, the rod becomes a conductor in a magnetic field. The rod will experience a force at right angles to the magnetic field (indicated by the lines of force) and at right angles to the direction of the current through the rod. The rod will move to the right.

(b) Another version of the motor effect. Here the current-carrying rod is mounted to swing freely. If the horseshoe magnet is brought near, the bar will swing to the right for the given orientation of the magnet, to the left for the reverse orientation.

(c) Note that the direction of motion of the conductor in a magnetic field is at right angles to both the field and the direction of the current.

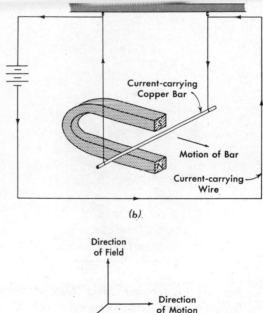

Current-carrying
Copper Bar

Motion of Bar

Current-carrying
Wire

(b)

Direction
of Field

Direction
of Motion

Direction
of Current

(c)

reasoned that since a magnet (compass needle) free to move would do so in the presence of a current-carrying wire, then the reverse should happen—a current-carrying wire free to move should do so in the presence of a magnet fixed in position. He successfully devised an experiment to check his reasoning, and in doing so, discovered the relationship between the direction of the magnetic field of the magnet, the direc-

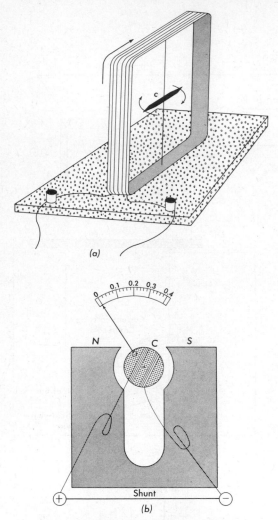

tion of the current in the wire, and the direction that the wire moved. We may state the principle involved in the discovery as follows:

If an electric current is made to flow through a conductor placed in a magnetic field, there will be exerted on the conductor a force at right angles both to the magnetic field and to the direction of the current (Fig. 21-10 *a, b*). This is called the motor effect, for the device that Faraday made to establish the principle was a crude type of electric motor. The same principle underlies the construction of such current-measuring instruments as galvanometers, ammeters, and voltmeters (Fig. 21-11). We will discuss them first, for their construction is simpler than that of the electric motor.

GALVANOMETERS, AMMETERS, VOLTMETERS

If compass needles—which are really small magnets that are free to move—will orient themselves with respect to the magnetic field of a current-carrying wire, then Newton's third law demands that a current-carrying coil of wire that is free to move should *attempt* to orient itself with respect to a magnet fixed in position. How successful the coil will be in orienting itself will depend in part on how it is suspended, in part on its inertia, and in part on the

Fig. 21-11. Motor Effect Applied to Galvanometers and Ammeters. **(a)** A magnetic needle, c, is mounted within a fixed coil of wire attached to a source. Since the needle is free to move and the coil is not, it will tend to orient its magnetic field with that of the coil. More commonly the magnet is fixed and the coil free to move as in **(b)**. Here (in **b**) the coil, C, and the magnet are shown in cross-section. When current passes through the coil it turns to the right, mov-

ing the pointer attached to it along the scale. The greater the current the farther the coil turns. A known fraction of the current passes through the coil; most flows through the shunt, as in an ammeter. Note that the movement of the needle in **(a)** or of the coil in **(b)** is due to the motor effect.

size of the current passing through it. Consider an example in which the magnet is a permanent horseshoe type; the coil is flat, rectangular, and made of many turns of fine wire (Fig. 21-12); it is suspended by a fine stiff wire between the poles of the horseshoe magnet such that the plane of the coil is at right angles to the field of the magnet. When a current is passed through the wire it becomes a magnet; one flat face becomes a north pole, the other a south pole. The two like poles, one on the permanent magnet, the other on the coil, will repel each other, and the unlike ones, one on the magnet, the other on the coil, will attract. The result is that the coil is twisted on its supporting wire, which resists the twisting. The greater the current, the greater the twisting. A pointer attached to the coil and leading to a carefully graduated scale can measure the amount of twisting, hence the amount of current passing through the coil.

If a small coil is made of many turns of very fine wire, if an independently mounted soft iron core is placed inside the coil, and if the suspending wire is extremely fine gold wire, we will have a highly sensitive instrument for measuring the current in the wire, a current as small as a billionth of an ampere. Such a galvanometer is too delicate for ordinary use. More rugged ones, but still too sensitive [7] for normal use are made by modifying the suspension. The still more rugged ammeter has a wire of low resistance in parallel with the coil so that the major part of the current, say nine-tenths, will pass through it. Thus, only one-tenth of the current passes through

[7] Because of the heating effect of currents, such fine wire will easily get hot enough to melt if ordinary currents are passed through them.

the coil, so large currents can be measured without burning out the coil (Fig. 21-11*b*). The scale is, of course, designed to read the full current through the system. Am-

Fig. 21-12. Motor Effect Applied to Electric Motor. When a current flows through the flat coil of wire suspended between the poles of the magnet, the coil becomes an electromagnet. Its poles attempt to orient themselves with the poles of the horseshoe magnet. We "frustrate" the attempt by changing the direction of the current in the coil. If we continue the frustration by timing the reversal of current direction correctly, the coil can be kept turning in the same direction. Mount the turning coil on an axle and we have an electric motor.

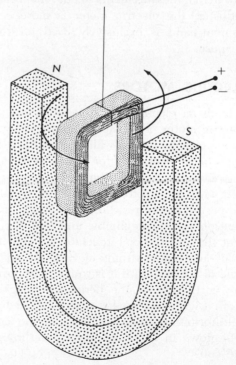

meters are always connected directly in the line in which the current is to be measured.

Galvanometers can easily be modified to measure the difference in potential between any two points in a circuit, i.e., they can be converted to voltmeters. Since $V = RI$, V can be measured if the product $R \times I$ is known. All we need is to know R and I, R by a previous separate measurement, I by the galvanometer itself, and then to devise a scale that will automatically multiply R by I. As the coil twists, a pointer indicates the product on the scale.

Since P (power) $= VI$, the power supplied by a circuit can be obtained by the readings of an ammeter and a voltmeter. The total energy supplied to the circuit is found by multiplying the product of these readings by the time the current flows. For actual measurements to households and industry, the electric meter is more convenient, and is exclusively used for that purpose.

ELECTRIC MOTORS

Such an electric meter, really a type of electric motor, is possible because the galvanometer has nearly all of the essential parts of an electric motor. Suppose that in Fig. 21-12 we replace the permanent magnet with an electromagnet. Let us also suppose that the resistance of the coil suspension wire is negligible and that a current through the coil generates a magnetic field sufficiently strong to turn the south pole of the coil until it is squarely opposite the north pole of the permanent magnet. Here it will stay, in what may be termed an equilibrium position, as long as the current flows in the same direction through the coil.

Let us start with no current through the coil. As we close the switch the coil turns to orient its field with that of the electromagnet. As it does so inertia carries the coil a bit past the equilibrium position mentioned above. Now suppose at this particular instant, before the coil can swing back, we reverse the poles of the electromagnet, thereby reversing the direction of its field. The coil cannot now swing back, because attraction has been replaced by repulsion, so it continues towards the other pole of the electromagnet, to which it is now attracted. As before, inertia carries it slightly beyond, at which instant we "frustrate" it again by switching the polarity of the electromagnet. Hence it continues on and on, being "frustrated" twice during every revolution. The reversal of the polarity of the electromagnet is accomplished by using alternating current for the electromagnet. Such current in the United States is generated to switch the polarity 120 times (60 cycles) per second. Thus, the coil is given 120 "kicks" in the same direction per second, enough to cause it to spin rapidly, which is what we want in a motor.

To be effective as a motor we must redesign the galvanometer. The suspension wire is replaced by a sturdy axle on which coarse wire is appropriately wound (Fig. 21-13). The electromagnet may be replaced by permanent magnets and alternating current fed through the coil. If so, it is the polarity of the coil that is changed 120 times a second instead of that of the magnet. In either case the axle with its coils of wire, called an armature, is kept spinning. A pulley on the end of the axle to which a belt may be attached, or a gear that will mesh with an appliance gear, and the motor is ready to convert electrical

Fig. 21-13. A Direct-current Motor. Only a single coil on the armature is shown. The field coils carry the current (from the source) for the electromagnet. The current from the source is fed into the armature coils by way of the brushes—which "brush" against the commutator. The commutator is needed to reverse the direction of the current in the armature coils—for the current in these coils *must* be an alternating current. If the source is alternating current, no commutator is needed. (After Semat, *Physics in the Modern World,* Ronald, New York, 1949.)

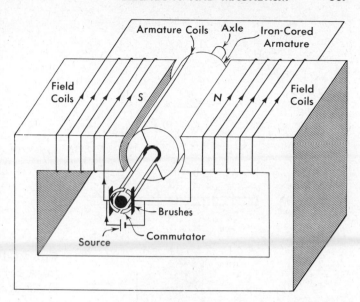

energy into mechanical energy (and into some of the inevitable heat energy).

ELECTRICITY FROM MAGNETISM

Again it was Faraday who pondered the question, "If an electric current is capable of producing magnetism, is it not possible that magnetism can be used to produce electricity?" It took him nine or ten years of sporadic experimentation to discover how.[8] Part of the difficulty was due to the crudity of the instruments available; part was due to the fact that only a feeble momentary current could be produced so that it could easily go undetected. To add to the difficulty, a stationary closed loop of wire (Fig. 21-14a) in a stationary magnetic field produces no current, but if either the loop or the magnet is moving, a

[8] Joseph Henry of the United States independently discovered how at about the same time (1831) but Faraday is usually given the credit because of priority of publication.

current is generated (Fig. 21-14 *b, c*). Moreover, the wire has to move *across* the field, not parallel to it. The faster the movement, the greater the current, and the stronger the magnet, the greater the current. The principle is further illustrated in Fig. 21-15.

The explanation is as follows: An electric current is a stream of electrons moving through a conductor (a wire, in this case). When a wire is moved *across* a magnetic field, the electrons in the wire experience a *sideways* push. Since the wire is moving perpendicular to the magnetic field, the electrons in the wire move sideways, i.e., along the wire. This movement of the electrons in the wire constitutes the current if the wire is part of a closed circuit. Reverse either the movement of the wire or the direction of the field and the electrons will be pushed the opposite way, i.e., the current will be reversed. Stop moving the wire and the electrons experience no sideways push, hence no current flows.

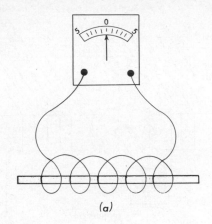

(a)

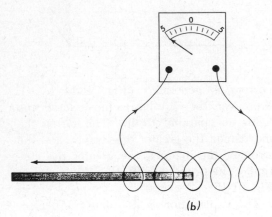

(b)

Fig. 21-14.   Electricity from Magnetism.
(a) A bar magnet at rest in a coil of wire
produces no current, as can be seen by the
galvanometer.   **(b)** When the magnet is
quickly moved to the left the galvanometer
registers a current through it.   **(c)** If the
magnet is moved to the right, the galvanometer registers a current in the opposite direction.   In any case the needle swings back
to 0 the instant motion stops.   Note that the
current is generated by the wire cutting
across magnetic lines of force as the magnet
is moved.

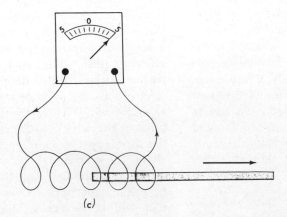

(c)

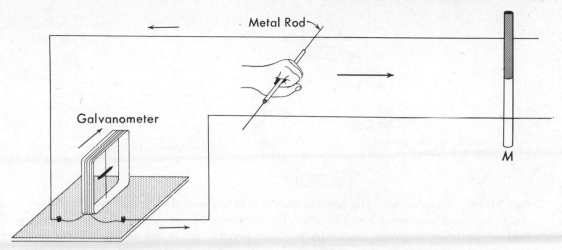

Fig. 21-15. The Phenomenon of Electromagnetic Induction. A strong magnet, M, is placed in a vertical position between the pair of bare horizontal rigid wires. A metal rod, with insulation in the middle, is placed in contact with the bare rigid wires and given a quick push towards the magnet. The galvanometer shows a current by the turning of the compass needle as the rod cuts the magnetic lines of force. Pulling the rod away from the magnet will cause the needle to turn the other way, showing that the current has been reversed. Compare with Fig. 21-10.

The actual apparatus that Faraday used was quite different. It was similar to that in Fig. 21-16. When the switch is closed, current from the battery flows through the primary coil. This magnetizes the circular soft iron ring, causing a magnetic field to build up about the whole ring. Note that there is no physical connection between the primary and secondary circuits. We could replace the circular ring with two soft iron cores entirely separated by a few inches, or we could even dispense with the cores entirely, without destroying the experiment. The cores, as we have already seen, strengthen the magnetic field, and so enhance the final effect.

While the switch is closed, the galvanometer reads zero. If we watch closely at the instant of closing it, we will see a momentary deflection of the galvanometer,

say, to the right but the pointer quickly settles back to zero. If we open the switch, we note another momentary deflection of the galvanometer, but to the left. If we rapidly open and close the switch, the pointer will swing back and forth, first to the left, then to the right, etc. Again we state that the pointer remains at zero when the switch is either open or closed.[9]

How can we explain this behavior? Actually it is similar to that for Figs. 21-14 and 21-15, but here we have a stationary wire and a moving magnetic field, whereas in Fig. 21-16 we have a moving wire and a stationary magnetic field. The stationary

[9] If Faraday had had alternating current (which was not possible until after he had made this discovery), he would not have had to open and close the switch to induce a current in the secondary coil.

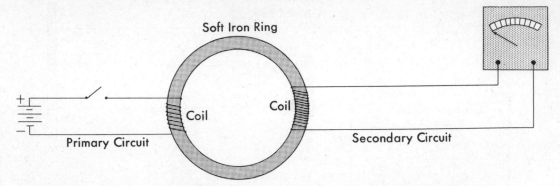

Fig. 21-16. Transformer. The wires in both circuits are insulated so that there is no electrical connection between the two circuits. The soft iron core merely intensifies the magnetic field set up when a current flows through either circuit. When the switch is closed, the alternating current in the primary coil induces a current in the secondary as a magnetic field about the primary is built up and collapsed 120 times per second (60-cycle current).

wire is the secondary coil, in which a current is induced on opening or closing the switch. The moving magnetic field builds up about the iron ring at the instant of closing the switch, and collapses at the instant of opening it. It is this building up and collapsing of the magnetic field that substitutes for the moving magnet.

Faraday thought of the building up of the field as consisting of lines of force "springing out from the core" at the instant of closing the switch. As they sprang out, they cut across the wire, exerting a sideways push on the charges. While the switch remained closed, the lines of force stayed in position out away from the coil. In other words, both the magnetic field and the wire were now stationary, so the charges experienced no push. When the switch was opened, the lines of force then collapsed back into the core, cutting across the coils again as they did so, and exerting a sideways push on the charges (electrons) in the opposite direction. Thus the current was reversed.

LAW OF ELECTROMAGNETIC INDUCTION

We may now state the general principle by which electricity is produced from magnetism, as follows: *Whenever a conductor cuts across magnetic lines of force, or the magnetic lines of force cut across a conductor, the electrons in the conductor experience a sideways push that causes them to move through the conductor as an electric current.* As stated, the assumption is made that the conductor is part of a closed circuit, as in the secondary coil in Fig. 21-16. A briefer but less explanatory statement of the law is as follows: *A current is induced in a conductor only while the conductor is in relative motion across lines of magnetic force.* The emphasis is on the words "motion across."

For a current to flow, the ends of the wire must be united in a closed circuit, as in Figs. 21-14, 21-15, but a difference of potential is established even if the ends are open. Move a short *straight* piece of insulated wire across one pole of a bar magnet. While the wire is moving, and only while it is moving, the electrons in the wire experience a push at right angles to the direction of movement, and also at right angles to the field of the magnet. Hence those electrons free to do so crowd towards one end of the wire. This end then has an excess, and the other end a deficiency of electrons. By definition, the former has a higher potential than the latter; work can be done by the electrons moving from the region of excess to that of deficiency. In any ordinary household electrical outlet there are the two open ends of a wire, between which there is a difference of potential of 110 volts. It is the function of the machinery in the power plant to maintain this potential difference. When you plug in a light, an appliance, or a motor and turn on the switch, you make it possible for the electrons to move from a higher potential to a lower potential, doing work as they pass through the light bulb, appliance, or motor.

ELECTRIC GENERATORS OR DYNAMOS

How does the power company maintain this difference of potentials? By use of Faraday's principle of electromagnetic induction, great electric generators, sometimes called dynamos, have been built. By means of steam or gas-powered engines or water turbines, great coils of wire are made to spin in a magnetic field or a magnetic field to spin about coils of wire. In either case a conductor (coil of wire) is cutting across magnetic lines of force; the electrons in the conductor move through it as an electric current (Fig. 21-17). The generator is thus a device that pushes electrons

through wires by means of changing magnetic fields. Note carefully that the device does not generate electric charge; it simply makes the charges flow.

The principle of the generator and that of the electric motor are much the same. In the generator the electrons are pushed along the wire; in the motor they are pushed perpendicular to the wire. In fact, either can be used for the other. In the motor we feed electrical energy into the coils and take out mechanical energy, whereas in the generator we put in mechanical energy and take out electrical energy.

There are two kinds of generators, direct current (DC) and alternating current (AC). The simplest, and most commonly used, is the AC type. As it spins in the magnetic field, the coil is moving upward across the lines of force on one side and downward across the lines on the other side. The result is that the current will flow in one direction half the time and in the other half the time (Fig. 21-17). Thus, in AC the electrons are surging back and forth through the wires of the electrical system, alternating their directions 120 times per second (if 60-cycle current is being generated).

TRANSFORMERS

The transformer also depends upon electromagnetic induction. In fact, Fig. 21-16 is one type of transformer. Whenever there is *alternating current* flowing in the primary coil (so called because it is the one connected to the source), a current, as we have already seen, will flow in the secondary coil even though there is no visible motion of either a coil or a magnet. We could cut the ring in two without affecting the current in the secondary just so long as we

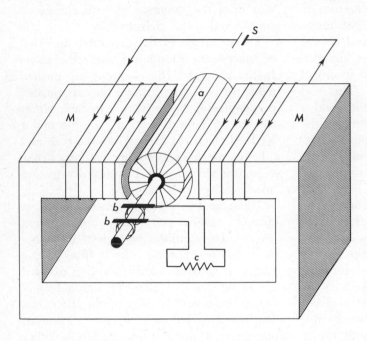

Fig. 21-17. Electric Generator, or Dynamo. A series of coils of wire are wound on the armature, a. The ends of the wire in these coils are attached to the rings on which the brushes, b, rub when a gas or steam engine or a water turbine spins the armature. The current for the electromagnet, M, comes from an outside source, S. There is no physical connection between the armature and the magnet. As outside energy spins the armature, the armature coils cut the lines of force of the magnet, causing a current to flow in the coils. The current is AC, for any one coil is first cutting down across the lines of force on one side and up across them on the other. The brushes at b are necessary to transfer the current to the outside circuit, c. (After Semat, *Physics in the Modern World*, Ronald, New York, 1949.)

keep the two coils close together. With alternating current, the magnetic field of the primary is building up and collapsing 120 times per second. As it does so, it cuts across the nearby secondary coil, inducing the electrons to move in it, thereby giving rise to a current.

If we have the same number of coils in the secondary as in the primary, the current and voltage generated in the secondary will be the same as in the primary, if we neglect any losses. If, however, the secondary contains twice as many coils as the primary, as is actually the case in Fig. 21-16, then the voltage generated in the secondary will be twice that of the primary, but

the current will be only half as much (neglecting losses). Since a transformer is actually a device for transferring electrical energy from a primary circuit to a secondary one, it is clear that the energy transferred to the secondary cannot possibly be greater than that in the primary. Therefore it follows that, neglecting losses,

$$V_p I_p = V_s I_s \qquad \text{(Eq. 21-2)}$$

The ratio of the number of turns, N, in the primary to the number of turns in the secondary determines the ratio of V_p to V_s.

$$\frac{V_p}{V_s} = \frac{N_p}{N_s} \qquad \text{(Eq. 21-3)}$$

It also determines the ratio of I_p to I_s.

$$\frac{I_p}{I_s} = \frac{N_s}{N_p} \qquad \text{(Eq. 21-4)}$$

Note that Eq. 21-3 is a direct proportionality and Eq. 21-4 an inverse proportionality. The three proportionalities can be combined, as follows:

$$\frac{V_p}{V_s} = \frac{N_p}{N_s} = \frac{I_s}{I_p}$$

If N_s is greater than N_p, the transformer is of the step-up type, i.e., the voltage in the secondary is increased and the current decreased. If N_p is greater, then we have the step-down type of transformer, i.e., the voltage in the secondary is decreased and the current is increased. Both types are abundantly used today. Our most familiar example of a step-down type is in doorbells that operate on house current. Here the voltage is reduced from 110 or 120 volts to about 6 volts.

Without the invention of the transformer our present electrical industry could never have developed as it has, for the transmission of electric energy over considerable distances would have been impossibly costly. High voltages must be used just as high pressures must be used to transport water over long distances, uphill and down or on level ground. If the pressure is too low, not enough water is delivered at the other end.

In the case of electricity the power, P, transmitted from the powerhouse to the consumer is calculated by multiplying the voltage, V, by the current, I, minus the losses due to the heating effect of the current. Since the heating effect of the current is given by I^2R, we can write

$$P = VI - I^2R$$

The problem is to keep I^2R low so that a larger percentage of the power generated reaches the consumer. Increasing the diameter of the wires (thereby reducing R) not only is costly but also with a fixed V, I is increased since $V = RI$ (Ohm's Law). Increase of I increases the amount of electrical energy transformed to useless heat energy; the amount is proportional to the square of the current. It is better to use a transformer to step up V at the generating station to allow a smaller current; this involves using another transformer to step down V for safe handling at the consumer end. This smaller current makes for a smaller value of I^2R, so the heat losses are reduced.

The step-up transformer allows us to increase the voltage (electrical pressure) to a thousandfold that generated by the dynamo, thus reducing the current, I, to a small fraction of an ampere. When this energy reaches the community where it is to be used, step-down transformers are used to reduce the voltage and increase the current to a usable value. Modern transformers are wonderfully efficient, making the transmission of electrical energy possible with little loss. They will not normally work with direct current for there is no changing magnetic field to induce a current in a nearby circuit. It is possible to make them work if a vibrator-interrupter is also used; it automatically makes and breaks the circuit very rapidly, thereby creating a changing magnetic field. Such devices are used only where high-voltage direct current is desired.

SUMMARY

Man knew some of the elementary facts about electricity and magnetism for centuries before he discovered, largely by accident, the relationship between them. The first magnets were specimens of a particular variety of the common mineral, magnetite. Man eventually learned to artificially magnetize iron and steel, and a very few other metals. Magnets will attract only those metals that can be made into magnets. A magnet free to turn orients itself with the magnetic field of the earth. The north-seeking end of a magnet is called its north pole. Like poles repel, unlike poles attract. The magnitude of this force of attraction or repulsion is given by Coulomb's Law of magnetic forces: $F = (Kq_1q_2)/d^2$.

The fact that the region about a magnet is different from that about a piece of metal of similar size and shape can be tested by sprinkling iron filings about each or by placing small compasses about them. This altered space is called the field of the magnet. The fact that it has direction can be observed by the way small compasses orient themselves in the magnetic field.

Electric charges have electric fields about them which can be detected by the behavior of other charges. Electric charges at rest ignore nearby magnets at rest, and vice versa. But one of the fundamental mysteries of nature is the fact that once that charge starts to move, it develops a magnetic field about it that can interact with the magnetic field of the magnet. Moreover, this magnetic field about the charge, absent while both charge and magnet are at rest, also instantly springs into being if the charge remains at rest and the magnet begins to move. Thus, the charge appears to have a dual personality, one side of which depends upon the motion of it *relative* to a nearby magnet.

The movement of neither the charge nor the magnet is necessary to bring into being the magnetic field of the charge. All that is necessary is to continuously change the strength of the magnetic field of the magnet. This is easy to do if our magnet is an electromagnet. The interaction between the magnetic fields about charges moving in a wire (which constitutes a current) and the magnetic field of a magnet will cause either the magnet or the wire or both to move if either or both are free to do so. The movement is neither one of attraction nor repulsion, and so the movement is neither towards nor away from the magnet or the wire. Instead it is at right angles to both the direction of the magnetic field of the magnet and the direction of the current. From this circumstance has come not only the current-detecting devices—galvanometers, ammeters, and voltmeters—but also electric motors.

Faraday reasoned that if an electric current is capable of producing a magnetic field, a magnetic field should be able to generate an electric current. If this were possible, it should relieve man from dependence on batteries as a source of electrical energy. Out of his researches came the Law of Electromagnetic Induction, and from the application of it came the electric generator, or dynamo. This device generates a current by causing the charges in the wire to move as the magnetic field about the wire is continuously changing. This changing of the magnetic field is accomplished by moving either the magnets with the wire fixed in position or the wire with the magnets fixed in position. External mechanical energy must be used to do the moving. Either alternating current or direct current may be generated, depending upon the method of leading the current away from the generator.

By using the fact that a continuously changing magnetic field exists about any wire carrying alternating current, the transformer was invented. By means of varying the number of turns of the secondary coil *relative* to the primary coil, voltages (hence the current) may be stepped up or stepped down. This allows electricity to be generated far from where it is needed, and is chiefly responsible for the great development of our industrial world.

EXERCISES

I. TERMS AND CONCEPTS

North-seeking pole
South-seeking pole
Pole strength
Coulomb's Law of magnetism
Unit pole
Magnetic field
Oersted
Electric field
Field intensity
Lines of force

Oersted's discovery
Motor effect
Armature
Law of electromagnetic induction
Transformer
Secondary coil
Primary coil
Alternating current
Direct current
Dynamo

II. PROBLEMS

1. How is the north pole of a magnet defined?

2. Could you locate the geographical north pole by means of a compass? Explain. In which direction would the north end of a compass point at the north pole?

3. Would you be wise to try to determine directions while standing

    a. Alongside an automobile.

    b. Near a wire fence.

    c. On a steel bridge.

    d. Beneath a high-tension electric power line (with copper wires)? Explain in each case.

4. The deep interior of the earth consists of a core 4000 mi in diameter presumed to be composed largely of iron with some nickel. It is probably, in part at least, molten. This molten iron has been said to be the direct cause of the earth's magnetism. Show why it cannot be.

5. Note that it was Coulomb who produced the evidence that the forces of attraction or repulsion between electric charges and between magnetic poles follow inverse-square laws. State both of these laws, in words and mathematically.

6. The field concept applies to three types of forces. What are they? Who originated the field concept? How can you detect the presence of a magnetic field? Of an electric field?

7. There are at least three differences between a gravitational field on the one hand and electrical and magnetic fields on the other. What are they?

8. Two unit poles are 2 cm apart. Let the force between them be represented by F. What will be the value of the force if the distance is increased to 4 cm? To 6 cm? Is reduced to 1 cm?

9. What sorts of things may be magnetized? What is the easiest way to demagnetize a magnet? Once demagnetized how might you magnetize it again? What is actually happening, according to our theory of magnetism, when you magnetize a steel bar? Why should tapping the bar during the magnetization process help?

10. You have a circular ring of iron. Can you magnetize it? If you did, what would be the north pole? The south pole? Can you have a magnet without poles? Consider our theory of magnetization. From it *alone*, would you expect that one could magnetize the ring? Do you need to go back and change your answer to the first question?

11. Describe Oersted's experiment. State exactly what his discovery was.

12. What is a helix? A solenoid? Does a solenoid have poles? What is an electromagnet?

13. Soft iron cores are not essential in the construction of an electromagnet, yet all commercial electromagnets have them. Why?

14. What is the motor effect? In what way is it related to Oersted's discovery? What devices depend upon it for their operation?

15. You have a bar magnet fixed in position. A solenoid free to move is suspended close to the north pole of the bar magnet. How will the solenoid orient itself? Suppose

your bar magnet is short, and just as the solenoid, in its "attempt" to orient itself, swings past (due to momentum) the end of the bar magnet, you quickly switch the ends of the bar magnet. If your timing is right, what happens to the solenoid? If you could keep doing this every time the solenoid attempted to orient itself, and your timing was perfect, what would you, in effect, have?

16. Suppose that in a particular set-up a flat current-free coil of wire is suspended between the poles of a horseshoe magnet in such a way that the plane of the coil passes through the poles. Both coil and magnet are free to move. The current is then turned on. Describe precisely what will happen and why. What will happen if the direction of the current in the coil is reversed? Explain.

17. A wire that is part of a closed circuit which includes a sensitive galvanometer is moved back and forth from the north pole to the south pole of a horseshoe magnet. The galvanometer registers no current. The wire is then moved back and forth at right angles to a line connecting the two poles. The galvanometer needle swings back and forth. Explain both cases.

18. How does a generator (dynamo) generate electricity?

19. How can a changing magnetic field be produced in a wire without moving either the wire or a magnet?

20. Suppose that you had a stream of electrons, not confined in a wire, traveling a straight course at high speed as they might do in a wire. Would their path be altered, and if so, how, if they passed the north pole of a magnet? The south pole of another magnet? A positively charged plate? A negatively charged plate?

21. Distinguish between AC and DC. What is meant by 60-cycle current?

22. What does a transformer transform? Why will it not work with DC?

23. A central power station transmits electricity throughout its area of distribution at 110,000 volts. Transformers scattered over the area step down this voltage to 220 volts for local use. What is the ratio of the number of turns on the primary to that of the secondary in these transformers?

24. A step-up transformer has 40 turns in the primary coil and 3200 in the secondary. The primary is supplied with AC at an effective voltage of 110 volts. What is the effective voltage developed in the secondary coils?

25. Suppose that you had a round bar magnet so suspended that it would swing back and forth like a pendulum following a true path with each swing. Near the ends of the path on each side the magnet enters the open ends of coils of wire in a closed circuit, generating a current in the coil, and thus establishing a magnetic field about the coil. This field is opposite to that of the magnet and so repels it, giving it a thrust the other way. Thus, the magnet gets a push at each end of the swing. It might seem that here we have achieved perpetual motion. Yet you would find that the swinging motion of the magnet is slowed down faster than if no coils were present. Explain.

26. If a straight piece of wire, say a foot long, is moved across a magnetic field, no current can flow because the two ends are not connected. Yet a difference of potential between the two ends is present as long as the wire moves across the magnetic field. Explain, remembering that electrons are negative charges.

27. The powerhouse supplying electric current to your home is a mile or more away. In the powerhouse are generators in which coils of wire are spinning between the poles of powerful magnets. Electrons in these wires are being "urged" back and forth by their interaction with the magnetic fields. How does the effect of this interaction reach your house to give you electricity?

PART

V

THE STRUCTURE
OF MATTER

The initial success of the atomic theory of Dalton was dimmed by its inability at the time to explain Gay-Lussac's Law of Combining Volumes as applied to gases. This failure loomed larger as the years went by until in the early 1850's many chemists were highly skeptical of the theory. Then in the late 1850's Cannizzaro resurrected Avogadro's hypothesis to explain Gay-Lussac's law and all difficulties with it vanished. The atomic theory of Dalton, however, soon ran into more difficulties, for it failed to explain the periodic chart. It offered not the slightest explanation for any of the periodicities in the chart and gave nary a glimpse into the whys or wherefores of a chemical reaction. Fruitful as the theory had been in its early days, it was proving wholly inadequate for further research.

Scarcely was this problem settled when another arose to perplex the physicist. This was the problem of bright line spectra. Each element had its own characteristic spectrum, and most of them were highly complex. The essential problem was, how could a simple indivisible particle like an atom give rise to such complicated patterns of line spectra? The evidence accumulated by the spectroscopists had indicated that spectra originated within the atom by the vibration of a highly complex set of oscillators. However, there appeared to be no order among the spectra. Knowing the spectrum of one element gave no hint of what the spectrum of either of its two nearest neighbors would be like. Neither were there any hints of order even among the members of the same family, at least in the visible part of the spectrum.

This failure to find order was not for want of search for it. The situation reminds us of the Greeks trying to reduce the apparent disorderliness of the motions of the planets to a series of circular motions, of Kepler searching through the data of Tycho Brahe to find relationships between the distances of the planets from the sun and their periods of revolution, and of the chemists' search for order among the chemical elements, the search that led to the formulation of the periodic chart. This search for order in the physical universe should not surprise us, for if we had to select one primary attribute of a scientist it would be a belief in a universe of law and order, a belief that nature does not ever act capriciously. This relentless search for order had always been eventually successful in the past; almost always long-held beliefs had had to be abandoned, or at least greatly modified. The belief that had to go here was that of the indivisibility of the atom.

The first hint, not apparent to anyone at the time, came with Faraday's discovery of ions in the 1830's. A positive ion is somewhat less than a complete atom, and a negative ion is somewhat more than a whole atom but less than two atoms. None of this was apparent at the time of discovery, even though many scientists undoubtedly speculated on what it was that made ions charged particles, hence different from atoms. To say that they carry electric charges is a description that explains nothing.

The first breaks came just preceding the opening of the present century (1896) with the discovery of radioactivity. The significance of this discovery was not immediately apparent; in fact, it was not until some years later that the full impact of the discovery was felt. Meanwhile, another discovery was made in 1897 by others who were investigating the nature of certain phenomena in gas discharge tubes, tubes through which an electric current was made possible by a high voltage and a very low density of the gas. The observations in both cases could mean only that the atom was divisible. Once this divisibility was accepted, a whole new field of research was opened up, the field of the structure of the atom. A moment's reflection will show why no research in this field could go on before 1900, for an indivisible atom could not logically consist of parts, and an elemental particle consisting of a single part could scarcely be said to have a structure.

Once the search for the structure began in earnest, it was quickly realized that no model of the atom would be at all satisfactory unless it succeeded in, (1) bringing order out of the chaos of spectral lines, and, (2) explaining the periodicities in the periodic chart, and, (3) at the same time making clear the whys and wherefores of chemical reactions.

It is the answer to these fundamental questions that we will seek in this section. Insofar as it is possible in a textbook which is devoted to the principles of physical science and is very definitely not just a book *about* science, we will relate the search in story form. To do so chronologically would serve only to confuse, for the research followed two apparently unrelated paths. Chronology would demand that we switch back and forth between these paths, a procedure which would destroy continuity of thought. We will not, however, ignore the chronology while following each of these two paths.

One path deals essentially with light as a wave motion, the theories of light and the problems of spectra, which finally culminated in the photon theory of light. The analysis of light is highly important, because by means of a beam of light we may travel in a figurative sense deep down into the submicroscopic world of the atom, or far out into the macroscopic cosmos of the stars. In the latter we in a sense do both, for the light of the stars comes from atoms in the stars, and so we are dealing with a submicroscopic world in a macroscopic cosmos. In fact, the spectra of the stars were studied before spectra here on earth. We include the study of all wave motions here because there seems no other way that is more satisfactory.

The other path deals essentially with particles. It starts with the discovery of ions and the particle nature of electricity, and reaches its culmination in the Bohr theory, where the two paths are united into one by the brilliance of this Danish physicist. The daring and revolutionary theory immediately furnished an explanation for line spectra, and, after considerable modification, made possible that crowning glory of science, *the explanation of the periodic chart by means of the electronic configuration of the atom,* and gave us an interpretation of chemical behavior of the atoms. Thus, the regularities in the periodic chart are explained in terms of regularities within atoms.

THE TWO LINES OF DEVELOPMENT

The Wave Line
1. Light as a wave motion
2. Early theories of light
   a. Corpuscular vs. wave
   b. Electromagnetic theory and its confirmations
3. Spectra: Kinds, problems, Balmer
4. Planck's quantum theory and Einstein's photon theory

The Particle Line
1. Faraday and electrolysis
2. Evidence for divisibility of atom
   a. Discovery of radioactivity
   b. Discovery of the electron
   c. Further evidence of the electron
3. Millikan's Measurement of e
4. Rutherford's nuclear theory

Union of the two lines in the Bohr theory and the immediate consequences

This method and order of presentation is, we believe, the best for presenting this difficult material to nonscience students. We believe that there must be some common thread to which a student may cling while attempting to find his way through this difficult forest of ideas. The student must always keep in mind this common thread, as he needs to be reminded repeatedly where he is going and where he is at each stage of the journey. Otherwise he is likely to become so lost that he gives up in despair.

CHAPTER XXII

Wave Motion

"An ocean traveler has even more vividly the impression that the ocean is made of waves than that it is made of water."—A. S. EDDINGTON

Waves originate from centers of disturbance. For a succession of waves to be generated, a succession of disturbances must occur. This is best accomplished by a vibrating source. As a result of the disturbance energy is transmitted from the center to a distant point with nothing of a material nature moving from the center to the distant point.

Throw a stone into the water near the shore of a quiet pond and shortly a leaf floating on the surface on the far side bobs up and down. Clearly the leaf gained kinetic energy. How was the energy transported? By the water moving from the center of the disturbance to the leaf? If so, why does not the water carry the leaf along with it? Let us try again, this time with several leaves scattered at random over the surface of the pond. We see the wave advance in all directions from the center, forming a circular wave front. As the wave reaches each leaf, the leaf bobs up and down but none shows any inclination to travel with the wave. We must conclude that the energy given to the leaves

is transmitted by the surface wave, but that no water molecules are transferred from the center to any of the leaves. Only energy is transmitted from water molecules to water molecules all along the path of the wave. We might also say that only the disturbance moves outward (Fig. 22-1).

Tie one end of a long rope to a fixed point, e.g., a tree, stretch it fairly taut, and give your end a shake by moving it quickly up and down several times in rapid succession (Fig. 22-1c). You can observe that the work you do on your end results in energy being expended at the other end. The visible evidence of this is that the tree, if it is not too big, begins to shake. Obviously, the particles in the end of the rope that you held in your hand do not travel along the rope and bump into the tree. All that travels along the rope is a series of waves. The energy transmitted by the wave must be transferred from rope molecules to rope molecules the full length of the rope.

Pluck the taut string of a violin and its energy is transmitted to all of the people in a concert hall, be they a hundred or a thousand in number. The tympanic membranes of each of their ears are set in vibration, and hearing results. It is not reasonable to suppose that air molecules are directly transferred from the plucked string to the hundreds of thousands of ears present. We must, therefore, conclude that the energy of the plucked string is transferred from the violin to the ears by the air molecules in some way that does not include their actual movement from the center of the disturbance to the ears of the music lovers. We say that a wave, a sound wave, passed from the violin to the members of the audience, carrying energy with it.

The methods of energy transmission in

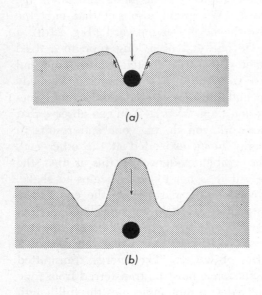

(a)

(b)

Fig. 22-1. Propagation of Waves. **(a)** Water waves. The heavy ball has pushed the water beneath it downward, forming a "hole." The displaced water rises above the general level, forming a circular crest around the hole. **(b)** The water forming the first crest reaches a maximum height dependent on the kinetic energy of the ball as it struck the water. Because it has inertia (and kinetic energy) the water of the crest, in returning towards its former level, is carried downward and outward below this level. This motion forms a circular trough outward from the crest. The water displaced in forming the trough rises to form another crest outward from the trough. Thus an ever-widening circular wave front disperses the original kinetic energy transmitted by the stone. Note that two motions are involved, a vertical up and down motion due to gravity and inertia, and a horizontal to and fro motion due to the impact of the ball and the inertia of the water particles. The latter cause the wave to move outward. The combination of the two motions cause the individual water particles to move in circular paths as these motions are transmitted ever outward from water particle to water particle. **(c)** Waves in a rope. The vibrating source is the hand. The rope vibrates vertically as the waves travel horizontally from the hand to the tree.

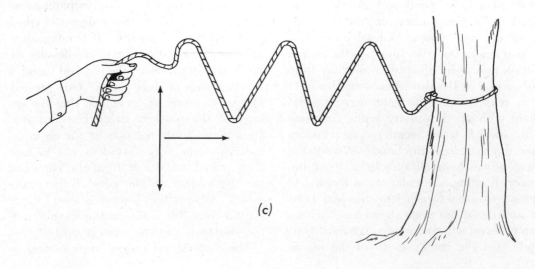

(c)

these three cases are clearly different from the familiar mechanical methods. The latter include transmission by gears (in your automobile), and belts (as in a washing machine or the fan belt of your car), or chains (as in a bicycle), or a falling weight (as in a pile driver). The transference of electrical energy by means of wires, and of heat energy by means of conduction are also mechanical in nature but less obviously so, but none of these resembles a method in which energy is transferred without anything of a material nature moving from the center of disturbance to the receiver.

The necessity of a physical medium for the water waves and the rope waves is clear, for we can see the energy advance as the wave moves over the water surface or along the rope. That we need a medium for the sound waves emitted by the violin can be proved by substituting an electric bell for the musical instrument and placing it in an airtight jar from which the air is being evacuated. As the air is pumped out, the ringing of the bell becomes fainter and fainter until it cannot be heard at all. We conclude that sound waves cannot be transmitted through a vacuum. It follows that the medium transmitting the sound is air, also a physical medium. Further investigation reveals that sound waves are also transmitted by liquids and solids in the same way as they are transmitted in air.

Suppose now, while we are energy conscious, that we step outside into the bright sunlight. We wonder how the light energy and the heat energy of the sun are transmitted to us through so vast a distance. We are prepared, tentatively at least, to accept wave motion as the method, but we are at a loss for the medium. We have learned that our atmosphere extends outward at most one or two thousand miles,

and that beyond we have "empty" space, space far emptier than any vacuum we can produce here on earth. If we accept the concept of wave motion, we must accept the fact that here we have a type of wave motion that needs no physical medium for its transmission, unless we wish to introduce another of those imponderables like phlogiston or caloric.[1] If we wish concrete evidence that no medium is needed, we can prepare a near vacuum in the laboratory and pass light energy from the sun through it. We find that the transmission is actually better than it is in air. We have read in the papers about radio waves coming through empty space from distant stars. Evidently they do not need a medium for their transmission, either.

We see, then, that waves can be divided into two groups, those that require a physical medium for their transmission and those that do not. The first group includes all mechanical waves; the second includes all electromagnetic waves. We will see later that waves can be classified in other ways.

SOME FUNDAMENTAL CHARACTERISTICS OF WAVES: WAVELENGTH, FREQUENCY, VELOCITY

All waves, mechanical or electromagnetic, have certain characteristics in common. The most fundamental are wavelength, frequency, and velocity. We will illustrate by a train of water waves produced by dropping stones in the same spot one after the other at regular intervals, because we can see them. The high points

[1] We will find later that such an imponderable was actually postulated for a time.

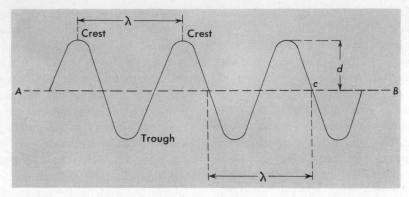

Fig. 22-2. Conventional Representation of Waves. The diagram resembles a water wave but is used for all types of waves, even light waves which cannot be visualized under any circumstances. Since all waves originate from a vibrating source, a wave motion traveling the path *AB* may be considered to consist of a vibration from crest to trough and back again, etc., thus producing a visualizable form. The diagram is actually a graph whose curve shows the displacement at any instant along the path of the wave. λ = wavelength, *d* = amplitude. Frequency, *f*, is the number of wavelengths passing a given point, *c*, per unit time. The velocity is given by $f\lambda$.

of the waves are the *crests*, the low points the *troughs* (pronounced "troffs"). The distance between two successive crests, or two successive troughs, is the *wavelength* (Fig. 22-2). The number of crests passing a given point per unit time is the *frequency*. The period of a wave is sometimes important. It is defined as the time interval during which the source emits a single wave, or as the time it takes one wave to pass a given point in its path. The period is related to the frequency by the formula, frequency = 1/period. Thus, if a wave has a period of $\frac{1}{10}$ sec its frequency will be 10/sec. The velocity of a wave is given by the product of the frequency and the wavelength.[2] In symbols,

$$v = f\lambda$$

where v is the velocity, λ the wavelength, and f the frequency. The wavelength divided by the period also gives the velocity.

The velocity of any wave depends upon the nature of the medium through which it travels—if there is a medium. For mechanical waves the velocity decreases as the density increases, and increases as the rigidity increases. For example, sound waves travel in air at about 1100 ft/sec, in water at about 5000 ft/sec, and in ice at

---

[2] If you have trouble seeing why this is so, consider a freight train passing a crossing. Suppose the number of cars passing is 20/min, and the length of each car is 50 ft. The first car will have traveled 1000 ft (20 × 50) by the time the twentieth car has passed. The velocity is therefore 1000 ft/min. The length of each car corresponds to the wavelength, and the number of cars passing per minute to the frequency.

about 10,500 ft/sec. Ice has a density only slightly less than that of water but it has a rigidity that is vastly greater, so the velocity of sound through ice is more than twice that through water. Despite the great difference in density between air and water, sound travels nearly five times faster in the latter. This is because water has some rigidity at least, whereas air has practically none. In cast iron, a dense medium of high rigidity, the speed of sound is about 15,000 ft/sec, and in rubber, a dense medium of low rigidity, it is only about 100 ft/sec. From this data it can be seen that rigidity is a far more effective factor in controlling the velocity of mechanical waves than is density.

For electromagnetic waves the situation is quite different. Light travels through a diamond, a substance of high rigidity and high density, only about half as fast as it does through air. It travels fastest through a vacuum, where its speed is about 3×10^{10} cm/sec (about 186,000 mi/sec). All electromagnetic waves, regardless of their frequency or wavelength, travel at this speed. Therefore, the greater the frequency, the smaller the wavelength.

The frequency of a wave governs one other property of sound and light waves. In the case of sound it is called *pitch*. The higher the frequency, the higher the pitch. The human ear can detect frequencies that range from about 20 cycles/sec to about 20,000 cycles/sec. Our ears react best to frequencies of about 2000 cycles/sec. To detect the very low frequencies, the energy of the waves must be enormously greater (a million times or more) than when in the optimum range. As a person grows older, the ability to detect the higher frequencies diminishes greatly. Certain animals, e.g., dogs and bats, can hear frequencies higher than can man. For purposes of convenience we refer to all such vibrations as sound waves whether they are within the range of the human ear or not. In the case of light the corresponding property governed by the frequency is *color*. Since this phenomenon can more adequately be dealt with under the subjects of refraction and dispersion, we will omit it here.

AMPLITUDE vs. ENERGY CARRIED BY A WAVE

If, in Fig. 22-2, the line *AB* is considered the level surface of the water before the stone is dropped, then the distance *d* represents the maximum displacement of the water above *AB* when the wave passes by. This distance is called the *amplitude* of the wave. It is half the distance between the top of a crest and the bottom of a trough.

A moment's reflection will show that the amplitude is a measure of the energy carried by the wave. A large stone will obviously create a bigger disturbance than a small one, and so the wave will be larger, will have a bigger amplitude, and will carry more energy. In sound waves greater amplitude means greater loudness; in light waves it means greater brightness. However, amplitude is not the only factor controlling loudness, if by loudness we mean the ease by which the sound may be heard by the human ear. The other factor is *pitch*. A high-pitched whistle can be heard above lower pitched sounds of much greater intensity—which is why most whistles are high-pitched.

The energy of a wave decreases as it travels outward from the vibrating source, varying inversely as the square of the distance from it (Fig. 6-1).[3] Consider a

---

[3] Note that here we have a fourth inverse-square law. What are the other three?

point source of light or sound. The waves are radiated outward in all directions. Their wave fronts (Fig. 22-3) will be spherical, and since the surface of a sphere increases as the square of its radius, the inverse-square law applies. Doubling the

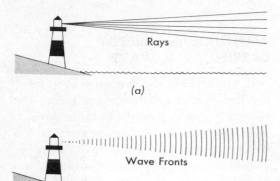

(a)

Rays

(b)

Wave Fronts

Fig. 22-3. Rays vs. Wave Fronts in Light. **(a)** Rays. **(b)** A series of expanding wave fronts. Note that the rays are at right angles to tangents to any wave front if the medium of transmission is uniform. The ray specifies the direction of transmission of energy.

distance to the source thus results in the energy being distributed over four times the area. If reflectors are used the inverse-square law does not apply.

It should be noted that the amplitude decreases with increasing distance from the source, but the frequency and the wavelength are not diminished as long as the medium is homogeneous. Thus, the frequency and the wavelength of the light from a star a million light years distant remains unchanged during the whole of its million-year journey through space.

DOPPLER EFFECT

If a source of sound waves is approaching the observer the frequency, as detected by the ear of the observer, is increased and the pitch rises; and if the source is receding from the observer, the frequency, as detected by the observer, is decreased and the pitch is lowered. Thus, if you were standing near a railroad track as the fast express approaches, blowing its whistle, the pitch of the whistle would rise until the engine reached you, then as it receded in the distance the pitch would decline, yet the frequency of the sound waves actually emitted by the whistle would be constant all of the time.

This apparent change in frequency due to the motion of the source is called the Doppler effect. As far as the source is concerned the change in frequency is only apparent; as far as the observer is concerned there is an actual change in the frequency. To understand this better let us consider our express-train analogy. We can illustrate it better by talking about wavelength rather than frequency. This is valid, for as one is increased the other is decreased proportionately, since the velocity is constant in any one situation.

In Fig. 22-4 let the train be moving from position 1 towards position 8 at a constant speed. The circles represent the wave fronts as they move outward from the train's whistle. The dots are the centers of the circles with the corresponding numbers. Since the situation is shown "frozen" at a particular instant of time (in this case immediately after the source—train—has reached position 8), the smaller numbered wave fronts are bigger because they have traveled longer than the higher numbered ones. They have traveled

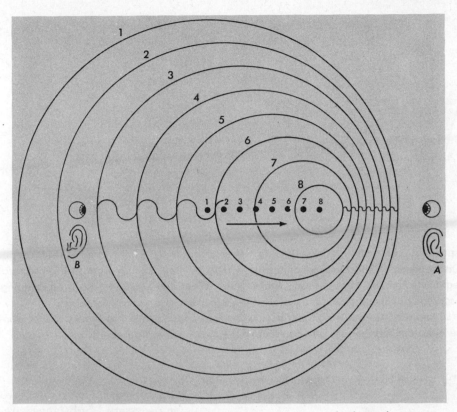

Fig. 22-4. Doppler Effect. The consecutive positions of spherical waves emitted by a source moving to the right. The successive positions of the source and the corresponding wave fronts are indicated by the same numbers. An ear at B hears a higher pitch than an ear at B because the number of waves reaching A per second, i.e., the frequency, is greater. (After George Gamov, *Matter, Earth and Sky*, Prentice-Hall, Englewood Cliffs, N. J., 1958.)

longer because they were emitted when the source was at 1, 2, etc. Note the squeezing on the right which results in shortened wavelengths (and higher frequency), and the lengthening on the left which results in longer wavelengths (and lower frequency). Note that if the relation $v = f\lambda$, is to hold, an apparent decrease in λ means an apparent increase in f and vice versa. A stationary observer at A would, in the case

of sound waves, hear a higher pitch than he would if the source were stationary also, since pitch increases with an increase in frequency. An observer at B would hear a lower pitch. A similar effect is produced if the source is stationary and the observer in motion.

The Doppler effect applies to light waves equally well. Changing of frequency by motion of the source of light towards or

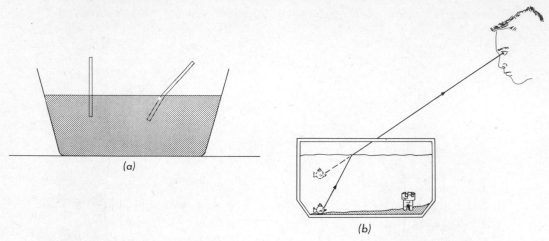

Fig. 22-5. Refraction. **(a)** A stick in water at an angle to the water surface appears bent because of the bending of the light rays as they change from the denser water medium to the far less dense medium of air. When the stick is vertical, no bending is observed, but the stick appears shorter than it actually is.

  (b) The fish is at the bottom of the tank but the observer sees it at some distance above. The eye does not perceive the bending of the rays coming from the fish.

away from the observer causes a change in color.

REFLECTION AND REFRACTION

We are all more or less familiar with the fact that water waves may be reflected from a wall, light waves from a mirror, and sound waves from a cliff or other surface. The latter we term an echo. We are also familiar with such terms as transparency and opaqueness, terms referring to the varying degrees with which objects reflect, absorb, or transmit light waves, but we are not so likely to realize that they apply equally well to most other sources of waves, especially to other types of electromagnetic waves. Thus, metals reflect radio waves, but glass, brick, and wood are largely transparent to them if they are not too thick. If this were not so, outdoor aerials for television and radio would always be necessary. Substances are said to be opaque if either absorption or reflection is complete or nearly so.

Waves of all kinds are also refracted, i.e., their rays are bent as they pass obliquely from one medium to another in which their speed is different. Accompanying the refraction is a change in the velocity; in fact, the velocity change is the cause of the refraction. If the boundary between the two media is at right angles to the path of the rays, there is still a change in velocity but no refraction. Thus, a stick partially submerged in water and at an angle to the vertical appears bent at the point where it enters the water (Fig. 22-5), whereas if it is at right angles to the water surface, it appears straight but shorter than it actually is. Thus, ponds of clear water never appear as deep as they actually are.

The following analogy will make clear why a change of the speed of waves causes them to refract. In Fig. 22-6 the dots represent soldiers marching abreast in parallel columns. On smooth, firm ground the columns maintain an even front, as the men are always taking steps of equal length in unison. If an area of loose sand is encountered as in the stippled area in the illustration, all members of any row encounter the sand at the same time, hence,

between rows. The distance between rows is roughly analogous to wavelength; thus, a wavelength is shorter when the wave passes into a medium where the velocity is less. Note that in the above case there

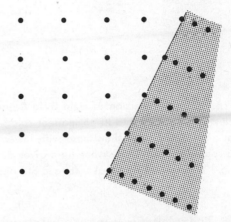

Fig. 22-7. Refraction Analogy. If, however, the boundary between solid ground and loose sand is oblique to the line of march, some rows will be slowed down sooner than others. If all maintain one length of step when on solid ground, and a shorter length of step in the loose sand, and all keep in step, then the line of march is bent, i.e., it changes direction, just as is the case when waves of any kind are refracted.

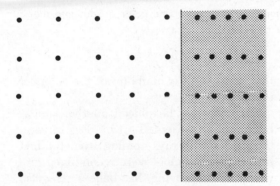

Fig. 22-6. Refraction Analogy. Soldiers marching with a steady cadence on solid ground remain properly aligned on a change to loose sand if they all enter the sand on the same step, but their steps will be shorter. Thus, their velocity is decreased.

all are slowed up at the same time. They are presumed to take the same number of steps per unit time as before, but the steps will be shorter. The rows behind them are not slowed up until a second or two later. Hence they "catch up" with the first row, i.e., they shorten the distance

was no bending of the column, because each member of each row reached the loose sand at the same instant.

Now let us suppose that the boundary between the firm ground and the sand is oblique to the line of march, as in Fig. 22-7. Not all the members of a row enter the sand at the same time. The ones who enter the sand first are slowed up first while the others continue at their original

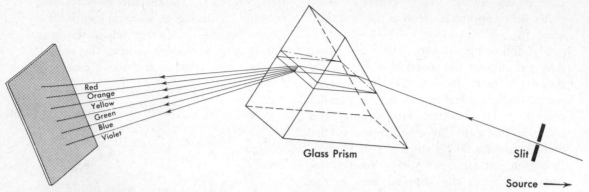

Fig. 22-8. Dispersion of Light by a Prism. White light, consisting of a mixture of frequencies, is separated into its component colors because the rays with higher frequencies (violet) are diffracted more than those with lower frequencies (red). Such a band of colors is called a spectrum. Ordinary white light gives a continuous spectrum, for one color grades into the next with no sharp break. (See plate opposite p. 362.)

rate. The result is that the original straight front has bent at the boundary between the two different media (firm ground and sand). When all are marching in the sand, the front will have a different direction. The greater the difference in speed of marching in the loose sand and on the firm ground, the more the column will have been bent, i.e., "refracted."

REFRACTION AND DISPERSION OF LIGHT

If we pass ordinary white light through a glass prism (a wedge-shaped piece of glass), the light rays are refracted on entering the glass and again on leaving it. The light leaving the glass is not white, but the colors of the rainbow (Fig. 22-8). Newton, who was the first to perform this experiment, believed that the colors were due to the dispersion (spreading out) of the various components of white light, i.e.,

that white light is made up of the colors of the rainbow.

To prove this he placed another similar but oppositely oriented prism (Fig. 22-9) in the path of the rays coming from the first prism. These colors were recombined into white light, proving his belief. He also placed a screen with a narrow slit in it between two properly oriented prisms (Fig. 22-10). Through this slit he could admit any one of the colors coming through the first prism and bar the others. He allowed these colors, one by one, to pass through the second prism, oriented in different ways, to see if each could be broken up any further. He found that they could not. Hence the colors emerging from the first prism are called the primary colors—red, orange, yellow, green, blue, violet.

How do we explain these facts? I.e., how does a prism break white light up into different colors? The answer is by the refraction of the components of white light.

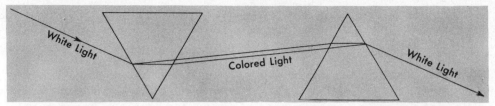

Fig. 22-9. Newton's Proof of Composition of White Light. White light passing through the first prism was dispersed into colored bands which were then recombined to form white light again by passing through an oppositely oriented prism.

White light consists of a band of rays with different frequencies.[4] On entering the glass prism (a different medium) the lower frequencies (red) are refracted less than the shorter. Thus, the prism sorts out the rays according to their frequencies, forming a band of colors called a *spectrum*. Actually each primary color consists of a group of frequencies which the human eye translates into color. These frequencies range from 7.5×10^{14} cm/sec (on the

violet side of the spectrum) to 4×10^{14} cm/sec (on the red side). There are also frequencies in ordinary light that are higher than the violet; these are the ultraviolet. The human eye is not constructed to translate them to visible light, but they can be detected by other means. The frequencies immediately lower than the red are called infrared. Our eyes do not register them as light, but our bodies detect them as heat.

This last statement should raise a question in our minds. If heat is molecular motion, why is it our bodies register the electromagnetic radiation we call infrared as heat rays? If our definition of heat means anything, the answer should be that

[4] Color is commonly explained as resulting from differences in wavelength. However, it can be proved that the eye detects differences in frequencies rather than wavelengths. See footnote 6, Chapter XXIII.

Fig. 22-10. Newton's Proof That Dispersed Color Bands Are Primary. He passed one of the colors of the continuous spectrum through another prism to see if it could be further broken up. The screen with a slit was used as a selector of the desired rays.

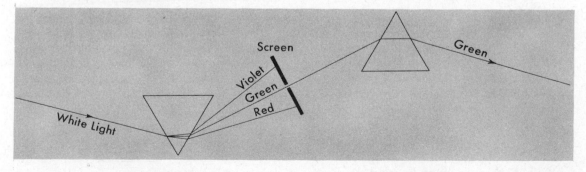

these infrared rays have the ability to increase molecular motions. This justifies calling them heat rays.

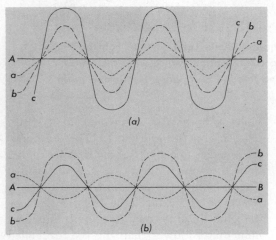

Fig. 22-11. Interference of Waves Traveling the Same Path. **(a)** Two waves, *a* and *b*, with different amplitudes are in phase. They therefore completely reinforce one another, producing a result like that of single wave, *c*, with an amplitude equal to the sum of the amplitudes of *a* and *b*. **(b)** Here the two waves are exactly out of phase. The final result is like that of a single wave, *c*, with an amplitude equal to the difference between the amplitudes of *a* and *b*.

PHASE

Two waves traveling in the same region will be exactly in phase if the crests and troughs from one arrive at a point at exactly the same time as the crests and troughs from the other. They will be completely out of phase if the crests of one arrive at a point at the same time as the troughs of the other. Two people walking together in step may be said to be in phase. All stages between exactly in phase and completely out of phase are possible.

Interference

That two beams of light may be combined to produce greater brightness we all know, but that two beams may be combined to produce darkness seems as unlikely as the production of silence by adding two sound waves of the same amplitude together. Yet both are possible; all that is necessary to produce darkness is to have the crest of one light wave arrive at a point exactly out of phase with another of the same intensity (amplitude). One wave cancels the other. If the two waves arrive in phase, they reinforce each other. Their amplitudes are added together, causing increased brightness in light or greater loudness in sound (Fig. 22-11*a*). If the two waves are not completely out of phase, nor completely in phase, there will be partial cancellation or partial reinforcement (Fig. 22-11*b*). The combined phenomena of cancellation and reenforcement constitute interference.

Interference accounts for the color patterns when white light, striking a thin transparent film, is reflected to the eye. The film may be a soap bubble, a film of oil on a water surface, etc. Some light is reflected from the front or top surface of the film and some light from the back or bottom surface. These two beams arrive together at the retina of an eye. The difference in the distance traveled by the two beams is equal to twice the thickness of the soap film. If this difference in path is an odd number of half wavelengths of red light, then the red component of white light will not be seen because the crests of the red wave coming from one surface of the film are canceled by the troughs of the red

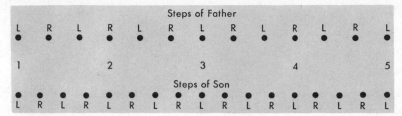

Fig. 22-12. Relation of Beats to Interference Shown by Analogy. A boy takes four steps to his father's three. It is seen that they are in step at 1, 3, and 5, and out of step at 2 and 4. If the steps were sound waves, the waves would reinforce each other at 1, 3, and 5, and cancel each other at 2 and 4, producing a tremolo effect.

wave coming from the other. What is seen will be white light minus the red component—which is the complementary color of red, green to bluish-green. If the difference is an odd number of half wavelengths of yellow light, then the yellow component of white light is canceled, etc. Because the film varies in thickness, different components are canceled out in different places, thus giving a multicolored pattern.

Beats and Interference

Beats are heard when two notes of slightly different frequencies are sounded together. The tone produced varies periodically between loud and soft, as the two waves alternately partially reinforce and partially cancel each other. To understand this let us use the following analogy: Suppose a small boy walking with his father takes steps 1½ ft long and the father takes steps 2 ft long (Fig. 22-12). They start out in step, but are at once partially out of step. They will be exactly in step again at the end of the father's sixth step (the boy's eighth step). Since they started in step and finished in step, but the son took more steps than the father, there must have

been at least one place along the way where they were exactly out of step; this was at the end of the father's third step. It should be obvious that they will be exactly in step again at the end of the father's twelfth, eighteenth, twenty-fourth, etc., step. They will be exactly out of step again at the end of the father's ninth, fifteenth, twenty-first, etc., step. If the steps of father and son were the wavelengths of two sound waves, they would reinforce each other at the sixth, twelfth, eighteenth, and twenty-fourth crests and cancel each other at the third, ninth, fifteenth, twenty-first crests. In between there would be partial cancellation or partial reinforcement, producing something of a tremulo effect as the tone rises and falls. Beats are made use of in tuning stringed musical instruments—two strings have exactly the same frequency when all beats disappear.

Standing Waves

When two identical wave trains travel the same path, but in opposite directions, and are exactly out of phase, waves are produced that appear to be stationary, i.e., they are standing (Fig. 22-13).

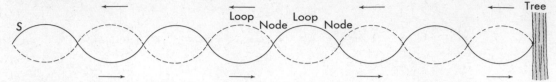

Fig. 22-13. Standing Waves in a Rope. The solid line is the transmitted wave, the dashed line the reflected wave. If the frequency is properly chosen, the rope at any instant will appear as if it were being traversed by two trains of waves traveling in opposite directions while the rope vibrates up and down in a number of segments; the number depends on the frequency. At high frequencies the eye sees a blur that appears to stand still. A necessary condition is that the two trains of waves be exactly out of phase.

Standing waves are best demonstrated in a rope, for here we are dealing with one dimension only. Consider the hand in Fig. 22-1. The wave that travels down the rope towards the tree can be reflected back from the tree so that the two waves are exactly out of step if certain conditions are met. Their frequency and wavelength must be adjusted so that by the time the reflected waves have returned to the hand, they are exactly out of step with the waves the boy is continuing to send along the rope. Pertinent to our discussion are nodes and loops (Fig. 22-13). The nodes are the points of little or no motion; the loops lie between the nodes. The distance between two adjacent nodes is half the wavelength. It is obvious that a node must exist at the point of contact of the rope with the tree in Fig. 22-1. If a standing wave is to be produced, then another node (not in phase) must be at the hand. Thus, the distance from hand to tree must be an integral number of half wavelengths; only those wavelengths that have a node at each attached end of the rope can exist as standing waves.

Standing waves can be produced by causing interference in any kind of wave motion in this manner. Such interference is common to all types of waves; this phe-

nomenon comprised a crucial test for wave motion, i.e., the production of any sort of interference pattern is evidence of wave motion.

DIFFRACTION

The spreading of a wave around the edges or corners of an obstacle in its path is called diffraction. In order for a disturbance to be transmitted from one point to another, the disturbance at one point must have an effect on all neighboring points. Consider a water wave passing through a gap in a breakwater. As the crest passes through it will obviously disturb the water directly in front of it. But it will also disturb the water on the sides of it to some extent, so that the wave spreads around the edges of the gap in the breakwater (Fig. 22-14).

If light from a source is passed through a tiny pinhole in a card and allowed to shine on another card placed a foot away and shielded from any other light, we will find that the spot of light on the second card is several times as big as the pinhole. If light were *not* diffracted, the spot on the second card would be no bigger than the pinhole. This would be the case if light were composed of particles. Therefore, diffraction is a test for wave motion. The fact that light can be diffracted suggests strongly that it is a wave phenomenon. The fact that it is diffracted only slightly as it passes through the pinhole suggests that the wavelength is less than the diameter of the pinhole.

new source of waves. The geometrical demonstration of this phenomenon is too complex to be presented here, but the principle can be illustrated as follows: Imagine a wall across a large body of water

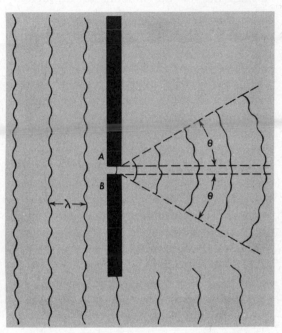

Fig. 22-15. Diffraction of Waves. The opening or slit, *AB,* is considerably smaller than the wavelength, λ. The waves are bent so much that the opening acts as a new source from which waves spread out in all directions beyond the wall.

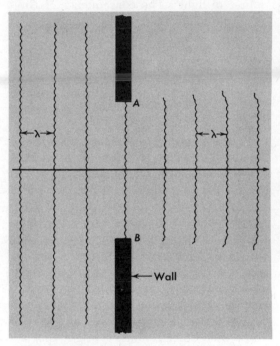

Fig. 22-14. Diffraction of Water Waves. A wall (breakwater) across a pond has a gap, *AB,* in it that is considerably wider than the wavelength, λ, is long. There is little bending (diffraction) of the waves as they pass the ends of the wall under these conditions.

HUYGENS' PRINCIPLE

Huygens' principle states that every point on a wave front may be considered as a

with two openings of different widths in it. Imagine also a series of waves initiated by a disturbance so far away that the wave fronts are approximately parallel when they strike the wall, i.e., they are plane waves. When the wave fronts strike the openings, part of them go through (Figs. 22-14 and 22-15). We note that the wave fronts spread out beyond the wall, that the waves are undergoing diffraction. We note also that the smaller the opening, the greater the amount of diffraction. The angle Θ (Fig. 22-15) is a measure of the amount of diffraction. This angle decreases as the size of the opening becomes larger. When the opening becomes as large as the wavelength or larger, the amount of diffraction is insignificant (Fig. 22-14). Hence small wavelengths will need small openings; for light they must be very small indeed. Note that each opening acts as a new source of waves, and that the smaller openings make better *new* sources of disturbance than the bigger openings. This is because they are more pointlike (see Huygens' principle on previous page).

YOUNG'S DOUBLE SLIT EXPERIMENT

We have already stated that unlikely as it may seem, two beams of light can be combined in such a way so as to produce darkness as well as to produce greater brightness. The phenomenon is analogous to that of beats in sound. This crucial experiment, which *seemed* to settle forever the nature of light in favor of the wave theory, was performed by the brilliant English medical doctor, Thomas Young, for whom physics was a hobby.

The following points must clearly be kept in mind in order to understand the experiment:

1. The waves emerging from the two slits will be, and must be, alike in wavelength, frequency, amplitude, and also in exact phase relation with one another.

2. Two crests (or two troughs) arriving at a point at the same time, i.e., arriving in phase, reinforce each other, producing greater brightness.

3. A crest and a trough arriving at a point at the same time, i.e., arriving out of phase, cancel each other, producing darkness.

4. Huygens' principle: Every point on a wave front may be considered as a new source of light. The consequence of Huygens' principle in Young's experiment is that the holes or slits in the middle screen, B (Fig. 22-16), act as new sources from which new wave trains emerge. Thus, if light did not act in accordance with Huygens' principle, light would appear on screen C only at points a_1 and a_2.

In the figure, S represents a source of light. A, B, and C are screens seen on edge. Screen A has a single slit in it, and B has two, each equidistant from the slit in A. Light from the slit in A passes through the two slits in B. Two new wave trains are initiated because, in accordance with Huygens' principle, slits S_1 and S_2 act like new sources of light. The wavy lines represent individual rays with their troughs and crests. Note that at L_1 a crest from S_1 and S_2 arrive exactly in phase and so reinforce each other. Thus, a bright spot occurs at L_1. There are the same number of crests between L_1 and S_1 as there are between L_1 and S_2 because the paths are the same length.

At L_2 a trough from S_1 and S_2 arrive exactly in phase, so again there is reinforcement, even though the distance traveled is different by exactly one wavelength. Thus, there is another bright spot at L_2. Similarly, there will be other bright spots at L_3, L_4, and wherever the difference in paths differ by a whole number of wave-

Fig. 22-16. Young's Experiment. Waves from two sources leave S_1 and S_2 exactly in phase. At L_1, L_2, etc., the waves arrive in phase because they have all traveled an integral number of wavelengths (an even number of half wavelengths). They therefore reinforce one another, producing light areas. Those waves reaching the screen at points marked D arrive exactly out of phase because they have all traveled an odd number of half wavelengths. They therefore cancel one another, producing areas of darkness. The experiment proved that light is a wave motion by demonstrating both interference and diffraction.

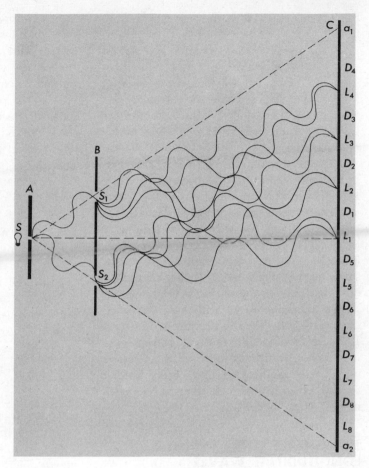

lengths—or we might say whenever the path difference is an even number of half wavelengths.

If there is a bright spot wherever reinforcement occurs, there must be dark spots in between (D_1, D_2, etc.) where cancellation occurs because a crest from S_1 and a trough from S_2 (or vice-versa) arrive at the same spot at the same time, i.e., they arrive exactly out of phase. This should be obvious, for if the path difference between S_1L_2 and S_2L_2 is exactly one wavelength and that between S_1L_3 and S_2L_3 is exactly two wavelengths, then there must

be a spot between L_2 and L_3 where the path difference is exactly one and one-half wavelengths, hence cancellation and darkness. Thus, dark spots will occur wherever the path difference is an odd number of half wavelengths.

One point needs to be clarified; these alternating dark and light spots will occur only if the light from S is monochromatic. If white light is used, different wavelengths will interfere at different spots because long wavelengths are diffracted more than short. The result is dispersion, the separation of white light into its component colors just as is the case with refraction.

In the figure we are looking at a screen edgewise, and so refer to our L and D regions as points. If we looked at screen C face on, i.e., as we would see it from points S_1 and S_2, we would see the L regions as bands of light and the D regions as bands of darkness.

The phenomenon of alternating dark and light bands may also be observed if, while in a darkened room, one looks through two very narrow, closely spaced slits in a piece of black paper towards a line source of light. The light coming through screen A is such a source. The explanation is the same as that just given. It should also be obvious that if there are three slits in screen B, three crests will reenforce each other at L_1, L_2, etc.; if 100 slits are present 100 crests will reenforce one another, causing the bands of light to be wider. Screens with large numbers of slits closely spaced are called diffraction gratings (see footnote 1, chap. XXIV).

TRANSVERSE AND LONGITUDINAL WAVES

So far we have avoided this classification of waves, because it has not been pertinent to our discussion. This classification is based on the direction of vibration with respect to the direction in which the wave is traveling. Three possibilities exist. The vibration may be back and forth in the same direction the wave is traveling, it may be at right angles to the direction of travel, or it may be a combination of both.

Sound is a common example of longitudinal wave. Superimposed upon the normal motions of air molecules are vibrations back and forth in the direction the sound is proceeding. For example, the vibrations of a violin string cause alternate condensations and rarefactions in the air in the immediate vicinity of the string. These alternate condensations (regions of increased air pressure) and rarefactions (regions of decreased air pressure) travel in the direction the wave is traveling. Such longitudinal waves "look" like Fig. 22-17. It is the regions of compressions and rarefactions that are propagated as the wave travels and not the air molecules that compose them. Graphically, we use the conventional wave diagram, Fig. 22-2, to represent a longitudinal wave; the crests represent the regions of compression, the troughs the regions of rarefaction.

The only other common type of longitudinal wave is the primary earthquake wave. It is the fastest of several types of earthquake waves, traveling at the rate of several miles per second through the earth, but it is not the wave that does the great damage to the works of man. All longitudinal waves are mechanical waves. They can travel through any medium, gaseous, liquid, or solid. As previously stated their speeds increase with increasing rigidity and decrease with increasing density, hence in most cases they travel fastest through solids.

Transverse waves are those in which the direction of vibration is at right angles to the direction of wave travel. A visible example is the waves in a rope. It is obvious that the molecules that compose the rope are not moving from the hand to the tree; instead, they are moving up and down, across, or transverse to the direction of wave travel.

Transverse waves may be either mechanical or electromagnetic. Rope waves are,

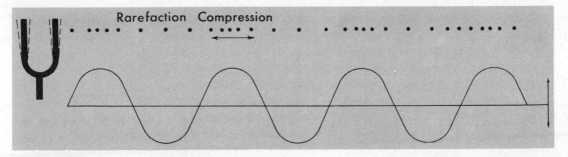

Rarefaction Compression

Fig. 22-17. Representation of Longitudinal Wave. A sound wave is emitted by a tuning fork. Regions of compression of the particles composing the medium alternate with regions of rarefaction as these regions (not the particles) are propagated through the medium. Such a wave may be represented as a series of crests and troughs in the manner as transverse waves in a rope.

of course, mechanical. The secondary waves of earthquakes are transverse. Like the longitudinal waves, they do little damage to the works of man. Transverse mechanical waves cannot travel through either liquids or gases. The fact that in these states of matter the molecules are not fixed in position does not allow one molecule to transmit its motion effectively to another in a direction at right angles to the direction of wave travel. Therefore, transverse waves quickly die out when they encounter such media. All electromagnetic waves are transverse. They can travel through any medium and in a vacuum as well. In fact their speeds are fastest through a vacuum. If this seems inexplicable to you, it may comfort you to know that no scientist can picture waves traveling through a vacuum either. This subject will be further discussed in the next chapter.

Water waves are combinations of both longitudinal and transverse waves. If a particle vibrates in a horizontal plane in the direction of wave motion while vibrating in a vertical plane at right angles to the direction of wave motion, the resultant path will be a circle.

POLARIZATION

Light in which vibrations take place in a particular direction at right angles to the direction of propagation is called polarized light. White light consists of vibrations in all directions at right angles to the direction in which the wave it traveling. It is therefore unpolarized (Fig. 22-18). It should be obvious from its definition that a longitudinal wave cannot be polarized. On the other hand, in a transverse wave the direction of vibration is in a plane that is perpendicular to the direction of wave travel; it can therefore be polarized. Some crystals will polarize light. So will the substance called polaroid, used in some sun glasses. Such polarized light is like ordinary light insofar as the eye can detect. If, however, a second crystal (or piece of polaroid) oriented at right angles to the first is now placed in the path of the beam coming from the first, none of the light passing through the first crystal will pass

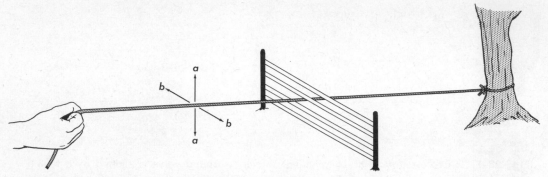

Fig. 22-18. Polarization. Polarization is most easily demonstrated by a rope and a rail fence. Waves parallel to *aa* will be stopped by the closely spaced rails in the fence, whereas those parallel to *bb* will pass through without hindrance. Consider a large number of ropes vibrating in many different planes, *aa, bb,* and at various angles to *aa* or *bb;* all waves that appear in those parts of any of the ropes *between the fence and the tree* will have vibrations that are in the plane *bb.* This restriction to one plane of vibration at right angles to the direction of propagation is called polarization.

through the second. One crystal blocks all light vibrating in one direction, and the other crystal blocks all light vibrating at right angles to the first direction (Fig. 22-19). If two crystals (or two pieces of polaroid) are oriented in the same way, light passes through them as it does through a single crystal. If one of the crystals is now slowly rotated, the intensity of the beam will slowly decrease until all rays are stopped. The planes of polarization of the two crystals are then at right angles to each other. Such crystals are used in some optical instruments.

Fig. 22-19. Polarization of Light. Light vibrations take place in all directions at right angles to the line of propagation. Only vertical vibrations pass through Polaroid B. Hence all light from the source S that reaches Polaroid C is polarized. If Polaroid C has its plane of polarization at right angles to that of B, this polarized light cannot pass through, and screen D will be dark. Only transverse waves can be polarized.

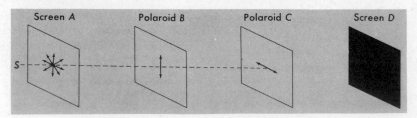

SUMMARY

A wave motion is one means of transmitting energy from one region to another without anything of a material nature moving from the first region to the second. Mechanical waves, such as water waves, waves in a rope, sound waves, etc., need a medium for their transmission. Electromagnetic waves, e.g., light waves, need no medium. All need a vibrating source to produce the waves.

All waves may be represented by a diagram showing crests and troughs as in a series of water waves. In such a diagram the wavelength is represented by the distance between two successive crests. The frequency is the number of crests passing a given point per unit time. It may also be considered the number of vibrations of the source per unit time, usually per second. The velocity of a wave is equal to the frequency multiplied by the wavelength. For mechanical waves the velocity increases with the rigidity of the medium and decreases with its density. The velocity of all kinds of electromagnetic waves is approximately the same in air as in a vacuum, i.e., 3×10^{10} cm/sec.

The amplitude of a wave is a measure of its energy. The energy of a wave decreases as it travels outward from its source, $E \propto 1/d^2$. The pitch of a sound wave is a function of its frequency. The apparent change in frequency due to the motion of the source or the observer is called the Doppler effect.

All waves are refracted, i.e., their velocity is changed, when they pass from one medium to another. There is also a directional change if the boundary between the two media is not perpendicular to the direction of wave travel. Light waves are refracted and dispersed into their component wavelengths (colors) when passed through a prism. The band of colors produced is a spectrum. Newton proved that the primary components of white light are red, orange, yellow, green, blue, and violet.

The wavelengths range from 4×10^{-5} cm (violet) to 7×10^{-5} cm (red).

All waves may be made to interfere constructively (reinforcement) or destructively (cancellation) with other waves of their own kind. Waves from two different sources will reinforce each other if they arrive exactly in phase, or they will cancel each other if they arrive exactly out of phase. All stages of partial reinforcement or partial cancellation are possible. Beats in music, the colors of soap and oil films, standing waves in a rope, and many other phenomena are produced by interference. Interference is a test for wave motion.

The spreading of a wave around the edges or corners of an obstacle in its path is called diffraction. Diffraction is also a test for wave motion. Huygens' principle states that every point on a wave front may be considered a new source of waves. Young, in his double slit experiment, made use of Huygens' principle to produce diffraction and interference of light, thus proving that light is a wave motion.

Waves may also be classed as longitudinal or transverse, depending upon the relationship of the direction of vibration to the direction of wave travel. Water waves are a combination of both. Transverse waves can be polarized but longitudinal waves cannot. This test proves that sound waves are longitudinal and light waves are transverse.

EXERCISES

I. TERMS AND CONCEPTS

✓ Vibrating source	Frequency period
✓ Medium	Wavelength
✓ Mechanical waves	Velocity
✓ Electromagnetic	$V = \lambda f$
waves	Crest
Wave front	Trough
Wave train	Amplitude

$E \propto 1/d^2$

Doppler effect
Reflection
Refraction
Dispersion
Prism
Spectrum
Primary colors
Phase
Interference
Reinforcement

Cancellation
Beats
Standing waves
Diffraction
Huygens' principle
Young's double slit
   experiment
Transverse waves
Longitudinal waves
Polarization

II. PROBLEMS

1. What are mechanical waves?

2. What determines the energy of a wave? *amplitude*

3. What finally happens to the energy of sound waves in open air? *heat*

4. What is the frequency of light with a wavelength of 6×10^{-5} cm in air? $f = \frac{186,000}{6 \times 10^{-5}}$

5. What is the wavelength of radio waves whose frequency is 1,500,000 vibrations per second (1500 kilocycles)?

6. What is the range of frequencies of light perceivable by the eye?

7. How far away did the lightning strike if five seconds elapsed between the flash and the sound of thunder? *5,000 ft away.*

8. Sonar devices on certain ships measure the depth of water by sending a sound wave to the bottom and then awaiting the echo. If the interval between the emission of the sound wave and the receiving of the echo is six seconds, how deep is the water? (Use 4700 ft/sec as the velocity of sound in water.)

9. Why does a timer on a straight-away track start his watch in a 200-yard race by the smoke from the starting gun rather than by its sound?

10. What is the relationship, if any, between

   a. Loudness and pitch?
   b. Pitch and frequency?
   c. Color and wavelength?
   d. Color and frequency?

11. If you were spearing fish from a boat, and you saw a fish directly below you, where would you aim? Suppose the fish were off to one side by a few feet? Explain your answers.

12. One star is receding from us and another is traveling towards us. Other things being equal, which should appear reddest to us? Why?

13. Suppose that blue light traveled faster than red. Assume a total eclipse of the sun. Describe the appearance of the sun as it emerges from behind the moon.

14. The fact that the light from the sun as it emerges from behind the moon at the time of a total eclipse is white instead of a succession of colors proves what with respect to the velocity of light?

15. a. How may ordinary light be dispersed?
   b. Why can monochromatic light not be dispersed?

16. How does refraction differ from diffraction?

17. What is meant when it is said that two wave trains are in phase?

18. a. Can two identical wave trains travel the same path without interference?
   b. Suppose one has a greater amplitude than the other?

19. What conditions must be met if two identical wave trains traveling the same path are to

   a. Interfere constructively?
   b. Interfere destructively?

20. What conditions must be met to produce a standing wave?

21. Ultraviolet and infrared radiation are frequently referred to as light. Why?

22. It is commonly said that transverse waves will not pass through a liquid or air. Yet light will pass through both. How must we qualify the original statement if we are to be correct? Explain your answer.

23. What is the proof that light is a wave motion?

24. Why can a sound wave not be polarized?

25. Why did Young need two closely spaced slits for his experiment?

26. The mass of an object in motion increases as the velocity increases according to Einstein's theory of relativity. The increase is given by the equation

$$M_v = \frac{M_o}{\sqrt{1 - \dfrac{v^2}{c^2}}}$$

where M_v is the mass at velocity v, M_o is the velocity at rest, and c is the velocity of light. Will the mass of a body change appreciably at a velocity of 1 mi/sec? What will its mass be if it travels with the speed of light? What force would be necessary to give it this speed? Is it possible for any material body to move with the speed of light?

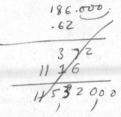

$v = f\lambda$

$\lambda = \dfrac{v}{f}$

$f = 1.500.000$

$v = 3x$

CHAPTER XXIII

Early Theories of Light

In our discussions of wave motion we have assumed that light is a wave phenomenon. We have assumed that it consists not of mechanical waves which need a physical medium for their transmission, but of electromagnetic waves which need no such medium. We will now briefly trace the development of the concept of light as an electromagnetic phenomenon.

The Greek philosophers and scientists could not conceive of light existing apart from the process of seeing. The realization that light is something that exists entirely independent of an eye to see it was first suggested in the eleventh century when some evidence was produced to show that light had its origin in what was perceived rather than in the eye of the perceiver. It was not until the seventeenth century that the emission of light was viewed as a transfer of energy.

As previously stated, there are only two mechanical ways of transmitting energy, one involves the transfer of matter from the source region to another region. The other is wave motion, which can transmit energy without a transport of matter from the source to another region. This method, in the eyes of all scientists until the latter part of the nineteenth century, depended upon the presence of a medium between the source and the observer to act as the carrier of the wave motion. These two methods of transporting energy found their expression with respect to light in the corpuscular and the wave theories.

NEWTON'S CORPUSCULAR THEORY vs. HUYGENS' WAVE THEORY

Newton believed that light consisted of particles of extremely small size, but he believed it with no great degree of positiveness, and he failed to specify the characteristics of the corpuscles. He rejected the wave theory because he could not detect diffraction, an essential characteristic of any wave motion. Yet he knew of experiments performed by Grimaldi, and repeated them himself, which indicated that light does bend very slightly as it passes an obstacle in its path. Newton attributed this bending (diffraction) to some obscure influence exerted on the corpuscles as they passed. Even his great genius did not prevent him from misinterpreting this scientific fact. Perhaps he might not have if he had realized the smallness of the wavelength of light.

Huygens, a contemporary of Newton, was a strong advocate of the wave theory and formulated the first well-rounded theory in 1678. The conflict between the two theories could not be resolved at the time, because the crucial experiment (concerning the velocity of light in different media) that could settle the matter could not be performed. According to the corpuscular theory light should travel faster through water or through a solid than through air, while the reverse should be true of the wave theory. All waves slow down on entering a denser medium, but Newton considered his particles of light to be attracted by the denser medium and therefore accelerated upon entering it. Failure to find a way of measuring these speeds led to the general acceptance of Newton's view because of his greater reputation.

In the very early part of the nineteenth century, Thomas Young of England and Augustine Fresnel of France both demonstrated that light definitely showed both diffraction and interference effects, and the weight of opinion shifted to the wave theory. About 1850, Foucault (the French physicist who proved that the earth rotated on an axis) found that the velocity of light in all media that he tested was smaller than in a vacuum, thus deciding the issue conclusively in favor of the wave theory. We shall see later that this conclusion does not prove the wave theory to be unqualifiedly correct, but only ruled out corpuscles of matter which obeyed the laws of Newtonian mechanics and which are speeded up as they enter a denser medium.

SPEED OF LIGHT

Any satisfactory theory of light must take into account a question that had been debated since the time of the ancient Greeks, namely, does light travel at a finite or at an infinite speed? The Greeks had assumed that light had a finite speed simply because moving means going from one place to another. Galileo had tried

without success to measure the speed of light in the simple way that speeds of finite objects are measured. That he could detect no time interval between the source and an observer several miles away could mean either that the speed was infinite or that it was too great to detect by ordinary means. The Danish astronomer, Roemer, settled the question of finiteness in 1676, and at the same time measured the speed with something like modern accuracy.

His method was simple. One of Jupiter's moons, Io, disappears behind Jupiter and reappears regularly as it revolves about Jupiter. The time interval between appearances should be constant if the speed of light is infinite, no matter where the earth is in its orbit. However, observation showed that when the earth is farthest from Jupiter, Io reappears about 16 minutes (1000 seconds) later than when the earth is nearest Jupiter (Fig. 23-1). Roemer explained the lateness was due to the greater distance that light had to travel, a distance equal to the diameter of the earth's orbit.

$$V = \frac{d}{t} = \frac{186,000,000 \text{ mi}}{1000 \text{ sec}} = 186,000 \text{ mi/sec}$$

These are modern figures. Roemer's figure was 192,000 mi/sec. The method was not entirely convincing to everyone.

The American physicist, Albert Michelson, made the first highly precise measurement of the speed of light by improving on a laboratory method used by Fizeau in 1849. The principle used by Michelson is shown in Fig. 23-2. A precision-built octagonal mirror was mounted on an axle and rotated at high speed by a jet of compressed air. Three of the eight faces of the mirror are labeled 1, 2, and 3. Con-

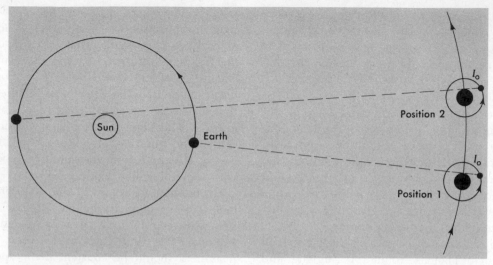

Fig. 23-1. Roemer's Method of Measuring Velocity of Light in 1676. One of Jupiter's moons, Io, is observed to be coming out of eclipse at two different times six months apart (during which time Jupiter has moved on in its orbit). The time between appearances of Io can be calculated. It arrives 16 minutes late in the second position because the light has to travel farther to reach the earth (2 × 93,000,000 mi farther).

sider the situation to be as follows before the mirror starts to rotate:

Light from a strong point source strikes face 1 of the octagonal mirror, which reflects it to another mirror about 22 mi away; this distant mirror reflects it back to face 3 of the octagonal mirror, which in turn reflects it into the lens of a fixed telescope, where it is focused on the crosshairs in the eyepiece. If the octagonal mirror is now turned slightly, the image of the light disappears from the telescope. Suppose now that we turn the air jet on so as to give the octagonal mirror moderate speed. No light will be observed in the telescope. But if the speed of rotation is increased sufficiently, face 2 will move from the position shown into the position

occupied by face 3 in exactly the same time as it takes the light to go from face 1 to the distant mirror and back again. The image of the light therefore reappears in the telescope and, if the speed of rotation is just right, it will be focused on the crosshairs. This speed of rotation can be measured and the time for one-eighth of a rotation calculated. This gives the time for the light to travel to the distant mirror and back again, a distance of 44 mi.

Michelson also measured the speed of light in other media and found it to be less than in air. This was in accord with the wave theory and in opposition to the corpuscular theory. He also found that red light travels at a considerably greater speed through liquids and solids than does blue light, yet travels at the same speed through a vacuum.[1] Michelson received a Nobel prize for his work on the speed of light.

The most modern measurement is 2.99876×10^{10} cm/sec. This is equal to 186,464 mi/sec. The speed of light in a vacuum is a most important constant, for it enters into calculations of the sizes, distances, motions, and energies of and within

[1] Through air all colors travel at practically the same speed. The difference is less than 0.03 per cent.

atoms. It is also a basic yardstick in astronomy. For almost all purposes we may round the figures off and remember them as 3×10^{10} cm/sec and 186,000 mi/sec.

"LUMINIFEROUS ETHER"

One disconcerting question remained, that of the medium for the propagation of light waves. To the scientists of the time, waves of any kind needed a medium for

Fig. 23-2. Michelson's Method of Measuring Velocity of Light. Light reflected from a face in position 1 travels to distant mirror and back to the face in position 3. The octagonal mirror is spun at high speed in direction shown by an air jet (not shown). If the speed is right, light from position 1 will travel to distant mirror and back to position 3 in the time it takes a face in position 2 to travel to position 3. From these data the speed of light is easily calculated.

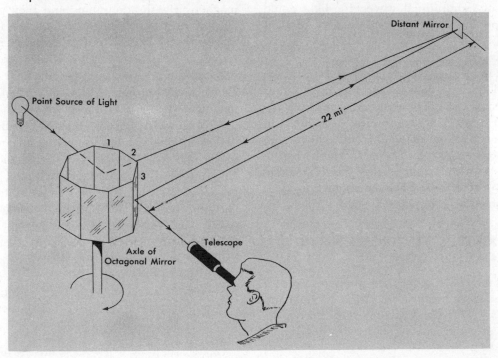

their transmission. They agreed with Lord Kelvin: "If I can make a mechanical model, then I can understand; if I cannot make one, I do not understand." Without a medium a mechanical model is impossible. All other known types of waves need media for their transmission. Sound waves, for example, cannot be transmitted through a vacuum. An undiscovered medium, named the luminiferous ether, was assumed to exist for light. The ether turned out to be another of those imponderable fluids comparable to phlogiston and caloric. It was assumed to pervade all empty space, even the space between atoms.

This creation of the ether posed another dilemma; if the ether was a fluid, light could not consist of transverse waves, for such waves can be transmitted only through solids. Light could not consist of longitudinal waves, for light could be polarized. The great velocity of light (known to be in excess of 100,000 mi/sec in Newton's time) demanded contradictory properties, very high elasticity and extremely low density for the medium of transmission. The concept of an invisible solid, the ether, would create the problem of the planets moving through it with no sign of slowing down. Various highly questionable solutions were offered for one phase of the problem or another, but no satisfactory progress was made.

MAXWELL'S ELECTROMAGNETIC THEORY OF LIGHT

Maxwell's theory had its inception in Faraday's concept of electric and magnetic fields. This concept proved to be one of the greatest contributions to the understanding of electric and magnetic phenomena. The concept, greatly simplified, is as follows: The space around an electrified (or magnetized) body is changed by the mere presence of the body. The fact that this space is changed can be detected only by bringing another electrified (or magnetic) [2] body into this space. Obviously, forces are present in this space that are not present when the body is removed. This changed empty space is the electric (or magnetic) field. The existence of this field is not explainable in terms of particles or waves or fluids, imponderable or otherwise. Faraday pictured this empty space as being occupied by lines of force. To him they were a kind of string, each having a tendency to contract, and to repel neighboring lines of force.

Maxwell, one of the world's outstanding theoretical physicists of all time, read the whole of Faraday's works on electricity and magnetism with admiration, and then proceeded to translate Faraday's ideas into mathematical terms. In the space surrounding a current-carrying wire, there is both an electric and a magnetic field—an electromagnetic field. If the current is D.C. and steady, then the electromagnetic field of the wire will also be steady. Both the electric field intensity, commonly represented by the letter E, and the magnetic field intensity, commonly represented by the letter H, while constant in magnitude and direction at any one point, will be smaller and smaller as the distance to the point from the wire increases. No electromagnetic waves are propagated in space under such conditions.

Suppose, however, that we suddenly change the amount of current in the wire. This can best be accomplished by the use

---

[2] A magnetic body is any body attracted by a magnet; it need not be another magnet.

of AC. If we use 60-cycle AC, the current will be changing direction 120 times per second, and the magnitude will vary from zero to a maximum value and back to zero again during the time involved in each change. What happens while the electrons [3] in the wire are being accelerated, first positively, and then negatively? Maxwell's equations indicated that accelerated charges will send out a series of pulses of energy. Now these pulses will spread out through space like waves and with speeds equal to that of light. The source of these pulses of energy is to be found in the accelerations of the electrons. As they slow down and stop before reversing their direction, their kinetic energy is converted into the radiant energy of an electromagnetic wave. In the propagation of a mechanical wave it is the to and fro movement of material particles as time progresses that causes the wave to travel through the medium, whereas in an electromagnetic field it is the values of E and H that oscillate.

The values of E and H oscillate in directions at right angles to each other, their values reaching both zero and a maximum together. Thus, the electric wave and the magnetic wave travel through space in unison (Fig. 23-3). The frequency of these electromagnetic waves will be the frequency of the pulses of energy sent out by the vibrating source, whatever that source may be. For our source, 60 cycle AC, it will be the frequency of accelerations of the electrons in the wire, 120 per second in the case of 60-cycle current. This means that as long as electrons have nonuniform motion, whether being accelerated back and forth in the wire or being accelerated in uniform circular motion about an atomic nucleus, energy should be lost by means of these wavelike radiations away from the vibrating source.

Maxwell's equations also showed that when other electrons are introduced into the fluctuating electromagnetic field, as are

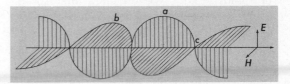

Fig. 23-3. "Model" of Electromagnetic Wave. It may be viewed as an electric wave and a magnetic wave always in phase and at right angles to each other as they travel through space. The electric wave is shown in the vertical plane, the magnetic wave in the horizontal. The electric field intensity, E, and the magnetic field intensity, H, reach a maximum (at a and b, respectively) and a minimum (c) at the same time.

electrons in an antenna of a television set in the path of the waves, they absorb some of this energy as they are acted on by electric and magnetic forces carried by the waves. These forces cause the electrons in the antenna to change their directions with the same periodicity as the transmitter's original oscillations. Thus, using mathematics alone, Maxwell predicted, without his knowing it, radio waves. Other predictions from his theory indicated that these waves should behave in all important respects like light. He was thus forced to the inferential conclusion that light is an electromagnetic phenomenon. He was

[3] Electrons were not known as such in Maxwell's time. He referred to them as charged particles. We will use the term electron to prevent confusion later on.

the first to perceive that light, electricity, and magnetism are intimately related.

You should not feel defeated if you cannot picture electromagnetic waves winging their way through empty space, for scientists freely admit that they do not know what electromagnetic waves "are." The "are" is in quotes because the word implies that these waves exist as such and we do not know that. We do know that something representing energy travels through space with a velocity of 186,000 mi/sec. This energy appears to travel as a transverse wave. The evidence is that it can produce diffraction and interference effects as all waves do and they can be polarized as only transverse waves can. One great difficulty in picturing electromagnetic waves is that no medium is needed for their propagation; thus, we have the anomaly of a wave without a waver. The waver for water waves is the water itself, and for sound it is air. If we must have a waver for electromagnetic waves, we should assume that they are Faraday's lines of force. We know no other way to describe the phenomenon graphically.

Maxwell's theory gives us a mechanical model which can be visualized and analyzed. Mechanical models, even though they are incorrect, may give us a great deal of information that may not be obtainable otherwise. Consider a map of the world. In a sense it is a mechanical model. It is not the world, nor is it even a small replica of it. In fact, it has no real resemblance to the physical world. Yet we can learn far more about the physical world from this map in an hour or two of study of it, than we could from years of actual exploration of the earth. Thus, we justify the use of mechanical models which may bear little resemblance to reality.

The use of Maxwell's theory advanced our knowledge of visible and invisible light far beyond what would have been possible otherwise. It has, and still does, serve as a unifying concept for many phenomena concerning light. It has been one of the most fruitful of all scientific theories, even though it cannot provide a complete explanation for all phenomena of light. The paper which announced this theory to the world in 1864, a paper synthesizing electricity, magnetism, and light, was probably the greatest scientific publication since Newton's *Principia*. Maxwellian electrodynamics was added to Newtonian mechanics to form the foundations on which all future advances in physical science must rest—or so it seemed at the time.

Maxwell was unable to prove that fluctuating electric currents gave rise to electromagnetic waves. He neither measured the speeds of such waves, nor did he prove that they were of the same nature as light. Why not, we may ask, set up an oscillatory current in a wire at the known frequency of red light and see if red light is emitted? The frequency of red light is 4×10^{14} cycles/sec (400 million million vibrations per second). Such frequencies could not be obtained mechanically, either at that time or the present, and so direct proof was out of the question.

Maxwell pointed out that his equations did not prohibit waves of frequencies higher than those of violet light, or lower than those of red light. These waves should have all the characteristics of light except visibility. The general concept that the range of our senses placed no limit on the range of wave motions was not new, for it had long been known that vibrations of the sort that we call sound were not limited to those within the range of detection by the human ear. In fact both ultraviolet and infrared radiation had been known since early in the nineteenth century. Thus, there existed the possibility that there were electromagnetic waves with frequencies low enough to be generated by apparatus available at the times. This turned out to be true, as Hertz soon showed.

HERTZ'S TEST OF THE ELECTROMAGNETIC THEORY

In 1888, Heinrich Hertz of Germany set up a simple spark gap device (Fig. 23-4), which was sufficiently charged to cause a spark to jump from one electrode to the other. According to Maxwell's theory, electromagnetic waves should be sent out every time a spark jumped; and these waves should be capable of causing electrons to move the same way in a secondary circuit some distance away, provided it were "tuned" to the original circuit. The original circuit was thus a transmitter, consisting of a source, two polished metal spheres as the electrodes, and an induction coil [4] (not shown) to build up large charges on the metal spheres. The secondary circuit was a receiver, consisting merely of two similar electrodes connected to each other by a wire. Current was actually induced in this circuit, observable as a spark between the receiver electrodes, whenever the spark jumped across the transmitter electrodes.

Above, we referred to the impossibility, even at the present time, of mechanically producing waves of the frequency of red

[4] An induction coil is used with DC, a transformer with AC. The principle is the same, except that an induction coil must have a device to rapidly make and break the circuit. Why?

light (4×10^{14} cycles/sec). In the above experiment Hertz obtained about 10^8 vib/sec. Figure 23-5 is a chart of the electromagnetic spectrum. We see that commercial radio broadcasts range from about 550,000 to 1,600,000 cycles/sec (550 to 1600

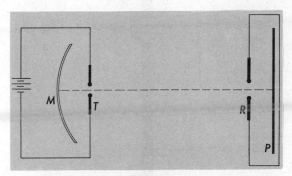

Fig. 23-4. Hertz's Proof of Electromagnetic Waves. Spark gap devices served as a crude transmitter, *T*, and receiver, *R*. A high-voltage source was necessary for the transmitter to emit a strong spark. A weak spark jumped the gap at *R* when a strong one jumped the gap at *T*. Energy was thus transmitted from *T* to *R* by means of a wave motion. *M* and *P* are concave and plane reflecting mirrors, respectively, which were used to prove the waves had the properties of light waves.

kilocycles). You might very well ask how such frequencies are produced. No mechanical device can be made to vibrate with anything like such frequencies.

It has been discovered that crystals, e.g., quartz crystals, have certain natural periods of vibration of their own, and these frequencies fall in the above ranges. This natural frequency is governed by the composition of the crystal, and the size and shape, in much the same way as the pitch (frequency) of a bell is determined by its

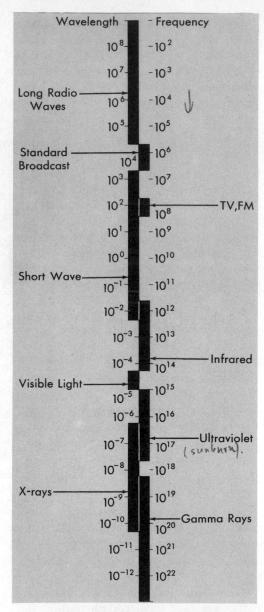

Fig. 23-5. Electromagnetic Spectrum. Wavelengths are shown on the left, frequencies on the right. In all cases $f\lambda$ equals 3×10^{10} cm/sec, the velocity of light. The arrows refer to the blocks, not to specific wavelengths or frequencies.

composition, size, and shape. Therefore, crystals of quartz are ground to the correct size and shape to produce the desired frequency of the waves emitted from the antenna of the broadcasting station. The smaller the crystal, the higher the frequency it emits. If the size is small enough, the frequency leaves the range of the ordinary radio for that of the short-wave radio. Still smaller crystals emit frequencies in the radar range.

It might seem possible to get down into the infrared invisible light ranges by choosing still smaller crystals. The trouble is that below the radar range the crystal size is too small to handle. If we calculate—and we can—the size a crystal must be in order to emit infrared waves, we find that it must be of *molecular* size. Remembering that infrared waves are heat waves, and, from kinetic theory, that heat is a kind of molecular motion, we should not be unduly surprised. Rather, we should feel gratified, for here we see how two apparently different concepts of heat, the molecular theory of heat and the wave theory of heat can be completely reconciled.

By further reasoning and calculation we can conclude that to produce frequencies as high as those of visible light and beyond, we will need to have particles smaller than molecules and atoms, which means that no crystals can do the job. Thus, according to Maxwell's theory of electromagnetic radiation, visible light, ultraviolet light, and *any possible radiations of still higher frequencies must be emitted by oscillating electric charges within atoms.*

Further experimentation revealed (1) that conductors, such as metals, reflected the waves, (2) that large concave metallic reflectors brought the waves to a focus just as a concave mirror focuses light waves, (3) that nonconductors allowed the waves largely to pass through them, refracting them as they do so, (4) that by varying the distance between a receiver and a reflector placed behind it, Hertz could produce standing waves (Fig. 22-13) with loops and nodes, and so proved both constructive and destructive interference, (5) that speed of the waves (frequency times wavelength) was about 3×10^{10} cm/sec, the same as the speed of light in air.

Direct measurement of the velocity came in 1895. Thus, Hertz verified the major predictions of Maxwell. These waves were called Hertzian waves; we now call them radio waves. The fact that, unlike light waves, they will pass through opaque nonconductors if they are not too thick, explains why indoor aerials for radio and television sets work very well. The fact that they are reflected or absorbed from metal surfaces explains why car radios are dimmed when crossing a metal framework bridge. In 1898, Marconi achieved reception and transmission of Hertzian waves over distances of many miles, and in 1901 sent and received them successfully across the Atlantic. Thus, radio is the result of the combined efforts of Faraday the experimenter, Maxwell the theorist, Hertz the experimenter, and Marconi the inventor and engineer.

Hertz appears to have been the first to realize that the electromagnetic theory needs only a set of equations varying in space and time, that no ether was needed for their transmission. An experiment which most experts in the field agreed was crucial, performed by Michelson in 1887, failed to find evidence for the existence of the ether. Nevertheless, the ether concept persisted in many quarters until Einstein sent it to join the graves of phlogiston and caloric with his relativity theory in 1905.

DISCOVERY OF X-RAYS

Further confirmation of the electromagnetic wave theory came in 1895, when

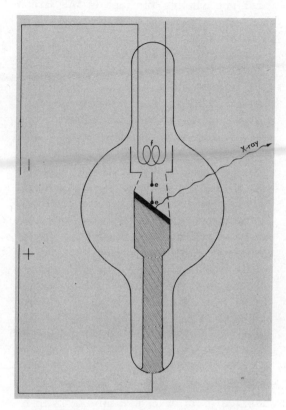

Fig. 23-6. Modern X-ray Tube. High-speed electrons, e, ejected from the filament, f, strike a target of tungsten metal where they "lose" most of their energy. This energy is transformed into electromagnetic radiation of extremely short wavelength. High voltage is applied to the tube to give the electrons the necessary speed.

Roentgen accidentally discovered X-rays. Roentgen was investigating cathode rays produced in a high-voltage gas discharge tube (Fig. 23-6) when he noticed that a fluorescent screen in his completely dark-ened laboratory glowed at each discharge, even though the tube was well covered by a black cardboard. Furthermore, it mat-tered not whether the face of the screen was turned towards the discharge tube or away from it. He quickly discovered the radiation causing the fluorescence had great penetrating power, i.e., all kinds of matter were transparent to it, though to different degrees. Paper, e.g., was nearly perfectly transparent, and so was human flesh;[5] even a sheet of aluminum half an inch thick failed to stop the radiation completely.

The fact that Roentgen failed in his ef-forts to determine the nature of X-rays is evident from the name he chose for them. That they were due to some kind of radia-tion was self-evident. Radiations are of two kinds. They may be streams of par-ticles, possibly charged, like Faraday's ions, or uncharged, like Newton's corpus-cles. Or they may be trains of electro-magnetic waves. X-rays were quickly proved not to be charged particles, for they were neither attracted nor repelled by strongly charged plates. Streams of them were directed against light paddle wheels, mounted in an evacuated tube so as to be almost frictionless, to see if they had kinetic energy as particles, charged or uncharged, would have. The results were negative. They showed no diffraction nor interfer-ence effects as they should if they were waves of any kind.

The problem was not solved for seven-teen years. By that time many new con-cepts had arisen, some of which were re-lated to X-rays, and so we will leave our final study of X-rays until we come to the new concepts (p. 425). However, it is profitable to consider certain facets of X-ray phenomena here.

Maxwell's theory of electromagnetic ra-diation was at its height at the time. You will recall that, according to this theory, electromagnetic waves have their origin in accelerations, positive and negative, of elec-tric charges. Roentgen, like so many of his fellow scientists, was investigating the na-ture of cathode rays when he discovered X-rays. Now cathode rays are known to be charged particles. If they were slowed down, or stopped, as they struck the walls of the discharge tube, their kinetic energy would be transformed into some other kind of energy, most likely to electromagnetic energy. Thus, from a theoretical view-point, X-rays should be a form of radiation akin perhaps to the ultraviolet, and they were generally considered so almost from the time of their discovery, even though final proof was in the distant future.

ELECTROMAGNETIC SPECTRUM

Infrared and ultraviolet radiations have been known to be parts of the solar spec-trum since early in the nineteenth century. Shortly after Hertz had proved the exist-ence of those electromagnetic waves that we now know as radio waves, it became ap-parent that visible light forms but a small part of what we now call the electromag-netic spectrum. Radio waves had proved

---

[5] This property of making opaque objects trans-parent, or partially so, caught the fancy of the public as soon as Roentgen announced his discov-ery. The possibility of "seeing" through opaque objects provided sensational material for certain newspapers of the day, for it was then easy to believe that X-rays could make fully clothed peo-ple appear naked. In a remarkably short time many of the modern uses of X-rays were devel-oped, particularly their use in the setting of broken bones.

to have the main properties of visible light, but they were of vastly greater wavelength and lower frequency. We now commonly represent the whole electromagnetic spectrum by a line, or a bar, like that shown in Fig. 23-5, so that we can indicate the relationships of the wavelengths and the frequency to one another. Wavelengths, given in centimeters are shown to the left of the scale and their corresponding frequencies on the right.

It has already been indicated that our eyes are constructed so as to receive only a limited range of frequencies [6] in the electromagnetic spectrum.

Various devices have been constructed to receive other parts of it, each being restricted to certain ranges. Radar and walkie-talkie sets, short-wave radios, television, and ordinary radio receivers, are all used to detect wavelengths greater than about 1 cm. Especially synthesized films of one sort or another will detect all wavelengths that are a bit shorter than 1 cm. Those wavelengths longer than 1 cm have an obvious connection with electricity, for we are all familiar to some extent with the broadcasting of radio and television waves. Those shorter than about 1 cm have no such obvious connection with electricity;

[6] It is far more common to state that the eye receives a limited number of wavelengths. However, the eye can be proved to be sensitive to frequency changes rather than wavelength changes, as follows: Light changes its velocity on entering water. This means that either f or λ or both must change, since $v = f\lambda$. Since frequency is a function of the source, we should expect the wavelength to change on entering water rather than the frequency. That the frequency remains constant, and that color is determined by frequency and not by wavelength, are both easily proved by a skin diver. Colors look the same to him while he is under water. If the wavelength governed color, colors seen under water should look different than when viewed in air.

nevertheless, we have already seen from Maxwell's theory that these shorter wavelengths should also be produced by oscillations of electric charges. To explain how this is done by electric charges that reside within the atom is one of the ultimate aims of this section.

SUMMARY

Newton and Huygens both advanced theories of light at about the same time, Newton a corpuscular theory, and Huygens a wave theory. Newton rejected the wave theory because he could not observe either interference or diffraction effects in any of his experiments with light. The preponderance of opinion went along with the man of greater fame. About 1800 Young of England and Fresnel of France (ca. 1805) both showed that light could produce both interference and diffraction effects, thereby establishing the wave theory.

Any successful theory of light would have to take into account its characteristics. One was the great speed of light. Roemer, a Danish contemporary of Newton and Huygens, made the first rough measurement of its speed by use of one of the moons of Jupiter, and came up with a figure of about 192,000 mi/sec, about 6000 mi/sec higher than our modern figure. Later measurements were made by the great American physicist, Albert Michelson.

In the 1860's Maxwell introduced his electromagnetic theory of light, based on concepts of electric and magnetic fields. By use of mathematics Maxwell showed that accelerated charges (e.g., electrons surging *back and forth* in a wire) should send out pulses of energy which should travel through space in the form of a wave and with the speed of light; the kinetic energy of the surging charges should be converted into the radiant energy of an electromagnetic wave.

Some twenty years later Hertz successfully tested Maxwell's theory by setting up a spark-gap device which sent out electromagnetic waves as the spark jumped from one electrode to the other, and another similar device to "receive" the waves. These were the first radio waves to be intentionally sent out.

Later confirmation of Maxwell's theory came with the discovery of X-rays by Roentgen. With the addition of infrared and ultraviolet radiation, known since early in the 1800's, the list of the different kinds of electromagnetic radiation grew to near its present size. Arranged in order of increasing frequency (or decreasing wavelength), the various kinds of electromagnetic radiation are referred to as the electromagnetic spectrum. It is common to speak of the shorter wavelengths —from the infrared to the gamma radiation— as light, some visible, some invisible.

EXERCISES

I. TERMS AND CONCEPTS

Corpuscular theory   Ray
Wave theory   X-rays
Speed of light   Infrared rays
  186,000 mi/sec   Ultraviolet rays
  3×10^{10} cm/sec   Radio waves
Electromagnetic theory
  electric field intensity, E
  magnetic field intensity, H
  accelerated charges
Electromagnetic spectrum
  range of frequency of visible light:
  4×10^{14} to 7×10^{14} vibrations/sec,
  range of wavelengths of visible light:
  7×10^{-5} to 4×10^{-5} cm

II. PROBLEMS

1. Distinguish between mechanical and electromagnetic waves.

2. What is the approximate velocity of electromagnetic waves in air?

3. What was the likely cause of error in Roemer's method of determining the velocity of light? (See Fig. 23-1.)

4. Distinguish between Newton's and Huygens' theories of light.

5. Why did Newton refuse to accept the wave theory?

6. What was the ether supposed to be? Why was the concept introduced? Who spelled doom for the concept?

7. State as simply as you can the fundamental assumption in Maxwell's electromagnetic theory.

8. What do the letters E and H stand for in electromagnetic theory?

9. Who tested Maxwell's theory, and how?

10. State four characteristics of electromagnetic waves.

11. To whom should we give credit for the "invention" of radio?

12. Name the various kinds of waves that constitute the electromagnetic spectrum in order of increasing frequency; in order of increasing wavelength.

13. Explain the *fundamentals* of radio transmission and reception. (This does not require any description of any of the complicated apparatus by which both are accomplished.)

14. X-rays emitted from a certain source have a wavelength of 0.000,000,008 cm. What is their frequency? (Calculate by use of standard notation, and show your calculations.)

15. How are X-rays of the kind that Roentgen discovered produced?

16. Why was there any difficulty about proving X-rays to be a kind of electromagnetic radiation?

17. Does DC electricity flowing through a wire send out electromagnetic waves? Does AC? Explain.

18. Would you expect the spark plugs in your car to send out electromagnetic waves while your car is running? Explain your answer. If so, why do they not interfere with your car radio?

19. Why does lightning interfere with radio reception?

20. What evidence is there that sound is not an electromagnetic radiation?

CHAPTER XXIV

Spectra

Today, I have made a discovery as important as that of Newton.—MAX PLANCK TO HIS SON (1900)

We cannot go much further in our understanding of the fundamental nature of light, nor in our investigation of the unraveling of the structure of the atom, until we have made a study of spectra. We have already noted that white light consists of a mixture of wavelengths and that a spectrum is a band of colors produced when light is passed through a prism or diffraction grating [1] so that the light is dispersed into its component wavelengths.

If the light consists of a single wavelength, i.e., if the light is monochromatic, a one-color band is produced. In an analogy with sound, we may say that this one-color light corresponds to a pure tone on

[1] You will remember that Young in his famous experiment (p. 337), used two slits to diffract light and cause it to interfere. Diffraction gratings are made to produce, magnify, and intensify the same result by making use of a large number of slits. Modern gratings are made by scratching fine lines on a piece of glass with a diamond point. The spaces between the lines serve as slits. As many as 30,000 lines per inch are scratched on the best gratings. Gratings used in student laboratories average about 15,000 per inch. A diffraction grating will disperse white light into a band of colors just as does a prism.

a musical instrument. Carrying the analogy further, we may say that white light represents a mixture of visual wavelengths just as common noise represents a mixture of auditory wavelengths. Thus, line spectra represent certain specific wavelengths just as pure musical tone represents certain specific auditory wavelengths.

RADIATION FROM SOLID BODIES

That hot bodies should radiate heat is known to all of us. We also know that if the temperature is high enough, they also emit light. The radiator in our room may emit heat but never light; the heating element of our electric stove glows a dull red as it emits a lot of heat but little light, and the electric light bulb appears to emit more light (of the white variety) than it does heat, even though its temperature is higher than that of the heating element of the stove. We note the same phenomenon if we place a poker in a hot fire—after brief heating we detect heat radiated from it long before it is hot enough to emit light.

These are the infrared or heat waves that have frequencies too low to affect our optic nerves, but still high enough to be absorbed by our skin, where their energy is converted to molecular kinetic energy, raising the temperature of the skin. Continued heating of the poker increases the amount of heat radiated, and soon the poker begins to glow red as frequencies are emitted sufficiently high for our eyes to detect. The reason is that, as the poker gets hotter, its molecules acquire more and more kinetic energy, hence more energy is radiated from it. As heating continues, the red color gradually changes first to orange, then to yellow, and finally to white. This means that the higher frequencies responsible for the green and blue colors are increasing in amount faster than those responsible for the red.

If we should continue the heating until the poker turns blue (a temperature we cannot attain in the laboratory, but which is attained in the hotter stars), the proportion of waves due to frequencies giving rise to blue would be greatly increased.

From these facts we can easily make the deduction that the higher frequencies have greater energy than the lower ones (Fig. 24-1). Note carefully that the total energy emitted by the infrared does not decrease with an increase in temperature. It actually increases, but red no longer determines the color that we see because of the greater abundance of the higher frequencies emitted. Thus, the intensity of light that a heated body emits increases as its temperature increases, and the color of it shifts from the red towards the blue end of the spectrum (Fig. 24-1b). In the interests of clarity, let us try to explain this in another way.

Without specifying its characteristics, let us call whatever it is that is emitting radiation from within the glowing body an emitter. It is apparent that there must be enormous numbers of such emitters in the body. It should also be clearly apparent that while the temperature is low, only the low-frequency emitters emit. A higher temperature is needed to bring the high-frequency emitters into play. Thus, as the temperature rises, more emitters of all frequencies are brought into play. Since the high-frequency emitters carry more energy than the low, the radiation peak shifts towards the shorter wavelengths as the temperature rises. It is thus easy to see that the color of the light emitted by an incandescent body is an index of its temperature.

In this way the astronomer can estimate the temperature of stars.

CONTINUOUS SPECTRA

If the radiation from the iron poker, or from any other solid or liquid body, is passed through a prism or diffraction grating, a continuous spectrum is formed, i.e., there are no wavelength gaps in it even when it is extended into the ultraviolet or the infrared. There are no distinct color bands; instead, one color merges into another, as in a rainbow. Therefore continuous spectra are not very helpful in understanding the fundamental nature of light.

SPECTROSCOPES

We have talked about analyzing light by passing it through a prism or a diffraction grating. A spectroscope is an instrument that allows the light to be analyzed to enter a tube through a narrow vertical slit, passes it through a system of lenses, then through the prism or grating, then through more lenses, and through another tube, from which it emerges to be seen by the eye (Fig. 24-2). If it passes through a prism (Fig. 22-8), various wavelengths are refracted (bent), the shorter ones more than the longer ones. The difference in the amount of bending is what causes the colors to be spread out into a spectrum, a continuous spectrum if the light is ordinary sunlight because all wavelengths are present.

If a diffraction grating is used, colors are also spread out because the different wavelengths are bent (or diffracted) by different amounts as they pass by the edges of the slits in the grating. The tube (but not the slit by which the light is emitted

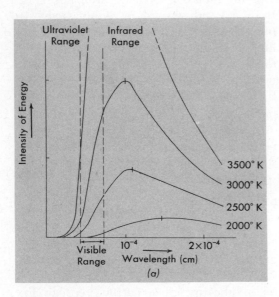

Fig. 24-1. Distribution of Electromagnetic Energy from a Glowing Body among the Various Wavelengths. The area below each curve represents the total energy at the given temperature. Note that almost all of it is in the infrared at the low temperatures, that the total energy rises in all ranges with increasing temperature, and that the proportion in the ultraviolet and visible ranges increases more rapidly than that in the infrared.

(a) The body barely begins to glow at 2000–2500° K. This is shown by the small amount of energy in the visible range. Not much is in the ultraviolet even at 3500° K.

(b) An appreciable amount of the radiation is in the ultraviolet range at 6000° K. The conclusion is that the higher frequencies (shorter wavelengths) must have greater energy than the lower ones. (After Gerald Holton, *Concepts and Theories in Physical Science*, Addison Wesley, Reading, Mass., 1952.)

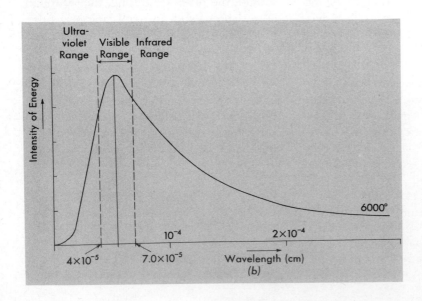

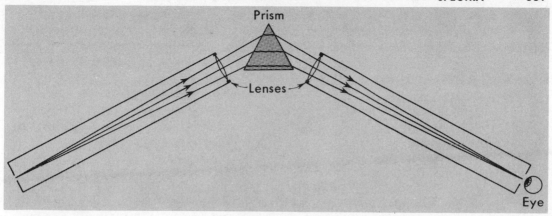

Fig. 24-2. Essentials of Spectroscope. Light enters the prism via the slit, is dispersed by refraction into its component wavelengths by the prism, and is focused for the eye. If mono-chromatic light enters the slit, the eye will see a bright band or line of light whose width depends on the width of the slit, and whose position depends on the amount of refraction. The prism can be rotated so as to bring widely dispersed rays into the viewing tube.

to the grating) may be dispensed with, but this is not always done. Commonly a third tube is added for the purpose of emitting light to illuminate a scale. This scale enables one to describe the positions of the spectral lines with respect to one another.

Spectroscopes vary in their resolving power, depending on how they are made. One of high resolving power, for example, may show two lines very close together that appear to have the same color, whereas, one of low resolving power may show only one line.

BRIGHT LINE SPECTRA

When gases or vapors are heated to incandescence or excited to luminosity by electricity, their light gives bright line spectra when passed through a prism or a diffraction grating, rather than the continuous spectra given by all incandescent liquids and solids. The reason is that their light does not contain all frequencies, but

only certain ones. In other words, there are gaps in the frequencies emitted, and these gaps show up as vacant spaces between the bands of color. Consequently, what is seen when such light is viewed through the eyepiece of the spectroscope is a colored line (or several colored lines) which is an image of the slit in color. If we limit ourselves to the spectrum of the first order we can generalize by saying that we will see as many distinct slit images as there are distinct frequencies in the light being analyzed. In the case of monochromatic light, only one bright line will be seen; if there are ten different wavelengths, there will be ten different images of the slit [2] (see Plate I).

Bright line spectra are remarkably different with different emitters, that is, with

[2] The number of colors seen when white light is analyzed will not necessarily be all of the colors of the continuous spectrum. The interfering of the complementary colors mixed in the proper portions will give white light.

different kinds of gases and vapors; each different kind of atom has its own characteristic pattern. Since any solid or liquid element may be converted to a vapor if it is heated to a high enough temperature, its bright line spectrum is a means of identifying it. The patterns of the spectra of the various kinds of atoms differ in the number of lines present, in the variety of the colors shown, and in the spacing of the lines, not only in the visible range but also in the infrared, ultraviolet, and X-ray regions. Thus, mercury vapor has two thin red lines, two intense lines close together in the yellow range, one intense line in the green, and several less intense in the blue and purple ranges. The relative order of the colors of the various lines is obviously the order in which they occur in the continuous spectrum. Sodium vapor has but two strong, closely spaced lines in the visible range, which in a spectroscope of low resolving power commonly appear as a single line. Contrast this with iron vapor which shows over six thousand lines. Clearly, the bright line spectra are the fingerprints of the atoms, and for that reason are often termed atomic spectra.

The discovery that the spectrum of any one kind of atom is unique made chemical analysis by flame spectra, i.e., by heating in a hot flame, possible for many of the metals. Salts of sodium, for example, give the same yellow line as does sodium heated alone. Two new elements, cesium and rubidium, were discovered by spectroanalysis of ores containing these metals. Later helium was discovered in the sun, some twenty years before its discovery here on earth. Astronomers are able to tell the composition of stars by their spectra. Some types of adulteration of food and other products may be detected by spectral analysis. Line spectra of gases are not produced by heating in a flame because gases cannot ordinarily be heated to incandescence. Instead, their spectra are produced by electric excitation in what is called a gas discharge tube.

ABSORPTION LINE SPECTRA

These spectra are also called dark line spectra, because they consist of black lines instead of bright lines. Glowing liquids and solids, as has already been stated, show continuous spectra rather than line spectra. If the light from a glowing liquid (or solid) is allowed to pass through a suitably large volume of *its* vapor on its way to the prism or diffraction grating in the spectroscope, then one or more dark lines may appear in the otherwise continuous spectrum. If the vapor is sodium metal, the resulting spectrum will show a dark line at exactly the same position on the scale in our spectroscope as a yellow line of sodium. The same light passing through some other vapor or gas will yield one or more dark lines in the positions of some other wavelengths (Plate I).

Joseph von Fraunhofer in 1814 noted these dark lines in the spectrum of the sun; they are known as Fraunhofer lines. Fraunhofer was a maker of optical glass. His interest was initially a practical one, that of improving the quality of the glass he was using to make spectacles. In this research he laid the foundations for solar and stellar chemistry. He constructed a "map" of 576 of these dark lines in the spectrum of the sun, and made other maps of various stars. He invented the forerunner of the modern spectroscope and diffraction grating, and in doing so, laid the foundations of the whole science of spectroscopy.

Experiment shows that each vapor or gas has its own characteristic absorption line spectrum because no two vapors or gases absorb exactly the same wavelengths from the light passing through them. The dark lines represent wavelengths that have been absorbed by the vapor or gas. Why is it that each dark line is assignable to the action of some specific gas or vapor?

The principle involved is as follows: Any mechanical system will absorb energy that falls on it that has the same period as its own vibrations, just as a child's swing is set and kept in motion by giving it a series of pushes that are "in tune" with its period. If the push is applied too soon, i.e., if it is not in tune with the swing's motion then no energy is absorbed and the swing is shortly stopped. For another analogy let us consider two tuning forks capable of emitting sound vibrations of the same frequency. We set fork 1 to vibrating. It sends out energy in all directions. The energy that strikes fork 2, which is nearby, will automatically start it vibrating. This fact can be observed by suddenly quenching the vibrations of fork 1. We will then hear the vibrations of fork 2, but only faintly, because it receives only that part of the energy of fork 1 that comes its way, which is only a small part of the total energy sent out.

We will now apply this principle to the Fraunhofer lines. Take sodium as an example. Sodium is present both in the hot interior of the sun and in the outer cooler (temperature 6000° K) gaseous envelope surrounding the interior. The sodium atoms in the hot interior radiate large amounts of energy; thus, the spectrum of the sun would, if there were no gaseous envelope, show the characteristic bright yellow line of sodium. But there is a hot, gaseous envelope, and so a dark line appears instead in the exact place where the sodium line should appear. The sodium atoms in the gaseous envelope absorb the energy radiated by sodium atoms in the hot interior and they then re-radiate the energy *in all directions,* some of it towards us, but not

enough to cause a bright line in our spectroscopes. Hence the comparatively dark line.

We can do the same thing in the laboratory by placing a sodium flame in the path of a continuous spectrum. A black line appears in the yellow part of the spectrum. We see, then, that dark line spectra represent wavelengths present in the original emitter, but which have been absorbed by a hot vapor or gas of the same composition as the emitter before they reach the observer.

PROBLEMS OF BRIGHT LINE SPECTRA

The great variety of patterns presented great problems to the early students of spectra, problems that were not resolved until after the first decade of the present century. That light is emitted by gases or vapors when their atoms are excited was known in the eighteenth century.[3] The first flame spectra were studied about 1750. Line spectra were first studied about 1800. Aside from that of Fraunhofer, not much significant work was done until the 1850's, when Kirchhoff and Bunsen began the work which shortly led them to the conclusion that each element had its own characteristic line spectrum.

Maxwell's electromagnetic theory of light stated that accelerated charges produced the electromagnetic waves that result in light when they strike our eyes. Charged atoms had been named *ions* by Faraday. It was recognized that either the atom or these charges had to be the emitter of the light. Something had to oscillate and give off radiation as it oscillated. But why the different wavelengths represented by the

---

[3] It should be remembered that any element can be made gaseous by heating it to a high enough temperature.

different lines, and why the exact line patterns? Why did atoms in the incandescent gaseous state emit these different bright line spectra, whereas these same atoms in the form of glowing liquids or solids emit continuous spectra only, and these all alike no matter what the element if the temperature is the same?[4] Why should sodium show only one or two (depending upon the resolving power of the spectroscope) yellow lines in the visible range, whereas iron vapor could give about six thousand lines? What complex arrangement of emitters could possibly give that many lines? Why should some closely similar elements, sodium and potassium, e.g., have such different patterns? Why was there no progressive change from element to element in the periodic chart? Why should the number of lines for any one element depend upon the intensity of the heating?

Clearly, these problems could not be solved until the structure of the atom was better understood, and, conversely, it is easy to see that no picture of the atom that failed to explain line spectra could be seriously considered. Therefore, we must turn our attention to the structure of the atom in order to find the answer; but before we do so we will consider two developments concerning spectra, each of which added to our knowledge, but at the same time created problems of their own.

We should also keep in mind one other fundamental problem, one more fundamental to this course than the explanation

of spectra or the unraveling of the structure of the atom. This book is entitled *A Study of Matter and Energy.* Energy is always associated with matter. All of the elemental kinds of matter in the whole universe are included in the periodic table. The table consists of an orderly arrangement of the elements into periods and families. Why the families? Why the periods? Why the transition elements? Why do the various elements combine with each other as they do? Why do some refuse to combine at all? In short, what is there in the structure of atoms that governs the behavior of matter? Our search for the cause of line spectra will not be fruitful unless it also leads us to a reasonably complete understanding of the periodic table.

BALMER'S EMPIRICAL FORMULA

In the 1870's and 1880's there was feverish research to find a numerical relation between the spacings of the spectral lines, to find some mathematical key to decode the secrets of the lines. In 1885, Johann Balmer (a Swiss schoolteacher who was neither a research scientist nor a recognized mathematician) made the first important break in the problem. By a straight trial-and-error method, he hit upon a formula that related the four principal (most intense) lines of hydrogen (red, green, blue, and violet) to their wavelengths. His formula is as follows:

$$\lambda \text{ (in cm)} = C \times \left(\frac{n^2}{n^2 - 2^2} \right)$$

where λ is the wavelength, n is an integer, 1, 2, 3, 4, etc., and C is an empirically determined constant whose value is 3645.6 $\times 10^{-8}$ cm. Specifically, for the hydrogen lines, n is 3 for the red, 4 for the green, 5

---

[4] We now know that the reason they are all alike at the same temperature is that in liquids and solids, or even in the dense gaseous core of the sun, the incessant mutual collisions among the atoms blur the individual characteristics, just as springs connected together in large groups can no longer vibrate with their own frequencies.

for the blue, and 6 for the violet. Let us calculate the wavelength of the red (alpha) line by substituting 3 for n and the numerical value of C in the equation:

$$3645.6 \times 10^{-8} \left(\frac{3^2}{3^2 - 2^2} \right) =$$

$$6562.08 \times 10^{-8} \text{ cm}$$

The experimental value obtained for this red line by Anders Angstrom, who had made the most careful wavelength measurements of his time, was 6562.10×10^{-8} cm, or 6562.10 A.[5] The agreement is within 0.02 per cent, which might seem to be remarkable considering the difference in methods Balmer and Angstrom used to obtain them. However, the agreement loses much of its strangeness when we learn that Balmer started with Angstrom's experimental value and worked backwards from it, juggling figures in a cut and try fashion until he came up with the right answer. Note carefully that he did not obtain his results by the formulation of a theory and/or by mathematical analysis. Balmer could give no reason for the success of his formula.

Far more remarkable is the fact that Balmer's formula is almost equally good for the wavelengths of the green, blue, and violet lines of hydrogen, and even for lines beyond the visible part of the spectrum, i.e., in the ultraviolet region, where the value of n is 7, 8, 9, etc. A total of 35 lines are now known in the Balmer series, most of them in the ultraviolet regions of the spectrum of hydrogen, and all are in close

agreement with his formula. Moreover, as the value of n gets bigger, the formula demands that the lines get closer and closer together. This is also in agreement with the spectra (Fig. 24-3).

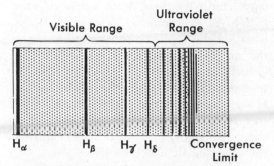

Fig. 24-3. Convergence of Spectral Lines of Hydrogen. The four principal lines of the visible range are individually labeled. Calculations from the Balmer formula show that as the value of n rises the wavelengths of the hydrogen spectral lines should become progressively closer together. This means that the difference between two successive wavelengths approaches zero. A spectrum of hydrogen that shows the ultraviolet range reveals that the calculations are in agreement with observation.

The wavelengths of all of the lines of hydrogen mentioned so far are given by the Balmer formula by varying the value of n while keeping the 2^2 in the denominator; all such lines are grouped together as the Balmer series. Balmer speculated on the possibility that there might be other series of hydrogen lines in which the wavelengths would be given by replacing the 2^2 with 1^2, or 3^2, or 4^2, etc. Such series were eventually found, as improvements in apparatus and techniques took place. The

[5] Instead of expressing wavelengths in centimeters, it is now customary for simplicity's sake to do so in Angstrom units (abbreviated A; named in honor of Angstrom). One such unit equals 10^{-8} cm.

first series, whose wavelengths are given when 2^2 is replaced by 1^2, is in the ultraviolet region of the spectrum; the others are in the infrared region.[6]

However, the formula had to be altered in some respects. If it was to give the wavelengths of these lines, a new constant had to be determined. This constant, R, is called the Rydberg constant in honor of the great Swedish spectroscopist who followed Balmer. (R is approximately equal to 4 divided by the previous constant, C.) If we rewrite Balmer's formula to give the reciprocal of the wavelength (instead of the wavelength) and use the new constant, the equation then becomes:

$$\frac{1}{\lambda} = R\left(\frac{1}{2^2} - \frac{1}{n^2}\right)$$

The value of R is 109,677.58 cm^{-1}. (The superscript, -1, in this constant simply means "reciprocal of.") The equation applies only to the Balmer series. We may now write the formula in the more general form, so it will be applicable to all of the series, as follows:

$$\frac{1}{\lambda} = R\left(\frac{1}{n_1^2} - \frac{1}{n_2^2}\right)$$

Here n_1 is a fixed integer (1, 2, 3, etc.) for any one series and n_2 is another integer (2, 3, etc.) that varies within the series (as n did in the original form of the equation). It should be noted that the equation does not apply directly to spectra of elements other than hydrogen. This should not surprise us, considering the range of the numbers of lines and the diversity of the pat-

terns of atomic spectra. Yet it served as a basis for the development of other formulas of similar form for the spectra of other gases and vapors.

It should also be noted that the Rydberg constant appears in all of them. These similarities suggest that all bright line spectra are caused by the same basic physical mechanism, a mechanism that must be extraordinarily complex in order to explain the great variety of spectral lines and spectral patterns. The understanding of this physical mechanism was not much advanced by Balmer's formula; such understanding had to await a better understanding of the nature of light and a model of the structure of the atom.

PLANCK'S QUANTUM THEORY

The first step towards a better understanding of the nature of light came about through the work of Max Planck, a German physicist, about the turn of the present century. Planck was trying to develop an adequate theory for the emission of continuous spectra. Let us return briefly to radiation from solid bodies. From the study of radiation from ideal emitters, called ideal black surfaces,[7] two laws, derived from the known laws of Hertz, and/or Maxwell's electromagnetic theory of radiation had been experimentally verified. The first is the Stefan-Boltzmann Law, which states that the total energy of all wavelengths emitted per unit time and per unit area is directly

---

[6] That in the ultraviolet region is called the Lyman series; those in the infrared region are the Paschen, Brackett, and Pfund series, all named after their discoverers.

[7] The ideal emitter of radiation is one that absorbs all the radiation that falls on it, for if it absorbs all wavelengths, it can emit all wavelengths. The total radiation from such an ideal body depends solely upon its temperature, no matter what its other characteristics are. No such ideal black body exists, but an equivalent was developed, which we need not describe here.

proportional to the fourth power of the absolute temperature of the emitting body. The second is Wien's Law, which, in general, states that the hotter the emitting body, the shorter the predominant wavelengths that are emitted (Fig. 24-1b).

The verification of these laws was a triumph for Maxwell's theory. However, there remained some questions without satisfactory answers. Most important was the failure to find a general law that would represent the energy emitted from an ideal black body as a function of the wavelength at different temperatures. This failure meant that no general formula for curves such as those in Fig. 24-1 that was consistent with Maxwell's theory could be formulated from the experimental data. The formula that fitted the curve to the radiation at one temperature was not valid for that of another temperature.

Planck finally succeeded in obtaining a formula by a trial-and-error method that did actually agree with the experimental data. He then determined what assumptions had to be made in order to deduce this formula theoretically. Note carefully the procedure he used:

1. He attempted to derive an equation from experimental data that was consistent with the accepted theory.

2. He was unable to do this (and neither were other able theorists), so he tried to derive a formula empirically that would fit the experimental data, and succeeded in doing so.

3. And finally, he formulated a theory from which not only the empirical formula could be deduced, but which also permitted him to derive by purely mathematical means the laws of Wien and Stefan-Boltzmann.

Planck, along with all other workers in the field, believed that spectra must be explained by the action of submicroscopic emitters within the atom, i.e., some part of the atom had to vibrate, and, in doing so, radiate electromagnetic waves of a particular frequency during the vibration. The radiated waves would carry the energy emitted, the amount varying with each particular emitter. However, and this is the crucial point, according to Planck's theory (now called the quantum theory), an emitter of a particular frequency, f, cannot send out just any part of its total energy at any instant. No matter how small the amount sent out it had to be some integral multiple of the quantity hf, where f is the particular frequency sent out and h is a constant determined experimentally.[8]

The amount of energy in each unit radiated may be equal to hf, $2\,hf$, $3\,hf$, etc., but never a nonintegral multiple of hf, such as $1.35\,hf$, $2.78\,hf$, or the like, any more than there are 1.35 or 2.78 atoms of any element. This means that there must exist a smallest portion of energy, each portion called a quantum of energy. It means that the rays of the sun, or rays from any other source, do not represent a continuous flow of electromagnetic waves in the visible range, but a stream of individual packets that Planck called quanta. The process of radiation is thus assumed to be discontinuous.

The size of each packet, or quantum, is inversely proportional to the wavelength, or what is the same thing, directly propor-

[8] This constant is now called Planck's constant. It has the value of 6.62×10^{-27} erg-sec. It has the dimensions of energy times time. It is one of the great universal constants of nature, derived experimentally. We will encounter it again and again. Get acquainted with it.

tional to the frequency. This means that there is no universal atom of radiant energy, since emitters of every conceivable frequency can occur in nature. A quantum of violet light thus contains more energy than a quantum of red light, because its frequency is higher. Here we have the concept of the indivisibility of packets of radiant energy somewhat analogous to the indivisibility of atoms, à la Dalton. More formally we can state the theory as follows: *An oscillator (vibrator or emitter) possesses energy only in discrete amounts called quanta. It can gain or lose energy only in integral multiples of these quanta, i.e., in integral multiples of hf.*

It was late in 1900 when Planck presented his quantum theory as a solution to the above problems of radiation. Planck's success in formulating the new theory did not please him at all, for the price of it was a radical assumption that was not at all in accord with Maxwell's theory of electromagnetic radiation, a theory in which Planck was still a staunch believer. He did his best to destroy his own theory, for it was not very convincing either to him or to most physicists of the time.

For one thing, how could one explain interference and diffraction with the quantum theory? Furthermore, his theory, insofar as he could see, contained no solution, no picture or model, for the puzzle of line spectra. Yet the experimental facts would not allow the destruction of either theory. To be accepted the quantum theory had to have more support, support from some other source. A theory made to suit one specific set of facts can probably be adjusted to fit that particular set of facts. However, the likelihood of that theory being universally applicable is very slender unless a very different phenomenon can be explained by the same theory. This is especially true if no adequate explanation of this different phenomenon has been yet devised. The strengthening of the evidence for Planck's quantum theory came in 1905, from a man who was to exert a profound influence on scientific thought in the twentieth century. That man was Albert Einstein, then only twenty-six years old.

PHOTOELECTRIC EFFECT

While Hertz was making the investigations that led to the successful emission and detection of Hertzian (radio) waves, he made the observation that the spark would jump more readily across the metal spheres that served as the electrodes of his receiver if they were well polished, and if the light from the transmitter spark were allowed to fall on them. Investigation revealed that radiation of high frequency, e.g., that in the ultraviolet region, impinging on the electrodes, could expel negative charges (electrons) from them. These charges helped to maintain the current between the electrodes and thus the spark jumped more readily between the spheres.

A simple device that demonstrates this phenomenon is an uncharged electroscope to which a metallic plate is attached (Fig. 24-4). Ultraviolet rays from a mercury vapor light shining on the plate causes the leaves of the electroscope to diverge, indicating the presence of a charge. A test shows that the sign of the charge is positive. Therefore, negative charges, i.e., electrons, must have been removed from the surface of the plate. *This ejection of electrons from metal surfaces by light of certain frequencies is called the photoelectric*

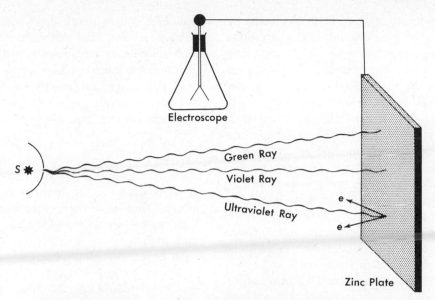

Electroscope

Green Ray

Violet Ray

Ultraviolet Ray

e

e

S ✹

Zinc Plate

Fig. 24-4. Photoelectric Effect. *S* is a mercury-vapor lamp which emits visible light of various wavelengths along with considerable of the ultraviolet. These rays strike a zinc plate. Only the ultraviolet rays have enough energy to eject electrons from zinc. Loss of electrons leaves the plate with an excess of positive charges, as is indicated by the electroscope. No matter how intense the visible light nor how weak the ultraviolet, the former will not eject electrons, the latter will.

effect. The surfaces of conductors act as barriers to the electrons that are free to move in them. To cross this barrier, i.e., to escape from the metal, electrons must acquire additional energy. If they do so by absorbing electromagnetic radiation, we have the photoelectric effect.

Further investigation revealed that while the ultraviolet and shorter wavelengths were effective in expelling electrons from practically any metal surface, those of visible light were effective only with the alkali and the alkaline earth metals. In fact, not all wavelengths of visible light will eject electrons from sodium. No matter how intense, red light will not do so, but no mat-

ter how faint, blue light will. This can mean only that more energy is associated with the blue wavelengths than with the red wavelengths.

Further experiments revealed that *for light of a given wavelength, the number of electrons ejected is directly proportional to the intensity of the light, but that the velocity of the electrons ejected was independent of the intensity.* This means that a greater intensity of light of a given frequency will result in more electrons being ejected, but will not increase the velocity of ejection. The experiments also showed that a decrease in the wavelength of light, i.e., an increase in the frequency, increased the velocity of the ejected electrons, no matter how low the intensity. In other words, a certain minimum frequency, often referred to as the threshold frequency, is necessary to eject electrons from any one metal, and this threshold frequency is different for different metals. Ordinary light will eject electrons from cesium and rubidium but not from zinc or iron. Furthermore, the ejection is instantaneous if the frequency is high enough showing that no accumulation of energy is necessary.

The following analogy may help to clarify these ideas. Suppose you have a large number of bottles all the same size lined up on a fence. You stand back and throw pebbles, one at a time, and all of a certain size (analogous to frequency) and with all your might. If the pebbles are too small, no bottles will be knocked over. If you increase the size of the pebbles from time to time (analogous to increasing the frequency), you will eventually find a certain minimum size that will knock a bottle over and send it a certain distance. But throwing more pebbles will not send any one bottle a greater distance, but will simply knock over more bottles. Still larger pebbles (greater frequency) will send the bottles a greater distance, i.e., give them a greater kinetic energy.

PHOTON THEORY OF LIGHT

The laws of photoelectricity may be summarized as follows:

1. The number of photoelectrons ejected is proportional to the intensity of the light striking the metal surface.

2. The maximum energy of the photoelectron is independent of the light intensity.

3. For every metal there exists a frequency (called the threshold frequency) such that lesser frequencies will not eject electrons no matter what the intensity.

4. The maximum energy of the photoelectrons depends on the frequency of the radiation causing the ejection.

The above facts could not be explained by Maxwell's theory of light. His theory required that the intensity of the radiation governs not only the number of electrons ejected, but also their velocities, just as high ocean waves (corresponding to a high intensity) will not only move more pebbles on a beach than low ocean waves (corresponding to low intensity) but will also give them greater speeds. Thus, the photoelectric effect remained unexplained from about 1890 until about 1905, five years after Planck had advanced his quantum theory. The name of the man who explained it was Albert Einstein.[9]

What Einstein did was to apply the quantum theory to the photoelectric problem in a simple and easy manner. Qualitatively, his method is as follows: Light is propagated through space in the form of individual packets of energy called photons (quanta). *On encountering an electron as it strikes a metal surface, a photon gives up its entire energy to the electron. If the amount of energy possessed by the photon is great enough, the electron will be*

[9] Einstein (1879–1955) did so poorly in high school that he was asked to leave. He did graduate from another school, and entered the Federal Institute of Technology in Zurich on the basis of excellent work in mathematics. He failed to get an assistantship for graduate study, so he became a custom's clerk. However, he pursued theoretical physics as a hobby. In 1905 he published three papers, any one of which would have brought him fame. One of them was his photon theory of light. He was twenty-six years old at the time.

ejected from the metal surface. Ejected electrons are called photoelectrons. The amount of energy in each photon increases with the frequency. Greater intensity simply means more packets, more photons, not greater energy in each packet or photon. Therefore, one packet of greater frequency will accomplish what many packets of lesser frequency will not.

Quantitatively, Einstein's explanation of the photoelectric effect is as follows: The amount of energy received by an electron (called a photoelectron) from a photon equals the total energy of the photon. According to Planck's theory, this energy is given by hf. If no work had to be done against forces tending to prevent the electron from leaving the surface of the metal, the photoelectron would be ejected with a kinetic energy given by the equation

$$\tfrac{1}{2}mv^2 = hf$$

i.e., the energy of the ejected photoelectron would equal the energy of the photon. This is in accord with the Law of Conservation of Energy. The attraction of the positive charges within the atom, however, constitutes a force that does tend to prevent electrons from being ejected from the surface of the metal. Work has to be done to overcome these forces, and energy is needed to do work. Therefore, the photoelectron is ejected with a kinetic energy that is less than that of the photon by the amount of energy needed to do the work. The equation therefore becomes

$$\tfrac{1}{2}mv^2 = hf - W$$

where W is the work done (in ergs). If W equals hf, $\tfrac{1}{2}mv^2$ is equal to 0, so the electron will not escape from the metal. The amount of work needed to eject an electron varies with the metal, and the amount of energy, hf, varies directly with the frequency. Thus, it is easy to see that for a particular metal, light of a particular minimum (threshold) frequency is necessary to eject electrons.[10] We might wonder why Planck did not develop the photon or quantum theory of light himself, since it is based on his work. The reason is that Planck could not cut himself loose from the Maxwellian electromagnetic theory, so that he could follow the consequences of his own theory to the bitter end, no matter where that end might be. Planck was convinced that his quantum theory would set the understanding of light back a century or more.

Thus, it was left to Einstein to follow through, and Planck was by no means pleased that he did so. The photon theory as proposed by Einstein did not abandon the wave concept completely, but stated that the energy of light was not distributed over the whole wave front as in Maxwell's theory, but rather is concentrated or localized in discrete small regions in the form of tiny bundles called photons. The intensity of the light is a consequence of

[10] Suppose we carry our reasoning a bit further and speculate on what might happen if the metal surface is heated strongly enough. Furthermore, let us remember that the phenomenon of electrons escaping from a metal surface for any cause whatsoever is analogous in most respects to the evaporation of a liquid. We may thus speak of the "evaporation" of electrons. As the temperature rises, the electrons gain kinetic energy, some more than others, and the additional energy needed to evaporate them becomes less. We might then assume that photons of lesser energy would eject them. This is found to be the case. In fact, as the temperature rises higher and higher, we eventually find the electrons evaporate without benefit of photons. This is called thermal emission of electrons, or thermionic emission. As in liquids, the evaporation is easier and faster with some substances than it is with others (Fig. 26-4).

the closeness of the spacing of the photons on the wave front. As a light wave progresses away from its source, the light becomes weaker, not because the photons lose energy, but because the distances between neighboring photons becomes greater, and the energy per unit area becomes less. Ordinarily in experiments dealing with reflection, refraction, interference, diffraction, and polarization we are dealing with enormous numbers of photons on each wave front. They are so closely spaced that the individuality of each photon is masked, and the wave front appears to be continuous and homogeneous, just as any material solid appears to be made of continuous matter rather than of individual atoms. That is why Maxwell's theory is still most useful when dealing with ordinary problems of optics, but when we get down into the finer structure of matter, i.e., inside the atom, the finer structure of the light wave becomes important. Therefore, we will use Einstein's photon theory in our attempts to explain the relationship between light and individual atoms. You will recall that this has been our chief problem throughout this section, and that we have not yet solved it.

We must not think that the photon theory is a reversion to Newton's corpuscular theory. Newton's corpuscles were thought of as actual particles of matter, whereas photons represent bundles of energy that have no rest mass.[11] This means that once the photon stops it ceases to exist, its energy being transferred to whatever stopped it.

The photon theory has a set of problems

all its own. For example, how large is the "spot" on the wave front where the photon is located? How does an electron absorb a photon? What is the meaning of frequency and wavelength if the photon is only a dot on the wave front? And so on. Our real difficulty is that we want a mechanical model that we can visualize pictorially. We can picture either waves or moving particles, but we cannot picture a wave–particle duality, something that acts like a wave under some circumstances and like a particle under others, or possibly acts like both at the same time. All we can say is that the wave and the photon concepts are both needed to explain the phenomenon of light; we must learn to regard them as complementary ways of viewing one and the same process.

We have been delving into the phenomenon of radiation, into spectra in particular, with the hope that we would unravel the structure of the atom, for, as we have already stated, no picture of the atom that failed to explain atomic spectra could be at all seriously considered, and, conversely, the problems of atomic spectra could not be solved without a better understanding of the nature of the atom.

It was universally agreed that a complex set of oscillators had to exist within the atom in order to account for atomic spectral lines and patterns. It followed that the atom could not be the simple, indivisible unit of matter postulated by Dalton and widely believed in for the better part of a century. Spectral research failed to identify the parts, although it supplied problems aplenty for atomic structure to solve. Therefore, we will turn our attention to that second line of research that we mentioned at the beginning of this section. It began, curiously enough, with that same

---

[11] It has become something of a fad to refer to photons as bullets. It is, to say the least, unusual for a bullet to cease to exist once it has stopped moving.

great experimenter, Michael Faraday, who started Maxwell on the work that resulted in his electromagnetic theory of radiation.

SUMMARY

Hot bodies radiate electromagnetic waves which range from the infrared to the ultraviolet inclusive. At lower temperatures only the infrared is given off, but as the temperature rises the bodies become incandescent, radiating the red frequencies almost exclusively at first. At still higher temperatures the higher frequencies form a greater proportion of the radiation, until the body becomes white hot. However, at *all* temperatures the infrared and red radiation form the larger proportion of the total radiation. The proportion of green and blue radiation, negligible at the lower temperatures, increases rapidly as the color of the body changes from red to white. The conclusion is that the higher frequencies have greater energy. The spectrum of such glowing bodies, solid or liquid, shows all frequencies and so is a continuous spectrum.

When gases or vapors are heated to incandescence, or excited to luminosity by electricity, a bright line spectrum is observed when viewed by means of a spectroscope, because not all frequencies are radiated. These bright line spectra are the "fingerprints" of the atom, for each kind of atom radiates a different set of frequencies, and so has a characteristic spectrum. Some new chemical elements were discovered by means of spectra that were different from those of any of the known elements. The great number of spectral patterns created problems for those who were trying to find out how spectra were emitted.

Balmer arrived at a formula by trial and error that gave the wavelengths of the four principal lines of hydrogen:

$$\lambda \text{ (in cm)} = C \times \left(\frac{n^2}{n^2 - 2^2} \right)$$

The formula, however, was in no sense an explanation, and there was no discernible reason why such a formula should give the wavelengths of the hydrogen lines with an error of less than 0.1 per cent.

Planck developed his quantum theory in 1900 while investigating radiation from so-called black bodies. This turned out to be one of the most revolutionary theories in modern science. It conflicted with Maxwell's theory in that it assumed that light was emitted as discrete amounts of energy which Planck called quanta, and which Einstein later called photons. The amount of energy carried by a photon varied with the frequency. A radiating body emitted this energy, not continuously as assumed by the Maxwell theory, but in discrete amounts. The theory was not at all acceptable until Einstein used it to explain the photoelectric effect in 1905. The photoelectric effect had gone unexplained for over a decade. It seemed to be a rather unimportant phenomenon with no great significance. However, Einstein's use of the quantum theory to explain it made it of immense importance, for it provided evidence for the nature of light.

EXERCISES

I. TERMS AND CONCEPTS

Spectrum	Photon theory of light
Continuous spectrum	
Bright line spectrum	Photoelectric effect
Flame spectra	
Spectroscope	Planck's constant
Angstrom unit = 10^{-8} cm	Einstein's photoelectric equation,
Quantum theory	
Quantum	$\frac{1}{2}mv^2$
Photon	$= hf - W.$

II. PROBLEMS

1. What range of frequencies of the electromagnetic spectrum are emitted by all incandescent bodies? (The numerical values of the frequencies are not wanted.)

2. What difference is there between the radiation of a red-hot body and a white-hot body?

3. What is the relationship between radiation of energy and frequency?

4. What is a continuous spectrum? Why is the spectrum of sunlight a continuous one?

5. What is the purpose of a spectroscope?

6. Glowing liquids and solids emit continuous spectra; glowing gases or electrically excited gases emit bright line spectra. Why?

7. List four of the problems of bright line spectra.

8. What was Balmer's formula designed to do? How did he obtain this formula?

9. What effect did Balmer's formula have on the problem of bright line spectra?

10. Calculate by means of the Balmer formula the wavelength of the violet line in the hydrogen spectrum.

11. What is Planck's quantum theory?

12. In what way is it different from Maxwell's theory?

13. Why was it not accepted at once?

14. What is the photoelectric effect?

15. Why could it not be explained by Maxwell's theory?

16. Name two metals from which ordinary light will eject electrons. What kind of light will eject electrons from zinc? From iron?

17. What effect does temperature have on the ease with which electrons will be ejected?

18. One ultraviolet photon will eject one electron from zinc but a hundred photons of blue light will not. Why?

19. Will X-rays eject electrons from zinc? Justify your answer.

20. What is the present standing of the two theories of light, the photon theory and the electromagnetic theory?

CHAPTER XXV

Faraday's Laws of Electrolysis

The things that any science discovers are beyond the reach of direct observation. We cannot see energy, nor the attraction of gravitation, nor the flying molecules of gases . . . nor the forests of the carbonaceous era, nor the explosions in nerve cells. It is only the premises of science, not its conclusions, which are directly observed.

—C. S. PIERCE (1898)

Experimenters began passing electric charge through various solutions shortly after Volta invented the battery in 1800.[1] The greatest of these experimenters was Faraday. The process of passing an electric charge through a solution, together with any accompanying changes due to the migration of solute particles, is called *electrolysis*. Chemical changes always occur if any charge passes through the solution. It was by this method that some compounds were broken up that heretofore had resisted separation into their component elements. Potassium and sodium were obtained by electrolysis in 1807 by Sir

[1] You will recall that before the invention of the battery a steady uniform flow of charge was impossible. Only static electricity, a violent, riotous, discontinuous flow of charge was possible.

Humphry Davy (the discoverer of Michael Faraday) from potash (K_2O) and soda (Na_2O), which at that time were both still considered elements. Chlorine was also discovered in this way.

The essence of the process of electrolysis is as follows: In any liquid solution the solute particles (molecules, atoms, ions), i.e., the particles of the material in solution, wander about as individuals among the particles of the solvent. Some solutions are good conductors and so are called electrolytes. Water solutions of salts, acids, and bases are excellent electrolytes. The pure molten salts themselves are also good conductors. If we remember that electric current in a wire consists of a stream of charged particles (electrons), then it is obvious that the passage of electric current through a solution is also a stream of charged particles, which is carried in some manner from one electrode to the other.

Observation of the process reveals that one kind of charged particle moves towards one electrode, while a charged particle of opposite sign moves towards the other. Faraday called these charged particles *ions*, from a Greek word meaning to travel. Experiment reveals that metallic ions and hydrogen ions (H^+) always travel towards the cathode (Fig. 25-1), thus proving that they carry a positive charge, whereas nonmetallic ions such as chloride (Cl^-) and oxide (O^{--}) ions and radicals such as NO_3^-, $SO_4^=$, etc., always travel towards the anode, thus proving that they carry a negative charge. It is therefore the ions that carry the charges from one electrode to the other; there is no stream of electrons as such flowing through the solution. Electrons are transferred, of course, since no current through the solution is possible without such transfer.

ELECTROLYSIS OF MOLTEN SODIUM CHLORIDE

The process of transfer of electrons can best be illustrated if we pass a current

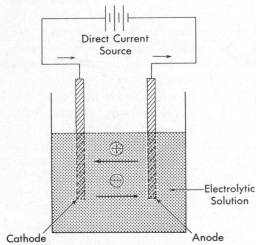

Direct Current Source

Electrolytic Solution

Cathode   Anode

Fig. 25-1. Process of Electrolysis of Molten Sodium Chloride. Because of electrostatic attractions the positively charged sodium atoms (ions) move to the cathode where they become neutral atoms and are deposited on the cathode; the negatively charged chlorine atoms (ions) move to the anode where they become neutral atoms and are released as a free gas.

through pure molten NaCl, in which there is no water present to complicate the electrolytic process. Sodium chloride is ionic not only in solution but in the solid and molten states as well. The ions that come into contact with an electrode become atoms; the positively charged sodium atoms do so by acquiring an electron from the cathode, and the negatively charged chloride ions by giving up an electron to the anode. The resulting sodium atoms are

deposited on the cathode as sodium metal. The chlorine atoms immediately pair up to form molecules, and these pairs escape in groups as tiny bubbles of gas which may be collected with proper apparatus.

The electrons, released at the anode, pass through the connecting wire to the battery, which in turn furnishes an electron to the cathode. The reaction at the cathode is

$$Na^+ + e^- \rightarrow Na,$$

and that at the anode is

$$2Cl^- \rightarrow Cl_2 + 2e^-,$$

where e^- is an electron. The combined reaction may be written:

$$2Na^+ + 2Cl^- + 2e^- \rightarrow 2Na + Cl_2 + 2e^-$$

Note that the electrons cancel out in the above equation. They have, however, played their part since they were transferred from the chlorine to the sodium, and it took electrical energy to do it. In the process the salt is decomposed into free metallic sodium and chlorine gas.[2] It should be obvious that the number of electrons acquired by the sodium at the cathode must exactly equal the number released by the chlorine at the anode. If each sodium ion acquires one electron and each chloride ion gives up one, then it follows that the number of sodium atoms deposited on the cathode exactly equals the number of chloride ions liberated at the anode. Therefore, if we collect one gram atomic weight of sodium (23 g) at the cathode, we should also collect one gram atomic weight of chlorine (35.5 g) at the anode, for there

[2] Metallic sodium and chlorine gas are produced industrially by this process. The same process is used for some other metals, notably aluminum.

are the same number of atoms in a gram atomic weight of any element. What will this number of atoms be?

ELECTROPLATING

In the process known as electroplating a somewhat different situation exists because of the electrodes used. When pure molten salts are decomposed electrolytically, as above, inert electrodes such as platinum or carbon are used. In the electroplating, e.g., of silver, the anode consists of a block of metallic silver, and the cathode of whatever is to be silverplated. The solution used is a dilute water solution of some soluble silver salt, say $AgNO_3$, which consists of positively charged silver ions (Ag^+) and negatively charged nitrate ions (NO_3^-). The silver ions move towards the cathode where they each acquire an electron and plate out, just like the sodium in the previous example.

At the anode, however, the situation is different. The nitrate ions accumulate there but they do not give up their electrons as did the chloride ions, despite the shortage of electrons there, a shortage which tends to increase as electrons are acquired by silver ions at the cathode. The anode in this case is a block of silver, a reactive metal; an atom of this insoluble silver gives up an electron more easily than does the nitrate ion. (Nothing happens to the nitrate ion.) For each loss of an electron to form a silver ion at the cathode, a silver atom gives up an electron at the anode, becomes a soluble silver ion, which in turn moves through the solution to the cathode where it is plated out as a silver atom. The process will continue until the silver block forming the anode is completely gone. The reaction at the anode is

$$Ag \rightarrow Ag^+ + e^-$$

and that at the cathode is

$$Ag^+ + e^- \rightarrow Ag$$

Note that there has been no change in the solution; silver has been transferred from one electrode to the other, the transfer involving a change from atoms to ions and back to atoms again. Again there is a one-to-one correspondence between the number of electrons acquired at the cathode and the number released at the anode. A consequence of this correspondence is that the mass of silver plated out, and that going into solution, is exactly proportional to the amount of electricity passed through the battery.

ELECTROLYSIS OF WATER

Another situation develops when dilute water solutions of salts of metals that react with water are used in conjunction with inert electrodes. An example is sodium sulfate (Na_2SO_4). The ions present in the solution will be singly charged sodium ions (Na^+) and doubly charged sulfate ions (SO_4^{--}). There will be twice as many of the former as the latter. As expected, the Na^+ ions travel to the cathode where they acquire electrons to become atoms. However, sodium atoms are highly reactive with water, so instead of plating out they instantly react with it. The complete reaction at the cathode, broken down into two steps is

$$2Na^+ + 2e^- \rightarrow 2Na$$

$$2Na + 2H_2O \rightarrow 2OH^- + H_2 + 2Na^+$$

Writing these two steps as a single reaction,

$$2Na^+ + 2e^- + 2H_2O \rightarrow 2Na^+ + 2OH^- + H_2$$

The sodium ions cancel out so that the net cathode reaction is

$$2H_2O + 2e^- \rightarrow H_2 + 2OH^- \quad \text{(Eq. 25-1)}$$

The net result of the reaction is that one hydrogen atom from each of two water molecules accepts an electron at the cathode to become a neutral hydrogen atom, which instantly combines with another to form a neutral hydrogen molecule. Groups of such molecules escape as bubbles of free hydrogen.

The SO_4^{--} ions migrate to the anode, but they do not release their extra electrons. Instead a water molecule breaks up, according to the following reaction:

$$2H_2O + 2SO_4^= \rightarrow 4e^- + 4H^+ + 2SO_4^= + O_2$$

Since the $2SO_4^{--}$ cancels out, we may write this anode reaction,

$$2H_2O \rightarrow O_2 + 4H^+ + 4e^- \quad \text{(Eq. 25-2)}$$

The oxygen escapes as bubbles of free gas.

The overall reaction is obtained by combining the reactions [3] (Eq. 25-1 and Eq. 25-2) at the two electrodes, as follows:

$$4H_2O + 4e^- + 2H_2O \rightarrow$$
$$2H_2 + 4OH^- + O_2 + 4H^+ + 4e^-$$

The electrons cancel out, and the H^+ and the OH^- ions react to form water, as follows:

$$4H^+ + 4OH^- \rightarrow 4H_2O$$

These four molecules of water, being on the right side of the overall equation above will cancel out four molecules of water from the left side. Thus, the net reaction at both electrodes [4] is

$$2H_2O \rightarrow 2H_2 + O_2$$

[3] The cathode reaction is doubled so that the electrons on the two sides of the equation will balance.

[4] An alternative and old-fashioned way is to write first the reaction at the cathode, omitting the electrons, then that at the anode, and finally the reaction between the products of the two electrodes, as follows:

$$4Na^+ + 4H_2O \rightarrow 4NaOH + 2H_2$$
$$2SO_4^= + 2H_2O \rightarrow 2H_2SO_4 + O_2$$
$$4NaOH + 2H_2SO_4 \rightarrow 4Na^+ + 2SO_4^= + 4H_2O$$

If we add the three reactions, canceling those quantities appearing on both sides, we have the same result:

$$2H_2O \rightarrow 2H_2 + O_2$$

To summarize, we started with a dilute water solution of sodium sulfate. The net result was to break up water molecules into atoms of hydrogen and oxygen which escaped as free molecules. Nothing happened to the sodium sulfate. It simply provided the means by which the electrons were carried through the solution. If water were a good electrolyte, i.e., if it formed abundant positive and negative ions in solution, as does molten NaCl, then the sodium sulfate would have been unnecessary.

FARADAY'S LAWS OF ELECTROLYSIS

Michael Faraday was the first to investigate quantitatively the electrolytic process. He found that the amount of the element liberated at an electrode was directly proportional to the strength of the current and to the time that the current was allowed to pass through the solution. From these facts he formulated his First Law of Electrolysis: *When an electric current passes through a solution, the total mass of the particular element deposited (or liberated) is directly proportional to the total charge passing through the solution.* This must mean that each ion of a given element carries a definite amount of electric charge.

The next step was to investigate the relative amounts of electric charge carried by ions of different elements, for it was quickly apparent that these amounts varied from one element to another. This can be done as follows: Suppose we have separate beakers of HCl solution, molten NaCl, molten $MgCl_2$ and molten $AlCl_3$ (dissolved in molten cryolite—a mineral composed of fluorine, sodium, and aluminum—to make it ionize). Let us connect these four beakers in series with a battery, a switch, and an ammeter (Fig. 25-2). Since the solutions

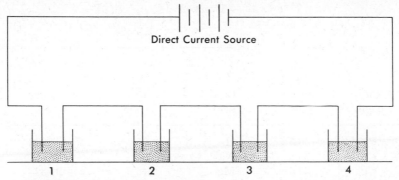

Fig. 25-2. Experimental Verification of Faraday's Laws of Electrolysis. Beakers numbered 1 through 4 containing HCl solution, molten NaCl, molten $MgCl_2$, and molten $AlCl_3$ (with a mineral, cryolite, to make it ionize), respectively, are connected in series with a battery and an ammeter (not shown). The same quantity of charge passes through each beaker. The ammeter and a clock are needed to determine the total quantity of charge. The quantity of each metal deposited, and the quantity of each gas liberated is carefully measured. The data confirm Faraday's laws. See Table 25-1.

are in series, the same number of coulombs will pass through each of them. The ammeter together with a clock will determine the number of coulombs, since $Q = It$. We close the switch and open it only after 1.008 g of hydrogen have been collected at the cathode.[5] A check of our ammeter and the total time the current was passing through the various solutions allows us to calculate that 96,500 coulombs of charge was transferred while 1.008 g of hydrogen was being collected. Note that the same amount of charge was passed through each of the solutions (for they are connected in series).

[5] We can determine the weight of hydrogen collected either by weighing, or by measuring its volume. Since 1.008 g of hydrogen is one gram atomic weight, or one-half gram molecular weight (mole) of it, its volume at STP will be one-half of 22.4 liters.

We now weigh the products deposited at each of the electrodes in all four beakers. The results are summarized in Table 25-1.

Let us examine the results one by one to see what conclusions we can draw. We note that for beaker 1, one gram atomic weight of hydrogen and one gram atomic weight of chlorine were collected at their respective electrodes. Since the number of charges released at the anode must be the same as the number released at the cathode, and since there are the same number of atoms in a gram atomic weight of any element, it follows that each hydrogen ion carried the same charge as each chloride ion. (We need not concern ourselves at the present time with the sign of the charge.)

For beaker 2 we see that one gram

TABLE 25-1

Beaker	Anode		Cathode			Total Charge Passed (coulombs)
	Element	Wt. Released (gm)	Element	Wt. Released	Atomic Weight	
1	Cl	35.5	H	1.008 gm	1.008	96,500
2	Cl	35.5	Na	23.0	23.0	96,500
3	Cl	35.5	Mg	12.16	24.32	96,500
4	Cl	35.5	Al	9.0	26.98	96,500

atomic weight of both sodium and chlorine were released. Following the same reasoning as above, we conclude that the sodium and chloride ions carry the same amount of charge. It follows that the sodium and hydrogen ions carry the same amount also.

The situation in the other two beakers is different with respect to the weights of the metals released, *although the amount of chlorine is the same.* We find that the weight of magnesium released is half a gram atomic weight, and that the weight of aluminum released is one-third of a gram atomic weight. This means that only half as many atoms of magnesium and only one-third as many atoms of aluminum were released as there were atoms of chlorine by the same quantity of charge. Since the number of electrons given up by the chlorine at the anode must equal the number acquired by each of the metals, it follows that each magnesium ion acquired two electrons in becoming an atom, and that each aluminum ion acquired three electrons. This means that the magnesium ion carries twice the charge of a chloride ion, and that an aluminum ion carries three times the charge. We also note from the formulas of

their chlorides that the valence of magnesium is 2 and that of aluminum is 3.

Investigation of other elements by electrolysis of their salts reveals (1) that no ion carries a smaller charge than an ion of H or Cl, and, (2) that 96,500 coulombs [6] of charge will release one gram atomic weight of any monovalent element, one-half gram atomic weight of any bivalent element, and one-third gram atomic weight of any trivalent element. We further note that the charges on all of these ions are in the ratios of small whole numbers, and that the number of charges on any ion of an element is equal to the valence of that element. We therefore feel justified in concluding that the charges carried by atoms are even multiples of some fundamental unit charge, a unit charge that is associated with atoms of elements whose valence is one. We may now state Faraday's Second Law of Electrolysis:

The same amount of charge will release different weights of different elements, and these weights are proportional to the atomic weights and inversely proportional to the

[6] This quantity of charge is now known as 1 faraday.

valence. Another way of stating the law is that the weights of different elements liberated by the same quantity of electricity are directly proportional to their equivalent weights. (The equivalent weight of an element is defined as its atomic weight divided by its valence. Equivalent weights are sometimes referred to as combining weights.)

If there is a fundamental unit of charge, i.e., if the charge on the electron is the smallest unit of charge that can exist, and if we know the charge carried by one electron, then we can calculate the number of electrons in one faraday (96,500 coulombs) of electricity. We now know the charge on the electron to be 1.6×10^{-19} coulomb. Therefore the number of electrons in 1 faraday is

$$\frac{96,500}{1.6 \times 10^{-19}} = \frac{9.65 \times 10^4}{1.6 \times 10^{-19}} = 6.023 \times 10^{23}$$

You will note that this is Avogadro's number, the number of atoms in a gram atomic weight of any element (or in a gram molecular weight of any compound or diatomic gas). We see now why it is that 96,500 coulombs of electricity will liberate one gram atomic weight (6×10^{23} atoms) of any monovalent element.

We must not think that Faraday knew all this. He made the experiments and formulated the laws of electrolysis, but he knew nothing of electrons, or the absolute quantity of charge on the ion, or of Avogadro's number. The fundamental concept in Faraday's laws is that the smallest charge that can exist is that associated with monovalent ions. Can we infer, then, that electricity, like chemical elements, consists of unit particles comparable to atoms? Faraday himself came very near making

that inference, but was held back, perhaps by a belief in the indivisibility of atoms.

In 1874, Johnstone Stoney, expressly stated that the charge on a monovalent ion was the smallest charge that could exist. His argument was as follows: A given weight of an element consists of a definite number of atoms; a definite quantity of charge liberates a definite quantity of atoms of that element; therefore, the total charge must be evenly distributed among the atoms. If matter comes in packets which we call atoms, then electricity must also come in packets which Stoney proposed to call electrons. Thus, each negative ion carried 1, 2, or 3 extra electrons, and each positive ion was missing 1, 2, or 3 electrons, the number depending upon the valence. In 1881, Helmholtz clearly stated that Faraday's laws imply the existence of "atoms" of electricity. Yet still another fifteen years was to elapse before the electron was discovered to be a universal constituent of all matter.

SUMMARY

Shortly after the invention of the battery experimenters began to pass electric current through certain kinds of solutions called electrolytes. Sodium, potassium, and chlorine were discovered in this way. Among these many experimenters was Michael Faraday, who appears to have been the first to study the phenomenon quantitatively.

By passing measured amounts of electric charge through various solutions and measuring the amount of metal (whose valence he knew) deposited on the cathode in each case, and the amount of gas (whose valence he knew) liberated at the anode, he was able to determine (1833) the two laws of electrolysis known by his name:

1. When an electric current passes through a solution, the total mass of the particular element deposited (or liberated) is directly proportional to the total charge passing through the solution.

2. The same amount of charge will release different weights of different elements, and these weights are proportional to the atomic weights and inversely proportional to the valence.

If the elements deposited (or liberated) are monovalent, then the amount of charge needed to deposit or liberate one mole at each electrode, is 96,500 coulombs (approximately), a quantity now known as 1 faraday. If it takes one charge to deposit one atom of a metal on the cathode, and if each charge consists of 1.6×10^{-19} coulomb (modern knowledge), then 96,500 coulombs divided by 1.6×10^{-19} (equal to 6×10^{23}) gives the number of charges needed to deposit one mole of the metal. If the metal is monovalent, then the number of atoms in one mole of the metal is also 6×10^{23}. It thus appears that the charge on a monovalent ion is the smallest charge that can exist. This conclusion was not reached by Faraday, perhaps because it suggested that perhaps the atoms were divisible. By 1881 it was clear that Faraday's laws imply a smallest basic unit of electricity of which all other amounts are integral multiples.

EXERCISES

I. TERMS AND CONCEPTS

Electrolysis	Monovalent
Electrode	Equivalent weight
Cathode	Faraday's laws
Anode	Faraday
Ion	

II. PROBLEMS

1. How are the charges transported through a solution during electrolysis? How does this differ from the transportation of charges through a wire?

2. To what electrode are metallic ions transported during electrolysis? Nonmetallic ions?

3. How does an ion at the cathode become a neutral atom? An ion at the anode?

4. On what *one* thing does the weight of a *given* element liberated at an electrode depend?

5. The weight of an element liberated during electrolysis depends on two things. What are they?

6. State Faraday's laws of electrolysis.

7. What purpose does the battery serve in the process? Be explicit, please. Could a source of AC be used instead of DC? Explain.

8. How much charge is 1 faraday?

9. A current of 2 amperes is passed through a molten salt for 80 min.

   a. How many faradays (approximately) passed through?

   b. How many electrons were transferred at the cathode? How many at the anode?

   c. How many atoms of a monovalent metal would be deposited at the cathode? How many of a bivalent element? Of a trivalent element?

   d. If this metal were potassium how many grams of it would be deposited? If it were cupric chloride $(CuCl_2)$?

   e. If the salt was a chloride, how many *atoms* of chlorine would be released at the anode? How many *molecules*?

   f. What would this amount of chlorine weigh? What volume would it occupy at STP?

10. If the salt in problem 9 is a chloride,

would the amount released depend upon the valence of the metal with which it is combined? Explain.

11. How many coulombs are required to liberate 1 mole of iron from $FeCl_2$? From $FeCl_3$?

12. How many molecules of chlorine would be released in the process of liberating 1 mole of iron from $FeCl_2$? What is this number called?

13. How many atoms of iron would be liberated from $FeCl_3$ by $\frac{1}{10}$ coulomb? How many *atoms* of chlorine? Suppose the solu-

tion to be $FeCl_2$. How many atoms of iron and how many atoms of chlorine would be liberated?

14. For compounds of magnesium, copper, aluminum, iron, etc., water solutions can be used to obtain the metals by electrolysis. We cannot obtain metallic sodium and potassium by use of their water solutions, but have to use their compounds in the molten state. Why?

15. State the argument for the existence of "atoms" of electricity (as shown by Faraday's experiments).

Evidence for the Divisibility of the Atom

The new discoveries made in physics in the last few years, and the ideas and potentialities suggested by them, have had an effect upon the workers in that subject akin to that produced in literature by the Renaissance.

—SIR J. J. THOMPSON (*1909*)

It should be apparent at this point that the scientific climate with respect to the atom was slowly changing. For nearly a hundred years Dalton's atomic theory had successfully weathered all attacks upon it. But now one postulate of it, that of the atom's indivisibility, was at last beginning to crumble. Speculations about how atoms could be electrical in nature, and how different atoms could possess different amounts of charge and yet be indivisible, had caused some skepticism. However, it was the phenomena of bright line spectra that caused most of the speculation. The large number of line spectra characteristic of many elements made it exceedingly difficult to believe that they were the result of complex oscillations of whole atoms; it would be much easier to think of various parts of the atoms as oscillating in different ways. But to have parts, the atom had to be divisible. Still, belief in the existence of bodies smaller than the atom came hard. However, in the 1890's there came two discoveries that made the indivisibility of the atom an untenable concept.

PASSAGE OF A CURRENT THROUGH GASES

The first gas discharge tube was invented in 1853 for the purpose of studying the passage of an electric current through gases. It was simply a partially evacuated glass tube with an electrode sealed in each end (Fig. 26-1). The common tubes used in fluorescent lighting or in advertising signs, e.g., neon tubes, are types of discharge tubes. In all of them a high-voltage electric current is passed through a gas under low pressure. The high voltage and low pressure is necessary if a continuous current is desired, for gases are poor conductors. For example, air at ordinary pressures is such a poor conductor that it takes a potential difference of about 30,000 volts to make a spark jump between two charged spheres placed 1 cm apart.

The current in the tube is carried from the cathode to the anode by electrified particles, i.e., by ions or by electrons. A few ions are always present in a gas because of collisions of its molecules with cosmic rays from outer space which knock electrons loose, or because of bombardment by particles derived through natural radioactive processes or even by collisions between the molecules themselves. When diatomic gases ionize they may or may not dissociate. Thus, both atomic ions and molecular ions are formed. That such electrified particles are present in gases can be demonstrated by surrounding a carefully insulated charged electroscope with the gas (or the atmosphere). The electroscope will slowly discharge in every case. If we heat the gas, the rate of discharge increases. We can explain this increase if we assume that the gas has become a better conductor because more ions have been formed. Heating increases the speed of the molecules, hence the energy of collision, which, if great enough, results in electrons being torn loose from the atoms. Of course, ions of opposite sign attract one another, and so recombine to form neutral molecules whenever they collide. However, more are being formed all the time, so that at any given temperature there is an equilibrium between ion formation and ion recombination.

If a high voltage is applied to the electrodes, this equilibrium will be upset by increasing the rate of ion formation. This is in part because some neutral gas atoms come into contact with one or the other of the highly charged electrodes and so lose or gain a charge to become positive or negative ions. As soon as they become charged, they are repelled from the electrode. In part, the rate of ion formation is increased by the accelerations given the ions by the repulsions from one electrode and the attractions towards the other. When ions reach the electrode to which they are attracted, they give up their charge and become neutral gas atoms. Thus, the current is carried as it is in the process of electrolysis.

More effective in increasing the rate of ion formation is the reduction in the number of molecules in the tube by means of a vacuum pump. This reduces the number of collisions, but the reduction in the density of the gas permits the ions to be accelerated over longer distances between collisions. The increased kinetic energy makes the likelihood of an ion being formed during a collision far greater, thus increasing the rate of ion formation despite a reduction in the collision rate.[1]

There is, therefore, a two-way migration of swarms of ions towards their respective electrodes. As the two swarms

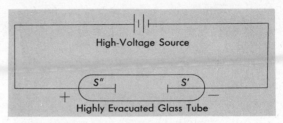

Fig. 26-1. Simple Gas Discharge Tube. The current will not flow unless the tube is highly evacuated because air is a good insulator. In some tubes holes are present in the electrodes, allowing rays to pass into the spaces S' and S''.

stream past and through one another, many ions of opposite charge collide and recombine to form neutral atoms. In doing so they give up their ionization energy, i.e., the energy needed to create them, in the form of light of various colors. The colors depend upon the gas present, red for neon, pale yellow for helium, green or blue-green for mercury vapor, pink for nitrogen, etc.

[1] At 0° C and normal atmospheric pressure the average velocity of air molecules is about $\frac{1}{3}$ mi/sec, and the number of collisions is of the order of 5 billion/sec. The mean free path, i.e., the distance traveled between collisions is of the order of 8.5×10^{-6} cm. When the pressure is reduced to about a millionth of an atmosphere, the number of molecules per cubic centimeter is about 2.68×10^{13} (compared to about 2.7×10^{19} per cm^3 at atmospheric pressure).

That there are two streams of rays [2] moving in opposite directions can be demonstrated by providing electrodes with holes in them (Fig. 26-1). Some of the rays will chance to pass through the holes into the spaces marked S′ and S″, forming luminous beams in these areas. Analysis shows that those which passed through the hole in the cathode into space S′ are positively charged ions of whatever gas the tube contains. They are called positive rays, or canal rays. Those which pass through the anode into space S″ are negative ions.

This two-way migration of ions constitutes the current in the early stages of the evacuation of the tube. The current does not start to flow immediately as the evacuation is started, because not enough ions are present. As the vacuum pump decreases the molecular population, the ions become more effective creators of new ions. When the pressure is reduced below 100 mm of Hg (the amount varies with the gas and the voltage) the flow of the current becomes apparent, first by writhing, twisting streamers of beautifully colored light moving sporadically from one electrode to the other. As the pressure drops further the light soon fills the whole tube with a steady glow. The pressure is now between 2 and 10 mm of Hg, the pressure at which the discharge is most easily maintained. This is the pressure at which neon and other such tubes operate because the conductivity of the gas is highest in this range of pressures. As the pressure drops lower and lower, other changes occur, the most significant of which is the dimming and final disappearance of the light as the pressure approaches a millionth of an atmosphere. This is because the gas has become so rarefied that not enough ions collide and recombine to emit light of sufficient intensity to be observed. We might also suspect that the current has ceased to flow, at least in observable amount, because of the decreased rate of ion formation.

Moreover, after the colored light has begun to dim but before it has gone completely out, a greenish glow appears on the walls of the tube, most intense near the anode. The glow is a fluorescence that comes from the walls of the tube, and is very different from the streamers of colored light that passed down the middle of the tube in the earlier stages of evacuation. As the pressure decreases further, only the greenish glow remains. The assumption that the low value of the current registered on the ammeter is due to the fewness of the ions formed leaves the glow unexplained. Also, calculations show that the ions remaining are too few to carry the current, and further evacuation causes no decrease in the reading. Apparently rays with different characteristics from those of the ions are now carrying the current, some striking the walls of the tube as they do so, and causing them to fluoresce.

That the rays come from the cathode can be proved in a number of ways. The most obvious is by reversing the polarity; doing so causes the most intense part of the greenish glow to shift away from the anode, towards the other end of the tube. If an opaque object, such as a maltese cross, is placed in the tube with a screen between it and the anode, a sharp shadow will be cast on the screen. The sharp shadow indicates that the rays follow straight lines.

[2] A ray is a catch-all term applied to any kind of radiation, be it a stream of particles or a beam of electromagnetic waves. It is particularly useful when the kind of radiation is as yet unidentified. However, the term has a habit of sticking even after identification. Examples are X-rays, gamma rays, etc.

Furthermore, a small paddle wheel mounted in the tube so that it can travel easily from one end of the tube to the other can be given momentum in the direction of the anode by the impact of the rays, but never in the direction of the cathode. If we reverse the polarity, the paddle wheel will travel the other way.

One more piece of evidence that these rays come from the cathode can be demonstrated by using a curved cathode. This brings the rays to a focus, as a lens does with light. A piece of metal foil placed at the focus becomes red hot from the impact of the rays, proving that they have kinetic energy. Nothing happens if only the anode is curved. Pending further identification these rays were called cathode rays. It was unlikely that they were "light" rays, comparable to ultraviolet or infrared radiation, because of their enormously greater energy. They not only cause fluorescence of various substances, travel in straight lines and cast shadows, convey momentum, carry energy that can be converted into heat, are attracted to a positively charged plate and repelled by a negatively charged one, but they also cause X-rays to emerge from any target that they strike. It is thus reasonable to expect them to be particles. At least one or two definite quantitative tests of the properties of the rays was necessary to make it certain that they were particles. The obvious measurements to be made were those of mass and magnitude of charge.

J. J. THOMSON'S DISCOVERY OF THE ELECTRON

Although others had tried to make such tests, it remained for Thomson to perform the crucial series of experiments that proved the rays were universal constituents of all matter, and to determine the ratio of their charge to their mass, a ratio commonly known as e/m (to be read as e over m). To determine the ratio, he had first to calculate the velocity. He did this by employing both electric and magnetic fields of known strength, for a beam of charged particles can be deflected by either electric or magnetic fields. It can be shown that the force acting on a beam of charged particles moving in a magnetic field is given by the following equation:

Force = Magnetic field strength

$\times$ charge $\times$ velocity

Symbolically,

$$F = Hev \qquad \text{(Eq. 26-1)}$$

It can also be shown that the force acting on the same beam in an electric field is given by

Force = Electric field strength $\times$ charge

Symbolically,

$$F = Ee \qquad \text{(Eq. 26-2)}$$

Thomson subjected the beam to both electric and magnetic fields at the same time by passing it between two charged plates and between the poles of an electromagnet (Fig. 26-2). The plates were charged so as to deflect the beam one way and the magnet oriented so as to deflect it the opposite way. By regulating the strength of the two fields the two forces could be made equal so that there was no deflection. Thus,

Magnetic field strength $\times$ charge $\times$ velocity

= Electric field strength $\times$ charge

(Eq. 26-3)

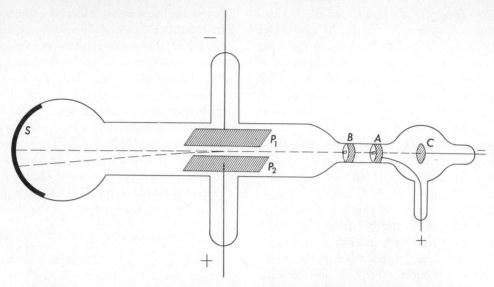

Fig. 26-2. Thomson's Apparatus for His Determination of e/m (somewhat modernized). C, cathode; A, anode with a hole in it; B, plate with a hole in it to provide a narrow beam of cathode rays; P_1 and P_2, plates charged so as to deflect the rays downward; S, a fluorescent screen to make the rays "visible." Not shown is the electromagnet whose field lies at right angles to the plane of the paper, and is oriented so as to deflect the rays upward. If the two deflecting forces are equal, there is no deflection.

Or in symbols,

$$Hev = Ee$$

Since the charge appears on both sides it cancels out. Transposing,

$$v = \frac{E}{H} \qquad \text{(Eq. 26-4)}$$

The electric field strength, E, is determined by placing a voltmeter in the circuit with the charged plates, and the magnetic field, H, by slightly more complex means if an electromagnet is used. From Eq. 26-4, v is determined. For the particular tube he was using, Thomson found the velocity of the rays to be about 10,000 mi/sec.

In the second part of the experiment he used the deflection in a magnetic field only (Fig. 26-3). The rays are deflected at right angles to the direction in which they are moving. If the magnetic field is uniform and large enough, the beam is continuously deflected; the resulting path is a circle. Recall that a change of direction is an acceleration, and that an acceleration at right angles to the motion is a characteristic of uniform circular motion, and it is apparent that the equations for uniform circular motion will apply. These equations are

$$a = \frac{v^2}{r}$$

and, substituting for a in $F = ma$,

$$F = \frac{mv^2}{r}$$

However, Eq. 26-1 is also an equation for the force acting on the beam in a magnetic field. Hence, the two expressions can be equated.

$$\frac{mv^2}{r} = Hev$$

Transposing,

$$\frac{e}{m} = \frac{v}{Hr} \qquad \text{(Eq. 26-5)}$$

The quantities, v, H, and r can be measured, v as already described, H as already indicated, and r by measuring the deflection of the beam in the field. The quantity, v/Hr, comes out to be 176,000,000 (1.76×10^8) coulombs/gm of particles.

This value for e/m means that 1 gm of the particles moving through a wire will furnish 1.76×10^8 coulombs of electricity.[3]

Thomson had to be content with the ratio alone, for he could conceive of no way of measuring e or m. He used many different substances as his cathode, and found that the e/m of the rays was the same regardless of the source. Cathode rays soon came to be known as electrons, the name that Johnstone Stoney had suggested for the charge on a monovalent ion. The "atomicity" of electricity seemed proved.

It is interesting to turn this ratio upside down so that it reads m/e. It is equal to about 0.00055 gm/faraday. This means

[3] This is enough electricity to keep a 100-watt light bulb burning twenty-four hours a day for nearly six years.

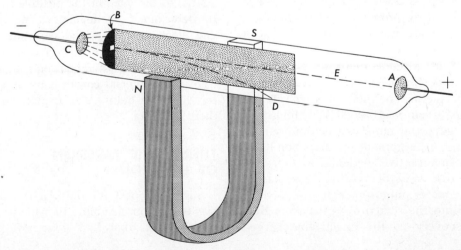

Fig. 26-3. Deflection of Cathode Rays in a Magnetic Field. C, cathode; A, anode; B, plate with hole in it to provide a narrow beam of rays; E, undeflected beam when the magnet is absent; D, deflected beam. Note that the direction of deflection is downward, i.e., at right angles to both the direction of the magnetic field (N to S) and to the direction of motion of the beam of rays.

that if Thomson had continued his experiment until 96,500 coulombs had passed through the circuit, the total weight of the electrons emitted from the cathode would be 0.00055 gm. The corresponding figure for hydrogen is 1.008 gm/faraday. The particles must therefore be far smaller than a hydrogen atom, the smallest of the atoms.

Thomson was very reluctant to advance the idea that atoms are not the indivisible particles envisaged by Dalton, but are complex mechanical systems composed of positively and negatively charged parts. It was only after repeated experiments had convinced him, that he said: "There is no escape from the conclusion that we are here dealing with particles far, far lighter than atoms." At first he had very few converts. Further evidence was needed to remove the last vestiges of doubt.

POSITIVE RAYS: ELECTRONIC EXPLANATION OF IONS

We have referred to ions as charged atoms, atoms that have at least one more or one less charge than neutral atoms. The term charge is a nondescript one. When we say that an atom has lost or gained a charge, we are not really stating what it has lost or gained. The concept of the electron as a constituent of all neutral atoms is much more definitive, even though we can picture neither an atom nor an electron. You may recall that Johnstone Stoney gave the same explanation of ions. However, his argument was based on logic, not on quantitative evidence.

The discovery of positive rays was of vastly greater importance in the investigation into the structure of the atom than the discovery of the negatively charged ions in the cathode ray tube, for the former are not complete atoms, whereas the latter are—with something added. Positive rays, or positive ions, are the so-called canal rays that passed through holes (or canals) in the cathode. They are what is left after one or more electrons have been torn loose from atoms of whatever gas was used in the tube. It took electrical energy to tear them loose. The process may be symbolized, in the case of hydrogen, as follows:

$$H \rightarrow H^+ + e^- \quad \text{or} \quad H_2 \rightarrow H_2^+ + e^-$$

The ions may be either atomic or molecular, as indicated. For helium,

$$He \rightarrow He^+ + e^-$$

or

$$He \rightarrow He^{++} + 2e^-$$

Helium atoms may thus lose one or two electrons.

What happens to the electrons torn from the atoms? Some attach themselves to other atoms of the gas in the tube, forming negative ions. Some find their way to the anode, to which they are attracted, and help carry the current. The ratio of the charge to the mass of the positive rays may be determined by deflections in magnetic and electric fields in the same manner as that used for the determination of e/m. The assumption of Thomson's that electrons are universal constituents of all matter therefore helps us to explain ions and their behavior.

THERMIONIC EMISSION OF ELECTRONS

Strong support for the electron concept also came from its ability to explain another phenomenon that had gone unexplained since its discovery in 1883 by Thomas Edison. Edison was attempting to improve the electric light bulb. The observation, now called Edison effect, was not further investigated by Edison, however, for he could see no way in which it would help him improve his bulb.

We can illustrate the phenomenon best by drilling a small hole in one side of an ordinary light bulb, inserting a plate with a wire leading to the outside, resealing the bulb and re-evacuating it to a pressure of about 10^{-6} atmosphere (Fig. 26-4). The wire leading from the plate is then attached to a galvanometer, which in turn is connected to a power source, say to the positive terminal of the battery that supplies the current to the bulb. If the circuit is now closed, the bulb lights up, but the galvanometer shows no immediate deflection. Then, suddenly it does, showing that a current has begun to flow even though the plate is connected to nothing inside the bulb; the current must be flowing across the gap between the plate and the filament of the bulb.

How is this current carried across this highly evacuated space? It cannot be by ions of gas in the bulb, for we have seen from our cathode ray experiment that there are insufficient ions to carry the current at the very low pressure of the gas inside the bulb. Moreover, if we connect the plate to the negative terminal of the battery, no current flows. Thus, the current is unidirectional. If we now decrease the amount of current flowing to the bulb filament so that the filament is no longer heated to incandescence, no current is detected by the galvanometer even when the plate is connected to the positive terminal. Conversely, the hotter the filament, the

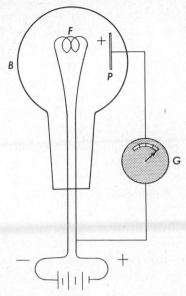

Fig. 26-4. Edison Effect: Thermionic Emission of Electrons. *P* is a metal plate inserted in an ordinary electric light bulb, *B*. The plate is connected to the positive side of the circuit that lights the bulb via the galvanometer, *G*. The plate is therefore positively charged. Note that this circuit is apparently not complete, for there is no visible connection between *P* and *F*. Yet a current flows as soon as *F* gets hot. Electrons ejected from *F* by the heat are attracted to *P*, completing the circuit. Ejection of electrons from a hot metal is called thermionic emission. Compare with the photoelectric effect.

greater the current flowing across the gap [4] up to a point called the saturation point. (Compare with evaporation of a liquid, and see p. 371n.)

---

[4] If tungsten with ½ per cent of thorium oxide dissolved in it is used as the filament and we increase its temperature from 1000° K to 2500° K,

If we use the electron concept, we have a ready explanation. Electrons are ejected from the hot filament, and the hotter the filament, the greater the number ejected. The process is similar to the evaporation of a liquid. It is also reminiscent of the photoelectric effect. Since the escaping electrons carry a negative charge, they are attracted to the plate if it is positively charged, but are repelled from it if it is negatively charged. Thus, the charged plate acts as a valve which allows electrons to move only in one direction. Implied in our explanation is that an electric current, at least in most cases, consists of a stream of electrons flowing through a conductor. Thus, we chalk up another success for the electron theory.

We can also deduce the reason for the emission of electrons from a hot metal and at the same time explain the difference between conductors and insulators, and, in part at least, the difference between a metal and a nonmetal. Conductors are substances that allow electrons to move through them readily, while insulators do not. Metals must therefore hold at least a few of their electrons rather loosely, whereas nonmetals hold all of theirs rather tightly. Heating a metal increases the energy of the electrons. If heated sufficiently, these loosely held electrons may gain enough kinetic energy to escape from the metal surface, just as molecules do from an evaporating liquid. We now see why the current continues to flow in a cathode

ray tube at a very low pressure (but only if the cathode is kept hot).

The electron theory also explains why the current flows in the photoelectric effect, i.e., when light of sufficient frequency shines on certain metals. Photons striking a negatively charged plate eject electrons from it. The electrons move towards the positively charged plate because they are attracted to it, and in so moving constitute the current.[5]

Thus, we find that the electron theory explains and coordinates a wide variety of phenomena, and opens up a possible explanation of spectra. For if atoms are divisible, if they have various parts, the kinds of oscillations that take place become vastly increased, and so the large numbers of spectral lines emitted by some atoms can more easily be accounted for. Soon even the most skeptical were convinced of the reality of electrons.

MILLIKAN'S OIL DROP EXPERIMENT

In the years following Thomson's discovery of the electron, attempts were made, first by Thomson and then by others, to measure the charges carried by very small amounts of matter. The object was to measure the charge on the electron, for if the charges on enough samples were determined, perhaps one sample would be found that carried a single charge. One difficulty was that of being able to recognize such a sample; perhaps some other sample would carry a smaller charge.

---

the current flowing across the gap is increased a billionfold.

The cathode in Thomson's experiment was cold, so he had to rely on a very high voltage to eject electrons from it. Today a hot cathode is used as a convenient source of electrons in radio and television broadcasting and receiving sets, in radar, in electron microscopes, in X-ray tubes, etc.

[5] We have now discussed three ways in which electrons can be ejected from a metal. One is to put a high voltage on the plate in a cathode ray tube, a second is by photoelectric emission, and a third by thermionic emission. There are other ways.

The principles involved are really quite simple. The mass of any body can be determined by a measurement of the force acting on it when it is accelerated (for $F = ma$). Similarly the charge on a body can be measured by the force it experiences in an electric field. It is neither practical nor necessary to measure the force on a single electron. However, the total number of electrons on a body must be small enough so that a change of one electron makes a noticeable difference. Since the force on the charged body is most likely to be very small, the body itself must be very light. The fact that the force of gravity must be reckoned with also demands that the body be very light if the very small electric force is not to be masked by a relatively large gravitational force. Optimum conditions will exist if the electric and gravitational forces are nearly the same order of magnitude.

For the body to carry the charges an American physicist, Robert A. Millikan, used oil drops from the mist sprayed from a small atomizer of the type used for perfume. These spherical drops were so small that they could be observed only in a beam of light and by the use of a microscope. A drop that small falls slowly through the air because of countless collisions with air molecules. However, the velocity of such spherical drops can be determined by the application of Stokes' Law, the derivation of which will not concern us here. Suffice it to say that such drops accelerate only briefly after they start to fall, and then attain a velocity that is constant from then on. This constant velocity, called the terminal velocity, is far easier to determine than an acceleration, and it is a measure of the forces acting on the body.

Millikan brought the measurements of the charges on the drops to a high degree of precision and was able to present convincing evidence that he had determined the charge on the electron. His method was ingenious. He started with two parallel metal plates connected to a source of direct current whose voltage he could carefully control. Thus, he could vary the charge on the plates at will. The upper plate had a tiny hole drilled in it so that if oil were sprayed in the region directly above the plates, an occasional drop would drift downward through the hole into the space between the plates. This region was strongly illuminated so that Millikan, by means of a small telescope, could see the droplet as it wafted downward, slowly because of air friction. The droplet would probably be charged by friction as it was sprayed from the nozzle of the atomizer, and so be attracted by one charged plate and repelled by the other. The whole apparatus was enclosed to protect the droplets from air currents. Once a droplet came into view, Millikan could close the hole to prevent any others from coming through. He would then put a small charge on the plates, a charge that was opposite to that which was on the drop. If this plate were given a charge exactly large enough to counteract the gravitational attraction, the droplet would remain stationary or move with constant velocity between the two plates. Millikan was able to watch one drop continuously for eighteen hours.

In such a situation the upward electrical force, Eq, would equal the downward gravitational force, mg. Hence,

$$Eq = mg \quad \text{and} \quad q = \frac{mg}{E} \quad \text{(Eq. 26-6)}$$

E, the strength of the electric field, is determined from the voltmeter reading, g is the acceleration due to gravity, m the mass of the drop, and q the charge on the drop. He could determine m from Stokes' Law, which relates the terminal velocity of a spherical drop falling through air to the mass of the drop, the density of the material composing the drop, and the viscosity of the air. Since the last two quantities are known and the terminal velocity can be measured directly as it slowly falls between the plates, the mass is easily calculated. This leaves q as the only unknown, and so it is easily found. Because electrons have a unique charge, the quantity q (for the electron) is now denoted by e.

Millikan not only measured the charge on scores of droplets, but he also varied the experiment in many ways. One way was to ionize the air between the plates by means of X-rays or other radiation. The droplets would pick up one or more of the ions, thus acquiring a new charge. This would upset the balance between the electric and the gravitational fields, and a new equilibrium would have to be made by changing the value of the charge on the plates. The difference between the original charge and the new one gave the charge on the ion, or ions, acquired by the drop. He also varied the experiment by using oils of different viscosities, by using atomizers that gave smaller or larger drops, by using different gases in his enclosed apparatus, and in various other ways.

Millikan made thousands of such measurements. When he tabulated and analyzed his results, he found that all his charge measurements were whole-number multiples of a certain number, which *might* or *might not* be the constant minimum charge on the electron. Some representative examples are listed in Table 26-1.

TABLE 26-1

CHARGES (IN COULOMBS) ON OIL DROPS [MILLIKAN]

1. 3.2×10^{-19}	6. 8.0×10^{-19}
2. 9.6×10^{-19}	7. 20.8×10^{-19}
3. 6.4×10^{-19}	8. 11.2×10^{-19}
4. 14.4×10^{-19}	9. 17.6×10^{-19}
5. 19.2×10^{-19}	10. 12.8×10^{-19}

Obviously, the charge on the electron cannot be the smallest of the values in the table, for 3.2 is not evenly divisible into all the other values. It must therefore be smaller than 3.2×10^{-19}. Numbers greater than 0.01 that are evenly divisible into 3.2 are 1.6, 0.8, 0.4, 0.2, and 0.1. We can eliminate the last four by noting that the values in the table (assumed to be representative) do not include values that are not also evenly divisible by 1.6. For example, if the value is 0.8 why are there not values such as 4.0×10^{-19}, 5.6×10^{-19}, 2.4×10^{-19}, etc., values divisible by 0.8 but not by 1.6? *Thus, the charge on the electron is 1.6×10^{-19} coulombs.* Millikan obtained even multiples of this unit, some up to nearly 200 times it. Many measurements have been made by many experimenters since Millikan first announced his results in 1910. The accepted modern value for the charge on an electron is $(1.601864 \pm 0.000025) \times 10^{-19}$ coulomb.

Once e was known, the mass of the electron could be calculated from Thomson's e/m ratio:

$$\frac{e}{m} = 1.76 \times 10^8 \text{ coulombs/gm}$$

Transposing,

$$m = \frac{e}{1.76 \times 10^8} = \frac{1.6 \times 10^{-19}}{1.76 \times 10^8} =$$

$$9.1 \times 10^{-28} \text{ gm} \qquad \text{(Eq. 26-7)}$$

The more accurate value is $(9.1084 \pm 0.0004) \times 10^{-28}$ g. It takes nearly 2000 electrons to equal the mass of a single hydrogen atom, the lightest of all the atoms.

Confirmation of the size of the charge on the electron was made by measurements of the amount of charge carried by monovalent ions in liquid solutions. The basic constant, Avogadro's number, could now be computed by using the above value of e. Dividing the faraday by e, we get

$$\frac{96,500 \text{ coulombs}}{1.6 \times 10^{-19} \text{ coulomb}} = 6.023 \times 10^{23}$$

(Eq. 26-8)

Avogadro's number has been verified in a number of quite different ways. Thus, the "atomicity" or particle concept of electricity rests on a sound basis.

CHARGE ON POSITIVE RAYS

As previously stated, positive, or canal rays had been discovered about ten years before the discovery of the electron. Thomson, among others, had attempted to measure the ratio of their charge, q, to the mass, m. This ratio turned out to be far less, using the same units, than for electrons, and it varied with the gas used in the cathode ray tube. The method was the same as that used for measuring e/m, i.e., by deflecting a beam of the rays in a magnetic field. They were deflected far less than were the electrons in fields of the same strength. If we assume that the ions carried a charge equal and opposite to that on the electron, the much smaller deflection is obviously due to a much greater mass. The smallest ratio was obtained when the gas used was hydrogen. The mass of the hydrogen ion turned out to be 1836.13 ± 0.01 times the mass of the elec-

tron. Once e was determined, the actual mass of the hydrogen atom could be calculated; it is 1.67×10^{-24} gm. This value closely agrees with that obtained by dividing the atomic weight of hydrogen by Avogadro's number:

$$\frac{1.008}{6.023 \times 10^{23}} = 1.65 \times 10^{-24} \text{ gm}$$

(Eq. 26-9)

When helium was used as the gas in the cathode ray tube and the positive ions were deflected in a magnetic field, it was found that some ions were deflected more than others. Thus, two beams of helium ions were formed. The m/e ratio of one beam was 4 gm/faraday, four times greater than that for hydrogen. This beam therefore consisted of helium atoms carrying a single positive charge. Since chemical evidence indicates that a helium atom has four times the mass of a hydrogen atom, it follows that the charge on these particular helium ions is the same as that on a hydrogen ion. The m/e ratio for the second beam is only half that for the first one. These helium ions must therefore carry two positive charges.

The same methods may be used with all gases, and comparisons with the charge and mass of hydrogen made. All elements, under proper conditions, give positive rays. We infer, then, that all atoms contain positive electricity, which comes in units that are even multiples of the charge on the hydrogen ion. This charge, in turn, is quantitatively equal to that on the electron but of opposite sign.

RADIOACTIVITY

Even if Thomson's discovery of the electron had not been made until much later, revision of the atomic theory would have been necessary because of a very different sort of discovery. In 1896 Henri Becquerel of France was working with fluorescent minerals to see if they emitted X-rays (which had been discovered only a few months previously). He had been exposing well-wrapped photographic plates to certain fluorescent minerals in full sunlight. Because of a cloudy spell of weather, he placed his minerals and a new set of unexposed well-wrapped plates in a drawer. Some days later he returned to his experiments, and, being a careful experimenter, he did not want to use plates that had been in the vicinity of his fluorescent minerals for several days. However, he decided to develop these plates without further exposing them. He found them fogged.

Before drawing any conclusions he placed a new well-wrapped plate in the drawer with the same minerals. On developing it he found it was also fogged. He began testing the minerals to find out which was emitting some kind of radiation that was capable of passing through opaque materials. It turned out to be a uranium mineral called pitchblende, whose composition is U_2O_8. Since oxygen is known not to emit such radiation, the emitter of the rays was probably uranium. The use of pure uranium not only proved it but also showed that it was more effective gram for gram in fogging plates than was the oxide. Other minerals were tested and all those containing either uranium or thorium were found to produce the same effect. Becquerel failed to understand the meaning of the observations at the time, even though he was working on the problem of the highly penetrating X-rays.

There were two fundamental differences, however, between this radiation and that of X-rays. One was that the radiation flowed steadily from the uranium while resting on the table or in a dark drawer with no external source to excite its atoms, and the other, not immediately known, of course, was that nothing that man could do would stop it, slow it down, or speed it up. The rate at which it *spontaneously* emitted this radiation was found to be proportional to the amount of uranium present, and it mattered not whether this uranium was in the elemental state or chemically combined with other atoms.

Becquerel turned the problem over to Marie Curie who was one of his student assistants. She and her husband, Pierre, ultimately found that the radiation emitted from pure uranium oxide was less intense than that emitted from its ore. Marie rightly concluded that there must be some other substance (or substances) in the pitchblende that was more powerfully radioactive [6] than uranium. She and her husband began the long and arduous labor of extracting the element (or elements) responsible. Carloads of pitchblende were processed, for the percentage of the unknown material was extremely small. Years of labor, false leads, misinterpretations and discouragements followed, but eventually they isolated two new elements, radium and polonium, both highly radioactive. Far more important than the isolation of two new elements was the discovery that certain atoms, chiefly those of high atomic weight, break down spontaneously into other kinds of atoms by the emission of the radiation that fogged Becquerel's photographic plates.

[6] The term applied to elements, minerals or other compounds, capable of emitting a radiation that will darken a well-wrapped photographic plate.

The same problem arose with these rays as with cathode rays: were they particles or waves? The question was settled in the same way, by passing them through magnetic and electric fields (Fig. 26-5). The radiation was found to consist of three distinct types, called, for want of more descriptive terms, alpha, beta, and gamma rays. The alpha rays were found to carry a double positive charge but were only slightly deflected in a magnetic field, suggesting that their charge was small in comparison with their masses. Comparisons with the e/m ratios of hydrogen and helium ions suggested that they were helium ions. However, positive evidence was needed.

The radiations were allowed to stream from a radioactive mineral into a small evacuated tube for months on end. Eventually spectroscopic analysis revealed that helium ions were inside the tube. Alpha particles were indeed helium ions—helium atoms that have lost two electrons, and so carry a double positive charge.

Although alpha particles are emitted from the cores of these heavy atoms with a speed of about 1.5×10^9 cm/sec, their range is only a few centimeters in air, and sheets of metal 0.01 cm thick stop them completely. They produce intense ionization in the air through which they move. The man who did most of the work on this problem was Ernest Rutherford, later Lord Rutherford, probably the greatest of the investigators into the structure of the atom.

The beta rays were found to carry a single negative charge, to undergo the same direction of deflection in magnetic fields as do electrons in a cathode ray tube, and to have the same e/m. However, they had more energy, i.e., they had a higher velocity. They are far less effective in ionizing

a gas than the alpha particles, but they penetrate much farther through metals than do alpha particles, and are obviously much

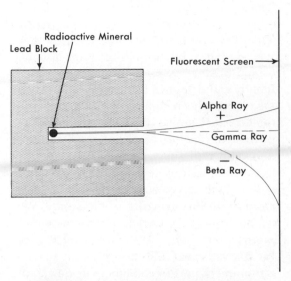

Fig. 26-5. Analysis of Rays Emitted from Radioactive Mineral. The lead block absorbs all rays except those traveling directly towards the screen. The rays pass through an electric field on their way from the block to the screen, with the deflections shown. A magnetic field is then substituted for the electric field. Alpha and beta rays are proved to be particles, charged as shown. Gamma rays are either waves or uncharged particles. Further analysis proves them to be waves.

smaller. Their velocity of ejection from radioactive minerals is extremely high, approaching that of the velocity of light. Since beta rays have all of the properties of electrons, they must be electrons.

Gamma rays proved not to be particles. They pass through glass as easily as does light, even through several centimeters of lead, a substance that is extremely effective in stopping all kinds of radiation. Gamma rays carry no charge and so are not deflected in electric and magnetic fields. They are indifferent ionizers of gases. Their velocity is that of light. In time they were found to be an invisible form of light, a kind of super X-ray with a shorter wavelength and a higher frequency. No waves have ever been found with higher frequencies. Gamma ray photons therefore possess the highest energies of all electromagnetic radiations.

Where does this energy come from? The answer will have to await further investigation into the structure of the atom. We cannot logically complete our discussion of radioactivity here. We introduced it here for two reasons. The first is that it played a prominent part in changing the viewpoint concerning the indivisibility of the atom, for there could be no doubt that these three types of rays were disintegration products of certain heavy elements. The second is that the discovery of radioactivity gave scientists a tool for further investigation into the structure of the atom. Before the nature of the alpha particle had been worked out, Thomson had discovered the electron. It was not long before scientists were "firing" electrons at other atoms to see if other parts could be knocked loose from them. They failed because the electron was too light and too small. It penetrated matter but that was all. The alpha particle weighed about 7500 times as much as the electron, and so was therefore far more effective as an atomic "bullet." It turned out to be the first really effective disrupter of other atoms.

RUTHERFORD'S NUCLEAR THEORY OF THE ATOM

That an atom had so definite a structure that scientists could confidently refer to different parts of it had now become certain. Electrons with their negative charges had been proved to be universal constituents of all matter, the existence of positive rays carrying positive electricity had been demonstrated, and alpha particles had been proved to be ejected from certain kinds of heavy atoms. Attention naturally turned to what the rest of the atom consisted of and to the number and arrangement of the electrons.

Various theories about the latter were advanced, none of them based on crucial experiments of any kind, so we will not review them here, except to state that one of them assumed the electrons to be scattered through the atom like seeds in a watermelon. One of the problems was the vastly greater amount of matter associated with the positive rays compared to that associated with the electrons. The belief was general, however, that all atoms contained positively charged hydrogen ions which were called protons (meaning primary). This concept was first advanced by William Prout, a British chemist, about 1817. He made the suggestion that hydrogen was the primordial substance out of which all other atoms were made. His evidence was that atomic weights, as then known, of many elements were almost even multiples of the hydrogen atom. The idea was abandoned as more careful atomic weight determinations showed that many were not even multiples. We will see later how right Prout was, although in a way that would have astounded him.

The alpha particle owed its effectiveness in causing ionization not only to its mass but also to the fact that it was ejected from radioactive atoms with velocities of about 10,000 mi/sec, and so had an enormous kinetic energy. As previously stated, it could knock electrons loose from gas atoms. At the time no way was known to see what actually happened to the alpha particles as they traveled through the gas. However, fired at a screen coated with zinc sulphide to make it fluoresce, their individual effect can be seen easily if a low-power microscope is used in a completely darkened room, for each produces a tiny flash of light on hitting the screen. By varying the distance of the screen from the source of the particles, their range could be determined. The rather amazing discovery was soon made that if a very thin metal foil was placed between the source and the screen, most of the particles passed through the foil as if it were not there. All were stopped completely, however, by slightly thicker foils. Most particles pass straight through thinner foils without loss of kinetic energy, some are slowed down, and some are deflected by varying amounts.

Rutherford decided to use a gold foil in his experiments, for it is the most malleable substance known, and can be hammered out without tearing into sheets so thin that a pile of about 250,000 sheets is only an inch thick. Nevertheless, each sheet is still several thousands of atoms thick. For his source of alpha particles, he used a speck of radium. By use of the apparatus shown in Fig. 26-6a he was able to obtain a thin pencil of particles. At first these were allowed to impinge directly on the screen. All of the hits were within a small circle whose diameter was approximately that of the beam.

The gold foil was then placed directly in the path of the beam. Most of the alpha particles went through without deviation, producing flashes on the screen. Many, however, were deflected by small amounts, so that the spot on the screen that included most of the "hits" had a diameter somewhat greater than that which was made by the thin pencil of alpha particles when the gold foil was absent. Some flashes were, however, observed on the screen far out from this central spot. Thus, on passing through the gold foil the particles are scattered somewhat (Fig. 26-6b), so this experiment is sometimes referred to as Rutherford's scattering of alpha particles experiment. Since some particles were very surprisingly deflected to the edge of the screen, and possibly beyond, the screens were moved in a circle about the gold foil in an effort to determine the maximum angle of scattering. A few were found to be deflected 180°, i.e., they seemed to have hit something head-on so that they bounced right back in the direction whence they came.

Rutherford could not interpret these results by any watermelon or plum-pudding model of the atom. Three inferences could be made from the observations. The first was that most of the atom appeared to be empty space, because most of the alpha particles went straight through the foil undeflected. The second was that those particles that had been deflected through angles that ranged from small to relatively large, had approached close enough to a concentration of positive charges to be turned away from it. The third was that a very few seemed to strike this concentration head-on.

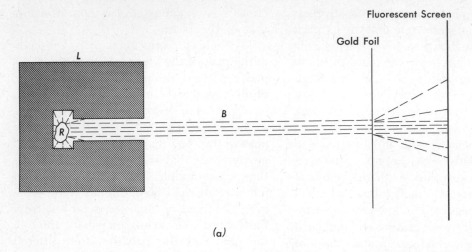

(a)

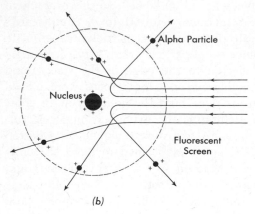

(b)

Fig. 26-6. Rutherford's Gold Foil Experiment. **(a)** The apparatus is much like that shown in Fig. 26-5 except for the presence of the gold foil. The beam, *B*, consists of alpha particles radioactively ejected from *R*. Note how some are deflected from a straight-line path after passing through the foil, whereas the great majority go straight through. In the actual experiment the screen could be moved completely around the foil. **(b)** The alpha particles are scattered by the repulsive forces of the similarly charged nucleus. Those that approach closest to the nucleus are deflected the most, some almost reversing their paths.

These inferences meant that the positive charges could not be scattered throughout the whole volume of the atom, for if they were, the maximum angle of deflection would be only a few degrees. The reason is that if the positive charges were scattered throughout the atom, no one alpha particle would "feel" the repulsive effect of more than a few positive charges. Striking these few head-on could not cause the alpha particle to rebound any more than a baseball striking a tennis ball in midair would cause the baseball to rebound.

Therefore Rutherford proposed a new model, a model that swept away the last vestiges of the classic solid-sphere model of the atom that had endured since Dalton.

He assumed that the whole of the massive positively charged part of the atom was concentrated in a very small region of the atom, which he termed the nucleus. The nucleus was assumed to be surrounded by a swarm of electrons, each carrying a negative charge. The total number of the electrons equaled the number of positive charges on the nucleus.

From this model Rutherford could calculate that no direct hits or head-on collisions were actually made, for the alpha particle and the nucleus carry charges of the same sign and would repel each other. We *now* know that gold has 79 of these charges, the alpha particle only 2. Therefore a particle headed for a direct hit with a nucleus would be slowed down to a stop by the repulsive force before it reached the nucleus, and would then be accelerated directly back along the same path. Others whose paths would carry them to the edge of a nucleus would be deflected through smaller angles ranging from less than 180° down to near 0°. Since most particles were not deflected at all, the distances between the nuclei must be very large, relatively. The mass of an electron was considered much too small to cause any deflection of the alpha particles.

Using foils made of atoms with fewer charges on the nucleus, e.g., aluminum, it was found that the average angle of scattering was smaller than that for gold. This is acceptable according to the theory, for the smaller the total charge, the smaller is the repulsive force on the particle and the smaller any deflection. The theory seemed to be standing up under repeated tests given it.

By the use of rigorous mathematics, the laws of motion, and Coulomb's Law of force between charged bodies, Rutherford could also make certain estimates concerning the total positive charge on the nuclei of various kinds of atoms. This was done by comparing the scattering in different materials by alpha particles emitted from the same source. The same source was necessary to insure the same average kinetic energy for the alpha particles. At first these estimates were crude, but they did indicate that the total of charges on the nucleus was about equal to half the atomic weight. His first estimate for gold was about 100, the actual number being 79.

Rutherford was also able to estimate the number of charges from other factors, e.g., the thickness of the foil, the actual percentage of particles that were deflected through various angles, etc. His results showed the diameter of the nucleus to be about 1/10,000 the diameter of the atom, and the volume of the nucleus to be about one-millionth of a millionth the volume of the atom. The diameter of the atom is of the order of 2×10^{-8} cm and that of the nucleus is of the order of 10^{-13} cm.

There remained the problem of the distribution of the electrons about the nucleus. Rutherford adopted the suggestion of a Japanese physicist that the electrons revolved about the nucleus, forming a miniature planetary system. The revolving was necessary to explain why the electrons did not "fall" into the nucleus, just as the earth would fall into the sun if it stopped revolving.

Several problems immediately arose. How could a large number of the positive charges be held together in so small a nucleus against their repulsive forces? How can solid bodies be rigid in the presence of these forces? Another had to do with revolution of the electrons about the nucleus. An electron is a charge and it is being accelerated as it revolves about the nucleus. (Recall that a change in direction is an acceleration just as much as a change in speed is.) According to Maxwell's electromagnetic theory, an accelerated charge should radiate "light," losing energy as it does so. As it loses energy, it should move closer to the nucleus, gradually spiraling down into the nucleus. It is obvious that under average conditions the electron does none of these things. Despite these difficulties the nuclear theory was soon widely accepted, for the interpretations of Rutherford could not be disputed. The problems would have to await some other explanation.

SUMMARY

The invention of the gas discharge tube in the early 1850's started a new line of investigation into the conductivity of electricity through matter, this time through gases. At normal pressure, gases are good insulators but at low pressure and reasonably high voltages, they become good conductors. Experiments show that in any normal gas there are a few electrified particles (ions) present. The more ions, positive and negative, the better the conductance. Ions are created in gases by collisions with one another, collisions which result in charges being torn loose from some atoms (making positive ions), which attach themselves to other atoms (making negative ions). Reducing the population of atoms in the tube by reducing the pressure allows more forceful collisions and so increases the rate of ion formation as long as the distances traversed between collisions are not so greatly increased as to reduce the collision rate too drastically.

When the collision rate is drastically reduced, however, cathode rays appear in the tube. The identity of the rays was long in question, even though it was known that they were particles rather than waves. Eventually J. J. Thomson showed that these rays were emitted from the cathode regardless of its composition. That the rays were the same from all cathodes was shown by their having the same properties. In particular, they had the same ratio of charge to mass. This ratio,

e/m, turned out to be 1.76×10^8 coulombs/gm. The method used included deflecting them (since they were charged particles) in electric and magnetic fields. The name, electron, was a word coined about twenty-five years earlier by Johnstone Stoney for the then assumed smallest particles of electricity. Thus, the atom was proved to be divisible by proving that electrons could be separated from the remainder of the atom.

Other support came for the concept of electrons as universal constituents of all matter by their emission from hot cathodes (thermionic emission). Also, the electron theory explained ions, positive and negative, and why the current flows in the photoelectric effect. Millikan succeeded in measuring the charge in the electron in the early 1900's by measuring charges on oil drops. The method consisted of balancing two forces, the electrical force of repulsion of a negatively charged plate for the negative charges on an oil drop, and the gravitational force acting on an oil drop. The charge turned out to be 1.6×10^{-19} coulomb. Knowing this, the mass of the electron could be calculated from e/m. So could the number of electrons in 1 faraday, thus giving us Avogadro's number. It was not long before the magnitude of the charge on positive rays was also determined, and from their e/m ratios, the masses of these ions was determined. Thus, the masses of hydrogen, helium, and other gaseous ions were calculated.

Further evidence for the divisibility of the atom came about the same time when Becquerel of France and his students, Marie Curie and her husband, Pierre, investigated radioactivity. Three products emitted by the atoms were tentatively called alpha, beta, and gamma rays. Ernest Rutherford proved that the alpha rays were helium ions emitted during this spontaneous disintegration (decay) of the radioactive atoms, and that they were doubly charged. Beta rays were found to be electrons of high energy, and the gamma rays were an electromagnetic radiation of extremely short wavelength.

Alpha particles ejected with great energy from radioactive atoms soon came to be used as "bullets" in an attempt to break up the atom into smaller parts. Rutherford and his students used them to bombard a gold foil, and from their results, Rutherford formulated his nuclear theory of the atom, a theory that postulated the great mass of the atom was concentrated in a very small space, i.e., it occupied only a very small part of the atom. The distances between adjacent nuclei were relatively great compared to the diameters of the nuclei. The electrons formed a miniature planetary system about each nucleus.

EXERCISES

I. Terms and Concepts

Gas discharge tube	Radioactivity
Cathode rays	alpha rays
e/m and m/e	beta rays
Positive rays	gamma rays
Thermionic emission	Alpha particles
	Rutherford's nuclear theory
Millikan's oil drop experiment	
1.76×10^8 coulombs/gm	
1.6×10^{-19} coulombs	
9.1×10^{-28} gm	

II. Problems

1. Why is a high voltage necessary to pass an electric current through gases? Note: To carry an electric current there must be something to carry it.

2. Why does a reduction of the pressure in a gas discharge tube result in a better conductance of a current?

3. What is meant by a ray of radiation?

How could you distinguish an electromagnetic ray from a particle ray? Would this method apply to all kinds of particles? Explain.

4. What did J. J. Thomson do with respect to cathode rays that previous investigators had not done?

5. What general principles did Thomson use in determining e/m? (The important thing here is not to describe in detail how he did it but to know the general principles involved.)

6. Why did the concept of the divisibility of the atom have such difficulty in becoming established?

7. From the value of e/m and the value of e, compute the value of m.

8. What general principles were used by Millikan in determining the value of e?

9. This problem is only for those having difficulty in understanding how Millikan arrived at a value of 1.6×10^{-19} coulomb from the date in Table 1.

Suppose oranges all weighed the same. You are given bags of oranges weighing 16 oz., 32 oz., 64 oz., 40 oz., 96 oz., 24 oz. Guess the weight of a single orange and state how many oranges are in each bag. Suppose now that you were given another bag of oranges of the same size but which weighed 20 oz. How would this affect your previous guess about the weight of a single orange?

10. How much does 6×10^{23} electrons weigh? 6×10^{23} atoms of hydrogen? What is the ratio of the weight of an electron to that of an atom of hydrogen (approximately)?

11. What are positive rays? Canal rays?

12. What is meant by thermionic emission of electrons? Why does the current not flow if the negative plate is connected to the terminal of the battery?

13. What practical uses are made of thermionic emission?

14. Why does a radio or television set not work instantly when you turn it on?

15. A rectifier is a tube in "plug-in" types of radio and television sets (as opposed to

battery-operated sets). It changes AC to DC. Explain how it does this.

16. How would the m/e ratio of singly charged helium ions compare with that of doubly charged helium ions?

17. What is radioactivity?

18. Name three naturally radioactive minerals.

19. What were the three types of rays emitted by various radioactive minerals? How could one tell whether they were waves or particles? How could one tell the sign of the charge on those that were charged particles?

20. Suppose one of the rays emitted were composed of uncharged particles. How would this complicate the identification process? Explain.

21. What is the simplest and most effective proof that beta particles are electrons?

22. Would alpha particles be deflected more or less than beta particles in magnetic fields? Why?

23. What use was made of alpha particles in the investigations of atomic structure?

24. Describe the principles involved in Rutherford's experiment which led to the nuclear theory of the atom.

25. Suppose that you had a box 10 ft square and 1 ft thick, standing on edge. You do not know what it contains. You fire bullets at it from a rifle, uniformly distributing your shots over one side of the box. You find that most of the bullets go straight through the box. A few are deflected, some slightly, some at appreciable angles, and once in a while one comes back right at you. What conclusions can you draw about the contents of the box?

26. Why did the electrons have no appreciable effect on the direction of the alpha particles?

27. An alpha particle headed *directly* for the center of a gold atom in the gold foil never actually crashed into the center of the atom. Why not?

28. Why did Rutherford postulate electrons circling about the nucleus like a miniature planetary system?

29. How did this planetary concept conflict with Maxwell's electromagnetic theory of light?

30. The diameter of a nucleus is only about 1/10,000 that of the atom. The volume of a sphere varies as the cube of the diameter. What is the volume of the nucleus compared to the volume of the atom?

CHAPTER XXVII

The Bohr Theory
of the Hydrogen
Atom

In order to reach the truth, it is necessary, once in one's life, to put everything in doubt—so far as is possible.—RENÉ DESCARTES

By 1910, it was clear that the fundamental constituents of the physical world are particulate in nature. Dalton had postulated that any mass is composed of discrete atoms or combinations of atoms that form discrete molecules. Avogadro had given him an assist in the case of the elemental diatomic gases. By 1860, atomicity of matter was beyond dispute, and it had been established that heat was intimately associated with the motions of these atoms and molecules. The particulate nature of electricity had been suspected from the time of Faraday's work on electrolysis in the 1830's, but the final proof had to await the experiments of Thomson and Millikan. Most difficult to accept was the particulate nature of light.[1]

[1] To avoid confusion here we need to define the word particulate. Webster defines it as "Existing as minute separate particles." This does not help

While light comes in individual packets of energy called photons, and is therefore particulate in nature, we must not allow ourselves to picture the photon as being a material body as an electron is. A photon may transfer its energy to an electron—as in the photoelectric effect—but when it does so, it ceases to exist. This means that it has no rest mass.[2] That energy could be transferred only in discrete packets seemed to contradict all previous ideas concerning the transfer of energy. Mechanical devices seem to convert their energy *continuously* from potential energy to kinetic energy, or from kinetic energy back to potential energy, as a swinging pendulum does. Thus, the quantum aspect of radiant energy, first advanced in 1900 by Planck in his quantum theory and extended in 1905 by Einstein in his photon theory, made little headway until Bohr used it in 1912 to formulate his theory of the hydrogen atom.

It should be realized that Rutherford's nuclear theory of the atom made no headway in explaining the old puzzle of bright line spectra, and, as has been stated before, no theory of the structure of the atom could be at all complete unless it could account for this. Rutherford's nuclear the-

much, for we need to know what a particle is in the scientific sense. *Scientists use it to mean the opposite of continuous.* If matter, or electricity, or light, is continuous, there can be no smallest amount that can exist. The electromagnetic wave, e.g., is continuous, according to Maxwell. To speak of the "particle" nature of light without defining particle (as many authors do) is misleading; and to speak of the photon theory as a corpuscular theory is to use the term corpuscle in a sense never intended by Newton.

[2] That the equivalent mass of a photon is sometimes given does not change matters any. Einstein's theory of relativity postulates the equivalence of mass and energy. This does not mean that a definite quantity of mass is associated with every definite quantity of energy.

ory, therefore, applied only to the nucleus. The concept of electrons revolving about the nucleus like a miniature planetary system was included only because atoms possessed electrons and there was no possible way of arranging negatively charged electrons in a *stationary* pattern about a positively charged nucleus, any more than one could conceive of stationary planets arranged about the sun. A theory that included normally stationary electrons could conceivably solve the problem of bright line spectra, for, as energy was absorbed by the valence electrons, they could vibrate and radiate the energy absorbed.[3]

With normally stationary electrons impossible, the problem of bright line spectra was still unexplained, and a new problem had arisen, namely, how could an electron revolving about a nucleus fail to radiate electromagnetic energy if Maxwell's theory of electromagnetic radiation were to hold? However, the Rutherford theory was a very necessary step forward, for the structure of the nucleus certainly would be a factor in determining the nature of the arrangement of the electrons.

The puzzle was soon resolved by Niels Bohr, a young Danish physicist, just out of graduate school, who came to England to work first with J. J. Thomson and then with Rutherford in 1911. Bohr was thoroughly familiar with Planck's quantum theory and Einstein's photon theory, theories widely publicized on the Continent, but which had gained little attention in

England,[4] probably for the reasons given on p. 368. Bohr accepted the main assumptions of Rutherford's nuclear theory and thought that he might be able to explain line spectra by combining Planck's quantum theory with it. Thus, he "married" Planck's theory to Rutherford's theory and came up, in 1913, with his theory of the hydrogen atom as the offspring. The reader is asked to keep in mind that the following discussion applies only to the hydrogen atom. Bohr chose it because it is the simplest of all atoms, containing a single charge on the nucleus and a single electron. It is easiest to test any hypothesis, theory, or postulate, by applying it to the simplest known case.

BOHR THEORY

Bohr first made a startling change in atomic theories of the time by postulating that *an electron revolving about the nucleus could do so only in certain specified orbits,* orbits that are at specified distances from the nucleus. These orbits are commonly referred to as permitted or stable orbits, because in them the electron can revolve without radiating. In these permitted orbits the electron has angular momentum. Linear momentum is defined as the product of a body's mass and its velocity at a particular instant. The concept is necessary to explain what keeps a body moving after the force that started it moving is removed, e.g., a baseball after it

---

[3] Such a theory was advanced by J. J. Thomson, the discoverer of the electron, but was abandoned when Rutherford advanced his nuclear theory. The discovery of the nucleus doomed Thomson's theory, a theory in which the electrons and the positive charges were "mixed."

[4] Eddington in 1936 wrote: "Let us go back to 1912. At that time quantum theory was a German invention which had scarcely penetrated to England at all. There were rumours that Jeans had gone to a conference on the Continent and had been converted; Lindemann, I believe, was an expert on it; I cannot think of anyone else."

leaves the pitcher's hand. A body moving uniformly in a circle possesses angular momentum, mvr. The additional quantity, r, is necessary and reasonable, as we can see if we remember that two points on our revolving wheel, one nearer the center than the other (hence having different radii), have different speeds, even though each revolves through equal angles in equal time intervals.

Thus, any electron circling a nucleus has a certain fixed quantity of angular momentum. Now the startling thing about Bohr's postulate is that this quantity of angular momentum is given by the equation

$$mvr = n\left(\frac{h}{2\pi}\right) \qquad \text{(Eq. 27-1)}$$

where n is an integer, 1, 2, 3, etc., and h is Planck's constant. This postulates that the angular momentum of revolving electrons is quantized, i.e., it comes in particulate units whose value is equal to $h/2\pi$. Orbiting electrons may have 1 unit, 2 units, 3 units, etc., but never 1.2, 1.3, 1.4, etc. units of angular momentum. Suppose we transpose 2π in the above equation to the left side. We then have:

$$mv \cdot 2\pi r = nh$$

We may then state the postulate in the following terms: The electrons can travel only in orbits for which the linear momentum multiplied by the circumference, $2\pi r$, is equal to a whole number multiplied by Planck's constant. This is analogous to stating that a person can walk in a circle 10 yd, 11 yd, 12 yd, etc., in radius, but that he can never walk in one with a radius of 12.6 yd, etc. Bohr placed no restriction on the number of permitted orbits; n might be any number.

Bohr evaded the conflict with Maxwell's theory simply by stating that Maxwell's theory did not apply to systems of atomic size. Thus, he could postulate that the electron could revolve in any one of the permitted orbits indefinitely without radiating energy. This may seem to be a purely arbitrary assumption—and it is. Bohr made no apologies for it. He simply presented it on a take it or leave it basis. Adherence to Maxwellian electrodynamics had long led only to wrong answers insofar as line spectra were concerned, so why not abandon them? After all, Einstein had abandoned the Maxwellian theory for Planck's quantum theory in his explanation of the photoelectric effect. Moreover, the assumption is obviously in accord with the facts; electrons do not continuously radiate as they revolve. If they did, the electrons would lose all their energy and fall back into the nucleus within 1/100,000,000 sec—and the atom would cease to exist as such. But atoms do exist permanently; conventional electrodynamics must therefore be wrong, at least for atomic systems.

One can test the adequacy of Bohr's first postulate, $mvr = n(h/2\pi)$ by applying it to the hydrogen atom in its normal, non-radiating state. Since the hydrogen atom consists of a single electron revolving about a nucleus, the radius of the electron's orbit is obviously also the radius of the non-radiating hydrogen atom. We know that its radius, calculated by entirely different methods, is about 0.5×10^{-8} cm. Let us see what we get by solving for r in the above equation. Transposing, we have

$$r = \frac{nh}{2\pi mv} \qquad \text{(Eq. 27-2)}$$

There are two unknowns in the above equation, r and v. We shall have to get rid of one of them by getting a value for v.

According to Newton's second law, $F = ma$. For motion in a circle $a = v^2/r$. Substituting,

$$F = \frac{mv^2}{r} \ (cgs \ \text{units}) \quad \text{(Eq. 27-3)}$$

But the net force acting at any instant on the revolving electron is also given by Coulomb's Law of Electrostatic Attraction.

$$F = \frac{Ke \cdot e}{r^2} \quad \text{(Eq. 27-4)}$$

where e, the charge on the electron (a known quantity) is equal to e, the charge on the nucleus, and K is a proportionality constant. Since things equal to the same thing are equal to each other,

$$\frac{mv^2}{r} = \frac{Ke \cdot e}{r^2} = \frac{Ke^2}{r^2} \quad \text{(Eq. 27-5)}$$

Solving for v^2, we have

$$v^2 = \frac{Ke^2}{rm}$$

Now if we square Eq. 27-2 and substitute this value of v^2 in it, we get

$$r = \frac{n^2h^2}{4\pi^2mKe^2} \quad \text{(Eq. 27-6)}$$

Now h, π, m, K, and e are all fixed quantities, i.e., they are all constants and n is an integer 1, 2, 3, etc. When n equals 1, r has the smallest possible value, which is the value of the radius of the lone electron in the nonradiating hydrogen atom. Substituting these known values in Eq. 27-6 we have

$$r = 0.53 \times 10^{-8} \ \text{cm} \quad \text{(Eq. 27-7)}$$

which is almost exactly the value calculated for the radius of the hydrogen atom by very different methods. It looks as if Bohr was on the right track.

It should be noted that in Eq. 27-6, n is squared; therefore, the radii of the permitted orbits are in the ratio of 1^2, 2^2, 3^2, 4^2, etc., i.e., the radii of the permitted orbits increase as the squares of the value of n.

Next, Bohr postulated that *in the normal, unexcited, nonradiating atom, the electron revolves in that permitted orbit that is closest to the nucleus,* i.e., in an orbit in which n is equal to 1. This orbit is sometimes referred to as the *ground state*, the state in which the energy of the electron is the smallest possible. All electrons in this state (in hydrogen atoms) have the same energy. It follows that an electron having greater energy than that in the ground state must shift to an outer permitted orbit, one with a value greater than 1, and to do so it must absorb energy. The greater the amount of energy absorbed, the more distant the orbit occupied by the electron after the shift. Thus, electrons in outer orbits have more energy than electrons in inner orbits. This shift to outer orbits takes place during a period of excitation which may be accomplished in one of several ways, as follows:

If the hydrogen is heated sufficiently to give the molecules high kinetic energy, the electron may be knocked into an outer orbit by collision with another molecule or atom. If the hydrogen is in an electric discharge tube, e.g., a cathode ray tube, a free electron which has been accelerated may hit it. If the atoms of the gas are illuminated by high-energy rays (ultraviolet, X-rays, gamma rays), they may absorb energy from photons. The electrons retain this absorbed energy as long as they remain in the excited state.

It also follows that to radiate a photon an electron must shift in the reverse direction, i.e., from an outer orbit to an inner one, and in doing so must radiate the same amount of energy as it absorbed in making the original shift (the Law of Conservation of Energy rules here inside the atom as well as outside). The amount of energy radiated is the difference in the energies of the electrons in the two orbits. The radiated energy is in the form of a single photon of light, light of a single frequency, wavelength, color. All electrons making the same shift emit light of the same color. When we see light in the hydrogen discharge tube, we are "seeing" the electrons go from higher energy states into lower energy states. The color of the light seen is a composite of all the different wavelengths emitted. If the great majority of electrons are making the transition between the same two energy levels, the light we see is essentially monochromatic. When an alpha particle strikes a fluorescent screen, it boosts electrons in some of the atoms of the fluorescent paint into higher orbits. The flash of light we see is caused by the electrons returning to lower energy orbits.

As demanded by the quantum and photon theories, the frequency of the light emitted is determined by the size of the "packet" of energy emitted. You will recall that Einstein, in explaining the photoelectric effect by means of his photon theory, stated that electrons were not ejected from metals by light shining on them, no matter how intense the light, if the frequency was too low; an electron cannot absorb just any quantity of light energy, but must absorb it in whole units (photons) whose energies are proportional to

the frequency, and hence are not all the same size. If the frequency is too low, no energy at all is absorbed. Similarly, when electrons that are revolving about atomic nuclei radiate energy (by transition from an outer to an inner orbit), they do so in units that are proportional to the frequency, i.e.,

$$E_2 - E_1 \propto f$$

where E_2 is the energy in the outer orbit (before radiation) and E_1 is that in the inner orbit (after radiation). If we use a proportionality constant, h,

$$E_2 - E_1 = hf \qquad \text{(Eq. 27-8)}$$

gives the frequency of the light emitted. You will recognize h as Planck's constant. The energy is radiated therefore in one fell swoop, and not continuously as the electron makes the shift from an outer to an inner orbit. If this is so, then the electron cannot spiral into an inner orbit from an outer one, but must make the change by a jump that takes place in zero time. Here again we have a departure from classical mechanics, for how can anything move through a finite distance in no time at all? Bohr says that the classical laws were not designed to explain intra-atomic behavior, and we should simply accept the idea that the electron emits a photon whose frequency is given by Eq. 27-8 during a transition between two energy levels in a manner that cannot be pictured.[5] He says that this,

---

[5] The term jump is commonly used to indicate that the shift from one orbit to another is instantaneous, but it is almost certain to give us a picture of the transition, a picture that Bohr himself says cannot ever be realized. The word "transition" is more nondescript and so probably is a better term. It will be used henceforth, but not exclusively.

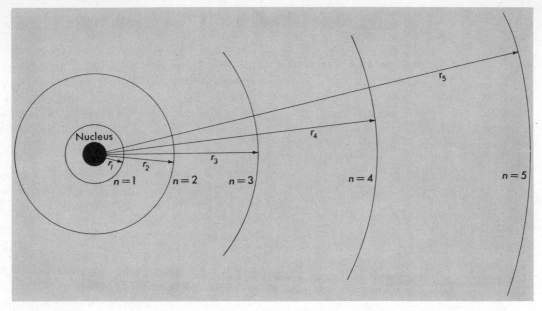

Fig. 27-1. First Five Permitted (Stable) Orbits of Electron in Bohr Hydrogen Atom. The circles represent the orbits (not drawn to scale). The radii r_1, r_2, etc., are in the ratios of 1, 4, 9, 16, and 25, i.e., the radii are proportional to the squares of the values of n.

Assumption . . . appears to be necessary to account for the experimental facts. . . . [Also] We stand here almost entirely on virgin ground, and upon introducing new assumptions we need only take care not to get into contradiction with experiment. Time will have to show to what extent this can be avoided but the safest way is, of course, to make as few assumptions as possible.

To summarize, Bohr's postulates may be stated as follows:

1. An electron can revolve about a hydrogen nucleus only in certain permitted or stable orbits, orbits in which the angular momentum of the electron is equal to n times a fundamental unit, $h/2\pi$ (Fig. 27-1). Symbolically,

$$mvr = \frac{nh}{2\pi}$$

2. A revolving electron in any of these stable orbits does not radiate energy.

3. When an electron absorbs energy from the outside, it makes a transition to a new stable orbit with greater energy, and on returning to the previous orbit, the energy difference is given up as a photon in accordance with the equation $E_2 - E_1 = hf$.

4. In all other ways the electron obeys the classical laws of mechanics and electrodynamics.

BRIGHT LINE SPECTRA

What, we may ask, has this to do with bright line spectra? Suppose, for example, that hydrogen atoms in a gas discharge tube are excited by passing a high-voltage electric current through the tube that we described in Fig. 26-1. What concerns us here are the collisions of hydrogen atoms and ions in which great numbers of atoms absorb energy as their electrons are knocked into outer orbits. Sooner or later they will return to orbits of lower energy, emitting photons as they do so. The light emitted from all atoms in which electrons are making the same jump will be exactly the same color. Commonly, certain transitions (jumps) are more probable than others, and so a larger number of atoms are emitting photons of a particular wavelength and frequency than any other. The Bohr theory tells us nothing about these probabilities or the resulting intensities of the light. In the case of hydrogen, the transition from the $n = 3$ orbit to the $n = 2$ orbit (Fig. 27-2) is more probable than any other, and since the wavelengths of the photons emitted during the transition are those of red light, the hydrogen in our gas discharge tube is reddish. It is not a "pure" red, because some electrons are making different jumps, and so are emitting other colors, principally green, blue, violet,[6] thus adulterating the color.

The spectroscope, however, separates these colors according to their frequencies, and since the light before separation is admitted through a narrow slit, we see the bright line spectrum of hydrogen consisting of a red, a green, a blue, and a violet line, the total width being that of the slit, and the intensities being governed by the numbers of photons making the same transitions per unit time. The spectrum is a line spectrum because only a limited number (four in the case of hydrogen) of fre-

quencies in the visible range are admitted in sufficient numbers to be visible. Dark gaps[7] separate the lines, the widths of the gaps depending upon what frequencies are *not* emitted.

TESTS OF THE BOHR THEORY

We have been assuming that the Bohr theory correctly explains how the hydrogen spectrum is produced, but we have given no evidence for it. True, the calculation of the radius of the first orbit and its comparison with the radius of the hydrogen atom as determined by other means was encouraging, but little more. If Bohr's third postulate, $E_2 - E_1 = hf$, is correct, then it should be possible to derive mathematically the frequencies, hence the wavelengths, of the four principal lines of hydrogen. Since these are already known, not only by measurements, but by calculation from the empirical Balmer formula, the test should be decisive, for we should now have a logical basis for Balmer's formula.

The first problem is to calculate the total energy of the electron as it revolves in a stable orbit,[8] say the orbit in which $n = 2$. Its energy is in part kinetic, because of its motion, and in part potential, due to its

[6] These colors, with the red, provide the four principal lines of the hydrogen spectrum.

[7] In continuous spectra, all frequencies are emitted, so there are no gaps. Each color forms a band that grades into the next. Thus, red forms a band which is deepest to the left (Plate I) and grades into orange to the right. Red is therefore due not to a single frequency, but to a group of frequencies. If not all frequencies of the red group are present, the spectroscope will separate them into a series of red lines of somewhat differing shades.

[8] The values of n designate the stable or permitted orbits, outward from the nucleus. For no very good reason, they are called quantum numbers.

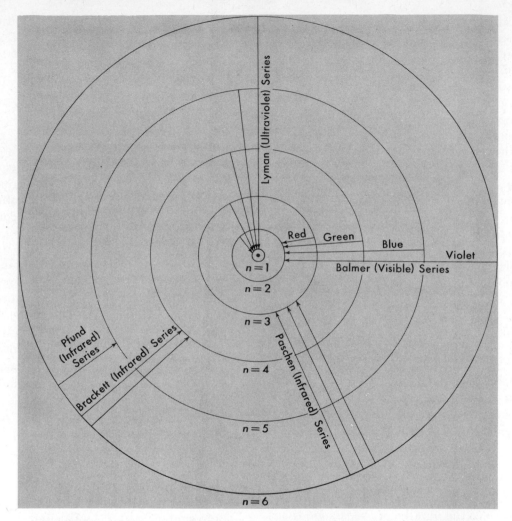

Fig. 27-2. Series of Spectral Lines Due to Transitions between Stable Bohr Orbits in Hydrogen Atom. Orbits not drawn to scale; radius of $n = 2$ orbit is 4 times that of $n = 1$ (Fig. 27-1). Each series belongs to a different final energy level. Thus, the final energy level of the Lyman series is the $n = 1$ orbit, that of the Balmer series is the $n = 2$ orbit, etc. The transition from the $n = 6$ to the $n = 1$ orbit involves a greater energy release than one from the $n = 6$ to $n = 2$, or to $n = 3$ orbit, etc. Therefore, the photons released by transitions to the $n = 1$ orbit are the most energetic; they are in the ultraviolet range. The same holds for the Balmer Series with respect to the Paschen, Brackett, and Pfund series. This can be more easily understood from Fig. 27-3.

position with respect to the positively charged nucleus. We start with Newton's second law, modified for uniform circular motion, $F = mv^2/r$, because it gives a centripetal force necessary to produce an acceleration [9] in a body. This force is an electrostatic force acting on the electron to hold it in its orbit. This force is given by Coulomb's Law in Eq. 27-4. We use the proportionality constant K because we do not wish to express E in the units of the cgs system (electrostatic units) but in coulombs. K takes care of this difference in units. Commonly another constant, Z, is used to indicate the number of positive charges on the nucleus. Z for the hydrogen atom is 1, so it may be omitted. It is omitted here in order to simplify equations that are already complex. Now from Eq. 27-5, we have

$$\frac{mv^2}{r} = \frac{Ke^2}{r^2}$$

We now multiply both sides by r, getting

$$mv^2 = \frac{Ke^2}{r}$$

Next we divide each side by 2,

$$\tfrac{1}{2}mv^2 = \frac{Ke^2}{2r} \qquad \text{(Eq. 27-9)}$$

and find that we now have the kinetic energy of the electron.

The calculation of potential energy is not so easy. It is equal to

$$\frac{-Ke^2}{r} \qquad \text{(Eq. 27-10)}$$

[9] Remember that a change of direction is just as much an acceleration as a change in speed.

where the minus sign is a consequence of the point chosen as our level of reference from which we measure the potential energy. As a matter of convenience, we choose for our reference a point infinitely far from the nucleus where the electrostatic attraction between the nucleus and the electron is zero. If the force between the electron and the nucleus were one of repulsion so that work would have to be done to move the electron in, the potential energy would be positive. Since it is one of attraction, the potential energy is negative.

As we move the electron towards the nucleus, say to the orbit in which $n = 2$, this electrostatic force will increase. Conversely, as we move it away, say to the orbit in which $n = 3$, the force will decrease. However, the work that this electron in orbit $n = 3$ can do by making a transition to the ground state where $n = 1$ is greater than what it can do in moving from the orbit $n = 2$ to the ground state. Since the work that can be done by a body due to its position is a measure of the potential energy of that body, it might seem that the potential energy is simply equal to force times distance, i.e., Fd. The flaw in this reasoning is that the force is not constant throughout the distance, d, but is continuously changing, varying inversely as the square of the distance from the nucleus. The problem is easily solved by use of the calculus, which, in effect, simply divides the distance between the two orbits into a large number of very small segments, segments so small that the force does not change appreciably when the electron moves from one end of the segment to the other, and then computes an average force for all the segments. By this method, as briefly stated

$$\text{P.E.} = -\frac{Ke^2}{r}$$

We started out to calculate the total energy, E, which is the sum of kinetic and the potential energy. Thus,[10]

$$\frac{Ke^2}{2r} - \frac{Ke^2}{r} = -\frac{Ke^2}{2r} \qquad \text{(Eq. 27-11)}$$

We have already found the value of r in Eq. 27-6. Thus,

$$r = \frac{n^2h^2}{4\pi^2mKe^2} = n^2\left(\frac{h}{4\pi^2mKe^2}\right) \qquad \text{(Eq. 27-12)}$$

is the radius of any permitted orbit. Before we go any further we will list the actual values of the above quantities.

n = an integer, 1, 2, 3, 4, etc.

h = Planck's constant, 6.63×10^{-27} erg-sec

π = 3.1416

m = the mass of the electron, 9.1×10^{-28} gm

e = the charge on one electron, 1.6×10^{-19} coulomb

K = the conversion factor from coulombs to electrostatic units, 9×10^{-18}

Z = the charge on the nucleus, equal to 1 for the hydrogen nucleus, and so neglected as long as we deal with the hydrogen atom.

Our next step in obtaining the wavelengths of the principal lines of the hydrogen spectrum is to calculate the difference in energy between two energy levels, i.e., between two of the permitted orbits.

[10] If this bothers you, ponder the following:

$$\tfrac{1}{2} - \tfrac{1}{4} = \tfrac{1}{4} \quad \text{and} \quad \tfrac{1}{4} - \tfrac{1}{2} = -\tfrac{1}{4}$$

$$E_2 - E_1 = hf \text{ or } f = \frac{E_2 - E_1}{h} \qquad \text{(Eq. 27-13)}$$

First we put the value of r obtained in Eq. 27-12 in the total energy equation, 27-11; we get for the energy in an orbit n,

$$\begin{aligned}
E_n &= -\frac{Ke^2}{2r} = -\frac{Ke^2}{2}\left(\frac{1}{\frac{n^2h^2}{4\pi^2mKe^2}}\right) \\
&= -\frac{Ke^2}{2}\left(\frac{4\pi^2mKe^2}{n^2h^2}\right) \\
&= -\frac{2\pi^2mK^2e^4}{h^2}\left(\frac{1}{n^2}\right)
\end{aligned}$$

$$\text{(Eq. 27-14)}$$

Remembering that what we are after, at the moment, is the difference in energy between two orbits, $n = 1$ and $n = 2$, let the quantum number n_2 represent a higher energy state than n_1. We then calculate the value of E_2 just as we did E_n in Eq. 27-14. Then we substitute these values of E_1 and E_2 in Eq. 27-13. The final result [11] is

$$f = \frac{2\pi^2mK^2e^4}{h^3}\left(\frac{1}{n_1^2} - \frac{1}{n_2^2}\right) \qquad \text{(Eq. 27-15)}$$

The negative value for the total energy, E_2 or E_1, arises from the fact that the potential energy is greater than the kinetic and has a negative value because of the level of reference we chose. We remind you that an object on the floor has negative potential energy with respect to the top of a table standing on the floor, or with respect to the ceiling.

Eq. 27-15 will give us the frequency of

[11] If you have trouble seeing why the parenthetical quantity is turned around, pay particular attention to the minus signs in the values for E_2 and E_1, and in Eq. 27-13.

the light emitted when the electron makes a transition from the $n = 3$ orbit to the $n = 2$ orbit if we let $n_2 = 3$ and $n_1 = 2$. Now what we really want is the formula for the wavelength of this light, so that we can compare it with the Balmer formula which we know will give us the wavelength. We know that the frequency and the wavelength are calculated by the formula

$$c = \lambda f$$

where c is the velocity of light, 3×10^{10} cm/sec. Transposing, we get $\lambda = c/f$, or, since eventually we will want the reciprocal of this equation,

$$\frac{1}{\lambda} = \frac{f}{c}$$

Dividing both sides of Eq. 27-15 by c and simplifying, we have

$$\frac{1}{\lambda} = \frac{2\pi^2 mK^2 e^4}{ch^3}\left(\frac{1}{n_1{}^2} - \frac{1}{n_2{}^2}\right) \quad \text{(Eq. 27-16)}$$

In the factor $2\pi^2 mK^2 e^4/ch^3$ all quantities are known. Putting in the values and solving, this factor turns out to be 109,678. Equation 27-16 then becomes

$$\frac{1}{\lambda} = 109,678\left(\frac{1}{n_1{}^2} - \frac{1}{n_2{}^2}\right) \quad \text{(Eq. 27-17)}$$

Now, if we set $n_1 = 2$ and $n_2 = 3$, we get [12]

$$\frac{1}{\lambda} = 109,678\left(\tfrac{1}{4} - \tfrac{1}{9}\right) \text{ cm}^{-1} \quad \text{(Eq. 27-18)}$$

Solving for λ, Eq. 27-18, gives 6.561×10^{-5} cm, or 6561 angstrom units (abbreviated A). The experimental value for this line (the red line) of hydrogen is 6562.7 A.

[12] The superscript -1 is read, "reciprocal of." This occurs because $1/\lambda$ is the reciprocal of λ.

We have here a truly remarkable agreement between theory and experiment, for the probability that all of the constants used in Eq. 27-16 with their large powers of 10 should combine to give the correct answers by mere chance is very close to zero. The agreement for the other principal lines of the hydrogen spectrum is equally good. They are obtained by substituting other integers (4, 5, and 6 for n_2). The value of n_1 is fixed for any one series of lines, thus, when $n_1 = 2$ the wavelength of the lines obtained are all in the Balmer series (Fig. 27-2). When $n_1 = 1, 3, 4,$ and 5, the lines obtained are in the Lyman, the Paschen, Brackett and Pfund series, respectively. Furthermore, if we compare Eq. 27-17 with the original Balmer equation on p. 364, we see that they are of the same general form. The difference in the two formulas is that Balmer's will give the wavelengths of only the principal lines of hydrogen, whereas the Bohr formula is equally good for lines outside the visible range of the spectrum, i.e., for the Lyman series in the ultraviolet, and Paschen, Brackett, and Pfund series in the infrared (p. 366n).

We should again emphasize the difference in the methods used by Balmer and Bohr. There was little mathematical logic in Balmer's method. Essentially it was one of trial and error with no theory behind it at all. The Balmer constant was obtained by working backward from the known values for the wavelengths. Balmer had no explanation whatever for the spectral lines. On the other hand, Bohr first formulated the theory that explained how atoms emitted light and why the spectral lines were spaced as they were, and by the use of mathematical reasoning, he then gave a logical basis for the Balmer formula.

True enough, Bohr also did some working backward from known answers obtained from experimental work, but that is commonly the way scientists work in formulating theories. Since a theory is essentially designed to explain a set of facts, and facts are obtained either through experiment or observation, this is not surprising. Perhaps we need, at this point, to summarize the initial successes of the Bohr theory. We can do this best by quoting Holton.[13]

Thus we have come to the initial successes of Bohr's model. It predicts the size of the unexcited atom, and the prediction is of the correct order of magnitude. It yields an expression for the wavelengths of all lines that are to be expected from radiating hydrogen atoms, and this expression coincides exactly with one that summarizes the experimental facts of line emission. It accounts for Rydberg's empirical constant in terms of physical quantities. It provides us with a visualizable (although therefore perhaps dangerous) system, and establishes physical order among the events accompanied by emission, whether the particular lines are well-known, or as yet beyond the region of the experimentation. The model introduces quantum theory into the atom and thereby gives on the one hand a physical basis for Planck's induction that the energy in the atom is quantized, and on the other hand removes the problem of the stability of electron orbits from the classical theory which could not provide the solution.

Bohr's theory also dealt successfully with energy levels, ionization potential, and the number of emission lines, all of which are discussed in the next section. It also successfully explained absorption spectra (p. 362).

[13] Gerald Holton, *Introduction to Concepts and Theories of Physical Science*, Addison Wesley, Cambridge, 1952, p. 596.

We have previously pointed out that the Bohr theory was originally designed to apply to the hydrogen atom. It accounted both qualitatively and quantitatively for the hydrogen spectrum, and was almost equally good for the helium *ion* carrying a single electron (as does hydrogen). It could not account for the spectrum of the helium atom with its two electrons, nor for spectra of other atoms with larger numbers of electrons. This means that Bohr's final equation (27-17) could not be used to calculate the wavelengths of their spectral lines.

We might hazard a guess that the reason for this is that in the hydrogen atom the single electron moves in the constant electrical field of a nucleus carrying only one positive charge, whereas in an atom with more than one electron and more than one charge on the nucleus, each finds itself in a rapidly fluctuating electric and magnetic field caused by the motions of the other electrons. Therefore, it is not likely that the radii of their orbits could be calculated by the single equation: $(mv^2/r) = (Ke^2/r^2)$. As a result, the energies of the electrons would not be the same as they would be if they were not under the influence of other electrons and of greater charges on the nucleus. Despite these failures, the Bohr theory stands out as one of the greatest conceptions the human mind has ever devised, for it opened the way for the elucidation of the structures of these more complex atoms. We will shortly show how the theory was altered to account for their spectra.

ENERGY LEVELS

Both the Bohr theory and Planck's quantum theory may be clarified to some degree by expressing some of their fundamental ideas in terms of the concept of energy levels. Moreover, the concept is a necessary one if we are to understand and interpret the periodic table in terms of the electronic configuration of the atom.

The energy levels of electrons are simply the energies of these electrons in any of the stable orbits. Making the transition from an inner orbit to an outer orbit, the electron must absorb at least one photon of energy; hence, the electrons in outer orbits have a greater total energy than those in inner orbits. The total energy is always an integral number of photons, or quanta. This was essentially the great discovery of Planck, that a vibrating emitter (what we now know to be an electron) of electromagnetic energy does not send out just any part of its total energy, no matter how small, but instead sends it out in whole number multiples of fundamental units, hf. This enables us to construct definite and distinct energy level diagrams (Fig. 27-3) showing discrete levels, which would be impossible if the emitters absorbed or emitted energy continuously as mechanically induced waves do.

Spacing of Energy Levels

You will note that the various energy levels (Fig. 27-3) are unevenly spaced, becoming closer together rapidly as we advance to the higher levels. This is in direct contrast to the radii of the orbits, which increase as the square of n, and so become farther and farther apart outward from the nucleus (Fig. 27-1). A moment's reflection should show why this is so. The energy in an electron is largely potential, which may be seen by comparing Eqs. 27-9 and 27-10. This potential energy is increased as we do work in lifting the electron to a higher energy level, work against the attractive force of the nucleus. But this attractive force is reduced as the electron is shifted farther and farther from the nucleus in accord with Coulomb's Law, so

Fig. 27-3. Energy Levels in Transitions between Stable Bohr Orbits. The ionization potential is the potential difference, expressed in electron volts, that must be applied under specified conditions to strip an electron from an atom. For hydrogen it is −13.6 ev if the electron is in the $n = 1$ orbit, −3.40 ev if it is in the $n = 2$ orbit, −1.51 ev if in the $n = 3$ orbit, etc. The minus sign is the result of our choice of a reference level for the energy of the electron in an orbit, energy that is largely potential. Note the relatively great difference between the energy in the $n = 1$ and the $n = 2$ orbits. In all transitions to the $n = 1$ orbit, the energy released is high; a photon in the ultraviolet range is emitted. Compare with Fig. 27-2.

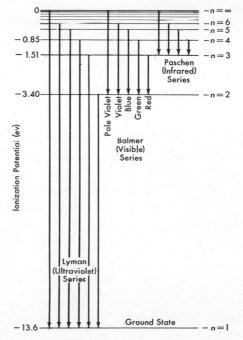

that the work necessary to shift it farther becomes less and less. Thus, the *increase* in energy becomes less and less and the difference in energy levels in the diagram are shown closer together.

The energy of an electron in a particular orbit may be calculated from Eq. 27-14 and is most conveniently expressed in terms of electron volts. An electron volt is an energy unit which is defined as the amount of energy equal to the change in energy of 1 electron when it moves through a potential difference of 1 volt. Since it is an energy unit, it may be converted to other energy units, such as the calorie, the dyne-centimeter (erg), kilowatt-hour, etc. Its abbreviation is ev. It is an exceedingly small unit of energy, equal to 3.80×10^{-20} calorie, or to 1.6×10^{-12} erg. However, the mass of the electron is only 9.1×10^{-28} gm, and so relatively the electron volt is a large quantity of energy.[14]

The minimum energy level is that of the ground state ($n = 1$), the state of the electron in the normal unexcited atom. If sufficient energy is absorbed by an electron in the ground state, it will leave the atom entirely, thus transforming the atom into an ion. For the electron in a hydrogen atom, this minimum energy required is 13.6 ev. *This is called the ionization potential of hydrogen.* Another way of saying this is that the ionization potential of the lone electron of hydrogen atom is the energy needed to lift it from the ground state to infinity, where infinity is defined as a distance so far away that the force of attraction is no longer sufficient to hold the elec-

tron in orbit;[15] the electron is completely free to move about, completely independent of the nucleus. Such a free electron can now absorb or emit energy in any quantity, i.e., it no longer absorbs or emits energy in units called photons (as it must when in the $n = 1$, $n = 2$, $n = 3$, etc. orbits).

In each of these orbits specified by an integral value of n, the electron has a specified amount of energy that it can emit in units of hf.[16] The amount of energy that the electron has in each of these orbits may be referred to as an energy level. This amount increases as the value of n increases, but the rate of increase becomes less and less with each shift to a higher value of n. This follows from Coulomb's Law; the force of attraction to be overcome varies inversely as the square of the distance. Thus, the energy levels in Fig. 27-3 are shown closer and closer together. When the difference between two successive energy levels becomes zero, the electron is at infinity, and the minimum energy it then has is equal to the ionization energy, 13.6 ev. This zero difference in energy levels marks the boundary line between the free state and the state in which the electron is *bound* to the hydrogen nucleus.

The energy we have been talking about is energy of position with respect to the nucleus. It is, therefore, potential energy, so we must select a level of reference from which to measure it. Most commonly a value of zero is given to the energy level represented by the ionization state. That

---

[14] It would take about 2.5×10^9 calories to boost 1 gm of electrons from the $n = 1$ to the $n = 2$ level. This is enough heat to raise the temperature of about 27 tons of water from the freezing point to the boiling point.

[15] Infinity for the electron of hydrogen is of the order of 10^{-5} cm.

[16] Except, of course, when it is in the ground state, where it has energy but which it is incapable of emitting.

of the ground state then becomes -13.6 ev. This simply means that the energy in the ground state is 13.6 ev lower than the ionization energy. From Eq. 27-14, we see that

$$E_n = \frac{-2\pi^2 m K^2 e^4}{h^2}\left(\frac{1}{n^2}\right)$$

Now the measured value of E_n for the hydrogen electron in the ground state is 13.6 ev. The factor $2\pi^2 m K^2 e^4/h^2$, must therefore be equal to 13.6 ev. Therefore,

$$E_n = \frac{E_I}{n^2}$$

where E_n is the energy for any value of n, and E_I is the ionization energy. With due regard to our level of reference, the energy in any orbit is given by:

$$E_n = \frac{-13.6 \text{ ev}}{n^2}$$

If $n = 1$,

$$E_1 = \frac{-13.6 \text{ ev}}{1^2} = -13.6 \text{ ev}$$

If $n = 2$,

$$E_2 = \frac{-13.6 \text{ ev}}{2^2} = -3.4 \text{ ev}$$

If $n = 3$,

$$E_3 = \frac{-13.6}{3^2} = -1.51 \text{ ev}$$

If $n = \infty$,

$$E_\infty = \frac{-13.6}{\infty^2} = 0 \text{ ev}$$

These values tell us that the first excited state ($n = 2$) is only 3.4 ev below the ionization energy, the second only 1.51 ev below it (Fig. 27-3). If we translate these converging energy levels to spectral lines, we see the reasons for the convergence of the lines towards a limit (Fig. 24-3).

We should now be able to see the reason for the various spectral series (Balmer, Lyman, etc.), and why they should be distributed among, and only among, the infrared, visible, and ultraviolet parts of the electromagnetic spectrum. Pertinent here are the previously stated facts that ultraviolet photons carry more energy than those of visible light, and those of visible light carry more than those of the infrared. Also pertinent is the fact that the energy of a photon is proportional to frequency, and this is equivalent to saying that the energy is inversely proportional to wavelength.

Let us start with an electron at infinity. If such a free electron comes close enough to a hydrogen *ion*, it may be "captured," and so occupy an orbit specified by some value of n. Let this be an orbit with the greatest possible value of n, i.e., the electron is as far away from the nucleus as it can get without being free. If it were now to make the transition from this orbit to the $n = 1$ orbit, the energy of the photon emitted, hence the frequency emitted, is the greatest possible; it is found to be in the ultraviolet range of the spectrum. This means that there can be no spectral lines of this type beyond the ultraviolet, i.e., in the X-ray part of the electromagnetic spectrum. X-rays must therefore be produced in other ways.

Jumps from any other orbit to the $n = 1$ orbit also are found to be in the ultraviolet range. Obviously the ultraviolet line of least energy should be from the $n = 2$ to the $n = 1$ orbit. Thus, ultraviolet radiations are produced by electrons making transitions from some outer orbit to the ground state in single jumps. Note carefully in Fig. 27-3 that the biggest part of *any* of these jumps is that made from the $n = 2$ to the $n = 1$ orbit. Hence the energy of the ultraviolet photon of greatest energy is only about one-third greater than that of least energy.

Let us return to our newly captured electron. Suppose that it makes the transition from the next-to-infinity orbit to the $n = 2$ in a single jump. The photon emitted would have a frequency detectable by the eye; it should be high in the violet part of the visible spectrum. All jumps from outer orbits to the $n = 2$ orbit are in the visible range, i.e., they are in the Balmer series. For the hydrogen electron, the jump from the $n = 3$ to the $n = 2$ orbit gives us the alpha (red line), that from the $n = 4$ to the $n = 2$ orbit gives us the beta (green) line, that from the $n = 5$ to the $n = 2$ orbit, the gamma (blue) line, and from the $n = 6$ to the $n = 2$ orbit, the delta (purple) line. From higher energy orbits, other purplish to violet lines result. Theoretically, a large number of such lines should be visible. Visibility, however, depends on intensity as well as on frequency, and the intensity of a line depends on the number of electrons making the same jump at the same time.[17]

[17] The eye can detect color only when extremely large numbers of electrons are emitting photons of the same energy at the same time. If the number is too small, no device whatever will detect them. Hence only the first 10 or 12 Balmer lines are obtainable from gas discharge tubes, whereas 33 such lines can be detected in the corona of the sun because of the far greater number of electrons making the bigger jumps. In gas discharge tubes a low density of the gas is required to allow more room for jumps without bumping into other atoms, for atoms with electrons in high-energy orbits are much bigger than the atoms with their electrons in the ground state. Interference with the jumps obviously complicates matters, so that the jumps do not take place unimpeded as the electron absorbs or emits energy. Some of the characteristic transitions become "uncharacteristic" transitions. In glowing liquids and solids where the atoms are far closer together than they are in gases, so much interference takes place that all

In gas discharge tubes the excitation of the atoms is not great enough to give large numbers of lines. The wavelengths of the hydrogen lines are 6562.1 A, 4860.7 A, 4340.7 A, and 4101.2 A, respectively. Note that the *differences* decrease rapidly from 1701.4 to 520.6 to 238.9 A, and if we carry this difference to lines beyond the purple, it would converge to zero, just as the difference in energy levels converged towards zero.

The Paschen, Brackett, and Pfund series are all in the infrared because the electron jumps that give rise to them are from outer orbits *to* the $n = 3$, $n = 4$, $n = 5$. The emitted photons do not carry enough energy to give us light in the visible range of the electromagnetic spectrum. In other words, the energy levels are too close together. Transitions from the outer orbits to the $n = 6$, $n = 7$, etc. orbits give rise to photons of too low energy to be perceived either by the eye or by a photographic plate.

Ionization Potentials vs. Energy Levels

Let us return to a consideration of the actual energy of the electron in its various stable orbits. You were told that it took 10.2 ev to boost the electron in the hydrogen atom from the normal, unexcited orbit, $n = 1$, to the $n = 2$ orbit. How do we know this? The experiment that gives us the answer is very simple. The general principle stripped of minor details is as follows:

We simply take a hydrogen discharge tube similar to the cathode ray tube that Thomson used in his measurement of e/m (Fig. 26-2). We will use a cathode which,

frequencies are emitted and continuous spectra result. Thus, we see why it is that only incandescent gases can emit line spectra.

when hot, will eject electrons (see thermionic emission, Fig. 26-4) and we will have it arranged so that some of the ejected electrons will pass through a wire mesh anode into a field-free region at the end of the tube. Un-ionized hydrogen gas of low density fills the tube. Before the current is turned on no light is observed, for the atoms are all in the unexcited state. We turn the current on, keeping the voltage low, say at 6 volts. The electrons ejected from the hot cathode are now accelerated in an electric field of 6 volts, i.e., each acquires an energy of 6 ev. We cannot see any light emitted yet, even with a spectroscope capable of detecting ultraviolet light and which is aimed at the field-free end of the tube. We slowly increase the voltage until our voltmeter registers 10.2 volts. We now "see" the first line of the Lyman series (Fig. 27-2). The reason is that the electrons ejected from the hot cathode that reach the field-free region of the tube, now have enough energy to "knock" the hydrogen electrons of the hydrogen gas from the $n = 1$ orbit to the $n = 2$ orbit when they make direct hits. Shortly these hydrogen electrons return to the $n = 1$ orbit, emitting ultraviolet light of a particular wavelength as they do so. Not until the voltage has reached 11.7 volts (10.2 plus 1.51, Fig. 27-3) does the second Lyman line appear, as some electrons, now boosted to the $n = 3$ orbit, return to the $n = 1$ orbit. At the same time, the Balmer line H_a also appears, for some of the electrons that were boosted into the $n = 3$ orbit return to the $n = 2$ orbit before going back to the $n = 1$ orbit.

If we increase the voltage still more, to 12.56 volts (10.2 plus 1.51 plus 0.85 volts, Fig. 27-3), we will get in addition to the previously mentioned lines, the third Lyman line, the second Balmer line, and the first Paschen line in the infrared (if our instruments are of the sort that will detect the infrared). The reason is that the voltage is now great enough to boost some electrons to the $n = 4$ orbit; they can return to the $n = 1$ orbit in more different ways. It must be remembered that the lines we see in the spectroscope are each formed by the combined radiation from countless billions of atoms. This experiment clearly shows that minimum energies are needed to lift electrons to successively higher levels and that they are lifted instantaneously *once that level is reached.* It thus gives proof that electrons absorb and radiate energy in discrete amounts, giving us further support for the Planck, Einstein, and Bohr theories.

Suppose that we carry our experiment a bit further. We increase the voltage to 13.6 volts and find that there is sudden increase in the current (Fig. 27-4). This increase can be explained in either of two ways; by an increase in the number of free electrons flowing through the main circuit, or by the appearance of ions to aid in conducting the current, or both. Where did these electrons and/or ions come from? They could come only from the hydrogen atoms. Electrons were knocked entirely free from them by the electrons ejected from the hot cathode, and which now have an energy of at least 13.6 ev each; they have reached infinity. This increases the number of free electrons, and it also creates just as many positive hydrogen ions, so that the current is carried better. This measured ionization energy of 13.6 ev is exactly equal to that of the electron in the $n = \infty$ "orbit" as calculated in Eq. 27-14. Since the energy of a photon making the transition from the $n = \infty$ orbit to the $n = 1$ orbit as calculated from theory agrees with the energy needed to free the electron from its nucleus as determined by experiment, support is thereby given to the Bohr theory.

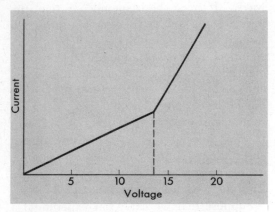

Fig. 27-4. Graph of Current vs. Voltage in Determining Ionization Energy of Hydrogen. Note that the current abruptly increases at 13.6 volts, indicating that there are now more particles (electrons, in this case) to carry the current. These electrons have been knocked loose from the hydrogen atoms, thus ionizing them.

The potential difference, expressed in electron volts, that must be applied in this manner to strip an electron from an atom, thus ionizing that atom, is called its *ionization potential*. The concepts of energy levels and ionization potentials are applicable to the atoms of all elements. We will shortly find that these concepts will help us in understanding the arrangement of the electrons in shells about atoms. First, however, we will find it advantageous to take a brief diversion into the concept of atomic number.

SUMMARY

By 1910 it was becoming increasingly clear not only that matter and electricity were particulate in nature but that light was also. Yet the old puzzle of bright line spectra still remained a puzzle. Rutherford's planetary atom did not explain spectra, but it furnished one of the two main leads that led Bohr to the solution of the problem. The other lead was Planck's quantum theory. To make even a beginning Bohr had to assume that some concepts of classical physics did not apply to the submicroscopic world of the atom. He kept, however, the number that did not apply to a minimum, i.e., he was careful not to make any unnecessary assumptions. His significant postulates were as follows:

1. Electrons travel about nuclei only in orbits for which the linear momentum multiplied by the circumference, $2\pi r$, is equal to a whole number multiplied by Planck's constant, h, i.e., $mv(2\pi r) = nh$, or $mvr = nh/2$. Such orbits are called permitted orbits.

2. In the normal unexcited state the electron moves in the orbit nearest the nucleus ($n = 1$) without radiating energy.

3. An electron may absorb energy in units proportional to the frequency. In doing so it shifts to a permitted orbit farther from the nucleus. It returns to an inner orbit by emitting a photon of light in accordance with the equation, $E_2 - E_1 = hf$.

Bright line spectra are explained by electrons from large numbers of atoms making characteristic transitions from outer to inner orbits and emitting large numbers of photons of the same frequency at the same time. The number of lines in the visible spectrum of an element indicates the minimum number of such transitions ("jumps") of different lengths; other lines may be (and commonly are) in the infrared and ultraviolet ranges of the spectrum.

The frequencies and wavelengths of the hydrogen lines are calculable by means of the equations, $E_2 - E_1 = hf$, or $f = (E_2 - E_1)/h$. These are found to agree with those calculated by use of the Balmer equation, which in turn agree with the measured values. The general form of the equation by which this is done is

$$\frac{1}{\lambda} = 109{,}678 \left(\frac{1}{n_1{}^2} - \frac{1}{n_2{}^2} \right) \text{ cm}^{-1}$$

Bohr's theory was applied successfully to the spectrum of the hydrogen atom (for which it was specifically designed) and to the spectrum of the singly charged helium ion, but it was largely a failure with multi-electron atoms because of the influences of the electrons on one another. The theory pointed the way, however, to the elucidation of the structure of these more complex atoms.

An electron has a certain definite quantity of energy when in any of the permitted orbits. This quantity increases as n increases, but the rate of increase falls off rapidly to become zero when the electron is at infinity. The energy needed to move an electron in the ground state to infinity, i.e., to free it from the attractive forces of the nucleus, is known as its ionization potential. For hydrogen this is 13.6 ev. The energy for each value of n is known as an energy level. The energy at infinity for the hydrogen electron may be calculated from the Bohr theory, or it may be determined by experiment. The experiment consisted of sending an electric current through a cathode ray tube that contained hydrogen gas of very low density. Cathode rays ejected from a hot cathode (Fig. 26-4) carried the current. If we start with a low voltage and gradually increase it we find that the current increases uniformly to a certain voltage (13.6 volts), at which point there is an abrupt increase in the current. Electrons knocked free from the hydrogen atoms now help carry the current. The common unit of energy here is the electron volt, although calories and ergs (or joules) are sometimes used.

EXERCISES

I. TERMS AND CONCEPTS

Permitted orbit	Electron volt
Ground state	Lyman series (ultra-
Angular momentum	violet)
	Balmer series (visible)
Energy level	Paschen ⎤
Ionization potential	Brackett ⎬ series
	Pfund ⎦ (infrared)
Infinity for the electron	$mvr = \dfrac{nh}{2\pi}$
Converging towards a limit	$E_2 - E_1 = hf$

II. PROBLEMS

1. State the four postulates of the Bohr theory of the hydrogen atom.

2. What reason did Bohr give for making assumptions that were in conflict with the classical physics of the time?

3. What does the quantity $h/2\pi$ represent? Orbits vary as n increases?

4. How was the adequacy of the first postulate tested?

5. The radius of a permitted orbit is given by $r = n^2h^2/4\pi^2mKe^2$. State what each one of the quantities on the right is.

6. If the radius of the first permitted orbit is 0.5×10^{-8} cm, what is the radius of the second permitted orbit? The third? The fourth?

7. Specifically, what use did Bohr make of Rutherford's nuclear theory, i.e., what did he abstract from it and include in his own theory?

8. Specifically what use, etc., did he make of Planck's quantum theory?

9. Why did Bohr have n equal only integers?

10. What equation gives you the energy difference between two permitted orbits?

11. What is meant by the excited state of an atom? State two ways in which this excited state may be attained.

12. By what process is electromagnetic radiation produced according to the Bohr theory?

13. What determines the frequency of the radiation emitted?

14. The bright line spectrum of sodium as viewed with an ordinary spectroscope consists of a single yellow line. The flame spectrum of sodium consists of a "mass" of yellow light. Why is the first a "line" whereas the second is a "mass" of light? Why are these spectra yellow? (The answer should include how these spectra are produced.)

15. Explain how each of the four principal lines of hydrogen is produced.

16. The intensity of the above lines is not the same for all. Why not? Luminous hydrogen has a reddish hue. How do you account for it?

17. Flame spectra, for the most part, may be seen only briefly when viewed either with a spectroscope or the naked eye, whereas the spectrum of a gas in a gas discharge tube may be viewed as long as the current is turned on. Explain.

18. In what state must an element be in order to obtain its bright line spectrum?

19. Why do incandescent solids and liquids give continuous spectra rather than bright line spectra?

20. What transitions give rise to ultraviolet radiation? How may spectral lines in the ultraviolet be detected?

21. What transitions give rise to visible radiation? Compare the color of the line produced by a jump from the $n = 12$ orbit to the $n = 2$ to one produced by a jump from the $n = 3$ to $n = 2$ orbit, and one produced by a jump from the $n = 11$ to the $n = 2$ orbit. In what part of the spectrum would you expect to find each?

22. Why should the energy that a hydrogen electron absorbs in being lifted from the $n = 1$ to the $n = 2$ orbit be so much greater than that absorbed in being lifted from the $n = 2$ to the $n = 3$ orbit?

23. What is meant by the ionization energy of an atom? What is it for hydrogen?

24. Calculate the energy of the fifth hydrogen orbit.

25. Calculate the energy of an electron volt in joules. (The charge on the electron is 1.6×10^{-19} coulombs. A volt is 1 joule/coulomb.)

CHAPTER XXVIII

X-Rays and the Concept of Atomic Number

While it is never safe to affirm that the future of Physical Science has no marvels in store ever more astonishing than those of the past, it seems probable that most of the grand underlying principles have been firmly established, and that further advances are to be sought chiefly in the rigorous application of these principles to all the phenomena which come to our notice. . . . An eminent physicist has remarked that the future truths of Physical Science are to be looked for in the sixth place of decimals.
—A. A. MICHELSON (*Nobel Prize, Physics, 1907*)

In Chapter XXIII we discussed the discovery of X-rays as one of the triumphs of the electromagnetic theory of Maxwell, but postponed their explanation because the proper background for understanding them had not yet been laid. Since X-rays played the star role not only in the development of the concept of atomic number, but also in the opening up of a wholly new field of research into the structure of crystalline solids, it is necessary that we understand something of their nature.

X-RAYS—PARTICLES OR WAVES

Within a few weeks of the announcement of their discovery by Roentgen in 1895, scientists everywhere were investigating X-rays. Among the properties discovered was their ability to make certain minerals fluoresce, to pass through most opaque matter, to darken a photographic plate, and to ionize the air through which they passed. The failure to determine conclusively whether they were waves or particles was not for want of trying. They passed beams of X-rays through electric and magnetic fields with negative results, proving that they were not charged particles. This left two possibilities, that they were either neutral particles or a form of wave motion. At first glance it might seem that the neutral particles hypothesis could be checked by setting up a nearly frictionless paddle wheel in their path to see if they possessed kinetic energy. The trouble was their great penetrating power; they go through the thin light blades of such a wheel almost as if they were not there. Attempts to produce diffraction and interference patterns failed. Nevertheless, Roentgen and many others believed that they were waves.

The problem was finally settled in 1912, when Laue, a German physicist, acted on the suggestion that they might be electromagnetic waves of such short wavelength that even the finest diffraction gratings had slits too far apart to produce diffraction. To show measurable diffraction, a slit must be small, the degree of smallness being determined by the wavelength. The slits in a grating with 10,000 per centimeter (25,000 per inch) are wide (10^{-4} cm) compared

425

with the wavelength of X-rays—which range from 10^{-6} to 10^{-10} cm. Laue thought that the atoms or molecules in some kinds of crystals might be arranged

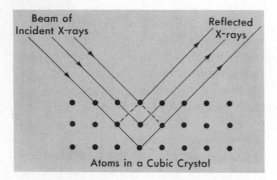

Fig. 28-1. Conditions for X-ray Interference Pattern. The dots represent layers of atoms in a cubic crystal. A beam of X-rays strikes the crystal from the left, penetrating to varying depths before being reflected (scattered is the better but less used term) to the right. The three-dimensional character of the beam is not apparent in the figure. Some rays reflected from atoms in the deeper layers may travel the same path as some reflected from atoms in the shallower layers. Those that do may now interfere constructively or destructively if they have the same wavelength.

in regular layers that were far thinner and more closely spaced than were the slits in even the best of diffraction gratings. Perhaps crystals could be used in place of diffraction gratings to produce interference patterns. Some of Laue's students tried, and succeeded in combining the rays constructively and destructively. Thus, both of the two unique experimental criteria for

wave motion were successfully applied to X-rays.

HOW X-RAY INTERFERENCE PATTERNS ARE PRODUCED

Sir William Bragg developed a method that is simpler than Laue's. The essence of his method is as follows: A beam of X-rays strikes the surface of a crystal at a certain angle. Some rays are reflected from the outermost layer of atoms, some penetrate to the second layer before being reflected, some to the third layer, etc. (Fig. 28-1). The waves reflected from the deeper layers travel slightly longer paths than those reflected from the shallower layers. For example, a wave that travels from a point source to the third layer before it is reflected to a given point occupied by the deflector travels a greater distance than one that is reflected from the second layer. If this difference in distance is equal to one wavelength or any whole number of wavelengths and the angle of the incident wave with the crystal is carefully adjusted so that the incident wave reflected from the third layer and that from the second follow the same path, they will constructively interfere. If the difference in distance traveled by the two waves is a half wavelength, or any odd multiple of a half wavelength, they will interfere destructively. The pattern produced (Fig. 28-2) is very different from that produced by gratings because crystals are three-dimensional whereas gratings are two-dimensional.

THE FRUITS OF ROENTGEN'S DISCOVERY

Once it was known that crystals could be used to produce interference patterns, pat-

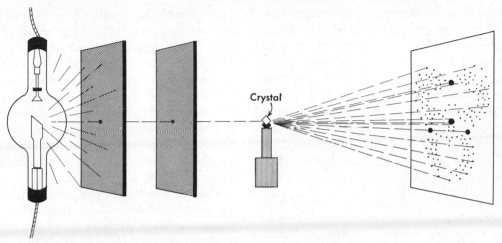

Fig. 28-2. Laue's Set-up for Production of X-ray Diffraction Pattern.   A single narrow beam of X-rays is produced by rays from the tube entering the holes in the two lead screens.   This beam passes through the crystal, where they are scattered in all directions.   Scattered rays grouped in separate pencils produce the dark spots on a photographic film.   The spots are produced by interference of waves diffracted from a number of atoms.   The arrangement of the spots is intimately related to crystal structure.

terns that were different for each type of crystal, it became possible to turn the experiment around and use X-rays to identify crystals (Fig. 28-3).   The mineralogist can now compare the interference patterns made by an unknown crystal specimen with the patterns made by known minerals.   Furthermore, the pattern made by a particular kind of crystal depends in part on how the atoms in that crystal are arranged.   Thus, a whole new field of research into the structure of crystalline substances was opened.

Further research into the mechanism of the production of X-rays led to the discovery that an X-ray tube produces two kinds of X-rays.   One kind was found to produce a continuous spectrum of all possible wavelengths, analogous to the continuous spectrum of visible light.   The other kind produces a line spectrum superimposed upon

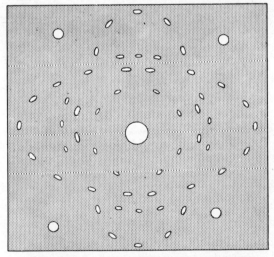

Fig. 28-3. X-ray Diffraction Pattern of NaCl. (After Michell Sienko and Robert Plane, *Chemistry*, McGraw-Hill Book Co., Inc., New York, 1957.)

the continuous spectrum.[1] Investigation of these line spectra revealed that different elements used as targets in the X-ray tube produced line spectra of different wavelengths. Still further investigation into this phenomenon by one of Rutherford's assistants resulted in the development of the concept of atomic number into a law of universal acceptance and usefulness.

J. J. Thomson, the discoverer of the electron, was truly correct when he said,

A striking discovery like that of the Roentgen rays acts much like the discovery of gold in a sparsely populated country; it attracts workers who come in the first place for gold, but who may find that the country has other products, other charms, perhaps even more valuable than the gold itself.

TWO TYPES OF X-RAYS

Before we proceed to the work of Moseley on X-ray spectra, we need to learn more about the production of X-rays. We have already learned that X-rays are akin to light in that they are a form of electromagnetic radiation produced when high-speed electrons ejected from a hot cathode under high voltage strike a target [2] and are abruptly stopped so that they give up most of their energy all at once.[3] To differentiate them from orbital electrons we

will refer to the bombarding electrons as cathode electrons. The wavelength of the X-rays will depend in part upon the abruptness of the stoppage of these cathode electrons, and in part upon their speeds. Because there are all sorts of collisions, from direct hits which cause instantaneous stoppage to collisions so glancing that no X-rays are emitted, X-rays of all wavelengths are produced. Thus, a continuous X-ray spectrum is produced.

The line spectra are produced in another manner, as follows: The cathode electrons that make direct hits may give their energy to electrons that belong to the atoms composing the target material. The orbital electrons in an atom are arranged in shells [4] about the atom, each shell representing a different energy level (or set of energy levels). These shells have been labeled the K (innermost), L, M, N, O, P, and Q shells by the X-ray spectroscopists. As we already know, the electrons in the outer shells have higher energies than those in inner shells. Suppose a cathode electron, accelerated to a high velocity by the high voltage of the tube, penetrates an atom and dislodges an electron from the innermost shell (the K shell). At once an electron from an outer higher energy shell "drops" into the "hole" left by the dislodged electron, where it has a lower potential energy. The electron filling this hole will radiate the difference in energy as a photon in the X-ray range. If the electron that fills the hole in the K shell is from the neighboring shell (the L shell), K_α radiation is produced. If it is filled from the next outer shell (the M shell), K_β radiation is pro-

---

[1] All X-ray spectra, like ultraviolet spectra, can be "seen" only by photography, for they affect certain film emulsions in the same way that ordinary light does.

[2] Note that this is just the reverse of the photoelectric effect, in which a photon ejects an electron from a metal target. Here an electron produces a photon by striking a metal target.

[3] Nearly 99 per cent of the electrons striking the target undergo collisions so glancing that they do not lose their energy all at once. They produce no electromagnetic radiation; their energy is converted into kinetic energy of the molecules of the target material, thus raising the temperature.

[4] These shells are actually occupied by electrons in the normal unexcited state. They are not the permitted orbits of the hydrogen atom. Elements of the first period have only a K shell, those of the second have a K and an L shell, etc.

duced. Since the former will occur more often, the K_α line is more intense than the K_β line. These two wavelengths give rise to two lines that are superimposed upon the continuous X-ray spectrum (Fig. 28-4). X-ray radiation may also be produced by the cathode electrons knocking electrons out of the L shell.

ORIGINAL CONCEPT OF ATOMIC NUMBER

The atomic number of an element originally referred to the position of the element in the periodic table. It was the "serial number" of the element when they were arranged (with one or two reversals) in order of atomic weight, due allowance being made for undiscovered elements by leaving gaps with serial numbers assigned to the gaps. The many regularities in the table excluded the possibility of elements being discovered that would fit anywhere except in one of the gaps, or at the high end of the table. Thus, the atomic numbers represented a "natural" order of the elements, but they did not represent any property or quantity that changed regularly from one element to the next element, i.e., they had no more significance than the numbers given to houses to identify them on a street. Actually the term used to refer to an element was not atomic number, but simply number. The former did not come into use until after Moseley's work had been announced.

MOSELEY'S CONCEPT OF ATOMIC NUMBER

The concept of a definite number of charges in the nuclei of atoms had been "kicking around" for some time before 1913. It was generally known that the

number of charges on the nucleus increased with atomic weight. Rutherford, in his work on the nuclear theory of the atom, had estimated that this total charge was equal to about half the atomic weight. It

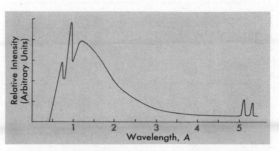

Fig. 28-4. General Form of Graph of X-ray Spectrum of Metal. Wavelength in Angstroms is plotted horizontally and X-ray intensity in arbitrary units vertically. The curve minus the spikes is that of the continuous spectrum produced when cathode electrons are stopped abruptly. The wavelength decreases (frequency increases) with the electron speed, which is governed by applied voltage. The spikes represent the line spectra. They are produced only at high voltages because cathode electrons must be given high speeds to penetrate into the K and L shells of atoms with enough energy to dislodge orbital electrons.

remained, however, for H. G. J. Moseley, one of Rutherford's assistants, to discover a method of definitely determining the number of charges on the nucleus.

By 1913 the main features of Rutherford's nuclear theory had been completely verified, and Bohr's original paper on his theory of the hydrogen atom had just been published. Moseley was investigating the wavelengths of X-rays, particularly those that were responsible for the line spectra mentioned earlier. He found that the character of the continuous spectrum depended mainly on the voltage, and hardly at all on the metal used as the target. On

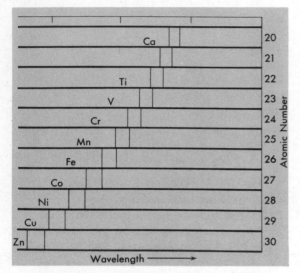

Fig. 28-5. Positions of X-ray Line Spectra with Respect to Wavelength. The spectra of all are much alike. Note that they shift towards the shorter wavelengths as the atomic number increases. Note the regularity of the shift. If No. 21 were unknown, the double shift from Ca to Ti would indicate a missing element. The increase in a regular manner of the energy of emitted X-rays with atomic number is explained by a regular increase of charge on the nucleus as the atomic number increases. A graph of the atomic number against the square root of the frequency is a straight line, thus showing a direct relationship between atomic number and frequency.

the other hand, the wavelengths of the line spectrum turned out to depend upon the target material. A graph of the continuous spectrum with the superimposed

line spectrum is shown in Fig. 28-3, in which the "spikes" represent the line spectrum. The spikes occur in groups to which the X-ray spectroscopist has assigned the letters K and L to correspond to the K and L series. We will concern ourselves only with the two K lines, K_a and K_β, inasmuch as the others are not essential to the concept of atomic number.

Using as many different metals as he could obtain for the target in his X-ray tube, Moseley found that the frequencies of these two lines increased progressively as the serial number of the target element increased. This is as expected, for the energy needed to knock electrons from the K shell increases with increasing charge on the nucleus, and the higher the frequency the higher the energy of the photon emitted. He deduced an equation that allowed him to calculate the frequency of the lines. The general form of the equation,[5] good for all elements, is

$$f = \tfrac{3}{4} cR(Z - 1)^2$$

where c is the velocity of light, R is the Rydberg constant (which occurs in both the Bohr formula and the modern form of the Balmer formula for the hydrogen spectrum), and Z is the number of charges on the nucleus.

Thus, $\tfrac{3}{4} cR$ is a constant. Therefore the frequency varies directly with $(Z - 1)^2$. More meaningful is the fact that the square root of the frequency of a particular line, say the K_a line, increases by the same amount from one element to the next in the periodic chart, (for $\sqrt{f} \propto Z - 1$). The

[5] Another form of this equation is

$$f = cR(Z - 1)^2 \left(\frac{1}{1^2} - \frac{1}{n^2} \right)$$

Note the resemblance to the Balmer formula, p. 364.

same is true for the K_β line (Fig. 28-5). Moseley said, "We have here a proof that there is in the atom a fundamental quantity which increases by regular steps as we pass from one element to the next in the periodic chart. This quantity can only be the charge on the central positive nucleus." The fact that the charge on the nucleus was more fundamental than its mass (given by the atomic weight) dovetailed nicely with the Bohr model of the hydrogen atom, for the charge was basic to his theory and the mass was not.

You will recall that Mendelyeev had had to make certain reversals in arranging the elements known in his time (1869) in a table according to atomic weight. The pairs that had to be reversed were argon [6] and potassium with atomic weights of 39.9 and 39.1, respectively; cobalt and nickel with atomic weights of 58.19 and 58.7; and tellurium and iodine, 127.6 and 126.9, respectively. Moseley showed that the number of charges on the nucleus of the cobalt atom was 27 and that on nickel was 28, thus justifying the reversal. The other reversals were similarly justified.

Certain known metals were not available to Moseley at the time, e.g., scandium. Nevertheless he calculated the wavelengths of its K lines, which were later found to be almost exactly correct.

The modern concept of the atomic number of any element is, then, the number of charges on the nucleus of an atom of that element. It is also the number of protons in the nucleus, for each proton carries one positive charge. And, since the atom is neutral, it is also equal to the number of electrons surrounding the nucleus.

[6] Argon was not known when Mendelyeev formulated his table. It was discovered in 1894.

PROTONS AND NEUTRONS

Just as we found it unavoidable to refrain from speaking of the electron before we were able to relate the story of its discovery, so we are finding it equally unavoidable to refrain from using the word proton until we discover it. To "discover" it here would destroy whatever continuity and integration we have managed to keep in our story. We will accept it as a nuclear particle that carries one charge equal to that on the electron but opposite in sign. The protons in the nuclei of the lighter elements carry about half the mass of the atom. For hydrogen one proton is responsible for the whole of the mass of the nucleus, and for the heavier elements the protons carry somewhat less than half the total mass. A proton and a positively charged hydrogen ion are identical.

The rest of the nucleus consists of neutral particles called neutrons. The number of protons plus the number of neutrons add up to approximately the atomic weight. We will also defer our "discovery" of the neutron to a more appropriate place in our story.

SUMMARY

X-rays were discovered in 1895, but whether they were waves or particles was not determined before 1912 because the diagnostic tests for both waves and particles gave negative results. Laue thought they might be waves with a wavelength too small to be affected by the finest diffraction gratings. By using crystals whose atoms were arranged in planes whose distances apart were far less than those in gratings, he got an interference pattern. This pattern was very different from those produced by gratings. Since each different kind of crystal produced a different pattern, X-ray diffraction patterns are used for crystal identification.

X-ray tubes produce X-rays in two different ways. One kind results from the energy of these high-speed cathode electrons that are stopped abruptly enough by the target. Their energy is given to X-ray photons. These produce a continuous spectrum. The other kind results from the fact that some cathode electrons penetrate the target material, ejecting orbital electrons. If these displaced orbital electrons are from the K shell (to take one case only), and the vacancy is filled from the L shell, K radiation is produced, giving rise to a "spike" superimposed upon the continuous X-ray spectrum. Moseley worked out an equation from his experimental data that gave the frequency of the superimposed lines. From this equation he found that $\sqrt{f} \propto Z - 1$. This means that some quantity in the atom increases regularly from element to element. This quantity could only be the number of charges on the nucleus, i.e., the number of protons in the nucleus. Thus, the concept of atomic number was given a new meaning.

EXERCISES

I. TERMS AND CONCEPTS

X-ray diffraction pattern	Atomic number
X-ray continuous spectrum	Charge on the nucleus
X-ray line spectrum	Proton
K and L shells	Neutron
K_a and K_β lines	

II. PROBLEMS

1. In what ways do X-ray photons differ from those of visible or ultraviolet light?

2. Why did the early attempts to obtain interference patterns of X-rays fail?

3. How did Laue solve the problem?

4. How are the X-rays that give rise to the continuous X-ray spectrum produced?

5. Compare this production of X-rays with the photoelectric effect.

6. What gives the high speed to the cathode electrons in an X-ray tube?

7. How are the X-rays that form the line spectrum that is superimposed upon the continuous spectrum produced?

8. What is the source of the energy of the K_a line? The K_β line? Which represents the greatest amount of energy?

9. If the "hole" left by an orbital electron ejected from the K shell of an atom having several shells is filled by an electron from the next outer (L) shell, then a hole must be left in the L shell, which may be filled by an orbital electron from a shell still further removed from the nucleus, etc. Would you expect the radiation produced by an orbital electron from the N shell filling a hole in the M shell to have a higher or a lower frequency than that produced by an orbital electron from the L shell filling a hole in the K shell? Explain.

10. What is the modern concept of atomic number?

11. Describe briefly what Moseley did to arrive at the modern concept of atomic number.

12. How does the arrangement of elements in the periodic table according to atomic number compare with an arrangement according to atomic weights?

13. How did Moseley use prediction to lend support to his concept of atomic number?

14. What are protons? Neutrons?

15. What is the mass of a proton as compared to an electron?

CHAPTER XXIX

Modifications of the Bohr Theory

Ah, a man's reach should exceed his grasp
Or what's a heaven for.—ROBERT BROWNING

Bohr's original concern had been only a single-electron system, i.e., the hydrogen atom and the helium ion with a single positive charge. As we have already stated, the theory was highly successful with them but failed with multi-electron atoms, in large part because of the mutual repulsion of the electrons. We might further reason that, because of the greater number of charges on the nucleus, the electrons in the innermost orbit would be held more tightly than in the hydrogen atom, that the radius of this orbit would be somewhat less, and that the energies during transitions from one permitted orbit to another would be correspondingly greater. The last is a consequence of their being held more tightly. We have also suggested, without presenting any evidence for it, that the electrons are arranged in shells about the nucleus, shells that the X-ray spectroscopists have labeled by the capital letters K, L, M, N, O, P, and Q. We will now attempt to apply the Bohr theory to the atoms of helium, lithium, and beryllium, as a check against our reasoning, and at the same time see if we can find evidence for the shells.

THE EVIDENCE FOR THE SHELL STRUCTURE OF ATOMS

We will consider the helium atom first, an atom with two electrons and two positive charges on the nucleus. We will make the simplest assumption as to the distribution of these electrons, that they are in the same orbit, but on opposite sides of it because of mutual repulsion. To change this atom into an ion we need to remove one electron. This is done by the method used in determining the ionization potential described on p. 420. This measured value we will call the experimental value. However, we will first make a rough estimate of the ionization potential of this electron by use of the Bohr theory. (A precise calculation is beyond the scope of this book; it is also unnecessary for our purposes).

If it were not for the repulsion of the two helium electrons, we might logically assume that the ionization potential of the first electron would be double that of the hydrogen, for the charge holding it in its orbit is doubled. It is also logical to assume that the repulsion of one electron for the other would reduce the ionization potential of the first electron that we remove. The amount of the reduction can be estimated from the following data:

1. The distance between the electrons is twice that of either electron from the nucleus.

2. The repulsive force between two electrons is half the attractive force between the electrons and the nucleus.

The first item results in a repulsive force on one electron equal to one-fourth the attractive force (Coulomb's Law), and the second item cuts this in half again (Coulomb's Law again). Thus, the reduction should be about one-eighth. Therefore we might expect that the ionization potential of the first electron of helium would be about one-eighth less than twice that of the hydrogen electron. Since the ionization potential of hydrogen is 13.6 volts, this ought to be reasonably near 25.5 volts. The experimental value of the ionization potential turns out to be 24.6 volts, which checks quite well with our rough estimate. Removing this one electron leaves a singly charged helium ion.

Now let us turn our attention to the second electron of helium. We might expect the spectrum of this helium ion to be more like that of hydrogen than that of the atom of helium, because the ion also is a one-electron system. Our expectations turn out to be correct. We can estimate the ionization potential of this second electron if we make due allowances for the changed conditions.

The attractive force of the nucleus is obviously larger in magnitude, not only because of the mere lack of the counteracting repulsive force, but also because the electron, lacking this repulsion, moves in closer to the nucleus. Remembering that Coulomb's Law in an inverse-square law, we can calculate that the attractive force is about four times as great as that between the hydrogen nucleus and its electron. This means that the voltage needed to remove it should be four times the ionization potential of hydrogen, or 54.4 volts. By actual experiment in our discharge tube, this second ionization potential turns out to be 54 volts, a bit more than twice the ionization potential of the first electron. This does not mean that the second electron is held any more closely than the first. Both electrons are exactly alike and both have the same amount of energy while they are a part of the atom. The difference is due to the electrons being removed *in succession*. Our assumptions that two electrons are in the same orbit checks out remarkably well with our rough estimates and with the actual ionization potentials obtained by experiment.

Now let us try the lithium atom. It has three electrons, and three positive charges on the nucleus. Let us assume that they are all in the same orbit. Again we can calculate the voltage necessary to remove the first electron. Allowing for the increased attraction of the nucleus and the repulsive force of the other two electrons, as we did for the first electron of the helium atom, we come up with a figure somewhat less than three times that to remove the sole electron from the hydrogen atom, i.e., an ionization potential of somewhat less than 40 volts, say 35 volts. However, our experimental value from the discharge tube turns out to be only 5.4 volts.

This great discrepancy shows that our assumption that all three electrons are in the same orbit is wrong. The electron is so loosely held that it must be in a more distant orbit. If it is in an orbit by itself we might reasonably expect that the spectrum of lithium would look more like that of hydrogen than it does helium. This turns out to be so. A check by measuring the ionization potential of the other two electrons would be helpful. We assume them to be in the same shell, and that they are in a shell somewhat closer to the nucleus than are the electrons in the helium atom because of the triple charge on the nucleus. These assumptions turn out to be correct, for the experimental value for the first of these two electrons that we remove turns out to be 75 volts. For the second (and last) electron we predict an even higher ionization potential, for the lack of repulsive force of the removed electrons make it now revolve in a still smaller orbit. Our prediction turns out to be correct. Thus, we are inevitably led to the conclusion that the lithium atom has two shells, two electrons in the first or K shell, and one in the second or L shell.

We will consider beryllium only briefly, because the story is much the same. Beryllium, atomic number 4, has four electrons and four positive charges on the nucleus. Since lithium has one electron in the second shell, we might reasonably expect beryllium to have its additional electron in the second shell also. If we assume that it is, make our estimation of its ionization potential, and compare it with the experimental value, we find the agreement extremely good. It takes only 9.3 volts to remove the first electron from beryllium, a bit less than twice the voltage necessary with lithium.

For the succeeding elements in the second period of the periodic table, boron, oxygen, carbon, fluorine, and neon, the energy needed to remove the first electron increases, going from 5.4 volts for lithium to a high of 21.6 volts for neon. True, there are a couple of small discrepancies, but these are not sufficient to invalidate our reasoning. The really significant thing is that when we remove the first electron from the next element, sodium, the ionization potential drops way back to 5.1 volts, even less than that for lithium. This can mean only that sodium has one electron in a shell still farther out, i.e., it is in the third or M shell.

Examine Fig. 29-1, which is a graph showing the ionization energy in electron volts plotted against the atomic number. Note the amazing drop in ionization potential after the end of a period. This can mean only that the outer shells of an inert gas can hold no more electrons, i.e., their outer shells are "closed." If more electrons are added, they must go into a new shell. Thus, an alkali metal starts a new period with one electron in its outer shell. A more striking evidence for the assumption that the electrons are really arranged in shells about the nucleus could scarcely be desired.

MODIFICATION DUE TO MOTION OF NUCLEUS

We have been using rough estimates of the ionization potentials against actual measurements in checking our assumptions. They served our purposes very well in the development of the concept of the arrangement of the electrons in shells about the nucleus. However, spectroscopy has developed into a precise science, and even close approximations are not good enough when we attempt to compare wavelengths calculated from the Bohr theory with the actual spectroscopic measurements. As always in science, when theory does not agree with observation, it is the theory that must be modified. One of the first modifications involved motion of the nucleus.

In the original theory, the assumption was made that the nucleus was motionless as the electrons swirled around it. The mutual attraction between the nucleus and the electrons cause the nucleus to have a motion of its own, just as the influence of

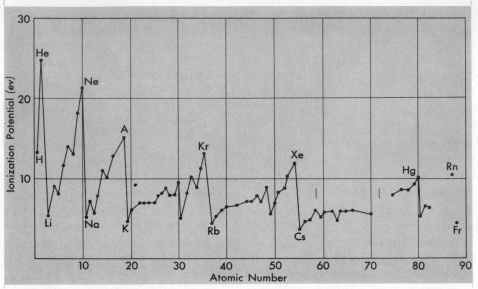

Fig. 29-1. Graph of Ionization Energy vs. Atomic Number. Note the drop in ionization energy at the end of each period, and the rise in the following period. This is excellent evidence that electrons are arranged in shells.

the moon causes the earth to move somewhat differently than it would if there were no moon. Bohr's correction for this motion of the nucleus changed the value of the Rydberg constant so that the calculated values of the wavelengths of even the hydrogen lines were in better agreement with their observed values.

MODIFICATIONS OF ORBITS

In a broad, general way, we might say that the trouble with the original Bohr theory was that not enough "jumps" were permitted to account for the spectra of multi-electron atoms, nor were most of these jumps exactly the right size. The latter accounted for most of the discrepancies between the measured wavelengths emitted and those calculated by the Bohr

theory. The full treatment requires the use of advanced calculus, and so the mathematical details are beyond us. We present it qualitatively in outline form here because we think it is possible for you to grasp the essential results of the theory—which include a rational explanation of both the periodicities in the periodic chart and in the chemical behavior of atoms. These explanations are prime objectives of this textbook. The modifications deal chiefly with Bohr's second assumption, i.e., that the permitted orbits must all satisfy the equation for angular momentum:

$$mvr = \frac{nh}{2\pi}$$

Different values of n specified the value of mvr, for both h and 2π are constants. The permitted orbits were considered circular.

Elliptical Orbits

The first change allowed elliptical orbits as well as circular ones (Fig. 29-2). This change was a natural one, for it allowed a comparison to be made with our solar system. The integer n no longer specifies the angular momentum, but is restricted to determination of the sizes of the orbits. This means that it determines not only the diameter of circular orbits, but also the diameters of the long axes in elliptical orbits. *For a given value of n all of these diameters are equal.* The diameter of the short axis was, however, different for each ellipse, and determined the degree of flatness (eccentricity) of the ellipse. For $n = 1$, only circular orbits are permitted; for $n = 2$, two orbits are permitted, one a circle and the other an ellipse; for $n = 3$, two ellipses of different eccentricities and one circle are permitted, etc. The number n is called the principal quantum number.

Elliptical orbits meant that another quantum number, associated with an electron in the given orbit, had to be introduced. It is designated by the letter l, and specifies the number of bits of angular momentum, $h/2\pi$. The value of l is an indication of the shape of the orbit. The permitted values range from 0 for the most elongated ellipse to $n - 1$. Thus, for $n = 3$, $n - 1$ is 2, and so the permitted values are 0, 1, and 2. Note that because one possible value of l is 0, the total number of values of l is equal to n, even though the maximum value is $n - 1$. Thus, as n increases by 1, so do the possible values of l. The size of the orbits increases as the square of n, as in the original Bohr theory.

The energy of the electron in the elliptical orbits for any one value of n turned out to be the same as for the circular orbits

(Kepler's third law), unless Einstein's theory of relatively was invoked; this involves a very slight change in mass, due to the higher speed [1] of the electron when it comes near the nucleus. (Remember that the earth moves faster when closer to the sun.) A slight effect on the total en-

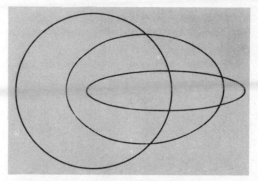

Fig. 29-2. Orbits Corresponding to $n = 3$. The diameter of the circle is equal to the diameters of the long axes of the ellipses. The quantum number, n, denotes the sizes of the orbits in the modified theory. The period and the angular momentum are the same for all orbits with the same quantum number. (After Sommerfeld.)

ergy in such an elliptical orbit results, so that there are slight differences in the wavelengths of the light emitted during transitions from outer to inner orbits. E.g., transitions from each of the four orbits with quantum number $n = 4$ to the circular orbit $n = 2$ result in four slightly different wavelengths being emitted; this results in four closely spaced lines in the spectrum, lines that in spectroscopes of low resolving power appear as a single line. Such

---

[1] The speed of the electron about the nucleus is of the order of 10,000 to 20,000 mi/sec.

spectroscopes reveal only the "coarse structure" of the atom. Spectroscopes of high
resolving power split up these coarse lines
into the several closely spaced lines, thus
revealing the "fine structure" of the atom.
It was to explain this fine structure that
several modifications of the Bohr theory

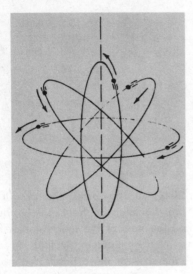

Fig. 29-3. Orientation of Orbits. The five
permitted orientations of the circular orbit
shown in Fig. 29-2.

were made, including those already mentioned.

Orientation of Orbits

Elliptical orbits solve some of the problems of the spectra of complex atoms, but
not all. In the original Bohr theory two
possibilities existed with respect to any permitted circular orbit, i.e., for any one value
of n. The orbits could all be in one plane,
giving a flat, two-dimensional disclike appearance to the atom (as pictured originally
by Bohr), or the circular orbit could shift
from one plane to another which would, by
taking into account the infinite number of

possible planes, give a spherical, three-
dimensional appearance. Which of these
was correct could be checked by applying
a magnetic field to a beam of hydrogen
atoms traveling through another gas.

If the hydrogen atoms were disclike, they
should orient themselves with the magnetic
field, as does a coil of wire in a galvanometer. For a given orientation of a magnetic field, the range (i.e., the distance it
will travel through the other gas before
being stopped) of the hydrogen atom will
be a specified amount. Now let us change
the orientation of the magnetic field by
90°, but keep the beam of hydrogen atoms
traveling in the same direction as before
through the gas. Again the hydrogen atoms
should orient themselves with the magnetic
field, but now instead of traveling through
the gas edgewise, they should be traveling broadside, hence their range should be
less. The experimental fact is that there
is no difference in the range under these
two conditions. The conclusion is, therefore, that the atoms are spherical, not disclike.

Now if atoms are spherical so that the
permitted orbits are not all in one plane,
the orientation of the orbits with respect
to one another becomes important, especially in atoms with more than one electron.
Each orbit has its own tilt, and only certain
tilts are permitted (Fig. 29-3). The energy levels in these different tilts are not
quite the same, giving rise to the emission
of slightly different wavelengths by the
emitting atoms.

This concept of orientation of orbits came
about through the discovery that a spectral
line that shows up as single when not in
a magnetic field may be split into several
lines when the emitting atoms are placed
in the field. This splitting of spectral lines
by a magnetic field is called the Zeeman

effect, after its discoverer. The different energies are explained by the fact that it takes more work to change the alignment of an orbit lined up with the magnetic field than to change one lined up against the magnetic field. The amount of tilt is specified by a third quantum number, m. The permitted values of m range from $+l$ to $-l$. If $l = 2$, the permitted values of m are $-2, -1, 0, +1,$ and $+2$. The electrons in orbits with plus values have the most energy.

ELECTRON SPIN

These values of n, l, and m gave a great variety of permitted orbits and so allowed a great number of spectral lines, yet there were some spectral lines not yet accounted for. Hence the concept that electrons spin on axes was introduced. A spinning electron is a tiny magnet with a magnetic field about it. The field will be oriented one way if the spin is clockwise, the opposite way if the spin is counterclockwise. There is also a field about the nucleus because the nucleus is a charged moving particle. The field of the electron may be parallel or antiparallel to that on the nucleus, giving rise to the clockwise or anticlockwise spins. The two spins, for our purposes, can be designated as plus and minus. The electron with the plus value has less energy. The discovery of electron spin greatly improved our understanding of magnetism.

We therefore have four quantum numbers to describe each electron in an atom, n, l, m, and s. The principal quantum number is n; it specifies the size of the orbit. The quantum number l is an orbital quantum number that characterizes the angular momentum. The values of l specify the shape (eccentricity) of the orbit. The magnetic quantum number, m, specifies the orientation (tilt) of the orbits. The spin quantum number, s, specifies the spin of the electron in its orbit.

PAULI'S EXCLUSION PRINCIPLE

The final solution of the mysteries of the arrangement of the electrons in atoms required the formulation of a new principle by Pauli of Switzerland. It is called the exclusion principle because it excludes large numbers of possible arrangements of the electrons. It states that *no two electrons in the same atom can have precisely the same energy or motion, i.e., they cannot have the same four quantum numbers.* This prevents congestion of electrons in the inner orbits, which might otherwise come about because of the attraction of the nucleus. This seems to be a fundamental principle which allows the positions of the elements in the periodic table to be explained. By use of the four quantum numbers and the exclusion principle, we can "build" the periodic table. First, however, we need to extend some concepts already mentioned and to introduce a few new ones.

It was the observations of atomic (line) spectra that demanded revision of the Bohr theory to provide a much greater variety of orbits, orbits that can be identified by sets of quantum numbers. This revision, however well they made it possible for the theory to account *qualitatively* for all atomic spectra, could not account *quantitatively* for them; i.e., the correct values for the wavelengths as calculated by the theory did not coincide precisely enough with the experimental values. Something clearly was fundamentally wrong, and by 1924 every

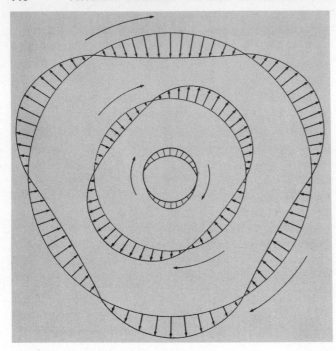

Fig. 29-4. De Broglie's Matter Waves. An electron can move only in an orbit whose circumference is an even number of wavelengths; all others are excluded. This gives a rational basis for Bohr's postulate, $mvr = nh/2\pi$. (After Gamov, *Matter, Earth and Sky*, Prentice-Hall, Englewood Cliffs, N. J., 1958.)

worker in the field knew it. Another perplexing problem was that there was no explanation for Bohr's first postulate, $mvr = nh/2\pi$. New ideas were needed.

DE BROGLIE'S "MATTER WAVES"

These new ideas came in 1924 when de Broglie,[2] a young French scientist, made a radical proposal. He pointed out that since light behaved like particles in some phenomena and like waves in others, perhaps electrons also behaved like particles and like waves. This is equivalent to saying that perhaps matter had two aspects, a particle aspect and a wave aspect.[3] He

suggested that somehow waves accompanied electrons just as waves accompanied photons.

His idea is not very difficult up to this point. Suppose we have an electron moving in an orbit about a nucleus. If a wave accompanies it (Fig. 29-4), going round and round in an orbit whose circumference is a whole number of wavelengths, we have a resemblance to a standing wave. Now a standing wave is stable (remember the rope waves that seemed to stand still). In such a wave there is a whole number of wavelengths in the *complete* circuit, so that

[2] Pronounced dĕ Broy or dĕ Bro-ee.

[3] Perhaps in macroscopic matter, i.e., matter in relatively large chunks, the wave aspect is so overwhelmingly overshadowed by the particle aspect that the former not only cannot possibly be de-

tected, but is probably meaningless. As the size gets smaller, perhaps the wave aspect becomes more important. It might be important in particles of atomic size if we could learn how to detect it. Perhaps in particles the size of electrons, the wave aspect is fully as important, and even possibly more so, than the particle aspect.

the wave can continuously interfere with itself. Why should not the integer n in the Bohr equation merely represent the number of whole wavelengths demanded for this interference? If so, we see why only certain orbits are permitted; all those whose paths are not an integral number of wavelengths are excluded.

Thus, de Broglie made the plausible assumption that an electron would move only along orbits whose circumference contained a whole number of wavelengths. Thus,

$$2\pi r = n\lambda \qquad \text{(Eq. 29-1)}$$

where n is an integer. Now Einstein in his relativity theory had developed the principle of the equivalence of matter and energy, $E = mc^2$, where c is the velocity of light. Let us use v for velocity in place of c. Hence, $E = mv^2$. Now the energy of a photon is proportional to its frequency. We can say that it is equal to its frequency times a constant. The constant relevant here is Planck's constant, h. Hence $E = hf$.

Therefore, $\qquad hf = mv^2 \qquad \text{(Eq. 29-2)}$

But $\qquad f = \dfrac{c}{\lambda} = \dfrac{v}{\lambda}$

Substituting, $\qquad \dfrac{hv}{\lambda} = mv^2$

Dividing by v $\qquad \dfrac{h}{\lambda} = mv$

Transposing, $\qquad \lambda = \dfrac{h}{mv} \qquad \text{(Eq. 29-3)}$

Substituting this value of λ in Eq. 29-1, gives us

$$2\pi r = \frac{nh}{mv}$$

Transposing,

$$mvr = \frac{nh}{2\pi}$$

which is Bohr's first postulate (p. 407).

De Broglie thus gave a rational explanation for Bohr's equation for permitted orbits, an equation derived by Bohr through a combination of mathematical reasoning and insight, high level imagination, and a willingness to break with a theory that was consistently giving wrong answers. De Broglie did not carry this simple explanation far enough to develop it into a complete theory. It remained for Edwin Schroedinger of Austria to supply the additional ideas to do that.

Confirmation of de Broglie's initial suggestion was not long in coming. Einstein stated that if de Broglie was right, then electrons should show diffraction. Shortly afterwards, G. P. Thomson, son of J. J. Thomson, the discoverer of the electron, showed that electrons could be diffracted so as to produce an unmistakable interference pattern. Davisson and Germer in the United States did the same thing almost at the same time as Thomson.

Thomson passed a narrow beam of electrons through an exceedingly thin layer of metal. If electrons have a wave aspect, then this should show up, and it did, as a consequence of the intensity of the electron beam being strong in some directions and weak in others, just as we should expect if reinforcement and cancelation take place. Such a pattern cannot possibly be explained by the particle aspect.

Meanwhile, Schroedinger, who had taken seriously the suggestion that waves accompanied particles, showed that if this were so, one could "guess" the form of the wave equation of the resulting wave motion in a relatively simple way—provided one is sufficiently versed in higher mathematics. Those of us who are not will have to take his derivation on faith. All that we need to know about it here is its implications. It asserts that you can never be sure where the electrons are in the atom at any particular time. All we can do is to make assertions about their positions on the average, i.e., probability replaces exact descriptions. Heisenberg's uncertainty principle is applicable here. It states that *it is impossible to obtain accurate values for the position and velocity of an electron simultaneously.*[4]

This impossibility is not due to the lack of sufficiently refined experimental techniques, but to the fact that you cannot observe electrons without disturbing them. Suppose that under certain conditions you could "see" an electron. Now you need light to "see" it, but when you turn on the light to do so, the electron absorbs light energy instantaneously and so moves out of its normal path. Thus, the very act of observing causes it to change both its velocity and its position. We are therefore reduced to talking about the region about the atom in which the probability of finding the electron is greatest.

Eventually Schroedinger's work led to an entirely new system of mechanics known as wave mechanics, in which Newton's equation, $F = ma$, is replaced with a more complicated equation called the wave equation. Unfortunately the wave mechanical concept of the atom cannot be visualized. Yet the mind of man, being what it is, never

gives up trying to visualize its concepts no matter how abstract they are. We therefore draw diagrams to represent or to picture atoms, many of which are shown in the following pages. We must remember that none of them are actually pictures or diagrams in any sense of the words. For justification we refer you to the analogy between a map of the world and the actual world.

This new wave mechanical theory correctly accounts for all the observable properties, both quantitatively and qualitatively, of even the most complex spectra. Oddly enough, the four quantum numbers and the exclusion principle appear unchanged in the new theory. However, they appear as a natural result of the wave equation, whereas in the patched-up Bohr theory (where they originated) they appeared as a result of special assumptions introduced to account for the observable facts concerning spectra.

RECONCILIATION OF THE WAVE AND PARTICLE THEORIES OF LIGHT

The work of de Broglie and Schroedinger went far in reconciling Maxwell's electromagnetic theory and Einstein's photon theory. The former explained interference and diffraction, but failed completely to explain the photoelectric effect. The photon theory explained the photoelectric effect but failed to explain interference and diffraction. Now we find that electrons, which are clearly particles, have wavelike characteristics such as those that cause interference and diffraction. Thus, along with the dual nature of light, we have the dual nature of matter. We should there-

---

[4] This is in contradiction to the macroscopic world of matter in which both position and velocity are easily calculable, e.g., the velocity of the earth at a particular position in its orbit.

fore no longer be surprised that light can be correctly described in terms of both waves and particles. We should not, however, say that light is both waves and particles, because waves and particles are not capable of being the same thing. Difficult though it may be to understand how, the gap between the two theories has been bridged.

MODIFIED ORBITS

The uncertainty principle ruled out the definite orbits of Bohr, orbits in which a definite location and velocity was assigned to each electron. In its place there was substituted a three-dimensional atom in which all one can do is to make assertions where they are on the average. In this three-dimensional atom there are not only shells, but subshells as well. In the $n = 1(K)$ shell, there is only one subshell; in the $n = 2(L)$ shell, there are two subshells; in the $n = 3(M)$ shell, there are three subshells; in the $n = 4(N)$ shell, and all other shells, there are four subshells. The electrons in any one group of subshells have energies that are nearly the same. The principle quantum number, n, designates the shell, and the orbital quantum number designates the subshell. In the ground (unexcited) state each electron in an atom is confined to its home shell and subshell. Except under extreme conditions of excitation (such as bombardment by high-energy X-rays or when subjected to heat as intense as that in the cores of stars), it is only the electrons in the outer shell that leave their home shells.

We are now ready to study in more detail the structure of the atom.

SUMMARY

The Bohr theory had to be modified for multi-electron atoms largely because the original theory did not take into account the repulsive forces of the electrons for one another. The X-ray spectroscopists had postulated that the electrons were arranged in shells, which they designated by the letters K, L, M, N, O, P, and Q. The evidence from ionization potentials confirmed the shell arrangement. Revisions of the Bohr theory had to be in agreement with the evidence from these sources. The revisions had to allow for more transitions ("jumps") to give more spectral lines, and to give more accurate values for the energies of the electrons when in any of the permitted orbits.

The original Bohr model was as nearly a mechanical one as he could make it. The first revised theory was also a mechanical one. It allowed elliptical as well as circular orbits, allowed orbits to be oriented in various planes, and allowed two directions of electron spin. Introduced to quantize these arrangements in space were the four quantum numbers, n, l, m, s. The principal quantum number, n, allowed only certain diameters of the orbits, l allowed only certain degrees of ellipticity, m allowed only certain tilts of orbits, and s allowed only certain spins. Pauli added an exclusion principle, which excluded large numbers of possible arrangements of the electrons in an atom.

These revisions improved the theory but failed to bring the observational data from spectra into close enough harmony with theory. The first step towards a solution was taken by de Broglie when he advanced his matter—wave concept, a concept that assumed matter had both a particle and a wave aspect, in the manner that light did. Schroedinger, aided by others, developed the ideas of de Broglie into a full-fledged wave mechanical theory, a theory which is so mathematical in nature that no mechanical model can be constructed for it. The four quantum numbers and the exclusion principle appear in it as they do in the empirically revised Bohr theory. The wave mechanical theory reconciled, to a very large degree at least, the electromagnetic and photon theories of light.

EXERCISES

I. TERMS AND CONCEPTS

Quantum numbers, n, l, m, s
Pauli's exclusion principle
De Broglie's "matter waves"

Heisenberg's uncertainty principle
Shells and subshells

II. PROBLEMS

1. What is meant by the ionization potential of an element?

2. Explain how ionization potentials of the various elements give us evidence for the arrangement of electrons in an atom.

3. What do all possible orbits for a given value of n have in common?

4. What do all orbits for given values of n and l have in common? In what way or ways do they differ?

5. Suppose that all of the electrons in an atom like sodium were spinning in the same direction. Sodium would then have one prominent physical property that it does not possess. What is this property?

6. How many different orbits are possible for electrons with a principal quantum number of 2? Of 3? Of 4? How many for any value of n?

7. How many different energy states are possible for electrons with a principle quantum number of 2? Of 3? Of 4? For any value of n?

8. State Pauli's exclusion principle.

9. Comment briefly but significantly on de Broglie's matter waves.

10. What effect did de Broglie's theory have on Bohr's first postulate, p. 407?

11. What experimental evidence supported de Broglie's theory?

12. What new theory replaced the revised Bohr theory?

13. Does the acceptance of this new theory mean that the Bohr theory of the hydrogen atom has been completely discarded? Explain.

14. What is Heisenberg's uncertainty principle?

15. How did the wave mechanical theory modify the physical model of the atom postulated by Bohr?

CHAPTER XXX

Electronic Configuration of the Elements

Orderly arrangement is the task of the scientist. A science is built out of facts just as a house is built out of bricks. But a mere collection of facts cannot be called a science any more than a pile of bricks can be called a house.—HENRI POINCARÉ

Mendelyeev (1869) formulated the first periodic chart that even remotely resembled our present chart. He arranged the elements in the order of their atomic weights, and placed elements with similar properties in the same group (or family), i.e., in the same vertical column. He could offer no reason why the elements could be so arranged. Moseley, about 1913, removed the few anomalies in the order of atomic weights by using atomic numbers as the basis for the order in the table. This, of course, did not help explain the periodicities. The fact that, in the modern table, there are two elements in the first period, eight each in the next two, eighteen each in the next two and thirty-two in the sixth, seemed odd to say the least, especially when it was seen that these numbers are related as follows:

$$2 \times 1^2 = 2$$
$$2 \times 2^2 = 8$$
$$2 \times 3^2 = 18$$
$$2 \times 4^2 = 32$$

The evidence for the groups came chiefly from the valences of the elements. If we neglect the transition elements, the valence of an element is related to its position in the chart. The suspicion that electric charges were somehow involved in chemical reactions had been growing since early in the nineteenth century, chiefly, possibly wholly, on the evidence from electrolysis. Berzelius, the great Swedish analytical chemist, was its strongest advocate. We have already seen that Faraday came very close to the concept of a smallest possible charge from his work on the passage of electricity through ionic solutions. The passage of electricity through gases yielded still more information, information that resulted in the discovery of that smallest possible charge, the electron. Later the amount of this charge on the electron was measured, and still later its relationship to the rest of the atom was postulated by Rutherford and his fellow workers.

Since both atomic number and valence are related to position in the periodic table, it seemed likely that the chemical behavior of atoms depended on the number of electrons (which is determined by the nuclear charge) around the nucleus of the neutral atom. These nuclei are, in general, well screened from one another by the shells of electrons, and so are relatively far apart, so far apart that the chemical activity of atoms must depend directly on the electrons, and most probably on the outer electrons only. Bohr's theory gave credence to the above concepts by postulating that visible light has its origin not only in the behavior of electrons in atoms but most probably in the behavior of the outer electrons at that. If so, then it was those outer shells of electrons that are responsible for the spectra of visible, infrared, and ultraviolet light. Moreover it was, as we have already seen, a study of these spectra that gave us vital information about the electrons and their movements within the atom.

It is therefore not at all surprising that the understanding of the periodicity in the periodic chart was achieved through the study of electricity and light. It must not be assumed that there was any overall planning of these investigations. The principles that lie behind the periodic chart were uncovered by scientists from many countries, each working on problems that were of particular interest to him. It is questionable whether many could have related their immediate work to the periodic table.

More directly, from the revised Bohr theory and the wave mechanical theory came the four quantum numbers, which together with Pauli's exclusion principle, made it possible to "build" the elements. This is done by adding successive electrons, one at a time as we proceed from one element to the next. Of course, we have to add to the nucleus also, but we are going to take this for granted so as to avoid needless repetition.[1]

---

[1] What is added to the nucleus each time is one proton with its single positive charge, and whatever number of neutrons are necessary to stabilize the nucleus—which results in the observed atomic weights.

"BUILDING" THE ELEMENTS

We need a few guiding principles, all of which are already familiar. The more general ones are as follows:

1. Each electron has four quantum numbers, n, l, m, and s.

2. The principal quantum number, n, designates the shell. We will refer to the shells as the $n = 1$, $n = 2$, etc., shells.

3. The second quantum number, l, determines the shape of the orbit, i.e., its degree of ellipticity. Each different value of l for the same value of n gives the shape of one of the subshells.

4. The quantum number m gives the tilt of the orbit to a particular subshell when the atom is in a magnetic field.

5. The quantum number s designates the direction of spin of the electron relative to an external magnetic field. We will designate the spin as plus or minus.

6. Pauli's exclusion principle: No two electrons in the same atom can have the same four quantum numbers.

To these guiding principles we need to add a few restrictions governing possible new combinations of n, l, and m.

1. The value of n is an integer, 1, 2, 3, etc.

2. The possible values of l for any subshell range from 0 to $n - 1$ (including 0).

3. The possible values of m range from $-l$ to $+l$ (including 0).

4. The added electron normally (there are a few anomalies) must go into the vacant orbit with the lowest energy.[2]

---

[2] This is not arbitrary. Macroscopic objects free to do so always seek a level where their potential energy is lowest. Thus, water runs down hill, etc.

Fig. 30-1. Diagrammatic Representation of Subshells in Relation to Shells. The K shell of all atoms has only one subshell. The L shell has two, the M three, and all others have four subshells.

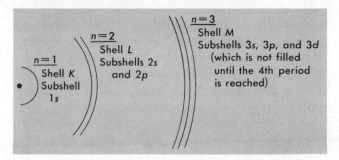

$n=1$
Shell K
Subshell 1s

$n=2$
Shell L
Subshells 2s and 2p

$n=3$
Shell M
Subshells 3s, 3p, and 3d (which is not filled until the 4th period is reached)

5. There never can be more than eight electrons [3] in the outermost shell, except for the first ($n = 1$) shell, in which the maximum number is two.

With these guiding principles, and the restrictions on the values of n, l, and m, we will now directly proceed to the building of the periodic chart. But first one caution: As we proceed from element to element in order, it is imperative to remember that each atom has all of the electrons of the preceding element (with their quantum numbers) plus one more with a set of quantum numbers that are different from any *preceding* it. In the following tables the spin quantum number will be indicated simply by $+$ and $-$.

First Period, $n = 1$ (Table 30-1)

If $n = 1$, then $l = 0$, $m = 0$, $s = -$, according to the second and third restrictions. These are the four quantum numbers of the lone electron in the hydrogen atom. Helium has two electrons. One of them will have the same four quantum numbers as the hydrogen electron. The other, according to Pauli, must have at least one quantum number that is different. For it, $n = 1$, $l = 0$, $m = 0$ and $s = +$; only the spin

[3] There are two anomalies which need not concern us here.

TABLE 30-1

POSSIBLE QUANTUM NUMBERS OF THE $n = 1$ SHELL (FIRST PERIOD)

Subshell 1s

l	0	
m	0	
s	$-$	$+$
Element	H	He

is different. There can be no more non-duplicating sets of quantum numbers as long as $n = 1$. The shell is therefore said to be closed. Note that it closes with an inert gas. Note also that there is only one subshell [4] in the $n = 1$ shell.

Second Period, $n = 2$ (Table 30-2)

All elements in this period have two shells, an $n = 1$ and an $n = 2$ shell. We will concern ourselves only with the electrons that will go into the $n = 2$ shell. From the second restriction (or Table 30-2) it is apparent that when $n = 2$, there are

[4] See Fig. 30-1 for a diagrammatic representation of shells and subshells.

TABLE 30-2

POSSIBLE QUANTUM NUMBERS OF THE $n = 2$ SHELL (SECOND PERIOD)

	Subshell 2s		Subshell 2p					
l	0		1					
m	0		−1		0		1	
s	−	+	−	+	−	+	−	+
Element	Li	Be	B	C	N	O	F	Ne

two possible values of l, 0 and 1. From $l = 0$ we get the one subshell for the first two elements, lithium and beryllium. Since this subshell is always filled when two electrons occupy it, the added electrons for the other six elements in the period must go into another subshell, one in which the value of l is 1. Note that this new value of l gives us two new values of m, so that there are six electrons in this subshell. Neon closes the period, for it has eight electrons in this shell. Note also that it is another inert gas.

Third Period, $n = 3$ (Table 30-3)

Elements in the third period all have all of the electrons present in neon, and also have electrons in the $n = 3$ shell. This gives us an additional value for l ($l = 2$). This shell is filled by electrons being added one by one, until, in argon, there are eight electrons in it. It thus *appears* [5] that the capacity of the $n = 3$ shell is the same as for the $n = 2$ shell. Since argon has eight

[5] We will find that the real capacity, as is shown in the later periods, is 18.

TABLE 30-3

POSSIBLE QUANTUM NUMBERS OF THE $n = 3$ SHELL (THIRD PERIOD)

	Subshell 3s		Subshell 3p						Subshell 3d
l	0		1						2
m	0		−1		0		1		
s	−	+	−	+	−	+	−	+	Not filled in this period
Element	Na	Mg	Al	Si	P	S	Cl	Ar	

TABLE 30-4

POSSIBLE QUANTUM NUMBERS OF THE $n = 4$ SHELL (FOURTH PERIOD)

Subshell 4s		Subshell 3d										Subshell 4p						Subshell 4d	Subshell 4f
			$n = 3, l = 2$																
l	0			2										1				2	3
m	0		−2		−1		0		1		2		−1		0		1			
s	−	+	−	+	−	+	−	+	−	+	−	+	−	+	−	+	−	+		
Element	K	Ca	Sc	Ti	V	Cr	Mn	Fe	Co	Ni	Cu	Zn	Ga	Ge	As	Se	Br	Kr	Not filled in this period	Not filled in this period

electrons in its outer shell, we are forced to invoke the fifth restriction, and so we start a new shell, $n = 4$, even though no electrons are in the subshell for $l = 2$ (Table 30-3). Note also that argon is another inert gas.

Fourth Period, n = 4 (Table 30-4)

Elements in the fourth period all have all of the electrons present in argon. In addition they all have one or more additional electrons in the $n = 4$ shell, and, of course different sets of quantum numbers. There is, however, one difference from the filling of the $n = 3$ shell. After potassium and calcium have gotten their added electrons in the $n = 4$ shell, the next *added* electron does not go into the fourth shell of the next element, scandium, but goes instead into scandium's unfilled $l = 2$ subshell (Table 30-3) of the $n = 3$ shell.

This continues for ten elements, scandium through zinc, for this subshell takes ten electrons. Thus, there are ten extra elements in this period. These constitute the first transition series, scandium through zinc. (See the chart on the inside of the front cover.) When this subshell is filled,

the elements following zinc get their added electrons in the $n = 4$ shell. Once again the period ends with eight electrons in the outer shell of krypton, another inert gas, even though no electrons with possible quantum numbers of $l = 2$ or $l = 3$ have gone into this shell. One of these subshells will be filled in the following period and the other in the period following that. This delayed filling accounts for the various transition series. The reason for the delayed filling is related to the close spacing of the energy levels for the higher values of n (Fig. 27-3).

ELECTRONIC CONFIGURATIONS AND PERIODICITIES IN THE PERIODIC TABLE

Before the development of the revised Bohr theory we might have guessed that the reason for the similarity in physical and chemical properties of members of the same family, e.g., the alkali metals or the halogens, was due to similarities in atomic structure. The experimental evidence for these similarities in atomic structure came from the long and arduous labor

TABLE 30-5

ELECTRONIC CONFIGURATIONS OF FOUR MAIN FAMILIES

Alkali Metals Family IA	Alkali Earth Metals Family IIA	Halogens Family VIIA	Inert Gases Family VIIIA
			He 2
Li 2, 1	Be 2, 2	F 2, 7	Ne 2, 8
Na 2, 8, 1	Mg 2, 8, 2	Cl 2, 8, 7	A 2, 8, 8
K 2, 8, 8, 1	Ca 2, 8, 8, 2	Br 2, 8, 8, 7	Kr 2, 8, 18, 8
Rb 2, 8, 18, 8, 1	Ba 2, 8, 18, 8, 2	I 2, 8, 18, 8, 7	Xe 2, 8, 18, 18, 8
Cs 2, 8, 18, 18, 8, 1	Sr 2, 8, 18, 18, 8, 2	At 2, 8, 18, 18, 8, 7	Rn 2, 8, 18, 32, 18, 8
Fr 2, 8, 18, 32, 18, 8, 1	Ra 2, 8, 18, 32, 18, 8, 2		

of spectroscopists working on atomic spectra. Some of the results are shown in Table 30-5.

The members of Family IA all have one electron in the outermost shell, those of IIA have two, those of VIIA have seven, and those of VIIIA have eight (except for helium). This is the only similarity that applies to *all* members of the same family, and at the same time is different from other main families. It is reasonable to suppose then that the essential character of the elements within a family must be determined by the number of electrons in the outermost shell. The other shells seem to make a difference in degree only, not in kind.

Note that the members of the inert gas family, except for helium, have eight electrons in the outer shell. No more can be put into this shell as long as it remains the outer shell. For that reason we call it a closed shell, for eight electrons in the outer shell closes the period. Two electrons in the outer shell does for helium (with only one shell) what eight does for those with more and larger shells. This eight-electron configuration, with the two-electron configuration of helium, are called stable octets; elements that have them are unreactive. *The essence of a chemical reaction is that the atoms involved reshuffle their electrons so that each atom has eight electrons in its outer shell, or at least has a share in eight electrons in that shell.* Each seeks to attain the stable octet configuration. Hydrogen is an exception since it is in the first period. Two electrons form its stable "octet." The atoms of the first and second periods, the first two elements of the third period, and uranium are diagrammatically represented in Fig. 30-2.

ELECTRONIC CONFIGURATION AND IONIZATION POTENTIALS

We have already seen that the closeness with which an atom holds an electron can be determined by measuring the energy required to pull it from the atom, and that this energy is called the ionization potential. While it is true that we used ionization potentials to aid us in determining the electronic configurations of atoms, we are still pleased to turn things around and see that, if we are able to determine the configurations *by other methods* (spectroscopy), the regularities in the increase of ionization potentials across the period and in the decrease downward in the families could be predicted.

ATOMIC SIZES

Atomic sizes are determined by nuclear charge and electronic configurations. The size of the nucleus plays no part, for the radius of the nucleus is only about 1/10,000 that of the whole atom. Atomic sizes play a role in all chemical reactions, more in some than in others. Knowledge of atomic and ionic sizes comes in part from experimental and in part from theoretical sources. The experimental data comes chiefly from X-ray diffraction experiments in crystals, and electron diffraction by molecules. The Bohr theory of the hydrogen atom predicts that the radius of an orbit is proportional to n^2, where n is the principal quantum number, a prediction that is confirmed by the wave mechanical theory. (The normal orbit of the hydrogen electron is in its $n = 1$ shell.)

This means that if the hydrogen atom had an electron in an $n = 2$ shell, its radius would be four times that of its $n = 1$ shell.

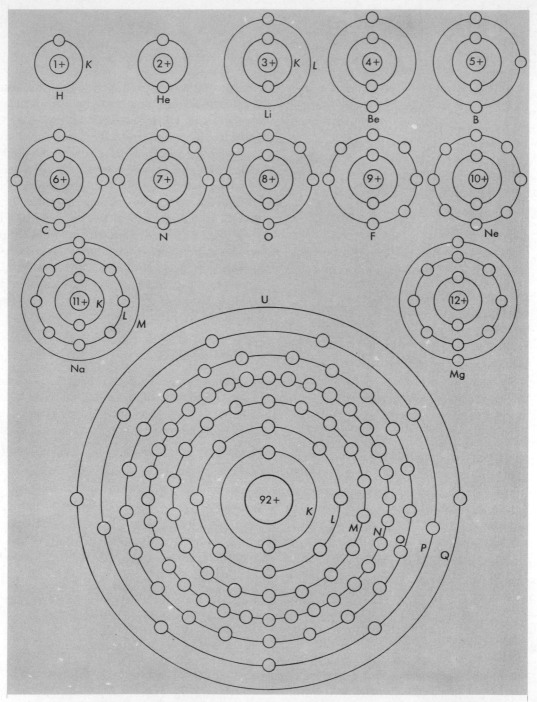

Fig. 30-2. Diagrammatic Representation of Atoms of Some Elements. Note the numbers of shells and the numbers of electrons (small circles) in each shell. Subshells are not shown. These drawings are not in any sense to be considered as pictures of atoms.

The radius of the $n = 3$ shell would be nine times that of the $n = 1$ shell. Actually these shells, and others farther out, may contain the lone electron of hydrogen when the atom is excited because it is to one of them that the electron "jumps" when in the excited state. Thus, we see that the radius of the hydrogen atom increases enormously when excited. However, our definition of atomic radius is that it is the radius of the largest shell when the atom is in its unexcited state. By analogy the radius of our solar system is that of the radius of the orbit of the planet farthest from the sun. Some orbits of atoms are circular and some are elliptical, but we may treat them as circular, for the sizes of the circular and elliptical orbits for any particular value of n average out the same. The radius of the hydrogen atom is 0.53×10^{-8} cm (0.53 A).

Let us do a little theorizing—and a little predicting—about the radii of atoms and ions with higher atomic numbers than hydrogen, i.e., atoms with more charges on the nucleus. Let us consider an atom of lithium, atomic number 3, with two electrons removed. This makes a doubly charged positive ion, Li^{++}, in which the remaining single electron revolves in the $n = 1$ shell about the triply charged nucleus. This makes possible a direct comparison of the radius of its $n = 1$ shell with that of the hydrogen atom because there are no other electrons in our lithium ion to alter the situation by their repulsive effects on one another. This radius, according to the Bohr theory, should be only $\frac{1}{3}$ that of the $n = 1$ shell of the hydrogen atom, and the wave mechanical theory confirms it. Following the same line of reasoning the radius of the $n = 1$ shell of sodium, atomic number 11, should be $\frac{1}{11}$ that of the hydrogen

electron, that of the K shell of potassium should be $\frac{1}{19}$, etc. Thus, the K shell becomes smaller and smaller with increasing atomic number.[6]

The same should be true of the $n = 2$, $n = 3$, etc. shells, and it is, but not to the same extent. The reason is that there are two effects that tend to counteract this "squeezing" of the electrons in a particular shell into orbits of smaller radius. One is due to the fact that the electrons in the outer shell are shielded, or screened, from the attractive forces of the nucleus by the nonvalence electrons in the intervening shells, which neutralize a like number of charges on the nucleus. Thus, the valence electrons of successive members of a family experience the same effective nuclear charge, a charge of about one in the case of the alkali metals. Thus, even though there are 55 charges on the nucleus of cesium, the valence electron experiences a charge of about 1 because of the "neutralization" of 54 charges by 54 electrons in the five inner shells. On the other hand, the $1s$ electrons are not screened at all, the $2s$ electrons by only the two in the $n = 1$ shell, the $3s$ electrons by those in the $n = 2$ and $n = 3$ shells, etc. Thus, screening gets better from one shell to the next, so the squeezing is less.

The other effect is that as we crowd more and more electrons into a shell, there is a tendency to increase the diameter of any

[6] For the elements with high atomic numbers—above 82—this decreasing radius of the $n = 1$ shell, brings the $1s$ electrons very near the nucleus. We might surmise that this might be the cause of, or at least in part contribute to, the instability of these radioactive atoms. For the lighter atoms there is still plenty of room for the $1s$ electrons to move in closer to the nucleus, for the radius of the $n = 1$ shell of hydrogen is about 10,000 times the radius of the nucleus.

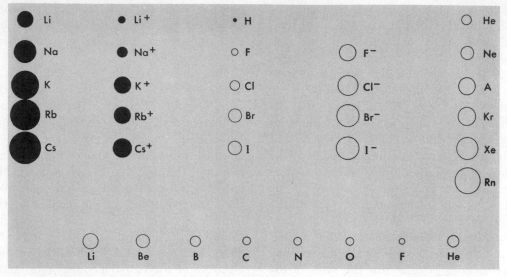

Fig. 30-3. Relative Sizes of Atoms and Ions. The atoms in the lower row are not drawn to the same scale as the others. Note that ions of the metals are smaller than their corresponding atoms, whereas in the nonmetals the reverse is true. Note the decrease in size in a period until an inert gas is reached. Note the increase in size within a family.

uncompleted shell because of the mutual repulsion of the electrons in it.

An examination of Fig. 30-3 shows that the increase in the number of nuclear charges in a period produces the dominating effect, and so the radii become smaller and smaller until the end of the period, i.e., until an inert gas is reached. Here the mutual repulsion predominates, and the radius of the inert gas atom abruptly increases.

The net effect of these tendencies to increase or decrease the radii of the various shells, is that the sizes of atoms (Fig. 30-3) vary within small limits, considering the enormous differences in their masses, 1 for hydrogen and 238 for uranium. Note that as the atomic number increases *within a period,* atomic size decreases, except for the inert gas at the end of a period. Note

also that as atomic number increases *within a family,* there is relatively slight increase of size except in the inert gas family.

Note also (Fig. 30-3) that the sizes of ions are very different from those of their parent atoms. Every positive ion is much smaller than its parent atom, and every negative ion is much larger than its parent atom. The reasons are not hard to find. Positive ions have one less shell than their parent atoms, and negative ions have eight electrons in their outer shells, so that what we said about the increase of size of the inert gas atoms at the end of a period due to the predomination of mutual repulsions applies equally well to negative ions.

This analysis of the electronic configurations of the various kinds of atoms has several satisfying and rewarding results. Chief among them is the emergence of certain regularities in electronic arrangements which permit us to demonstrate correlations between these regularities and the periodicities of the periodic chart, and, finally, between these regularities and periodicities on the one hand and the chemical properties of atoms on the other. Once these relationships are understood, the fundamental mysteries of chemical reactions disappear. We should constantly bear in mind that the electronic configurations of the atoms have been determined by experimental evidence, evidence acquired through the study of atomic spectra and by measurement of ionization potentials. By use of the Bohr theory, by use of the knowledge gained from the study of spectra and ionization potentials, and by use of a knowledge of certain chemical properties of the elements, e.g., valence, we have been able to deduce the structure of atoms. We shall now turn things around and see if we can use the structure of atoms to explain their chemical and physical properties.

SUMMARY

The suspicion that electronic charges associated with atoms were somehow involved with chemical reactions went back to the early days of experimentation with electrolytic solutions. This concept was a hundred years in reaching fruition. The first major step was taken when Bohr advanced his theory, a theory that also gave the first explanation of atomic spectra. Atomic spectra gave information about electrons that eventually led to an understanding of chemical reactions, and, eventually to an understanding of the arrangement of the elements in the periodic table.

Using the four quantum numbers that arose from the revisions of the Bohr theory, it is possible to "build" the elements if certain restrictions governing possible combinations of the four numbers are used. By doing this, the major structural features of all the atoms are made apparent, and the periodicities of the elements are explained. Many minor features still remain without completely satisfactory answers. Atomic and ionic sizes play a role in all chemical reactions. Knowledge of them comes from both experimental evidence (chiefly X-ray diffraction effects) and theoretical considerations.

EXERCISES

I. TERMS AND CONCEPTS
   Guiding principles
   Restrictions on combinations of quantum numbers
   Atomic and ionic sizes

II. PROBLEMS
   1. Give the four quantum numbers of the first electron in helium. Of the second electron in helium.
   2. Structurally what is the difference between an atom of hydrogen and an atom of helium?
   3. How many values of l are there when $n = 2$? When $n = 3$? When $n = 4$?
   4. How many *new* values of m are made possible by an increase of 1 in the value of l? How many new sets of quantum numbers are made possible by this increase in the value of l? Explain.
   5. How many electrons may occupy the same orbit? If more than one, how must they differ?
   6. No electron in an element in the third period has a quantum number $l = 2$, even though our restrictions (p. 446) do not forbid

it. Why? Do later periods have this $n = 3$, $l = 2$ subshell filled?

7. Normally the added electrons alternate with respect to spin. Sometimes, e.g., in iron, they do not, so that there may be several orbits of different tilt (but same value of l) that have electrons of the same direction of spin but none with the opposite spin. This may account for what property of iron? Explain.

8. How many elements comprise each of the first four periods?

9. The electronic configuration of an atom is given by writing the numbers of electrons it has in each shell, e.g., Na (2, 8, 8, 1). Without referring to the periodic chart write the electronic configurations of each of the following elements. (Note: None is beyond the fourth period. The number given with the element is its atomic number.) C (6), Ne (10), Mg (12), P (15), Ar (18), K (19), Br (35), Fe (26), Zn (30), F (9).

10. To what do the members of the alkali family owe their similar physical and chemical properties? To what do they owe most of their differences?

11. In what way does the charge on the nucleus influence atomic size? In what way does the electronic configuration influence it?

12. Positive ions are smaller than their parent atoms and negative ions larger. Explain.

13. How does atomic size vary within a period? Explain.

14. How does atomic size vary within a family? Explain.

15. Why does an atom with two shells not have twice the radius of an atom with one shell? (Make your answer meaningful.)

ATOMIC STRUCTURE AND CHEMICAL COMBINATION

We have seen that the original Bohr theory was greatly modified so that it might be applied to the atoms of the other elements. Several scientists, most prominent among whom was
Bohr himself, made a thorough revision of the theory in order
to bring it into closer agreement with the experimental evidence.
We have learned that the various quantum numbers arose artificially in order to explain the spectral observations, and how
they were used to "build" the periodic table. This revised theory
scored enormous successes, even though the agreement between
observations of spectral lines and measurements of the wavelengths involved were not precisely in agreement with the calculations from the theory. Many things were left unexplained, e.g.,
the character of the "jump" between orbits, and the fact that
electrons showed diffraction effects.

We have also learned that de Broglie made the suggestion that
perhaps matter had a wave aspect as well as a particle aspect, and
that this suggestion led to the development of a wave mechanical
theory that gave precise agreement between theory and observation. However, the revised Bohr theory, imprecise as it is, is
still retained because it gives us a visualizable model of the atom,
whereas the wave mechanical theory does not. It is completely
abstract and so highly mathematical and nonvisual that we can-

not present it here in any form. We cannot make a model of something that at times behaves like a particle and at others like a wave.

We simply cannot visualize either the structure of atoms or the phenomena of chemical combination by means of the wave mechanical theory. Apparently the conditions within the atom are so different from anything in man's ordinary experience that they cannot be pictured. Thus, the revised Bohr theory gives us the only possible model, and, as we have said before, the mind of man forever tries to interpret its conceptual schemes in terms of mechanical models. Incorrect though it may be, we can reason from it, and it leads us to the correct conclusions, for the most part at least. If we keep ourselves aware of its limitations, and check our results against those of the wave mechanical theory, we can prevent ourselves from falling into the traps that prematurely completed mental pictures often set for us.

The revised theory of the arrangements of electrons about the nucleus and their behavior is the result of the work of many men, and so no man's name can properly be attached to it. It has its roots firmly fixed in the Bohr theory of the hydrogen atom, however, and so we are apt to think of it and refer to it as a revised Bohr theory simply as a matter of convenience, particularly since Bohr played a prominent part in its revision. To a large degree the success or failure of the theory stands or falls on its ability to explain the nature of the chemical bond, the fundamental details of chemical reactions, the reasons for the distinctions between metals and nonmetals and a number of other physical and chemical phenomena. We shall therefore attempt to correlate atomic structures with the types of bonds in chemical reactions and certain physical properties of the elements.

By the chemical bond we mean the link that holds atoms together in molecules. We shall assume that only the electrons in the outermost shell are involved in chemical binding, an assumption that will have to be checked against the facts if it is expected to turn out to be valid. Of primary importance in this correlation is the question of valence. We will not deal with it in its entirety in a separate section, but will include much of it in the discussions of chemical reaction by electron transfer and by electron sharing, for much of the science of chemistry is included in the study of valence.

CHAPTER XXXI

The Electronic Theory of Chemical Bonding

The underlying physical laws necessary for the mathematical theory of a large part of physics and the whole of chemistry are now completely known.
—P. A. M. DIRAC (*Nobel Prize, Physics, 1933*)

We have dealt at some length with the arrangement of electrons in atoms because no understanding of chemical reactions is possible without it. In the hundred and fifty years after the laying of the foundations of modern chemistry by Lavoisier, an enormous amount of factual data had been accumulated, chiefly by empirical means, for the basic understanding was missing. Chemists from Mendelyeev on were struggling to correlate all of the physical and chemical properties of the elements, but not much could be done until the basic ideas of atomic structure had been developed. With Rutherford's theory (1911) that atoms consisted of positively charged nuclei with the negatively charged electrons circling them, and Bohr's theory (1912) that the electrons circled the nuclei in specified orbits with determinable

amounts of energy, it became possible for the theoreticians to attack the basic problems of chemical affinity with some chance of success.

These basic problems were solved in the period between the two world wars, after the essential data concerning electronic configuration had been accumulated and the interpretations had been made. Atoms obviously combine to form molecules because of some kind of affinity for one another, but this is in no sense an explanation, no more so than is the statement that objects fall to the earth when dropped because of gravitational affinity for one another.

The first step towards basic understanding came when the great American chemist, G. N. Lewis (1875–1946), suggested that atoms of elements other than those of the inert gases would be more stable if they could somehow acquire eight electrons in their outer shells. This hypothesis obviously assumes that it is the presence of eight electrons (two for helium) [1] in the outer shells of the inert gases that accounts for their chemical stability.

INTRODUCTION TO VALENCE

What the chemists once referred to as the chemical affinity of one atom for another, we now call the *chemical bond*. *The chemical bond is formally defined as the attractions between two atoms within a molecule,* attractions in part electrical, in part magnetic. [2] Valence was originally

---

[1] From now on we are going to include helium as an atom with a stable "octet" although its octet is actually a duet. This will save us needless repetition.

[2] Some atomic physicists now define valence

considered a measure of the combining capacity of atoms, a measure of the readiness of atoms to react, and even today, if we insist on a single definition, it is still as good a one as we can formulate. However, today we develop the concept of valence in more than one way. No single definition can possibly be broad enough to include all of the various shades of meaning that have been given to it. Valence signifies much more than combining capacity; it can tell us much about the structure of the atom, what it is likely to combine with, etc. In fact, much of the science of chemistry is a detailed study of valence.

IONIC OR ELECTROVALENT BONDS

Once one accepts the existence of ions as atoms that have lost or gained one, two, or three electrons, and so are electrically charged, it is not difficult to apply the laws of electrostatics to them. The positive and negative ions are easily visualized as being held together in pairs or groups because of the attractions between unlike charges. Thus, when we think of a "molecule" of sodium chloride, we somewhat loosely think of the positive sodium ion being held to the negative chlorine atom by a simple electrostatic attraction; the terms electrovalence or ionic valence are consequently applied.

Positive electrovalence is the number of electrons in the outer shell of a metal. More correctly, it is the number of electrons that an atom must lose to attain the stable octet. Thus, atoms with configurations of

2, 8, 1 and 2, 8, 8, 2 can attain the 2, 8 and 2, 8, 8 configurations of neon and argon, respectively, by the loss of one and two electrons, respectively.

Negative electrovalence is the number of electrons that an atom must gain to attain the stable octet. Thus, fluorine, 2, 7, must gain one electron to attain the configuration of neon, and oxygen must in fact gain two.

Experiments show that elements that are close together in the periodic table have little or no tendency to form ions [3] when they combine. It is therefore reasonable to expect that two atoms of oxygen, or of any other diatomic elemental gas, cannot be held together by ionic attractions, for any two atoms of the same element have the same electron-holding ability. Yet two atoms of oxygen *do* unite to form molecules, and this tendency is so strong that the elemental gases (other than the inert gases) do not exist free as discrete atoms, but are paired up to form molecules. Clearly there is more to valence than ionic valence.

COVALENCE

G. N. Lewis, therefore, introduced the concept of the covalent bond. This bond is an electron-pair bond; it involves the sharing of pairs of electrons rather than their transfer, and it applies particularly (but by no means exclusively) to the elements that are close together in the periodic table. *The covalence of an element is the*

---

as the number of free spins multiplied by 2. This is not a meaningful definition for us, and so we will ignore it.

[3] How ionic a compound is can often be tested by passing an electric current through a solution of it. Only ionic solutions conduct electric currents, and the more strongly ionic they are, the better they conduct it.

number of electron pairs that are shared. There are varieties of covalence, the chief ones being polar and nonpolar.

The terms *polar* and *nonpolar* refer to the distribution of charge *in* the molecule. We remind you that the nuclei of atoms carry positive charges, the electrons the negative charges. When atoms combine, the charges are necessarily redistributed in the resulting molecule. If the redistribution in this molecule is such that the two kinds of charge have a common center, the molecule is said to be nonpolar; the charges are symmetrically arranged so that there is no tendency for the molecule to orient itself in an electric field; perhaps this distribution of charge is analogous to that of a mythical magnet in which the north and south poles coincide.

If there is no common center, both the molecule *and* the bonds holding it together are polar; the distribution of the two kinds of charge is asymmetrical, so that one part, or end, if you like, of the molecule has a residue of positive charge, the other a residue of negative charge. There will, of course, be more or less tendency for such molecules to orient themselves in an electric field. The more asymmetrical the distribution of charge, the more polar the molecule. Or, we might say, the farther the two centers of charge are from each other, the more asymmetrical the distribution, and, at the same time, the more polar the molecule.

In ions the center of the positive charge is at the center of the positive ion, and that of the negative charge is at the center of the negative ion. This is as far away from each other as the centers can get. Thus, "molecules" that have ionic valence are the most strongly polar. In dilute solutions they are completely polar for here they act independently of each other.

It follows from this discussion that there are varying degrees of polarity, from the completely polar "molecule" to the completely nonpolar. In other words, there is no sharp line of demarcation between electrovalence and covalence.

DOT SYSTEM OF NOTATION

We find it desirable to make a brief digression here in order to introduce a useful method of picturing electron transfer and electron sharing before and after a chemical reaction. This system was made possible by the realization that it was only the electrons in the outer shells of atoms that played a role in chemical reactions. The nucleus of the atom together with whatever inner shells there may be is conveniently called the *kernel;* it is represented by the symbol of the element. Dots, arranged singly or in pairs, represent the electrons in the outermost shell, i.e., they represent the valence electrons. The atoms of the first three periods are represented below by the dot system. Note that all mem-

H·   ·He·

Li· ·Be· ·B· ·C· ·N: O: ·F: :Ne:

Na· ·Mg· ·Al· ·Si· ·P: S: ·Cl: :A:

bers of the same family have the same number of dots. Some examples of molecules written in this system are:

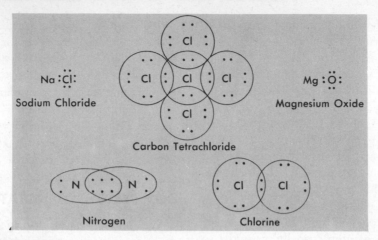

The circles are drawn to show that each atom has a share in eight electrons. We can now return to the problem of chemical reactions.

IONIZATION POTENTIAL, ELECTRON AFFINITY, AND ELECTRONEGATIVITY

These three concepts are useful in varying degrees in discussing the underlying principles of chemical reactions by electron transfer (as in electrovalent compounds) and by electron sharing (as in covalent compounds).

Some aspects of *ionization potentials* have already been considered on pp. 418–420. In chemical reactions we are concerned with its use as an aid to the understanding of the creation of positive ions. The equations for the formation of positive sodium and magnesium ions from neutral atoms are as follows:

$$\text{Na·} \rightarrow \text{Na}^+ + e^-$$

$$\text{·Mg·} \rightarrow \text{Mg}^{++} + 2e^-$$

In other words, neutral metallic atoms → positive ions + electrons.

The ionization potential is the energy (in electron volts) that is required to induce an atom *in the vapor phase* to part with an electron and form a positive ion. The ease (or difficulty) of transfer of the electrons in the outer shells of those elements that give up electrons during chemical reactions determines the readiness of these elements to react. Thus, a knowledge of ionization potentials helps us measure the reactivity of those elements forming positive ions.

Some nonmetals gain electrons to form negative ions. Equations for the process are as follows:

$$:\overset{..}{\text{Cl}}· + e^- \rightarrow :\overset{..}{\underset{..}{\text{Cl}}}:^-$$

$$:\overset{..}{\underset{..}{\text{O}}} + 2e^- \rightarrow :\overset{..}{\underset{..}{\text{O}}}:^{--}$$

It can be seen that these atoms have a tendency to gain electrons rather than to lose them, so their ionization potentials are not as pertinent as their *electron affinities*. This is a measure of the energy *released* when an atom acquires an extra electron to form a negative ion. A knowledge of electron affinities combined with that of

TABLE 31-1

ELECTRONEGATIVITIES OF SOME ELEMENTS *

H								He
2.1								0
Li	Be			B	C	N	O	F	Ne
1.0	1.5			2.0	2.5	3.0	3.5	4.0	0
Na	Mg			Al	Si	P	S	Cl	A
0.9	1.2			1.5	1.8	2.1	2.5	3.0	0
K	Ca	Sc		Ga	Ge	As	Se	Br	Kr
0.8	1.0	1.3			1.7	2.0	2.4	2.8	0
Rb	Sr	Y		In	Sn	Sb	Te	I	Xe
0.8	1.0	1.3			1.7	1.8	2.1	2.4	0
Cs	Ba			Tl	Pb	Bi	Po	At	Rn
0.7	0.9								0

* Data from Linus Pauling, *Nature of the Chemical Bond*, Courtesy Cornell Univ. Press, Ithaca, N. Y., 1940.

ionization potentials can be used to predict which kinds of atoms can remove electrons from other kinds.

For various reasons the *electronegativities* of the elements are used instead. The electronegativity of an element is a measure of its electron-attracting ability. A scale based on certain quantities characterizing a bond (e.g., the energy needed to break up a molecule into its component atoms), called the scale of electronegativity has been developed. The concept of electronegativity applies to all atoms, even to those with a greater tendency to lose than to gain electrons. It is reasonable to expect that atoms which hold their electrons most firmly should have the greatest tendency to gain another one,[4] and those that lose electrons most easily should have the least tendency. It should also be apparent that those elements with the highest ionization potentials have the highest electronegativity.

The element with the greatest tendency to gain electrons is assigned a value of 4.0 on Pauling's electronegativity scale. Cesium, the least electronegative of the naturally occurring elements, is assigned a value of 0.7 (Table 31-1).

The electronegativity scale [5] is useful for predicting which bonds are ionic (electrovalent) and which are covalent. The greater the difference in electronegativity between two atoms, the greater the likelihood of reaction, the greater the energy of the reaction, and the more likely that the bonds will be ionic. Thus, the bonds between the alkali metals and the halogens are expected to be ionic by a comparison of their electronegativities. We can predict that cesium and fluorine with the

[4] The inert gases, for reasons already stated, have zero tendency to gain other electrons, despite the fact that they hold their electrons firmly.

[5] An electronegativity scale (not this one) may be developed from the following formula:

$$\frac{\text{Ionization potential} + \text{electron affinity}}{2}$$

greatest disparity in their electronegativities of all reactive elements $(4.0 - 0.7 = 3.3)$ should form strongly ionic bonds. Conversely, we can predict that elements with a small disparity in their electronegativities will form covalent bonds. The polarity of covalent bonds can also be predicted, for the greater the disparity, the more polar the bond. We will find ample use for the concept later.

ELECTRONIC THEORY OF CHEMICAL BONDING

We have presented a number of ideas concerning the behavior of atoms during chemical combination, and, in doing so, have given explanations of one sort or another. We have not presented any theory in formal form. The theory that attempts to unify all of the facts, observations, concepts, etc. may well be called the electronic theory of chemical bonding.

The basic assumptions of the electronic theory may be stated as follows:

1. The only electrons involved in normal chemical reactions are those in the outermost shell. These are the valence electrons.

2. The most stable configuration of any atom is that of one of the inert gases. This configuration has eight electrons in the outermost shell (called the stable octet), except for helium, in which the stable configuration is two.

3. Atoms enter into chemical combination only if they can acquire a more stable configuration than they have in the atomic state. For most atoms this is the stable octet, or a close approximation to it. The stable octet is ideally obtained by electron transfer, and the close approximation by electron sharing.

METALS AND NONMETALS

The distinctions between metals and nonmetals present a number of problems that any fruitful theory of chemical bonding must be able to explain. One has to do with the position of the heavy diagonal (zigzag) line (in the periodic chart on the inside of the front cover) that separates the elements into metals and nonmetals. Why does this line cut diagonally downward to the right? Why do metals have almost no tendency to combine with one another [6] but combine readily with most nonmetals? Why do certain nonmetals combine so readily with one another, so much so that the number of such compounds is almost infinite? Why do metals have positive valence, and nonmetals, with the exception of hydrogen, negative valence? Why do metals conduct both heat and electricity so much better than the nonmetals? Why may both the photoelectric effect and thermionic emission be observed in metals but never in nonmetals? Why do the metals have the power to form bases, and the nonmetals acids? Why do metals have reducing power, the nonmetals oxidizing power? The electronic theory must be able to explain these phenomena, and in doing so it must explain the arrangement of the elements in the periodic table.

There should be a correlation between theory, electronic configurations, and the evidence from the experimentally deter-

---

[6] We will omit from consideration alloys in which some combination does occur.

mined ionization potentials of the various kinds of atoms. The metals, on the left side of the periodic table, begin each period, and nonmetals end them (except for the first, in which there are no metals). The ionization potentials (Fig. 29-1) rise in each period as we pass from the metals to the nonmetals, with the inert gas at the end having the highest. To start the following period the ionization potential drops sharply to slightly below that of the preceding period. Again it rises across the period but not to as high a level as for the preceding period. This behavior is attributed to the fact that the valence electrons in each succeeding period are in a shell that is at a greater distance from the nucleus, which is the dominating effect in spite of increasing nuclear charge.

Thus, the data from the ionization potentials shows that the electrons of the alkali metals are most loosely held. Activity is therefore highest among metals of the alkali family, for the energy to remove the one outer electron from any of them is (except for lithium) less than for any other element. Other atoms with higher electronegativities have little trouble removing them. Even photons of low energy can remove them.

As the ionization potentials rise across the period, the energy necessary to remove electrons rises until it becomes too high for the photon to be effective. Thus, one aspect of the photoelectric effect is explained. Electrons can be ejected from nonmetals, but it takes high energy photons to do it. A parallel situation exists in thermionic emission except that it is heat (kinetic) energy that ejects the loosely held electrons. If we remember that an electric current consists of a flow of electrons in a conductor, and that a potential difference between the two ends of a conductor causes a current to flow, it is apparent that the current will flow most easily in conductors where the electrons are held most loosely. Thus, conductivity decreases as we proceed from elements with one outer or valence electron to those with more. The valence electrons in the nonmetals are held so tightly that it takes a potential difference of many thousands or even tens of thousands of volts to make them move appreciably in a linear direction. Thus, the nonmetals make good insulators.

Normally metals do not combine with other metals, because it is not possible for them to obtain stable octets by electron transfer. To attain stable octets with other metals those metals with one, two, or three electrons in their outer shells would have to transfer their valence electrons, and no metal has a sufficiently high electronegativity to take electrons away from any other metal. Therefore, to combine, some kind of electron sharing must take place. We will not delve farther into this problem except to note again that covalence, for the metals, is most prevalent among those with more than three electrons in their outer shells. On the other hand, nonmetals can attain the stable octet by sharing electron pairs, for all of them contain at least four electrons in the outer shell. Discussions of the acid and base forming powers, and the oxidizing and reducing powers of nonmetals and metals are reserved for later chapters.

THE SPECIAL CASE OF HYDROGEN

In the first period hydrogen seems to occupy the place of a metal. In fact, it has the electronic configuration of a metal, one electron in its one and only shell. It is unique among the elements in that it is the only one with no neutrons in the nucleus.[7] When it loses its electron, it becomes a positive ion (as do the metals). Furthermore, its chief combining ability is with the nonmetals. On the other hand, it has a higher ionization potential than any of the metals; it does not conduct electricity as they do, even when it is liquefied; it does not generally give up an electron when it enters into chemical combination, but instead it shares electrons; it reacts with many metals to form hydrides as do the nonmetals to form chlorides, etc.; its compounds with the nonmetals are not salts as are most simple compounds of metals and nonmetals; and its physical properties are wholly nonmetallic.

Hydrogen has, then, a curious mixture of metallic and nonmetallic properties. Strictly speaking there is no proper place for it in the periodic table; different periodic charts show it in a variety of places. Let us look again at its electronic configuration. Take away its lone electron and a bare nucleus is left, which consists of a single proton. It is then a positive ion, like the metallic ions. But the hydrogen atom can gain an electron, attaining the configuration of the helium atom. It is then a negative ion, H^-; but since it has but a single charge on the nucleus, it does not have the great ability that the halogens have to attract and hold more electrons. Its compounds with metals are easily broken up because of this inability to hold their valence electrons. It has a high ionization potential, nearly three times that of

[7] A very small percentage of hydrogen atoms have neutrons in their nuclei.

the alkali metals; thus, it does not easily give up its electron. Having little ability to attract other electrons, and a relatively high ability to retain the one it has, it reacts chemically by sharing electrons. Thus, the unusual properties of hydrogen are explained by its electronic structure.

INERT GASES

These gases all have eight electrons in their outer shells, except helium, which has two. They are also completely inert chemically. They will neither combine with any other element, nor with their own kind of atom to form diatomic molecules. This antisocial behavior causes them to be the only monatomic gases, even down to very low temperatures. All atoms that do not have eight (two for helium) electrons in their outer shells are chemically active to some degree. All this seems to mean that the atoms of the inert gases have the most perfect stability possible for atoms of any kind. It is this stability that gives us the second assumption of our electronic theory.

CHEMICAL REACTIONS BY ELECTRON TRANSFER— ELECTROVALENCE

As we have already seen, the alkali metals (group IA) react readily with the halogens (group VIIA). Each atom of the alkali metals has one electron in its outermost shell. If each were to transfer this lone electron to another element, thereby becoming a positive ion, it would have the electronic configuration of the inert gas just preceding it in the periodic table. Thus the sodium *ion* would have the configuration of the neon *atom*, the potassium *ion* would have that of the argon *atom*, etc.

All members of the family have an electro-valence of +1 because each transfers one electron per atom.

The halogens each have seven electrons in their outermost shells, one short of the stable octet, and so have an electrovalence of −1. If an atom of a halogen acquires another electron, thereby becoming a nega-tive ion, it would have the electronic con-figuration of the inert gas nearest it in the periodic table. Thus, the fluoride *ion* would have the configuration of the neon *atom*, and the chloride *ion* would have that of the argon *atom*, etc.

The reaction can be written as follows:

$$Na\cdot \; + \; \cdot \overset{\cdot \cdot}{\underset{\cdot \cdot}{Cl}}: \;\rightarrow\; Na : \overset{\cdot \cdot}{\underset{\cdot \cdot}{Cl}}:$$

Note that all of the electrons are around the chlorine ion; the lone sodium electron has joined the seven electrons of chlorine to make a stable octet. The sodium ion is also surrounded by eight electrons (as is neon, the preceding element) but the dot system does not show this because these electrons are not in the outer shell of the sodium atom.

If magnesium, with two electrons in its outer shell, combines with chlorine to form $MgCl_2$, one atom of it combines with two atoms of chlorine. In order to attain the configuration of the nearest inert gas (neon), magnesium must transfer two elec-trons per atom. Since a chlorine atom has seven electrons in its outer shell, it can ac-cept only one more in attaining the stable octet, and so each of two chlorine atoms takes one electron from magnesium. Mag-nesium, and all members of its family, has a valence of +2. In the dot notation we write the reaction as follows:

$$\cdot Mg\cdot \; + \; : \overset{\cdot \cdot}{\underset{\cdot \cdot}{Cl}}: \overset{\cdot \cdot}{\underset{\cdot \cdot}{Cl}}: \;\rightarrow\; : \overset{\cdot \cdot}{\underset{\cdot \cdot}{Cl}}: Mg : \overset{\cdot \cdot}{\underset{\cdot \cdot}{Cl}}:$$

Certain questions are in order here, chief among them one concerning the underlying reason for the transfer of electrons from a metallic atom to a nonmetallic one. We have stated that the stable octet configura-tion is attained for both atoms, but this is no reason at all, for neither atom can

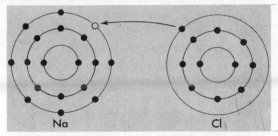

Fig. 31-1. Chemical Reaction by Elec-tron Transfer. If the two atoms come close enough together, the lone outer electron of sodium will "fall" into the outer shell of the chlorine atom simply be-cause the chlorine nucleus has a greater electrical attraction for it than does the sodium nucleus, i.e., because chlorine has a much greater electronegativity than sodium.

"know" that the transfer will result in a stable octet. Electrical and magnetic forces must be involved in one way or an-other. We are sure that in those reactions in which the net result is a liberation of energy, the energy state of the system is lower than before the reaction. The mech-anism by which this energy is released is a complex one that has not yet been success-fully investigated. That ions are formed in electron transfer reactions is easily checked by passing an electric current through either a water solution of the compound, or the molten compound. Such compounds form one class of ionic compounds. All chemical reactions between members of Families IA and IIA on the one hand, and the halogens on the other result in the formation of ionic compounds. There are many other examples.

It is also fair to ask why certain compounds are formed by transfer of electrons, forming ions, while many others are formed in other ways. The phenomenon can be simply explained in terms of Coulomb's Law. The simplest case is that of two atoms of a diatomic gas combining to form a molecule. Consider hydrogen as an example. All hydrogen atoms attract their lone electrons with equal force. Therefore when two atoms of hydrogen get close enough together to interact, there is no way in which one atom can attract the electron of the other away from it. Thus, no ions can be formed. In order to form an ionic compound from two atoms, the electron-attracting ability of one must be sufficiently greater than that of the other. This is equivalent to saying that the disparity in their electronegativities must be large.

The energy needed to remove one, two, or three electrons from metallic atoms can be measured (p. 434). For members of the first two families this amount is not prohibitively high, so these elements almost always form compounds by electron transfer. For the third family the energy needed to remove three electrons so as to form ions approaches this prohibitive value, so that many of their compounds are not ionic. Members of the fourth family with four electrons to be removed to ionize them almost never form ions by electron removal.

CHEMICAL REACTIONS BY ELECTRON SHARING—COVALENCE

Most generally, if atoms do not enter into chemical combination by electron transfer, they do so by electron sharing. The type of bond involved is covalent. The ability to form covalent bonds is spread throughout the whole of the periodic table; it is especially prevalent in compounds of the heavy metals. Yet it is the elements in the fourth family that we think of as having the most completely covalent bonds. The valence of an element in a covalent compound is the number of electron pairs that are shared, one, two, three, or four pairs. Thus, a carbon atom, with a valence of four, shares four pairs of electrons with one, two, three, or four other atoms to form a covalent compound. Each of the atoms involved in the sharing usually contributes one electron to each pair; *each pair constitutes a single bond.*[8]

For example, the carbon atom—which is the covalent atom par excellence—with four valence electrons, may share them with the single valence electrons of four chlorine atoms to form carbon tetrachloride, CCl_4:

Note that there are eight electrons inside each circle. Thus, each kernel is surrounded by eight electrons. The shared pairs are shown in the overlapping areas of the circles. None of the atoms has an

[8] In each pair the two electrons have different (opposite) directions of spin.

exclusive right to eight electrons; in fact, the carbon atom has an exclusive right to none. Instead it has a half interest in eight electrons.

It might seem that a half interest in eight electrons is equivalent to a full interest in four, and so it might seem that the carbon atom has not gained anything. Yet the chemical reaction has taken place, and therefore it seems that a closer approximation to the stable octet has been attained. It follows from our "stone rolling down hill" analogy that energy has been given up in the process. If we remember that the electrons move around the nuclei with incredible speeds, and that those forming the inner shells take no significant part in chemical bonding, perhaps we can form a simple mental picture of one of the electrons from each chlorine atom spending half its time in the outer shell of the carbon atom, while at the same time the four carbon electrons spend half of their time in the outer shells of the four chlorine atoms. Thus, all of the atoms have a configuration of one of the inert gases at least part of the time.

You may well ask why we have to introduce the concept of electron sharing in this chemical reaction. How do we know that the carbon atom does not transfer its four electrons to four chlorine atoms, thus making it a case of electrovalence? Let us assume that it is electrovalent. Carbon tetrachloride (CCl_4) would then consist of positive carbon ions and negative chloride ions, and so be ionic. We have learned that ionic liquids and gases conduct electric currents. Carbon tetrachloride, a liquid, is not a conductor; therefore it is not ionic and cannot be electrovalent.

DIATOMIC ELEMENTAL GASES: A CASE OF ELECTRON SHARING

We remember how the problem of the common chemically active elemental gases (hydrogen, oxygen, nitrogen, chlorine, and fluorine) bothered the chemists for dec-

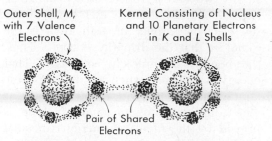

Outer Shell, M, with 7 Valence Electrons

Kernel Consisting of Nucleus and 10 Planetary Electrons in K and L Shells

Pair of Shared Electrons

Fig. 31-2. Chlorine Molecule (Cl_2) with Its Electron Cloud. The 14 electrons in the outer shells of the two atoms move about the two nuclei in more complex paths than do the electrons of the inner shells, because they are not so tightly held by the electrostatic attraction of the nuclei. While we speak of there being one pair of shared electrons, we must not think of any particular pair being shared.

ades. The problem had been solved by Avogadro (but not accepted until more than forty years later) when he suggested that these gases probably existed as double atoms (molecules) instead of single atoms, and that these double atoms broke up on entering chemical combination. How can we explain these facts by the present theory of atomic structure?

They are easily explained if we consider the joining together of two atoms of these gases as a simple case of chemical union by the sharing of electrons (Fig. 31-2).

The details of this union are best illustrated by use of the dot system:

$$\text{H:H} \quad :\ddot{\text{F}}:\ddot{\text{F}}: \quad :\ddot{\text{Cl}}:\ddot{\text{Cl}}: \quad :\ddot{\text{O}}::\ddot{\text{O}}: \quad :\text{N}:::\text{N}:$$

Note that fluorine and chlorine molecules share one pair of electrons, while oxygen shares two and nitrogen three pairs. The sharing in these gases is exactly equal, for the electronegativity of each atom is the same, so that the disparity is zero. Thus, the bond is completely nonpolar. That energy is released when any two of these atoms combine to form a molecule, just as when different kinds of atoms combine, is proved by the fact that energy is needed to separate them.

MORE ABOUT BONDS AND VALENCE

We have already learned that, in general, all chemical reactions result in a more stable state for the atoms than they had before the reaction. This state is achieved by a rearrangement of the electrons of the atoms involved, a rearrangement that almost always results in the attainment of the stable octet. Even in the exceptions there is always some increase in stability.

In the discussion of electrovalence and covalence in the last few pages, they were treated as if they were separate and distinct concepts. However, we made the statement that they graded into one another. If we examine the electronegativities of carbon and chlorine (Table 31-1), we see that the disparity between them is relatively small (0.5). From this fact we are able to reach the conclusion that there is little tendency to transfer electrons. The bonds between carbon and chlorine will,

however, be slightly polar because chlorine, with its higher electronegativity, will hold the shared pair of electrons a bit more closely than will the carbon atom. The molecule of CCl_4 will, however, be nonpolar because the centers of positive and negative charge are both at the center of the molecule, i.e., the distribution of charge is symmetrical. Carbon tetrachloride is then a case in which *a nonpolar molecule has polar bonds.*

Consider hydrogen chloride gas, HCl. Here the disparity in electronegativities is greater than in CCl_4 but not great enough to make the gas ionic. The bond is more polar than those in CCl_4, but the molecule is also polar, for in molecules composed of two atoms of unlike electronegativities there can be no symmetry in the distribution of the charge. The elemental diatomic gases are the only molecules that are nonpolar and have nonpolar bonds.

Consider two three-atom molecules with two of the atoms the same, CO_2 and H_2O. The differences in the electronegativities of C and O on the one hand, and H and O on the other suggest that all bonds are polar. Symmetry of distribution of charge is possible in three-atom molecules if two of the atoms are the same. Using the dot system of notation, we can write

$$:\ddot{\text{O}}:\text{C}:\ddot{\text{O}}: \quad \text{and} \quad \text{H}:\ddot{\text{O}}:\text{H}$$

The properties of CO_2 indicate that the molecule is indeed nonpolar; but the properties of water indicate that it is polar—the charge cannot be symmetrically distributed. It is therefore said to be polar covalent. We indicate this by writing the formula of water by the dot system like this:

$$\begin{array}{c} \ddot{\text{O}} \\ \text{H} \quad \text{H} \end{array}$$

The properties that are used to judge polarity or nonpolarity of molecules are discussed in Chapter XXXIII.

Now let us consider chemical reaction between elements with a high disparity between their electronegativities. The greatest disparity is that between fluorine and the inert gases. But the inert gases will take part in no reactions whatsoever, a fact that we could predict by their zero electronegativity if we did not know it otherwise. From the way the electronegativities are distributed among the elements we would expect francium to have the lowest. It probably has, but it has never been determined, because francium is not a naturally occurring element; it has been produced artificially only in almost infinitesimal quantities.

The next lowest is cesium. The disparity between it and fluorine is 3.3. We should expect the bond between their atoms to be the most polar of all bonds, and it is. However, if we are considering individual molecules of CsF (cesium fluoride), the bond is not completely ionic but only 90-odd per cent ionic, because the transfer of the one outer electron of cesium to the fluorine atom is not complete. The cesium atom maintains a slight interest in it. Since CsF is the most ionic of all compounds, this means that in the discrete molecular (gaseous) state, there are no completely ionic compounds, and that all compounds in this state are, to some slight degree at least, covalent.[9]

[9] We carefully limit this statement to the discrete molecular state because both in crystals and

It is apparent from this discussion that the character of a bond in a discrete molecule may vary from 100 per cent covalence (zero ionic) down to less than 10 per cent covalent (90+ per cent ionic). Those compounds that are so ionic that they completely dissociate[10] into ions in water, are said to consist of atoms that are electrovalent; they are helped to become, by dissociation, completely ionic when dissolved in a liquid whose molecules are polar. In general, those compounds that will not dissolve in polar liquids are said to be covalent.[11] Between the electrovalent and the covalent types of bonds, and showing all gradations, lie the polar covalent bonds.

It may help to clarify the concepts of electrovalent and covalent bonds and all of their intermediate gradations if we return to our simple mental picture of the Bohr atom. In a purely (100 per cent) electrovalent compound the valence electrons would spend all of their time circling the nonmetallic ion and none of the time circling the metallic ion. This is the situation with ions in water solution. In a completely covalent molecule the electrons divide their time equally between the atoms. For those molecules that are polar-covalent, the electrons spend more of their time circling the most electrovalent atom. The greater the disparity in electronegativity, the greater the amount of time the electrons spend with the atom of greatest electronegativity. This follows from the very definition of electronegativity.

in water solution cesium fluoride is completely ionic.

[10] A crystal of salt, NaCl, placed in water, dissociates into Na+ and Cl− ions.

[11] There are exceptions. Silver chloride, AgCl, e.g., is ionic but is only slightly soluble in water.

SUMMARY

The first step towards understanding the causes of chemical reactions came with the suggestion that the inert gas configuration of electrons in the outer shell was completely stable, and that perhaps other atoms would be more stable if they could attain this configuration. Perhaps the attainment of this configuration is the essence of a chemical reaction. If it is, then it must be the outer electrons that are involved in chemical reactions; it must be these outer electrons that are involved in the formation of a chemical bond between atoms in a molecule. The presence of discrete ions, positively and negatively charged, in certain water solutions led to the concept of ionic valence (or electrovalence). Elements that donate or accept electrons exhibit electrovalence; the ions in the resulting compounds have ionic or electrovalent bonds.

That ionic bonds do not hold the atoms together in many compounds is made apparent by the fact that their water solutions do not conduct an electric current. The covalent bond, consisting of shared pairs of electrons, was introduced to account for their reactions. The valence of an atom held in a molecule by such bonds is the number of electron pairs that it shares with other atoms. Covalent bonds may be polar or nonpolar depending upon whether the sharing is equal (nonpolar) or unequal (polar).

The concepts of ionization potential, electronegativity, and electron affinity are useful in a study of the types of bonds holding atoms together in ions or molecules. Of especial use in predicting which bonds are likely to be ionic and which covalent is a scale of electronegativity. The greater the disparity in electronegativities between elements the more ionic the bond.

Considerations of electronic structure and its relationship to valence give rise to the electronic theory of chemical bonding which is now firmly established. The theory explains the differences between metals and nonmetals, the reason hydrogen is an abnormal nonmetal, the chemical reactions that take place by electron transfer, and those that take place by electron sharing, the pairing up of the atoms of the elemental diatomic gases to form molecules. It explains the polarity or nonpolarity of bonds and the polarity or nonpolarity of the resulting molecules.

EXERCISES

I. TERMS AND CONCEPTS

Combining power of atoms	Dot system of notation
Chemical bond	Kernel
Ionic or electrovalent bond	Ionization potential
Covalence	Electron affinity
Polar and nonpolar covalence	Electronegativity
Distribution of charge	Scale of electronegativity
	Electronic theory of chemical bonding

II. PROBLEMS

1. What is meant by a chemical bond?

2. Distinguish between ionic valence and covalence.

3. Distinguish between polar and nonpolar covalence.

4. Draw dot pictures to represent the following: Cs, Zn, Br, Pb, Sr, As, Rn, KBr, $FeCl_2$, Na_2O, SO_2, H_2S.

5. Define electronegativity.

6. How is electronegativity related to ionization potential?

7. For what is the electronegativity scale used?

8. From the scale predict the character of the bonds between the atoms in the following compounds: CH_4, K_2O, $SnCl_4$, CI_4, H_2S, $AlCl_3$.

9. Which is the more highly polar, H_2S

or H_2O, CO_2 or H_2O, $SnCl_4$ or CCl_4? Justify your decisions.

10. State the assumptions of the electronic theory of chemical bonding.

11. State the difference between metals and nonmetals with respect to electronic structure.

12. Which metals form ions most easily? Which nonmetals?

13. Why is sodium more active than magnesium? Magnesium than aluminum?

14. Why is hydrogen placed both on the right and on the left in some periodic charts?

15. In chemical reactions that take place in nature here on earth, what is the energy level of the valence electrons after the reaction, with respect to what it was before? Is this in accord with what we said towards the end of Chapter XIV?

16. What *ultimately* determines whether a chemical reaction will take place by electron transfer or electron sharing?

17. How can you tell whether carbon tetrachloride is ionic or covalent?

18. Explain why nitrogen (in the air) exists as diatomic molecules.

19. The molecules of diatomic gases are completely nonpolar. Would you expect these gases to be easily liquefied? Explain.

20. Why is it possible to ignore the electrons of the inner shells in our electronic theory?

CHAPTER XXXII

Oxidation and Reduction

Knowledge is proud that he has learned so much;
Wisdom is humble that he knows no more.
—WILLIAM COWPER (1760)

In treating oxidation and reduction in a separate chapter we are yielding to historical precedent, for both processes involve electron transfer in most cases, and electron sharing in the remainder. All of the reactions considered under electron transfer in the preceding chapter are oxidation–reduction reactions, oxidation being a loss of electrons, reduction a gain of electrons during the reaction. Thus, when sodium combines with oxygen to form sodium oxide, the sodium atoms lose electrons and so are oxidized, the oxygen atoms gain electrons and so are reduced.

As previously stated we are yielding to historical precedent. Before the electronic theory of chemical bonding was developed, oxidation was defined as the chemical combination of oxygen with other elements. All of the common "burning" processes, whether they involved ordinary combustion, spontaneous combustion, the instantaneous combustion that constitutes one type of explosion, the slower combustion of foods in living animals, or the slow decay of many substances, organic or inorganic, exposed to the weather, were called oxidation if oxides were produced. It therefore became customary to treat reactions of this and the reverse type under the heading of oxidation–reduction.

Many burning processes, however, do not involve oxygen. Sodium will burn brightly in chlorine, powdered zinc will do so with sulfur, and potassium will "burn" in water. There is no significant difference between these cases and the burning of magnesium and steel in oxygen. In all cases there has been a transfer of one or two electrons from the metal to the nonmetal. There is no sound reason for a separate treatment. We do so here, in part because most elementary chemistry texts still do so; thus, students who have had high school chemistry might be confused if we omitted separate mention.

There is, however, one distinct advantage. Separate treatment allows us to discuss such topics as displacement reactions, the activity (electromotive) series, reactions in current-producing cells, and metallurgy without making the general discussion of chemical reactions by electron transfer and electron sharing cumbersome. It should be clearly understood, however, that oxidation–reduction reactions (commonly called redox reactions for short) do not constitute a separate class of chemical reactions.

It should be evident from what has been said that oxidation cannot occur without reduction, nor reduction without oxidation. They occur not only simultaneously but always to the same extent. The element that is oxidized is the reducing agent. In the cases cited the metals were oxidized and so they were the reducing agents. Similarly, the nonmetals were reduced and so they were the oxidizing agents. We can say, in general, that metals are reducing agents and nonmetals oxidizing agents.

Consider the reaction, $Na + Cl \rightarrow NaCl$. The sodium atom transfers (loses) an electron and so is oxidized; at the same time the chlorine gains the electron that sodium loses, and so is reduced. The reaction, broken down into half reactions, is as follows:

Oxidation:

$$Na \rightarrow Na^{1} + e^{-}$$

Sodium   Sodium   Electron
atom   ion

Reduction:

$$Cl + e^{-} \rightarrow Cl^{-}$$

Chlorine   Electron   Chlorine
atom   ion

Adding the two together we get the whole reaction,

$$Na + Cl + e^{-} \rightarrow Na^{+} + Cl^{-} + e^{-}$$

Eliminating e^{-} from both sides, [1]

$$Na + Cl \rightarrow Na^{+} + Cl^{-}$$

DISPLACEMENT REACTIONS

The displacement of one metal by another in a solution is a redox reaction. If we place an iron nail in a copper sulfate ($CuSO_4$) solution, we will find that the

nail will become coated with copper. Copper sulfate is an ionic compound, a fact which can be checked by passing an electric current through the solution. The valence of the sulfate ion is always -2. Hence the copper ions in the solution have a valence of $+2$. To become an atom a copper ion must gain two electrons. These it obtains from an atom of iron. In the process, the latter becomes a doubly charged positive ion and passes into solution. The copper has taken the place of the iron in the nail. The equation for the reaction is

$$Fe + Cu^{++} + SO_4^{=} \rightarrow$$
$$Fe^{++} + SO_4^{=} + Cu$$

or more simply,

$$Fe + Cu^{++} \rightarrow Fe^{++} + Cu$$

The iron has spontaneously displaced the copper. We naturally ask the question, "why?" The answer lies in the configuration of atoms. We have learned that the metals give up their valence electrons with varying degrees of ease, those that have the fewest and are shielded by the most inner shells giving them up most easily. Thus, cesium, atomic number 55, holds its lone valence electron less tightly than potassium or barium. As a result it is the most active of the naturally occurring metals. (Francium, just below it in the periodic table, is still more active but it does not occur naturally.) In any competition for electrons the more active metals *yield* to the less active. This means that under proper conditions the less active metallic ions can take electrons away from more active metallic atoms. Thus, iron, being more active than copper, loses electrons to the copper ions, transforming the former into ions and the latter into atoms. We

[1] The chemist would say that the valence number of Na has been increased by one, and that of Cl reduced by one. The concept of valence number, also called the oxidation number, was developed to deal with the balancing of equations in complex redox reactions. Balanced equations are a necessity for every chemist no matter how complex they are. As nonchemists we will be content to balance simple equations by inspection—as we have already learned in Chapter XVII.

say that iron displaces the copper in solution.

ACTIVITY SERIES

If we wish to find out whether metal *A* is more or less active than metal *B*, all we have to do is to place metal *A* in an ionic solution of a compound of metal *B* and see if *A* replaces *B*. If it does, it is more active than *B* because it has yielded electrons to *B*. This method allows us to list metals in a series in the order of activity. Such a series is variously called an activity series, an electrochemical series, a displacement series, or an electromotive force series.[2] Hydrogen is also placed in the series (Table 32-1) because it will displace many metals in solution. For example, hydrogen is set free when zinc is placed in an acid solution.

Any element in the series will displace any of the others below it in an electrolytic (ionic) solution of the latter. The sequence is in the order of decreasing ability to lose electrons. Such a series is extremely useful to a chemist because he can tell at a glance the likelihood of many chemical reactions taking place. Redox reactions furnish a precise experimental method of measuring the degree of activity of each of the metals. A similar series may be constructed by the same methods for the nonmetals. The degree of activity of the metals is measured by their reducing ability, that of the nonmetals by their oxidizing ability.

[2] The last name comes from the fact that displacement of one metal by another in electrolytic solutions is used in the construction of a current-producing chemical cell to produce an electromotive force, i.e., a potential difference.

TABLE 32-1

ACTIVITY SERIES FOR SOME OF THE
MORE COMMON METALS
(AND HYDROGEN)

K	Pb
Na	H
Mg	Cu
Al	Ag
Zn	Hg
Fe	Au

REDOX REACTIONS IN CURRENT-PRODUCING CELLS

Any chemical change that takes place spontaneously liberates energy which, in theory at least, is capable of being transformed into work. If such changes take place in solutions that are capable of carrying an electric current, i.e., if the solutions are electrolytes, then it is possible to obtain the liberated energy in the form of electrical energy. A device that does this is called a voltaic cell (Fig. 20-2). Flashlight batteries are voltaic cells (Fig. 32-1). The chemical reactions that take place in them are redox reactions.

In such a cell at least two substances must participate in the reaction, electrons must be lost by one substance in one part of the cell and gained by the other substance in another part of the cell, and these two substances must not be in physical contact with each other. This may seem somewhat paradoxical, but it can be done if the two substances are included in an electrical circuit consisting partly of metallic conductors and partly of an electrolytic solution (Fig. 32-2). Note carefully that the Zn electrode is immersed in a $ZnSO_4$ solution and the Cu electrode is immersed in a $CuSO_4$ solution. If the two

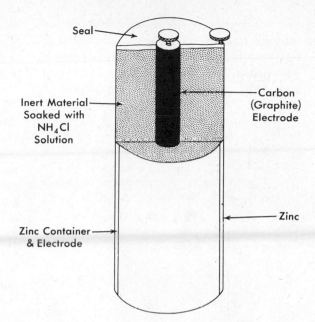

Fig. 32-1. Common Dry Cell. The upper part is sliced away to show the construction.

electrodes were reversed, nothing would happen to the Cu electrode in the $ZnSO_4$ solution, but the Zn electrode would soon be coated with Cu as the Zn displaced it, and all of the liberated energy would appear in the form of heat. To obtain electrical energy the reactants must be kept apart. Each part is called a half cell. There are various ways of keeping the two half cells apart. No reaction will occur when they are kept apart unless the switch is closed.

As soon as the switch is closed a redox reaction begins. The zinc–zinc-ion half cell reaction is

$$Zn \rightarrow Zn^{++} + 2e^-$$

For the zinc atoms to become zinc ions as they go into solution they must leave two electrons behind on the zinc electrode, thereby causing it to become negatively charged. The copper–copper-ion reaction is

$$Cu^{++} + 2e^- \rightarrow Cu$$

For the copper ions to become copper atoms they must gain two electrons from the copper electrode. This would leave a deficiency of electrons and so cause that electrode to become positively charged. Thus, there is a difference of potential between the two electrodes; a current will flow if they are connected by a wire. If the switch is not closed the repulsions of the electrons accumulated on the zinc electrode quickly stops the accumulation; the electrons have no place to go. The negative ions pass through the porous cup so as to keep the positive and negative ions inside and outside the cup in balance as to numbers.

Liquid cells such as the one in Fig. 32-2

are not practical for many purposes for obvious reasons. The "dry" cell, which is not exactly dry, is far more widely used. The principle is the same, however. The zinc (Fig. 32-1) container acts as one of

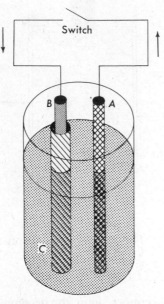

Fig. 32-2. Liquid Cell. *A* is a zinc electrode immersed in a Zn^{++} solution, indicated by *C*. *B* is a copper electrode immersed in a porous cup containing Cu^{++} solution. Electrons can pass freely through the porous cup, but the ions cannot.

the electrodes. The other electrode is of graphite. The electrolyte is a water solution of ammonium chloride. It is soaked into a porous inert substance (sawdust, paper pulp, cotton waste and mixed with MnO_2) and this fills the space between the two electrodes. The sealing prevents the dry cell from becoming dry, for if it did, no ions could move. When a current is flowing, Zn dissolves to form Zn^{++} (and

so is oxidized) and the manganese is reduced to a lower oxide.

The storage battery is a voltaic cell which, after it has acted as a source of electrical energy for a time and is weak or "dead," can be restored to its original condition by an outside source of electrical energy, i.e., it can be recharged. This is done by sending the recharging current through in the opposite direction so as to reverse the electrodes and the reactions taking place at them. One electrode consists of lead–antimony plates packed with finely divided lead, the other of similar plates packed with lead dioxide. The electrolyte is H_2SO_4. During discharge, the half reaction at the anode is

$$Pb + SO_4^= \rightarrow PbSO_4 + 2e^-$$

The half reaction at the cathode is

$$PbO_2 + 4H^+ + SO_4^= + 2e^- \rightarrow$$
$$PbSO_4 + 2H_2O$$

The electron flow is from the lead to the lead dioxide electrode.[3] During the discharge water is formed. This reduces the amount of the H_2SO_4 in the solution and reduces its density. Thus, an instrument that measures the density is used to determine whether or not the battery needs recharging. A recharging current causes reversals of the above reactions so that the H_2SO_4 is reconstituted.

METALLURGY

Redox reactions are of great importance in the smelting of ores. An ore is any naturally occurring mineral aggregate from which one or more metals can be extracted

[3] By convention the lead dioxide electrode is positive.

at a profit. A few metals, e.g., gold and platinum, commonly occur in the free, or native, state. The pure metals may be recovered by purely mechanical methods, such as panning, but in almost all ores the metal is in chemical combination in the form of oxides, sulphides, carbonates, etc. The common ores of iron are Fe_2O_3 (hematite), Fe_3O_4 (magnetite) and $Fe_2O_3 \cdot nH_2O$ (limonite, or hydrated oxide of iron). Other ore minerals are CuO, ZnS, PbS, Ag_2S, CuS, $PbCO_3$, $MnCO_3$. The valuable minerals (do not confuse a mineral with a metal) are commonly associated with more or less (mostly more) worthless minerals, called the gangue minerals, from which they can be separated by mechanical means. However, the separation of the metal from the oxygen, sulfur, or carbonate ions, or from other elements, must be done by chemical processes that are grouped under the term smelting.

Some metals are very easy to smelt, some very difficult. The first metals known to primitive man were those that occur native, either usually (e.g., gold), or under certain circumstances (e.g., silver and copper). Next came those that were easy to smelt, e.g., copper, tin, lead, and, much later, iron. The more difficult the smelting process, the later, in general, the discovery of the metal was.

Many metals may be obtained from their ores by electrolysis. To do this the ore must either be in the molten state or in an aqueous solution so that free ions of the metal are present. In the process of electrolysis reduction takes place at the cathode, oxidation at the anode. The most active metals, as we might suspect, are those that are the most difficult and expensive to smelt. Electrolysis can reduce even the most active metals.[4] The process is described in Chapter XXV.

More common and less expensive than electrolysis is the original process of smelting by heating the ores with hot carbon in the form of charcoal or coke. A flux, such as limestone ($CaCO_3$ essentially) is mixed in proper proportions with the ore and the fuel, and then the fuel is burned to melt the ore and the flux together. If the ore is one of the iron oxides, the iron is reduced and the carbon is oxidized. The purpose of the flux is to combine with the impurities (chiefly silica) to make them liquid. The process is carried on in a blast furnace (Fig. 32-3).

The mineral used in the United States is chiefly hematite (Fe_2O_3) which has been, and still is, mined in prodigious quantities in northern Minnesota and northern Michigan. The ore consists of hematite mixed with other rock material generally classified as impurities. The blasts of hot air introduced at the bottom keep the coke in the coke–ore–limestone mixture burning furiously. The ore, the limestone, and the impurities are all melted together. The calcium in the limestone combines with the SiO_2 and other impurities to form the slag.

[4] Aluminum, the most abundant element in the rocks of the earth's crust, used to be prohibitively expensive for most purposes because it resisted all attempts to free it from the oxygen with which it was combined, except by use of the expensive alkali metals. Charles Hall, a chemistry student, heard his professor state that if any member of his class wanted to become a millionaire, all he had to do was to find a way to dissolve aluminum oxide so that the process of electrolysis could be used. Within two years (1886) he had done so. His discovery was that a mineral from Greenland, cryolite, would, when molten, dissolve the aluminum oxide, allowing the process of electrolysis to be used. Aluminum is deposited at the cathode and oxygen is liberated at the anode. Charles Hall did, indeed, become a millionaire.

Since it is less dense than the liquid iron, it floats on top and so can be drained off periodically. Once started a blast furnace is operated continuously. The essential reactions take place in a series of steps in

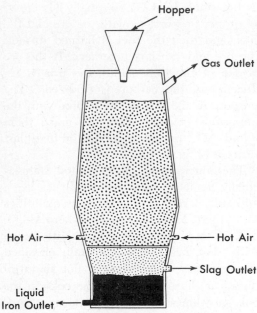

Fig. 32-3. Diagram of Blast Furnace. A mixture of iron ore, coke, and limestone are continuously introduced into the furnace via the hopper. A continuous blast of hot air is fed in at the bottom to burn the coke and so reduce the ore. Liquid slag and iron are periodically removed from the bottom.

which the carbon combines with the oxygen in the hematite. The net reaction is

$$2Fe_2O_3 + 3C \rightarrow 4Fe + 3CO_2$$

The reactions that form the slag are

$$CaCO_3 \rightarrow CaO + CO_2$$

$$CaO + SiO_2 \rightarrow CaSiO_3$$

The calcium silicate is essentially glasslike.

REDOX REACTIONS IN COVALENT COMPOUNDS

At the beginning of this chapter we stated that most redox reactions were electron transfer reactions. Some of the commonest cases, e.g., the combining of carbon with oxygen, however, involve electron sharing. Perhaps the equations dealing with smelting made you pause, for until we dealt with the smelting of iron we had been concerned solely with electron transfer redox reactions. In those equations you note that carbon is the reducing agent, and at the same time you should remember that carbon always forms covalent bonds, no matter whether its valence is considered positive or negative. Whether we burn wood, coal, paper, or oil, all of which contain both carbon and hydrogen, the following covalent reactions take place:

$$C + O_2 \rightarrow CO^2$$

Nonpolar covalent molecule   Nonpolar covalent molecule

$$2H_2 + O_2 \rightarrow 2H_2O$$

Nonpolar covalent molecules   Nonpolar covalent molecule   Polar covalent molecules

In these cases, and all similar ones, the electrons are not transferred but are displaced to form covalent bonds. It should be clear from the definition of oxidation and reduction that in the absence of electron transfer, it is not obvious which is the oxidizing agent and which is the reducing agent. Oxygen is more electronegative than either hydrogen or carbon, and so the positions of the shared electrons average out somewhat closer to the oxygen atom than to the hydrogen or carbon atom.

SUMMARY

Oxidation and reduction reactions are commonly electron transfer reactions although the common burning reactions in which carbon and/or hydrogen combine with oxygen to form CO_2 and H_2O involve the formation of polar covalent bonds. Oxidation always involves reduction and vice versa; one cannot take place without the other. In general, metals are reducing agents, i.e., they donate electrons, and nonmetals are oxidizing agents, i.e., they accept electrons. In any redox reaction the metal is oxidized and the nonmetal is reduced.

Typical redox reactions include displacement reactions in which one metal may replace another in a solution of a salt of one of them. In every case the more active metal replaces the less active one, never the other way around. Reactions in either current-producing cells or in storage cells are redox reactions. The ore of any metal can be reduced by electrolysis. Some can be reduced economically only by electrolysis, e.g., aluminum. Less active metals are reduced by other means, e.g., iron by the use of coke and limestone in a blast furnace.

EXERCISES

I. TERMS AND CONCEPTS

Oxidation	Oxidizing agent
Reduction	Reducing agent
Displacement reaction	Current-producing cell
Activity series	Dry cell
	Storage cell

II. PROBLEMS

1. In the reaction $2K_2 + O_2 \rightarrow 2K_2O$ what is oxidized and what is reduced? Justify your answer.

2. Metallic K is placed in water. Predict, from your knowledge of the activity series (Table 32-1), what would happen chemically.

3. Would you expect the same thing to happen if copper were placed in water? Explain.

4. What is it that determines the position of an element in the activity series?

5. If you were to add cesium, calcium, and beryllium to Table 32-1, where would you put each of them? Why?

6. Which elements are most easily reduced? Which most easily oxidized?

7. In a region where the color of the soil is commonly reddish brown (due to Fe_2O_3), the color in the marshes, where vegetation is exceptionally abundant and the soil constantly moist, is black. Explain.

8. What causes a "dry" cell to go dead?

9. During the discharge of the storage battery, where do the two electrons released come from? How many electrons and how many coulombs of electricity will the cell deliver while one mole of lead is being oxidized?

10. Common brass is an alloy of zinc and copper. It is commonly badly corroded by sea water. State the details of the chemical reaction involved.

CHAPTER XXXIII

Binding of Ions, Atoms, and Molecules into Solids

A problem is not solved in the laboratory. It is solved in somebody's head, and all the apparatus is for is to get his head turned round so he can see the thing right.—CHARLES F. KETTERING

Only in the gases do substances exist as discrete particles, i.e., as either atoms (in the inert gases) or as molecules, very largely independent of any of the others about them at ordinary temperatures and pressures. It is only when this independence becomes greatly restricted that attractive forces of one kind or another cause the discrete particles to form aggregates that we call liquids. This restriction can be brought about by reduction of temperature alone in all cases except that of helium, which ultimately requires an increase in pressure also. In all other cases, pressure is an aid but it is not necessary. Still further restriction of the movements of the atoms or molecules results in the formation of solids. As the term is used in everyday life, there are two kinds, the crystalline and the noncrystalline. In crystalline solids there is an orderly arrangement of the atoms or molecules, forming characteristic patterns that are repeated over and over indefinitely in the crystal. Most solid inorganic and many organic substances are crystalline.

The noncrystalline substances are not so easily defined. A few, like glass, are considered to be supercooled liquids because, as in a liquid, there is no arrangement of the atoms or molecules into patterns that are regularly repeated.[1] Instead, they are randomly distributed throughout. Other examples are sealing wax, asphalt, and certain substances that have been rapidly cooled from the molten state. Another group that cannot be considered crystalline are the tissues of organisms, such as the woody tissue of plants, the skin and flesh of animals. In them there are orderly arrangements of molecules, chiefly to form fibers, but these patterns are not repeated over and over again with anything like the precision of crystals. We will concern ourselves here only with the crystalline state.

An individual discrete atom or molecule cannot be considered a liquid, a solid, or a gas. These terms apply only to relatively large aggregates of atoms or molecules. We have already learned that the same aggregate can exist in any one of the three states, depending on the temperature and the pressure. It is reasonable to assume that the state in which they exist at the moment will depend upon the magnitude of the forces existing between them, forces that tend either to keep them apart or to keep them together. It is also reasonable to assume that many of the physical and

[1] Other reasons are that they have no definite melting points, i.e., as they are heated they gradually soften until they become molten. The same is true of their boiling points.

chemical properties of these aggregates of matter, properties such as melting points, boiling points, heats of fusion and vaporization, solubilities, and even the hardness of crystalline solids, will also depend upon the magnitude of these forces.

To understand these forces we should know something more about the types of bonds. When we do, we will be able to make reasonable predictions about many of the physical and chemical properties of matter. In Chapter XXXI we considered the question of how atoms are bound together to form molecules. Our answer was formulated in terms of the degree of polarity of the chemical bond. The electronegativity scale was used to give us a measure of the degree of this polarity. Our problem here is to investigate the forces that hold atoms and molecules of crystalline solids in those aggregates that we call crystals, and what are the limits, if any, to the size of individual crystals. We also wish to relate the physical properties of the crystals to the type of bonding.

CRYSTAL SPACE LATTICES

Perfect crystals are solids with smooth plane surfaces called faces. These faces give a crystal a visible geometric form such as a cube, a prism, a doubly terminated pyramid, etc. (Fig. 33-1). They vary in size from microscopic to several feet long. The faces themselves may be square, rectangular, triangular, hexagonal, rhombic, etc. The angles between corresponding faces on all crystals of the same species are always the same. All crystals start as individual discrete atoms, ions, or molecules and grow by accretion of more of the same kind of atoms, ions, or molecules. There is no limit to the size as long

as the supply of the same kind of atoms, ions, and molecules holds out, and as long as there is space to grow. Perfect crystals of most substances occurring naturally in the earth are rare because of (1) crowding during growth, (2) defects in the space lattice, or (3) breakage in collecting them.

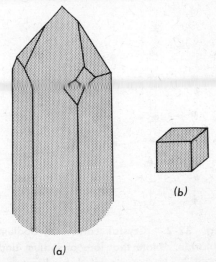

Fig. 33-1. (a) Half a Crystal of Quartz. If complete, the other end would look the same. Perfect crystals (rare) are six-sided with pyramids of six main faces on each end. **(b)** A Cubic Crystal. Halite (table salt) and pyrite have this form.

It should be apparent that the regularities in the same species of crystal is proof of the orderly arrangement of the atoms, ions, and molecules making up the crystal. While these regularities yield some information about the internal structure, a great deal more is obtained from a study of X-ray diffraction patterns. Figure 28-3 shows such a pattern. A detailed mathematical analysis of a spot pattern enables the expert to calculate the positions the atoms, ions, or molecules might occupy in order to produce such a pattern. The process is an indirect one and so must be carefully checked by experiment. The pattern of points that describes this internal arrangement is known as a space lattice. Compare the lattice in Fig. 28-3, which shows only the positions occupied by a

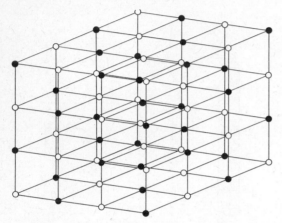

Fig. 33-2. Crystal Lattice of Sodium Chloride. Note that ions of sodium and chlorine alternate in all three directions.

few of the centers of the ions, with the model in Fig. 33-2, which attempts to portray the actual ions. The space lattice is an abstract concept only; *we think of its lattice points as existing even though unoccupied by any kind of matter.*

The mineralogist classifies crystals according to the symmetry of the arrangements of their crystal faces. The physicists and chemists find it more useful to classify them by the atoms, ions, or molecules and the forces that bind them together. Unfortunately there is no universally accepted classification scheme.[2] We will

classify them as the covalent (sometimes called atomic), the molecular, the ionic, and the metallic types of lattice.

COVALENT LATTICES

In the covalent lattice the lattice points are occupied by atoms which share electrons with their neighbors. These covalent bonds extend in fixed directions. For example, in the diamond crystal each carbon atom is at the center of a regular tetrahedron[3] and is bonded to four other carbon atoms which are at the vertices of the tetrahedron (Fig. 33-3). At the same time the carbon atom at each vertex is also at the center of another tetrahedron. From the theoretical viewpoint there is no limit to the number of carbon atoms that can be bonded together in this way. Carbon with its four valence electrons is ideally suited to this type of *polymerization* (see p. 544). The resulting interlocking structure can extend indefinitely in three dimensions, giving a very strong interlocking structure that, no matter how big, is a single molecule. The strength of the covalent

---

[2] The student should not allow himself to be confused by the multiplicity of classification

schemes in the various fields of science. All such schemes are made by man in the attempt to bring order out of what would otherwise be a chaos of apparently unrelated facts. A scheme devised to serve certain purposes may be unsatisfactory or even useless for some other purpose. Thus, the scheme that classifies crystals according to the forces that hold the particles together is not at all useful for the crystallographer, whose interest is chiefly in classification according to their external symmetry and geometric form. Most, if not all, such schemes for natural phenomena break down if pushed too far. We have just had an example of this when we tried to classify chemical bonds either as electrovalent or covalent. Classification schemes, even if imperfect, help to bring order out of chaos.

[3] A regular tetrahedron is a triangular pyramid made by assembling four equilateral triangles.

bonds and their interlocking character are responsible for the great hardness of the diamond. Since the bonds must be broken to melt the crystal, the diamond has an extremely high melting point, 3500° C.

Graphite is another form of carbon but the visible properties are about as differ-

each carbon is bonded to three others in the same plane, forming a sheetlike structure (Fig. 33-4). Since the sheets are weakly bonded to one another, they slide over each other easily. This is the reason for the softness of graphite and its greasy feel. However, the bonding *within* the individual sheets is strong, as is shown by the

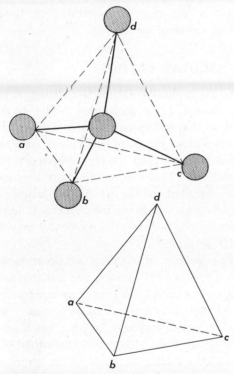

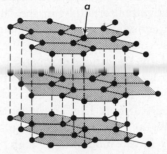

Fig. 33-4. Layer Structure of Carbon in Graphite. Each carbon atom within a layer is bonded to three others in the same layer, e.g., the atom *a*, and to one in either the layer above or the one below. Thus, the bonding within the layer is far stronger than that between layers.

Fig. 33-3. Tetrahedral Structure of Carbon in Diamond. Carbon atoms are at the four corners, *a, b, c, d,* with one in the center. The latter is bonded to each of the other four. Each atom at a corner is the center atom of an adjoining tetrahedron.

ent from those of the diamond as one could imagine. The difference is in the arrangement of the carbon atoms. In graphite

fact that graphite has about the same melting point as the diamond.

Other covalent crystals are SiC (silicon carbide), WC (tungsten carbide) and SiO_2 (silicon dioxide, or silica).[4] The first two can be thought of as analogous to a diamond in which half of the carbon atoms have been replaced by silicon or tungsten molecules. The same general arrangement prevails, the covalent bonding continuing indefinitely. These crystals have very high melting points, 2600° C for SiC and 2900° C for WC. They are high because,

[4] The chemistry of silica will be further treated in Chapter XXXIX.

as in the diamond, strong covalent bonds must be broken in the melting process.

IONIC LATTICES

In the ionic lattice positive and negative ions occupy the lattice points. It is the electrostatic attraction between these oppositely charged atoms that holds them together. These positive and negative ions are arranged alternately in the three cardinal directions of space. One cannot pair up these charges, since each ion is surrounded by six others of opposite charge, one in front and one behind, one above and one below, and one on each side. The whole crystal acts like one gigantic molecule. These attractions are large, so ionic crystals have moderately high melting points. To melt the crystal the attractions of these ions for one another must be overcome.

The amount of energy needed to separate the ions depends on two factors: (1) the distances between the ions, i.e., on ionic sizes, and (2) the magnitude of the charges. Table 33-1 shows the effect of the first factor.

TABLE 33-1

EFFECT OF IONIC SIZE ON MELTING POINTS OF IONIC CRYSTALS

Increasing Size of Metallic Ions		Increasing Size of Nonmetallic Ions	
Compound	Melting Pt. (°C)	Compound	Melting Pt. (°C)
NaCl	804	NaF	1980
KCl	776	NaCl	804
RbCl	715	NaBr	755
CsCl	646	NaI	651

The ions of all the compounds in the table have a charge of +1 or −1. For the effect of the second factor, consider the melting point of a compound in which both ions have a charge of 2, MgO(Mg^{++} and $O^=$); it is 2800° C. The melting points of ionic crystals are, in general, much lower than those of crystals with covalent lattices, for the energy needed to pull the ions apart is less than that needed to break strong covalent bonds.

MOLECULAR LATTICES

In the molecular lattice the lattice points are occupied by molecules. The forces *within* the individual molecule, i.e., the atom-to-atom bonds, are covalent, and are much stronger than the forces *between* the molecules. This distinction must be carefully kept in mind. It is the latter, of course, with which we are concerned here.[5] These bonds between the molecules may be polar or nonpolar.

The polar type consists of polar molecules, molecules in which the positive and negative charges are not symmetrically distributed. As a result there is a net residue of positive charge on one "end" and one of negative charge on the other. A molecule of HCl, or of H_2O, in terms of this electrostatic charge distribution, is a dipole. This polarity is a consequence of the inequal sharing of the pair of valence electrons between the chlorine and the hydrogen atoms in the case of HCl, and between the oxygen and the hydrogen atoms in the case of H_2O (Fig. 33-5). A crystal of either HCl or H_2O is simply a geometric

[5] Note that no such distinction was necessary in atomic or ionic crystals, for in these the crystal is just one big molecule.

array of these dipoles arranged alternately in the three dimensions of space. The binding energy of the crystal arises from the mutual attractions of the dipoles.

As we would predict, the greater the inequality of the sharing of the electron bond, i.e., the more highly polar the molecules, the higher the melting point. The melting point is a measure of the thermal energy required to separate the dipoles. It should be apparent that the melting points will be considerably lower than those of

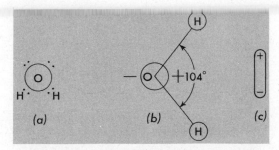

Fig. 33-5. Polar Water Molecule. **(a)** The two hydrogen atoms are not symmetric about the oxygen atom. This lack of symmetry leaves the left side **(b)** with a slight residue of negative charge; the right side with a slight residue of positive charge; hence its polarity. **(c)** A simple way of portraying the water molecule— as a dipole. The angular shape of water molecules, plus the fact that the forces are strongest at certain angles, results in Ice occupying a greater volume than the same number of water molecules.

ionic crystals, for the attraction between two dipoles in contact is always less than that between two ions. The melting points will be still lower in crystals with covalent bonds because the bonds *within* the molecules of molecular crystals are *not*

broken during melting, whereas in covalent crystals they are broken. (See Table 33-2.)

TABLE 33-2

MELTING POINTS OF POLAR MOLECULAR CRYSTALS (°C)

H_2O	0
HCl	−50.8
HI	−88.5
HBr	−112

In the nonpolar type of molecular crystal the bonding *within* the molecules is covalent as in the polar molecular lattice. The difference is that the individual molecules are nonpolar, i.e., no dipoles exist. What, then, holds the molecules together in a solid like dry ice (solid CO_2)? Presumably there are no forces between the molecules. There are, however, weak attractions between the molecules, mentioned on p. 205, called van der Waals forces. Our previous explanation of them was a non-electronic one, and so was not much of an explanation.

These forces have their origin in the motion of the electrons that take place in all atoms and molecules. We remember that in all atoms the electrons are kept from falling into the nucleus only because of their incredible speeds in orbits about the nucleus. It should therefore be obvious that even in nonpolar molecules the distribution of charge cannot be symmetrical at all times. When we say that it is, we mean that on the average it is symmetrically distributed. Therefore, at any particular instant the molecule may be slightly polar; an instantaneous dipole exists. At the next instant the molecule may be completely polar, and at the next the instantaneous dipole is reversed. The weak di-

TABLE 33-3

MELTING POINTS OF NONPOLAR MOLECULAR CRYSTALS (°C)*

Compounds			Monatomic Elemental Gases			Diatomic Elemental Gases		
Carbon Dioxide			He †	(4)	−272	F_2	(38)	−223
	(44)	−79	Ne	(20)	−249	Cl_2	(71)	−102
Naphthalene	$(C_{10}H_8)$		A	(40)	−189	Br	(80)	−7
	(128)	80	Kr	(84)	−157	I	(127)	113
			Xe	(131)	−112	H_2	(2)	−259
			Rn	(222)	−71	O_2	(32)	−218
						N_2	(28)	−210

* The figures in parentheses are the molecular or atomic weights. Note that within any one group the melting point rises as the atomic weight rises.

† Helium cannot be solidified at any temperature unless the pressure is at least 25 atmospheres.

poles are constantly fluctuating. It is clear that the more electrons there are in the molecule and the farther they are from the nucleus (and therefore less tightly bound), the greater the van der Waals forces are. These forces are, of course, present in all types of crystals but they are so small in comparison to the other forces in covalent and ionic crystals that they are negligible. In the molecular crystals their importance in binding molecules into solids increases with decreasing polarity.

Since van der Waals forces are weak at best, the melting points of nonpolar molecular crystals are low, and the weaker these forces, the lower the melting points. Since van der Waals forces increase as the number of electrons in the molecule increases, they are larger in the larger molecules, i.e., they increase as the atomic weights increase.

From Table 33-3 we can conclude that even the van der Waals forces are almost nonexistent in helium. They are effective only when the random kinetic energy of the helium atoms has been reduced to al-most zero, i.e., the temperature has been reduced almost to absolute zero.

METALLIC CRYSTALS

Ions of metals occupy the lattice points in metallic crystals. Neither ionic nor covalent bonds can account for the binding of metals into the large, generally strong, aggregates that we use in everyday life. Consider a bar of iron, or any other metal. What forces hold the atoms together? We can eliminate those in either type of molecular crystals on the basis of strength alone. And they are not due to the attractions of oppositely charged ions, as in ionic crystals, for the metal ions all have the same sign. The bonds cannot be covalent because metals cannot achieve the inert gas electronic configurations by sharing as do nonmetals such as carbon, sulfur, hydrogen, the halogens, etc. The van der Waals forces that hold discrete molecules together into a crystal lattice are much too weak, even if present, to account for the great strength of most metals.

We defined a metal as an element in which the valence electrons were relatively weakly held. *In metallic crystals the valence electrons are shared communally by all of the metallic atoms.* Each atom contributes its valence electrons to an "electron cloud" that belongs to the whole crystal. This contribution to the cloud leaves the rest of the crystal a mass of positive ions. The valence electrons of this cloud form floating, nonrigid bonds between positive ions. This random wandering of the electron cloud throughout the crystal accounts for the high electrical conductivity of metals and their deformability without breaking. However, it is difficult to account for the hardnesses and melting points in terms of the lattice.

Cesium (and the rest of the alkali metals) can be cut with a knife, and has a melting point only slightly above room temperature, whereas tungsten is very hard and has a melting point (3370° C) only a little less than that of carbon. In general, the melting points depend (1) upon the size of the atom, thus decreasing downward within a family (Table 33-4), and (2)

TABLE 33-4

MELTING POINTS OF METALLIC
CRYSTALS (°C)

Effect of Atomic Size		Effect of Number of Electrons	
Li	179	Na	98
Na	98	Mg	651
K	64	Al	660
Rb	39		
Cs	26		

upon the number of valence electrons, thus increasing across a period. The decrease downward in the family cannot be due to charges, because all have the same charge; it is due to the increase in average distance between neighboring atoms due to increasing atomic size. There are some exceptions, however, to the general rule.

SUMMARY

Crystals are solids in which the molecules, atoms, or ions are arranged in an orderly manner, made obvious in those specimens that have regular geometric shapes. In nature most crystalline materials do not have regular geometric shapes, chiefly because of crowded conditions during the formation of the crystals. These irregular specimens are nevertheless called crystals. We infer from crystal faces and crystal form that there must be an internal arrangement of the molecules, atoms, or ions, for such external regularity could never result from internal disorder.

If the temperature is high enough all elements and compounds exist in the gaseous state. Conversely, if the temperature is low enough, they exist in the solid state. At temperatures in between they are liquids. In the change from the liquid to the solid state, most substances form the orderly arrangements of atoms, ions, or molecules that we call crystals.

X-ray diffraction patterns give information that allows the various kinds of space lattices to be deduced. The physicist classifies crystals according to the kinds of particles (molecules, atoms, ions) that occupy the space points, together with the kinds of bonds that hold the particles in the lattice. Thus, we have molecular, covalent, ionic, and metallic types of crystals. We investigated the bonds holding the three kinds of particles together to form macroscopic masses of matter, carefully attempting to distinguish these bonds from the bonds that hold atoms together in discrete molecules. The bonds themselves turned out to be the same—all electrostatic in origin.

In the covalent crystals no distinction whatever could be made, for the bonds holding the atoms together were identical with those holding the crystal together. In other words, such crystals are in reality single molecules, no matter how big. The same was true of the ionic crystals, i.e., no distinction between the bond in a discrete molecule and the bonds of ions in the mass could be made. Hence they, too, consist of a single molecule, no matter how big.

Molecular crystals consist of actual molecules bound together by dipole-dipole attractions and by van der Waals attractions in the polar types, and by the latter alone in the nonpolar crystals. Metallic crystals consist of ions all of which are positive, so the crystal bonding cannot be ionic. Instead, these ions are held together by an electron cloud made up of floating valence electrons contributed by all of the ions in the crystal. The mobility of the bonds is the mobility of the electrons. Here again we find that the term molecule has no meaning. Thus, for covalent, ionic and metallic crystals, the term molecule is not a useful one.[6]

EXERCISES

I. TERMS AND CONCEPTS

Crystal lattice   Covalent lattice
Lattice points   Ionic lattice

Molecular lattice   Tetrahedron
Metallic lattice

II. PROBLEMS

1. Distinguish between crystalline and noncrystalline substances.

2. What is meant by:
    a. Crystal form.
    b. Crystal face.
    c. Lattice point.
    d. Crystal lattice.

3. In a general way state how the positions that atoms, ions, or molecules occupy within a crystal are determined.

4. What sorts of particles (atoms, ions, or molecules) make up each of the four types of crystals?

5. What types of forces hold the particles in each of the four types of crystals?

6. What properties of a crystal are determined by the strength of the bonds holding the particles together?

7. What is the size or range of sizes of a "molecule" in the diamond? Explain.

8. Graphite and the diamond both have extremely high melting points but extremely different hardnesses. Explain.

9. What two factors control the melting points in ionic crystals? Relate each to the periodic table.

10. Which have the higher melting points, polar or nonpolar molecular crystals? Explain.

11. Solid HCl has a melting point of −112° C. What crystal lattice would you expect it to have? Why? Would you expect its molecules to be more or less polar than those of water? Would you have reached the same conclusion from the electronegativity scale (p. 463)?

12. What type of crystal lattice do you have the most trouble in understanding? Why?

[6] It is, however, useful for molecular crystals, all liquids (except mercury) and all gases (except the monatomic gases).

CHAPTER XXXIV

The Process of Solution

*The brain is continually searching for fresh information about the rhythm and regularity of what goes on around us.—*J. Z. YOUNG

Much of our knowledge of the behavior of matter has come from the study of solutions. We find solutions everywhere. The waters of the oceans, the lakes, the rivers, and even the water we drink are solutions. Coffee, tea, soda pop, beer, wine, hard liquors, and even the liquid medicines that we take are solutions. The air we breathe is a solution composed of a number of gases dissolved in nitrogen, its most abundant constituent. Almost all metals as we see them in everyday life are solutions of solids in solids. Notable examples are brass, bronze, pewter, coins of all kinds. Our concern here will be almost exclusively with solutions of solids in liquids. It should be clearly understood that in all cases we are dealing with such solutions unless otherwise specified.

The process of solution is analogous to the process of melting—but it is very definitely not melting. The two processes are similar in that in both the cohesive forces between the atoms or molecules of the solid are overcome. In melting this is done by the increase in their kinetic energy by the application of heat. In solutions the cohesive forces of the atoms or molecules are overcome by the action (chiefly) of the solvent molecules. No solvent is involved in melting.

SOLUTIONS, SUSPENSIONS, AND COLLOIDS

Three types of systems in which solid particles are dispersed throughout a liquid are recognized, namely, suspensions, colloidal dispersions, and solutions. They are differentiated from one another by the size of the dispersed particles. In suspensions the solid particles are easily visible, either by the naked eye or by an ordinary microscope. The material in a muddy river is suspended material that ranges from the size of pebbles or even boulders down through sand to fine flour if the water is moving rapidly enough. If the motion is decreased sufficiently, the coarser material, even the fine sand and most of the clay, is dropped. If the water stands long enough, a day, two days, or a week, all, or almost all, of the flourlike material settles to the bottom.

Colloidal dispersions consist of particles that are aggregates or clusters of hundreds or even thousands of molecules that are observable only with high-powered ultramicroscopes. These particles are so fine that they remain in suspension indefinitely, prevented from settling by the constant collisions with the molecules of the solvent. The Brownian movement (p. 207) is commonly observed in certain colloidal dispersions. Other examples of colloidal dispersions are gelatin, "liquid" starch, protoplasm, rubber latex, etc. The colloidal state is not limited to solid particles dispersed in liquid media. Colored glass, opal, and certain other precious stones are examples of solids dispersed in solids. Milk is the most familiar example of a liquid dispersed in a liquid.

Solutions are intimate homogeneous mixtures of particles of atomic or molecular size. Whereas colloids will disperse light, solutions will not; the particles are too small. Hence, colloidal dispersions can be distinguished from solutions by passing a beam of light through them; the path of the light through the colloid is clearly visible,[1] whereas through the solution it is not. Colloidally dispersed matter cannot be removed from the solvent by filtering, frequently to the annoyance of the chemist.

SOLVENTS AND SOLUTES

In every solution there is both a solvent and a solute. (There may, of course, be several solutes in the same solution.) With solids or gases dissolved in liquids, the liquid is the solvent and the solid or gas the solute. With solutions of gases in gases, liquids in liquids, and solids in solids, it is not always clear which is the solvent and which the solute. In these cases we assign the role of solvent to that substance present in greatest quantity. Water is by far the best general liquid solvent.

SATURATION AND SUPERSATURATION

Solutions differ from compounds in that they do not have fixed compositions. A solution may be varied continuously with-

[1] This is called the Tyndall effect.

out causing any abrupt changes in its properties. Thus, we may have dilute solutions, e.g., weak coffee, or more concentrated solutions, such as strong coffee. We can dissolve three, two, one, or a fraction of one lump of sugar in our tea or coffee. If we add much more than three lumps we may find that not all the sugar will dissolve. No matter how much we stir, some of it will be found in the bottom of the cup after we have finished drinking the liquid. The coffee or tea is said to be saturated.

There is no such thing as saturation for solutes that are miscible in all proportions, e.g., certain alcohols and water. Gasoline, kerosene, motor oils, etc., are each solutions of several substances miscible in all proportions, and any of them may be dissolved in any or all of the others in all proportions. There is, however, a maximum amount of solid or gaseous solute that can be dissolved in a given quantity of a liquid solvent. This amount varies with the temperature of the solvent. For most solid solutes this maximum amount increases with the temperature; for a few it decreases. Thus, if we like sugar in our iced tea we find it faster to dissolve the sugar in the tea before we add the ice. If we *saturate* hot tea with sugar and then ice it, we will find that some of the sugar will crystallize out into the bottom of the glass because of decreasing solubility with decreasing temperature.

If we allow a hot saturated solution to cool down without disturbance, we may find that the solute does not crystallize out even though it is one that is more soluble at higher temperatures than at low. The solution is then said to be *supersaturated,* for it contains more solute than is normal for that temperature. Supersaturated solutions are unstable; if they are jarred, or if a crystal of the solute, no matter how tiny, is dropped into them, the excess solute will crystallize out suddenly. For gases dissolved in liquids, the quantity of solute always decreases with increasing temperature if the system is open, i.e., not under pressure, as in an unopened bottle of soda pop. An open bottle of soda pop will go flat a lot more quickly out of the icebox than in it because of the decreased solubility of the gas with rising temperature. The flat taste of boiled water is due to the fact that the air originally dissolved in it has been driven out of solution by the rise in temperature.

It must not be assumed that conditions are static in a saturated solution. If there is excess solute in the bottom of the container, and the temperature is kept constant, there is an equilibrium between the molecules in solution and those of the undissolved solute. Molecules, atoms, or ions are constantly going into solution while others are going out of solution, always in equal numbers so that the concentration does not change.

SOLUBILITY

The maximum amount of a substance that can be dissolved in a solvent at a given temperature is termed its solubility *at that temperature*. Solubilities may be expressed in various ways. The simplest is to use percentages. For example, we can state that air is a solution of gases of which about 78 per cent (by volume) is nitrogen, 20 per cent oxygen, etc. For gases and liquids the percentage can be expressed by either weight or volume. For solids it must be by weight only. We can also state that the solubility of sodium chloride in water is 360 gm/liter (1000 cc) at 20° C. There

are other methods, which are discussed below.

MOLAR CONCENTRATIONS

The chemist is more likely to be dealing with the concentration of the solute in a solution than he is with its solubility (which is the maximum concentration possible at a given temperature). He can use the methods listed above, but far more useful is the method that expresses concentration in the number of moles of solute per liter of water, giving what is called molar concentration. You will remember that a mole is the amount of substance containing the same number of molecules (or atoms, or radicals, or ions, or electrons as the case may be) as there are atoms in 12 gm of ^{12}C. The concentration is expressed by stating the number of moles of solute dissolved in 1 liter (1000 cc) of solution (not solute). A one molar (1 M) solution of sodium chloride in water is made by weighing out 58.45 gm of NaCl and then adding enough water to make 1 liter of solution. Note carefully that the amount of water added is somewhat less than a liter, and that the total volume of solution is constant regardless of the concentration if the temperature is constant. A two molar (2 M) solution would contain 2 moles of NaCl per liter of solution, etc.[2]

This method of expressing concentrations is preferable to other methods, because there is always the same number of atoms, ions, or molecules, as the case may be, in a mole of anything. This number is our old friend, Avogadro's number, 6×10^{23}. Since in chemical reactions atoms combine in

[2] A normal, or 1 N, solution is one that contains 1 gram-equivalent of solute per liter.

simple whole number ratios, e.g., 1:1, 2:1, 1:2, 3:1, 1:3, 2:3, 3:2, 4:1, 1:4, 3:4, 4:3, etc., it should be easy to see that if we are dealing with molar concentrations, we know just how many atoms or ions or molecules are involved. Consider the following equations:

$$Na^+ + Cl^- + Ag^+ + NO_3^- \rightarrow$$
$$Na^+ + NO_3^- + AgCl \downarrow \quad \text{(Eq. 34-1)}$$
$$2H^+ + SO_4^= + 2Na^+ + 2OH^- \rightarrow$$
$$2Na^+ + SO_4^= + 2H_2O \quad \text{(Eq. 34-2)}$$

Let us assume that we have 1 M solutions of each of the compounds on the left. Equation 34-1 tells us that if we mix equal volumes of the reactant solutions, the reaction will be complete with none of either reactant left over because the combining ratio is 1:1. Equation 34-2 tells us that we need twice the volume of 1 M NaOH solution than we do of 1 M H_2SO_4 solution, because the combining ratio here is 1:2.

SOLUTION vs. CHEMICAL REACTION

It is advisable at this point to clarify what we mean by a solution, again restricting ourselves to solid solutes in liquid solvents. Such clarification is necessary because many chemists, as well as most laymen, have fallen into the habit of using the term "dissolve" for any process in which a solid placed in a liquid disappears. Zinc, for example, will disappear if placed in sulfuric acid, but not by the process of solution. It is not soluble in the acid to any appreciable extent. The zinc reacts with the acid, forming zinc sulfate and releasing hydrogen, which escapes into the air. The zinc sulfate is soluble in water and so a true solution exists after the zinc has disappeared. The solute is, however, zinc sulfate, and not zinc. If we evaporate the water, it is zinc sulfate that is recovered. In a true solution, the solid solute can be recovered unchanged chemically by evaporation of the solvent. We will restrict our use of the term solution to true solutions as defined above.

Still, not all processes of solution are alike. No clear-cut boundary can be drawn between purely mechanical (or physical) processes and processes that are in part, at least, chemical. That some are chemical is attested to by the fact that heat can be given off, for example 18,000 cal/mole for sulfuric acid dissolved in water; with most solid substances, however, heat is absorbed when they are dissolved. Conversely, heat is given off when these solids crystallize out of solution. This is analogous to the heat of fusion, in which heat is given off as a liquid freezes (crystallizes), and is absorbed as the crystals melt. Melting is analogous to the dissolving process, for in both it takes energy to pull the molecules, or ions, away from the crystal, energy that can come only from the kinetic (thermal) energy of the solvent in the process of solution, or from an outside source in the process of melting.

The solution of many gases in water represents instances in which no clear-cut boundary between solution and chemical reaction can be drawn. Carbon dioxide dissolves in water to form H_2CO_3 and ammonia to form NH_4^+ and OH^- ions; hydrogen chloride dissolves in water to form hydrochloric acid, etc. Heating these gaseous solutions in an open receptacle will, however, drive off the gases unchanged in composition.

Another case where the cleavage between the processes of solution and chemical reaction is not clear cut is that of the formation of hydrates. The process of hydration involves the association of loosely bound aggregates of water molecules with solute ions or molecules, very commonly those of a salt. In other words, these salt "molecules" crystallize from water solution in association with one or more molecules (sometimes five, six, seven, or even more) of *water* of hydration. Examples are $MgCl_2 \cdot 6H_2O$, $ZnSO_4 \cdot 7H_2O$, $Na_2SO_4 \cdot 10H_2O$, and $Na_2S_2O_3 \cdot 5H_2O$ (sodium thiosulfate). All are extremely soluble in water. Heating the hydrate will drive off the water of hydration, leaving a dehydrated salt.

We might logically ask the whereabouts of the ions, atoms, or molecules of solute in a solution, for a glass of colorless solute dissolved in water looks no different from pure water. At this stage of our study of science we should be able to guess that the atoms or ions or molecules must occupy spaces between the molecules (rarely atoms) of the solvent. That there are spaces is attested by the fact that the volume of a solution is never the sum of the volumes of the substances involved. Thus, if we dissolve a quart of pure alcohol in a quart of pure water, we find that we have a bit less than two quarts of solution. That there are *nearly* two quarts of solution makes it clear that these spaces between the water molecules are not nearly large enough to accomodate the alcohol molecules without moving them somewhat apart. Therefore the volume of the solu-

tion is always somewhat greater than that of the solvent alone.

POLAR vs. NONPOLAR SOLVENTS AND SOLUTES

It is common knowledge that water will not dissolve grease but that carbon tetrachloride, benzene, gasoline, kerosene, etc. will. Conversely, water will dissolve such things as sugar, salt, and a host of other things that the other solvents will not. Can we explain these phenomena by our electronic theory?

We have already discussed the question of polarity. Some molecules are polar and some are nonpolar. We can find out if solvents are polar by seeing if their molecules orient themselves in an electric field.[3] The polarity of solutes can be checked by dissolving them and then performing the same test. The results of all such tests show that polar solvents will dissolve polar solutes and that nonpolar solvents will dissolve nonpolar solutes. They also show that polar solvents will not dissolve nonpolar solutes, and that nonpolar solvents will not dissolve polar solutes to any appreciable extent. Once having established this principle, we can use it in reverse, i.e., if the polarity of a solvent has been established, we know that anything that dissolves in it at all readily is also polar or ionic. The same can be said for nonpolar solvents and solutes.

Let us consider a few examples. We know that a water solution of NaCl will conduct an electric current from our discussion of electrolysis. Salt is therefore

[3] This does not mean that if they do they will carry an electric current. Only if they are ionic will they do that.

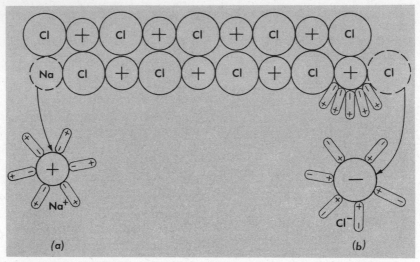

Fig. 34-1. Process of Solution in Polar Solvent (e.g., sodium chloride in water). The negative parts of the water molecules are attracted to the positive sodium ions and the positive parts (of other molecules) to the negative chloride ions. The end result is that the ions are pulled loose from the crystal and floated away, as in (a) and (b).

highly polar. Experiment has also shown that water is the most highly polar of all ordinary liquids. How does a crystal of salt go into solution? In our discussion of chemical reactions by electron transfer we learned that Na and Cl react by the transfer of one electron from the sodium atom to the chlorine atom, thus making positive and negative ions of them. In the solid state these ions are held together by electrostatic forces between the oppositely charge ions, forces that must be overcome if the Na^+ and Cl^- ions are to be pulled away from the crystal. How this is done is illustrated in Fig. 34-1. The polar water molecules may be represented as having one end slightly positive, the other slightly

negative, i.e., they are dipoles. The negative ends of water molecules cluster around a sodium ion on the exposed surface of the crystal because of the electrostatic attractions. They pull it loose, thus overcoming the attraction of the neighboring chloride ions. Other water molecules do the same with a chloride ion by the attraction of their positive ends.

It should follow that the solubility of a solute in a liquid at constant temperature depends upon the relationships among the forces between:

1. Solute particles and solute particles.
2. Solvent particles and solvent particles.
3. Solvent particles and solute particles (or vice versa).

Solubility in all proportions, e.g., alcohol and water, exists when the third set is equal to the other two. When the third set is far less than the other two, insolubility results. Limited solubility lies between these two extremes. The principle can be illustrated by the insolubility of fats and oils in water. Fats and oils are nonpolar, so the forces between the molecules are the van der Waals forces. If our concept of the polarity of the water molecule is correct, then we should expect that the negative ends of the water molecules are attracted to the positive ends of other water molecules. Thus, they would tend to line up somewhat like a group of parading circus elephants (Fig. 34-1), "squeezing" the nonpolar molecules out. In other words, the second set of forces prevails.

Some ionic substances, AgCl, e.g., are insoluble in water because the first set of forces prevails. A few ions may have enough kinetic energy to escape from the crystal; this explains its slight solubility.

We see, therefore, why nonpolar solutes are generally insoluble in polar solvents. If soluble at all, they will be so in nonpolar solvents. In both solute and solvent the attractive forces between the molecules of either are of much the same magnitude so that there is no "squeezing" out. A grease spot on clothing is not removed in the same way as a sugar spot. A nonpolar cleaning fluid, such as carbon tetrachloride or benzene, will mix with nonpolar grease molecules as the fluid passes through the spot, carrying grease molecules with it. The action is a passive one. On the other hand, a sugar spot is actively removed by the water molecules attaching themselves to the sugar molecules and forcibly pulling them away from the fabric.

THE PROCESS OF EXTRACTION

The generalization that "like dissolves like" is not absolute, for some substances are soluble to an appreciable extent in both polar and nonpolar solvents. An example is iodine, whose solubility in water at room temperature is about 1 gm/1000 gm of water. We might predict that it would be more soluble in a nonpolar or slightly polar solvent if our generalization is valid. Our prediction turns out to be true, for its solubility in chloroform (which is slightly polar) is about 250 gm/ 1000 gm of chloroform.

If we dissolve 1 gm of iodine in 1000 gm of water and then add 1000 gm of chloroform (which is well-nigh insoluble in water), and shake the mixture well, we will find that the iodine will distribute itself between the two solvents in the ratio [4] of its solubility in each. The chloroform will remove all but $\frac{1}{250}$ gm of iodine from the water. If we now separate the two solvents by decanting,[5] and then add 1000 gm of fresh chloroform to the water fraction, the chloroform will again absorb $\frac{249}{250}$ of the iodine remaining in the water, leaving only 1/62,500 gm of iodine in the water. Practically all of the iodine may be removed by this method—which is called extraction. Extraction is used to isolate and purify many industrially useful chemicals.

INSOLUBILITY

Strictly speaking there is no such thing as absolute insolubility. When you drink from a glass, you drink a few molecules of the glass. Therefore, when we say that a

[4] This generalization is called the *Law of Partition.*

[5] The process of decanting makes use of the facts that the two solvents are insoluble in each other and are of different densities. Thus, the lighter one can be poured off, leaving the heavier one behind.

substance is insoluble, we mean that for all except the most precise analytical work, its solubility may be ignored.

SUMMARY

Solutions are important because so much of our knowledge of matter has been obtained from study of them. Solutions consist of a solvent and a solute even though it is not always clear which is which. Solutions have no fixed compositions; within limits they may be varied continuously. The solubility of a solute in a solvent may be defined as the maximum concentration possible at a given temperature. Concentration is commonly expressed in moles per liter. Not all processes of solution are alike. The student should distinguish between chemical reaction and solution.

In general, polar solvents will dissolve polar solutes but not nonpolar solutes, and nonpolar solvents will dissolve nonpolar solutes but not polar solutes. The reason lies in the relationships between the attractions of the solute particles for each other, the solvent particles for each other, and the solvent particles for the solute particles.

EXERCISES

I. TERMS AND CONCEPTS

Solution	Supersaturation
Solvent	Solubility
Solute	Insolubility
Suspension	Molar concentration
Colloid	Process of extraction
Saturation	

II. PROBLEMS

1. Distinguish between the solution process and the melting process.

2. Distinguish between a material in suspension and one in solution.

3. What is meant by the solubility of a substance?

4. In general, are solids more or less soluble in hot water than in cold? Is the case the same with gases?

5. How is the solubility of a substance commonly expressed?

6. One mole of HCl dissolved in water to make one liter of solution is a normal solution, whereas one-half a mole of H_2SO_4 similarly dissolved is also a normal solution. Explain.

7. How many grams of H_3PO_4 are there in a normal solution of it?

8. How many moles of NaOH would it take to react completely with a water solution of H_3PO_4 containing one mole of the latter?

9. What solvent or solvents would you use to remove a sugar stain? A grease spot? A stain made by spilling soda pop on a rug? A stain made by heavily sugared coffee containing heavy cream? Give reasons for your answers.

10. Knowing that CCl_4 is nonpolar, would you use it to remove a sugar stain? Explain.

11. How could you tell experimentally whether a salt solution was saturated or not?

12. Cite from your own experience an example that shows that gases are less soluble in warm solutions than in cold.

13. What is meant by miscible in all proportions?

14. Is the process by which a crystal of salt goes into solution an endothermic (heat-absorbing) or an exothermic (heat-evolving) one or neither? Explain.

15. Considering your answer to the above question and the Law of Conservation of Energy, which would you expect the crystallization of the same salt from a solution to be, exothermic, endothermic, or neither?

CHAPTER XXXV

Ionic Theory

*Every new theory . . . believes that it is the for-
tunate theory to achieve the right answer. . . .*
—P. W. BRIDGMAN (Nobel Prize, Physics, 1946)

ELECTROLYTIC SOLUTIONS

In the study of the laws of electrolysis
(Chapter XXV) we learned that Faraday
applied the term ion (meaning "wanderer")
to the two kinds of charged particles present in the solutions through which he
passed an electric current. Solutions containing ions are electrolytic solutions. The
water solutions of all salts and bases are
both ionic and electrolytic. A few covalent
substances form electrolytic solutions because their molecules react with water to
form ions. The only ones we will be concerned with are acids, which we will learn
more about in Chapter XXXVI.

Solutions, then, may be divided into electrolytes and nonelectrolytes on the basis of
their ability to carry an electric current.
The presence of charged particles is necessary for the conductance. It should follow
that the greater the number of charged particles the greater the conductance. If this
is so, then we can gain information about
the concentration of the charges in a solution by using an ammeter to measure the
conductance quantitatively. By this means
we learn that electrolytes can be divided
into two groups, strong electrolytes and
weak electrolytes, even though there is no
sharp line of demarcation between them.
Strong electrolytes are those in which the
compound is completely dissociated [1] so
that great numbers of ions are available
to carry the current. Weak electrolytes are
those in which only a few per cent of the
molecules are dissociated to form ions; most
of the molecules remain intact, each surrounded by clusters of water molecules.
The percentage dissociation in the weak
electrolytes increases as the concentration
decreases, i.e., dilution favors dissociation.
The reason for this is discussed on p. 505.
To avoid any confusion due to the extent of the dilution we separate strong from
weak electrolytes on the basis of the extent
of dissociation in a 1 M concentration.[2]

MOLTEN SALTS AND BASES AS ELECTROLYTES

Molten salts and bases will also conduct
an electric current, but solid salts and bases
will not. The fact that ionic solutions and
molten ionic compounds will conduct currents, but ionic solids will not, suggests a
flow of ions in the liquids where freedom
of movement exists, a freedom that is lacking in solids. By reasoning backward from
our present state of knowledge, we can see
that it is but a short step from the concepts
to the conclusion that the ions must be pres-

[1] Dissociation is the separation of "molecules"
of a compound into ions in the presence of a
solvent.
[2] Strictly speaking we should be dealing with
molal instead of molar concentrations here. The
distinction is not significant to students in a course
of this kind.

ent in the solid state, too. However, the atom was still indivisible in the eyes of the scientists of the nineteenth century, and until the essential structure of the atom had been unraveled, no such conclusion could be validated.

ELECTROLYTIC THEORY: HISTORICAL BACKGROUND

Aside from the fact that the development of one concept must frequently await the establishment of another, there is also the circumstance that a wrong concept frequently must be gotten rid of before a new one can be formulated. Thus, more than fifty years elapsed after Faraday had established his laws of electrolysis on the assumption that ions carried the current through his solutions, before the development of a coherent ionic theory.

We should realize that no concept of ions was possible before the discovery of current electricity, about 1800. A few years later the fundamental observation was made that led to the science of electrolysis; this was the dissociation of water into hydrogen and oxygen. By 1815 both Berzelius and Sir Humphry Davy, Faraday's mentor, had put forth the idea that electric charges were in some way involved when elements combined to form compounds. Although Faraday had interpreted his laws to mean that the charge on the ion was quantized, progress in understanding the nature of ions was held up by the fact that Dalton's atomic theory was in disrepute because of its failure to explain Gay-Lussac's Law of Combining Volumes, a failure that would have been eliminated had Avogadro's distinction between atoms and molecules been accepted earlier. This distinction was finally accepted about 1860 through the ef-

forts of Cannizzaro. This allowed the kinetic theory of gases to be worked out in great detail in the years that followed. It was not until 1887, however, that the theory was applied to solutions by assuming that the solute particles moved about independently in their solvent, just as the molecules of a gas move about independently in their container.

This concept of ions meant, of course, that the old Dalton concept of molecules had to undergo a change. The Dalton concept can be illustrated by dissolving sugar, a nonelectrolyte, in water. The molecules disappear in the liquid, but they remain intact, as they should according to the Dalton concept. If, however, we dissolve common salt in water, the solution will conduct an electric current; one kind of charged particle goes to the anode and another to the cathode. This means that the salt must dissociate into two kinds of particles; not all of the molecules can remain intact, perhaps not any. Dissociated molecules are therefore molecules no longer. Thus, the *old concept* of molecules is no more meaningful with ionic solutions than it was with ionic, covalent, or metallic crystals. The study of the colligative properties of solutions led to a better understanding of ionic and nonionic solutions.

COLLIGATIVE PROPERTIES OF SOLUTIONS

The properties of liquid solutions are not the properties of the solvent, even in very dilute solutions. Some of the significant physical properties of the solvent that have been altered by the presence of the solute are the lowering of the vapor pressure, the lowering of the freezing point, the elevation of the boiling point, and the development of osmotic pressure. Since the alteration of all of these properties is dependent upon the number of particles present, and not at all on the nature of the particles, they are called colligative properties.

Vapor Pressure Lowering

Suppose we put a beaker of pure water, a beaker of a sugar solution, and a beaker of salt solution, all filled to the same level, under an airtight bell jar and leave them there for a while (Fig. 35-1a). In a day or two we will note that the level of the water has decreased in the beaker of pure water and it has increased in the other two (Fig. 35-1b) although there is no physical connection between them. We ask how and why. The how is easy. The only possible answer is that the transfer must have occurred by means of the vapor phase, i.e., more water must have evaporated from one beaker than from the others. What makes this possible is not so obvious.

We can be sure that once the bell jar is placed over the beakers, evaporation will continue until the air in the bell jar is saturated. Furthermore, enormous numbers of molecules will continue to escape after the saturation point is reached but as many will return to the beakers, as long as the temperature remains unchanged. An equilibrium situation has been established, in which the number of molecules returning to *each* beaker is the same. This must be so, for there is nothing to hinder their return to either beaker. It follows that, to produce the inequality of levels, fewer water molecules must escape from two beakers than from the other.

At this point we need to recall that in the process of evaporation only those molecules that have more than average kinetic energy manage to break through the sur-

face of the liquid, and so escape. Fewer water molecules from the sugar and salt solutions attain the necessary speeds because of collisions with the bigger non-

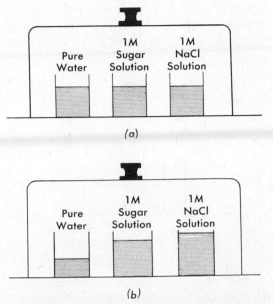

Fig. 35-1. Vapor Pressure Lowering of Water. **(a)** Three beakers filled to the same level and placed under an airtight bell jar. **(b)** The same beakers a day or two later. The water levels have changed even though there is no physical connection between them except by way of the atmosphere.

volatile sugar or salt particles (molecules or ions).[3] I.e., the sugar or salt particles hinder their escape. The net result is a decrease in the volume of pure water in one beaker and an increase in the volume of water in the other two.

Let us return to the equilibrium stage

---

[3] Cane sugar is $C_{12}H_{22}O_{11}$, the salt is NaCl, whereas water is H_2O.

described above. If only the beaker of pure water were under the bell jar, or if we had a closed container of water (Fig. 35-2), a similar equilibrium stage would soon be attained. Since the vapor is a gas, it exerts pressure in the manner of all gases. This pressure at the equilibrium stage is called the vapor pressure of the water. At

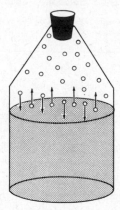

Fig. 35-2. Equilibrium in a Stoppered Container of Water. The same number of molecules of water are returning to the liquid as there are escaping from it.

a given temperature it is a fixed quantity that under proper circumstances can be measured.[4] If only the beakers with the sugar and salt solutions were under the bell jar, the equilibrium situation described above would have been reached sooner. The fewer molecules that escape per unit time, the fewer that need to return per unit time to establish equilibrium. Therefore, there will be less vapor in the bell jar

than there was at the equilibrium point for pure water, and so the vapor pressure of the sugar and salt solutions will be less than for pure water.

The addition of sugar or salt to water lowers its vapor pressure. We can say that the escaping tendency of molecules of pure water is greater than that of the molecules of water in a sugar or a salt solution, and this escaping tendency is a measure of its vapor pressure. We can generalize by saying that the escaping tendency of water molecules from *any* water solution is less than from pure water, and so the vapor pressure is less; it has been depressed by the solute particles. Further investigation will show that the amount of the lowering will vary with the amount of nonvolatile solute in the solution. Two moles dissolved in 100 liters of water will depress the vapor pressure nearly twice as much as one mole dissolved in 100 liters of water.[5] The lowering will be greater for electrolytes (like salt) than for nonelectrolytes (like sugar) because the ions in the solid salt separate in solution, forming twice (in NaCl) the number of particles. See p. 505.

Freezing Point Depression

It has long been known that solutes of any kind depress the freezing point of water. In fact, Fahrenheit (about 1700) had determined the zero point on his thermometer by finding the lowest temperature that he could obtain from any mixture of water, ice, and common salt.

If we freeze the water in the three beak-

---

[4] At room temperature the vapor pressure of water is about 24 mm of mercury. At the boiling point it is 760 mm, equal to one atmosphere. This is, in fact, the definition of the normal boiling point of water.

[5] We use dilute solutions because these ratios do not hold at high concentrations. Increasing the concentration always increases the lowering of the vapor pressure but the rate of increase drops off even with moderate concentrations.

ers discussed in the previous section, we will find that the sugar and salt solutions will not freeze at 0° C. The freezing point of water is depressed for the same reason the vapor pressure was depressed, i.e., because of the interference of the solute particles. They interfere with the occupation of the lattice points by the water molecules in a potential ice crystal. The interference is so successful that no crystals can form until the average kinetic energy of the particles has been reduced somewhat, i.e., until the temperature of the solution has been reduced. The effect of the lowering has been to extend the liquid range of the water to a lower temperature. Again further investigation reveals that doubling the concentration nearly doubles the freezing point depression as long as we limit ourselves to dilute solutions.

Boiling Point Elevation

Surprising as it may seem, a nonvolatile solute raises the boiling point of a solution. Thus, the solute causes the liquid range of the water to be extended upward to higher temperatures as well as downward. The nonvolatile solute particles hinder the escape of the water molecules so effectively that a vapor pressure of 760 mm is not attained until the temperature of the solution has risen somewhat above 100° C. Again the amount the boiling point is raised varies directly with the concentration in dilute solutions.

Osmotic Pressure

To demonstrate this we can use our beakers of water and sugar solution in a somewhat different manner. We will divide another larger vessel into two compartments by means of a semipermeable membrane.[6] We now pour the sugar solution into one compartment and the pure water into the other. After a time we find that the water level is higher on the sugar side than on the other, just as it was when the two beakers were under the bell jar. The cause cannot be the same, because the bell jar is absent; the surfaces of the two liquids are exposed to the atmosphere. Putting a separate cover over each compartment would not alter the situation as long as they were not quite airtight. The only way for water to pass from one side to the other is through the membrane.

Again we can call on interference of the sugar molecules. If we have pure water in both compartments, or sugar solutions of the same concentration in both compartments, we find that their levels do not change, for in both cases just as many water molecules pass through the membrane one way as the other. The sugar molecules cannot pass through because they are too big. All they can do is get in the way of water molecules, which happen to be moving towards one of the exceedingly tiny openings in the membrane. Hence more water molecules pass one way than the other.

The water level in the sugar solution will continue to rise, and in the other beaker it will continue to drop, thus creating a pressure difference on the two walls of the membrane. As this difference in pressure

[6] A semipermeable membrane is a membrane one kind of particle can pass through but another cannot, the chief reason being that it is too big. Many types of animal tissues are semipermeable, for many biological processes involve osmosis. A common nonbiological example of such a membrane is cellophane. A better one is made by precipitating insoluble copper ferrocyanide in the pores of an unglazed porcelain cup.

becomes greater, water molecules find it more and more difficult to move (against this pressure) from the pure water side to the sugar solution side. Fewer get through. When the number is reduced to the same number passing from the sugar side to the pure water side, the difference in elevation of the two surfaces is at a maximum. This maximum pressure difference is called the osmotic pressure of the solution. Just as with the other colligative properties, the osmotic pressure varies with the concentration in dilute solutions.

One thing that was unexplainable before 1887, and that we have deliberately omitted so far, was that these alterations in the colligative properties were two, three or even four times greater for electrolytes than they were for nonelectrolytes. That is to say, a 0.1 M concentration of NaCl was just about as effective in lowering the freezing point of water as was a 0.2 M concentration of sugar; a 0.1 M solution of $MgCl_2$ was nearly as effective as a 0.3 M solution of sugar or any other nonelectrolyte. The explanations of these facts, and others concerning electrolytes, were still awaiting a unified theory in 1887.

DISSOCIATION THEORY OF ARRHENIUS

Svante Arrhenius, a young Swedish chemist, advanced his dissociation theory in 1887 in an attempt to correlate the known facts about electrolytic solutions. The facts of electrolysis, and the facts concerning the colligative properties of solutions obviously were related.

The theory of Arrhenius is really a recapitulation of ideas that we have already discussed in laying the foundation for it. We find it best to introduce the theory in

this manner, for none of the postulates was original with Arrhenius. He put them together and used them to explain a variety of facts. We may summarize his theory as follows:

1. "Molecules" [7] of electrolytes when dissolved in water dissociate into ions.
2. An equilibrium exists between the electrolyte "molecules" and the ions. Dilution favors the formation of more ions.
3. The ions move about in the solvent independently of one another.

The first of the postulates has already been discussed except for the origin of the ions. Faraday had believed that the electric current "created" the ions from the molecules of the solute, and that they existed only so long as the current flowed through the solution. Arrhenius thought that the ions were created by the action of the water on the solute. He had to eliminate the need of a current for their formation if he was going to use the presence of ions to explain their greater effectiveness in altering the colligative properties. It was not until the electronic concept of chemical bonding was advanced, well along in the present century, that it was realized

---

[7] The old definition of a molecule does not apply to solids with ionic, covalent, or metallic crystal lattices. It does apply to those with molecular lattices, and to the gaseous or vapor state of all compounds. See the definition of molecule on p. 242. Some chemists use the term "formula unit," but this gives rise to a certain awkwardness of expression. For example, if one states that "formula units of electrolytes dissociate, etc.," one is making a misstatement, for it is the particles of the compound that dissociate. Arguments can be raised against the use of the terms particle or ion in the sense that we are using molecule here. We will use the word "molecule" here in its original meaning, but we will keep it in quotation marks to indicate that we are taking liberties in its use.

that the ions were present in the solid state of the solute.

The second postulate assumes both the presence of ions and of "molecules" in the solution, so that there is a resemblance to the equilibrium in a saturated solution, described on p. 493. Thus, "molecules" are breaking down into ions, and ions are recombining to form "molecules" *at the same rate* when equilibrium is reached.

Dissociation, therefore, was never complete in the view of Arrhenius. Dilution should favor the formation of more ions, because the greater the volume of the solvent with respect to the quantity of solute, the less chance two oppositely charged ions would have of finding each other to pair up to form a "molecule." Creating more ions increases the chances of pairing up.

The third postulate is valid at low concentrations where the ions are relatively far apart. It needed revision in concentrated solutions where the ions are relatively close together so that they *do* have an effect on one another, just as the kinetic theory of gases needed revision at high pressures because the molecules are close enough together for the van der Waals forces to be appreciable.

Successes of the Dissociation Theory of Arrhenius

The theory could explain the instantaneous chemical reaction between electrolytes because the "molecules" have already been broken down into their components. These components are then all ready to react. If a solution of silver nitrate, e.g., is poured into a solution of sodium chloride, an instantaneous precipitate of silver chloride is formed. Nonelectrolytic reactions, on the other hand, are not instantaneous, for time is consumed in the breaking up of the molecules into their component parts. Only after this has taken place can the reaction begin.

The theory could explain conductance in electrolytes and nonconductance in nonelectrolytes. This has been repeatedly discussed, so we will not elaborate it here. The theory could also explain why electrolytes were more effective in altering the colligative properties of solutions than nonelectrolytes. All we need to do is assume that the amount of alteration is determined by the number of particles present, be those particles ions, atoms, or molecules. If each of these particles splits into two ions, as does a particle of NaCl when it goes into solution, or into three ions, as does a particle of $MgCl_2$, or into four ions as does a particle of $FeCl_3$ then we have two, three, or four times the number of particles that we have in the same volume of solvent when the solute is a nonelectrolyte. Therefore, these electrolytes should be two, three, or four times as effective in altering the colligative properties as the nonelectrolyte.

Revisions of the Dissociation Theory

As already indicated, the effectiveness is doubled, tripled, or quadrupled only when the solutions are dilute. Moreover, the evidence was increasing that strong electrolytes were completely dissociated in water. For example, salts were ionic in the solid state. If they dissolved completely, they should dissociate completely. Eventually the theory was altered by Debye and Hückel in 1923. This altered theory is sometimes called the interionic attraction theory of electrolytes.

It not only assumes complete dissociation for strong electrolytes but also allows, as the name suggests, for the attractions of oppositely charged ions, attractions that play an increasingly important role as the concentration of the solute particles increases. Thus, in a solution of NaCl the Na^+ ions are accelerated away from other Na^+ ions and towards Cl^- ions; Cl^- ions are accelerated away from other Cl^- ions and towards Na^+ ions. Thus, neither kind of ion is a completely independent unit. The result is that when an electric current is passed through the solution, the ions are hampered in their movements towards an electrode. Dilution increases the distance between ions and so decreases the hampering; increasing the concentration decreases the distance between ions and so increases the hampering.

SOME TYPICAL REACTIONS BETWEEN ELECTROLYTES

If positive and negative ions exist as more or less independent particles in an aqueous solution, then it should follow that a negative ion ought to be able to enter into chemical combination without regard to what happens to a corresponding positive ion. Consider a tiny crystal of NaCl. Put it in water and the two ions of each "molecule" separate, moving about independently. The Cl^- ions have a set of properties that are quite distinct from those of molecules (or atoms) of chlorine. They have no tendency to escape from solution, even if the water is boiled (as do dissolved chlorine molecules). They do not react with hydrogen or most metals, as do chlorine molecules; they are almost inert. The reason for their inactivity is easy to find; chloride ions have eight electrons in their outer shell, and so have attained the stable octet.

The independence of the chloride ion can be demonstrated by adding a solution of a silver salt—anyone will do—to a solution of any chloride, e.g., NaCl, KCl, $MgCl_2$, $CaCl_2$, $BaCl_2$, etc. In every case the silver ion combines with the chloride instantly to form an insoluble precipitate of AgCl. Suppose we add NaCl solution to $AgNO_3$ solution. This reaction used to be written as follows:

$$NaCl + AgNO_3 \rightarrow NaNO_3 + AgCl \downarrow$$

(Eq. 35-1)

The electronic way of writing it is

$$Na^+ + Cl^- + Ag^+ + NO_3^- \rightarrow$$
$$AgCl \downarrow + Na^+ + NO_3^- \quad (Eq. 35-2)$$

Since the Na^+ and the NO_3^- ions occur on both sides we can cancel them, and write

$$Ag^+ + Cl^- \rightarrow AgCl \downarrow \quad (Eq. 35-3)$$

This tells us that whenever we bring silver ion and chloride ion together in the same solution, *regardless of the source*, AgCl will be precipitated (because it is insoluble in water). Since a chemical equation should be a summary of the actual chemical change, we see that Eq. 35-3 is entirely satisfactory. The other ions are merely "spectator" ions, for they take no part in the reaction.

Suppose, however, we mix molar solutions of $NaNO_3$ and Ag_2SO_4 in equal amounts. The ionic equation is

$$Na^+ + NO_3^- + 2Ag^+ + SO_4^= \rightarrow$$
$$Na^+ + NO_3^- + 2Ag^+ + SO_4^= \quad (Eq. 35-4)$$

The same substances appear on both sides, so no reaction has taken place; all four kinds of ions remain in solution. Suppose, however, we evaporated the $NaNO_3$—

Ag_2SO_4 mixture to dryness. Presumably we might get crystals of four compounds— $NaNO_3$, Na_2SO_4, $AgNO_3$, and Ag_2SO_4. If all were equally soluble and we had two moles of $NaNO_3$ to one of Ag_2SO_4, we would get equal numbers of "molecules" of each of the four. They are not equally soluble and so we would get a larger proportion of the least soluble of the above four compounds.

Consider another case among the salts. Let us mix solutions of $BaCl_2$ and Na_2SO_4. Instantly a precipitate of $BaSO_4$ forms. The summarizing equation is,

$$Ba^{++} + SO_4^{=} \rightarrow BaSO_4 \downarrow \quad \text{(Eq. 35-5)}$$

Again we have a reaction because an insoluble precipitate can form.

Consider a case among the bases, which are also ionic compounds. They dissolve in water, dissociating into metallic [8] and hydroxide (OH^-) ions. Arrhenius defined a base as a substance whose water solution contained OH^- ions. When these basic solutions are mixed with other ionic solutions, *acids excepted*, no reaction occurs unless an insoluble precipitate can form. For example, $Ba(OH)_2$ does not react with $NaCl$ because the possible reaction products are soluble in water. However,

$$Ba^{++} + 2OH^- + 2Na^+ + SO_4^{=} \rightarrow$$

$$BaSO_4 \downarrow + 2Na^+ + 2OH^- \quad \text{(Eq. 35-6)}$$

The positive ions may also react independently of the negative ions. Consider separate solutions of $CaCl_2$, $CaBr_2$, and CaS. If we add Na_2CO_3 solution to each, we will get in each case a precipitate of insoluble $CaCO_3$. Here the chloride, bro-

[8] There are a few bases in which there are no metallic ions.

mide, and sulfide ions are the spectator ions in the reaction,

$$Ca + CO_3 \rightarrow CaCO_3 \quad \text{(Eq. 35-7)}$$

If we added $NaNO_3$ solution to the above three soluble calcium compounds, no reaction would occur, for calcium nitrate is also soluble in water.

We should now be able to make the following generalization:

When water solutions of two electrolytes that are ionic in the solid state are mixed, no chemical reaction will take place unless some insoluble compound like $BaSO_4$, $AgCl$, $CaCO_3$ can be precipitated.

These insoluble precipitates should make us ask a question or two. Are they ionic compounds in the solid state? The answer is "yes," for X-ray diffraction patterns show it. If they are ionic, why did they go out of solution?

We should be able to find the answer in the electronic theory of chemical combination if our theory is valid. We have already learned that water is the best known solvent for ionic substances because of its relatively high polarity. In other words, if the highly polar water molecules cannot pull the Ba^{++} and $SO_4^{=}$ ions away from a crystal of $BaSO_4$, the molecules of no other liquid are likely to do it, either. This means that the interionic attractions are greater than the attractions between the ions and the polar water molecules. In the "tug-of-war" the water molecules lose.

SUMMARY

Solutions are divided into electrolytes and nonelectrolytes on the basis of their conductance of an electric current. All salts, bases, and acids form electrolytic solutions. All of them contain ions. In general, we classify electrolytic solutions as either strong or weak, although there are all gradations. Strong electrolytes are completely dissociated in water, weak electrolytes only to the extent of a few per cent.

Molten salts and bases will conduct an electric current even if no water is present. This suggests that the ions are present in the solid state of these compounds, and that they conduct a current only when free to move.

No concept of ions was possible before the invention of the battery. The elementary facts of electrolysis demand the presence of two unlike particles to carry the charges. Further clarification of electrolytic phenomena was blocked by problems concerning atomic and kinetic theory. Such clarification came in the years following 1860 with the acceptance of Avogadro's Law and the extension of the kinetic theory of gases to solutions.

Other facts to be explained were those concerning the colligative properties of electrolytic and nonelectrolytic solutions. These properties are vapor pressure lowering, freezing point lowering, boiling point elevation and osmotic pressure. All are due to the same thing, the interference of solute particles. A problem was presented by the fact that electrolytic solutes were at least twice as effective as nonelectrolytic solutes as producers of the colligative properties.

Arrhenius formulated an ionic theory largely by organizing into a coherent whole the various ideas that had developed since the time of Faraday. To explain colligative properties he abandoned Faraday's concept of the creation of ions by an electron current, substituting the water as the "creator" of the ions. In the dissociation into ions, more particles were created, and this was used to explain the phenomena of colligative properties. The theory also explained the differences in the speeds of reaction between ionic solutions on the one hand and nonionic solutions on the other. The inadequacy of the theory in other than dilute

solutions, and the recognition that salts and bases were ionic in the solid led to a revision of the Arrhenius theory by Debye and Hückel in 1923.

Some typical reactions between ionic electrolytes show the independence of the oppositely charged ions in solution. Some of these reactions give precipitates of insoluble compounds. X-ray diffraction patterns showed that these compounds were ionic in the solid state. Why, then, should they be insoluble in a polar liquid like water? The answer lies in the magnitude of the electronic attraction of their ions for each other compared to that of the polar water molecules for them.

EXERCISES

I. TERMS AND CONCEPTS

Electrolyte
Nonelectrolyte
Dissociation
Colligative properties

Vapor pressure
Osmotic pressure
Semipermeable membrane

II. PROBLEMS

1. Name the three groups of substances that conduct a current when dissolved in water.

2. Molten salts and bases conduct electric currents but solid salts and bases do not. Explain.

3. How did the Dalton concept of atoms and molecules inhibit atomic theory?

4. A lump of common salt and a lump of sugar look almost exactly alike. Before the invention of the battery, was it possible to know that one was ionic and one was not? Explain.

5. Faraday believed that ions were created when a current was passed through certain solutions. Considering the state of electric theory at the time, and the fact that atoms were considered indivisible (electrons

were unknown), how might you explain the method by which the two kinds of charges were carried to their respective electrodes?

6. Name the colligative properties of solutions. Why are they so named?

7. Explain the general method by which the physical properties of a solvent are altered by the presence of a solute.

8. What is a semipermeable membrane?

9. State the assumptions of the Arrhenius theory of ionic solutions.

10. Why are ionic solutes more effective than nonionic solutes in altering the physical properties of solvents? Explain the differences in the water levels of the beakers in Fig. 35-1b.

11. Why is the effectiveness doubled by doubling the concentration of the solute in dilute solutions, but not by doubling the concentrations of more concentrated solutions?

12. Why should dilution favor the formation of ions in weak electrolytes?

13. How did the strong electrolytes of Arrhenius differ from those of Debye and Hückel?

14. Cite one piece of evidence that in an ionic solution the two kinds of ions can react independently of one another.

15. What are "spectator" ions?

16. A water solution of NaCl and one of $MgSO_4$ are mixed. No reaction takes place. Yet if the water is evaporated, some Na_2SO_4 and some $MgCl_2$ will be precipitated. Explain.

17. Explain the insolubility of some ionic compounds in a polar solvent like water.

CHAPTER XXXVI

Acid–Base Reactions

To science, pilot of industry, conqueror of disease, multiplier of the harvest, explorer of the universe, revealer of nature's laws, eternal guide to truth.
—INSCRIPTION ON THE NATIONAL
ACADEMY OF SCIENCES BUILDING

Most commonly these reactions are between covalent and ionic electrolytes. Most bases are, as we have just learned, ionic electrolytes. Acids are covalent electrolytes. All contain hydrogen, which, we have also learned, forms covalent bonds. The *pure* acids are therefore nonionic and nonelectrolytes, no matter whether they are gases, liquids, or solids.[1] In water solutions all acids ionize to some extent by reacting with water. Arrhenius defined an acid as a substance whose water solution contains hydrogen ions. Water solutions of acids react with metals *that are above hydrogen in the activity series* (Table 32-1), with liberation of free hydrogen. For example,

---

[1] Pure HCl is a gas at room temperature; pure H_2SO_4 is a liquid; many pure organic acids, e.g., oxalic, benzoic, salicylic, etc., are solids.

$$Zn + 2HCl \rightarrow ZnCl_2 + H_2 \uparrow$$

(Eq. 36-1)

Written ionically,

$$Zn + 2H^+ + 2Cl^- \rightarrow$$
$$Zn^{++} + 2Cl^- + H^2 \uparrow \quad \text{(Eq. 36-2)}$$

Summarizing,

$$Zn + 2H^+ \rightarrow Zn^{++} + H^2 \uparrow \quad \text{(Eq. 36-3)}$$

In the reaction the zinc "forces" its valence electrons on to the hydrogen ions, thus making them neutral atoms, which pair up immediately and escape as molecules. Or we could equally well say that the hydrogen ions "take" the outer electrons of zinc away, giving the same result.

The Arrhenius concept of acids and bases was eventually found to be inadequate, so Brønsted, a Danish chemist, proposed a new one in 1923. He defined *an acid as a substance that can donate protons, and a base as a subsbtance that can accept protons during a chemical change.* Pertinent to these definitions is the knowledge that the protons referred to are *always* derived from hydrogen atoms by the loss of an electron; these protons never come from other atoms. The hydrogen ion is but a bare nucleus and is extremely small —about 1/10,000 the diameter of the chlorine ion. In the reaction between acids and bases there is a transfer of protons. This gives a new type of chemical reaction to add to those already studied, i.e., to electron transfer and electron sharing.[2]

We have stated that pure acids ionize when dissolved in water. Why should a covalent compound that is a nonconductor

---

[2] Another concept of acids and bases considers that a base shares one of its pairs of electrons with acids.

510

ionize in water? First, let us look at the ions formed.

$$HCl + H_2O \rightleftharpoons H_3O^+ + Cl^-$$

acid₁ → $acid_1$ base₂ → $base_2$ (hydronium (chloride
ion) acid₂ → $acid_2$ ion) base₁ → $base_1$

(Eq. 36-4)

Inspection of this equation shows that a hydrogen ion (proton) has separated from the HCl molecule and attached itself to the water molecule, turning it into a positive hydronium ion. Note that this positive ion is not formed in the way a metallic ion is formed, i.e., by removal of an electron. Instead a positively charged proton (hydrogen ion) has been transferred to a molecule of water. What caused the transfer?

We have already noted the extremely small size of the hydrogen ion, and that in HCl it shares a pair of electrons with chlorine. Since chlorine has a higher electronegativity than hydrogen, the hydrogen–chlorine bond is polar covalent, with the chlorine holding the shared pair of electrons a bit more closely than does the hydrogen nucleus. In water these polar HCl molecules find themselves in a new environment, one in which they are completely surrounded by water molecules. Since solute and solvent molecules are both polar, the HCl dipoles are surrounded by H_2O dipoles, with the result that they have a tendency to rip one another apart. The water molecules have two pairs of unshared electrons,

$$H : \overset{..}{\underset{..}{O}} : H$$

and the proton attaches itself to one of these pairs, forming an hydronium ion. We say that the HCl molecule has donated a proton to a water molecule. The HCl is

thus the donor, and therefore an acid, whereas the H_2O is the acceptor, and is therefore a base.[3]

Water ionizes to an extremely slight extent by breaking up into hydronium and hydroxide ions, as follows:

$$H_2O + H_2O \rightleftharpoons H_3O^+ + OH^-$$

acid₁ → $acid_1$ base₂ → $base_2$ acid₂ → $acid_2$ base₁ → $base_1$

(Eq. 36-5)

The process is the same as in acids, the transfer of a proton from one molecule to another. One water molecule acts as a proton donor and the other as a proton acceptor. Thus, again we see how different the Brønsted concept is from the Arrhenius concept, for here water acts as both a base and an acid. We have also seen how water acts as a base with HCl in Eq. 36-4. In the equation

$$H_2O + NH_3 \rightleftharpoons NH_4 + OH^-$$

acid₁ → $acid_1$ (ammonia) (ammonium (hydroxide
base₂ → $base_2$ ion) acid₂ → $acid_2$ ion) base₁ → $base_1$

(Eq. 36-6)

water acts as an acid.

By comparing the conductance of electricity in pure water with that in solutions in which the concentration of ions is

[3] We noted above that water has two pairs of unshared electrons, whereas ammonia has one pair, and methane has none. Also hydrogen fluoride has three pairs of unshared electrons. This may be seen from their dot formulas:

$$\overset{..}{\underset{..}{:O:}}_{H \cdot \cdot H} , \quad H:\overset{..}{\underset{..}{N}}:H , \quad H:\overset{H}{\underset{H}{C}}:H , \quad H:\overset{..}{\underset{..}{F}}:$$

Now all four of these elements, C, N, O, F are in the same period, and in that order. Of their hydrogen compounds only methane shows no acidic or basic properties. This is because it has no unshared pairs of electrons. Ammonia, with one pair, is the strongest base, hydrogen fluoride the strongest acid.

known, it has been determined that only one water molecule in over 500,000,000 is dissociated into ions. This is so trivial that it could be entirely neglected if it were not for the fact that it turns out to be responsible for some of the important properties of water. Many metabolic reactions in living organisms depend upon the hydrogen ion and hydroxide ion concentrations in the blood and other body liquids. Acids and bases, as we will have occasion to note later, can be defined on the basis of how they affect these concentrations, as follows: An acid is a substance that increases the hydrogen ion concentration and a base is one that increases the hydroxide ion concentration.[4]

Other acids react with water similarly to HCl.

$$H_2SO_4 + 2H_2O \rightleftharpoons 2H_3O^+ + SO_4^=$$

acid$_1$ base$_2$ acid$_2$ base$_1$
(sulfuric)   (sulfate ion)

$$(\text{Eq. 36-7})$$

$$HNO_3 + H_2O \rightleftharpoons H_3O^+ + NO_3^-$$

acid$_1$ base$_2$ acid$_2$ base$_1$
(nitric)   (nitrate ion)

$$(\text{Eq. 36-8})$$

$$HC_2H_3O_2 + H_2O \rightleftharpoons H_3O^+ + C_2H_3O_2^-$$

acid$_1$ base$_2$ acid$_2$ base$_1$
(acetic)   (acetate ion)

$$(\text{Eq. 36-9})$$

That acids are not ionic in the pure state but that their water solutions are, can be easily checked by means of an electric current. HCl, H_2SO_4, and HNO_3 show themselves to be strong electrolytes, hence strong acids, by the ease with which they conduct current. Acetic acid conducts it

[4] This was the Arrhenius concept, a concept that is still useful to biologists today. We will use it later.

only feebly at best. It therefore follows that acetic acid is only partially ionized in water solution, and is therefore a weak electrolyte and a weak acid. Most of the solute particles in the solution are acetic acid molecules, relatively few are hydronium and acetate ions. This may be indicated as in Eq. 36-9, where the shorter arrow indicates that the number of ions present is small compared to the number of acetic acid molecules present in the solution.

We might reason that the attraction of the acetate ion for a proton is slightly greater than that of a water molecule for it, so that very few actually escape from the acetic acid molecule, and these only temporarily. As soon as a hydronium ion collides with an acetate ion, they recombine to form an acetic acid molecule and a water molecule. However, new hydronium ions are constantly forming so that at any given temperature and concentration the number is constant, i.e., an equilibrium situation exists. We can now perhaps better understand why the *percentage* of particles that ionize in weak electrolytes increases with the dilution. *Dilution does not in any way affect the rate at which ions are formed,* but *it does affect the rate at which they recombine,* for the likelihood of a hydronium ion colliding with an acetate ion decreases as the dilution increases. Therefore, if we further dilute a weak acid, the number of new ions formed per unit time remains the same, but the rate at which they recombine is decreased. The number of ions present thus increases. This increases the likelihood of recombination. Eventually the rate of formation is again equal to the rate of recombination and a new equilibrium situation exists.

Bases that have metals for their positive

ions are ionic compounds and so dissociate in water just as do the salts. The ions are freed from their lattices by the water molecules in the manner previously described (Fig. 34-1). In the process a great deal of heat is given off. The strongest bases commonly available are metallic hydroxides in aqueous media. Simple bases with positive ions that are not metals are rare; NH_3 is the only common one.[5]

Generalizing with respect to both acids and bases, we can say that (according to Brønsted) those substances that form H_3O^+ ions in water are acids, and those that form OH^- ions are bases.

CONJUGATE ACIDS AND BASES

Consider again the definitions of acids and bases in terms of proton donors and proton acceptors, respectively. Note also that below each item in Eqs. 36-4 to 36-9 inclusive we have written the term acid or base. Consider, e.g., Eq. 36-9. Acetic acid is, according to the Brønsted concept, an acid because a molecule of it can donate a proton to a water molecule. This, however, makes the water molecule a base because it accepts the proton. Now let us look at the right side of the equation. The hydronium ion can donate a proton to the acetate ion. Thus, the former must be an acid and the latter a base. The same reasoning can be applied to Eqs. 36-4, 36-7, and 36-8. Generalizing, we can write

$$\text{Acid}_1 + \text{Base}_2 \rightarrow \text{Acid}_2 + \text{Base}_1$$

$$\text{(Eq. 36-10)}$$

[5] One should not assume that the presence of the OH^- radical in a compound makes it a base. C_2H_5OH, common grain alcohol, does not ionize to a measurable extent in water solution.

These acid–base pairs (acid$_1$–base$_1$ and acid$_2$–base$_2$) are called conjugate acid–base pairs. It is apparent that according to the Brønsted concept both molecules and ions may be acids or bases. It is also apparent that the reaction between one acid–base pair gives rise to another acid–base pair. Not so apparent is the fact that this second acid–base pair will have relative strengths that differ radically from the first. To understand this we need to discuss further the distinction between strong acids and weak acids.

STRONG ACIDS vs. WEAK ACIDS

In Eqs. 36-4 through 36-9 we used pairs of arrows, one long and one short, pointing in opposite directions, in place of single arrows pointing to the right. In Eqs. 36-4, 36-6, 36-7, and 36-8, the long arrows point to the right, the short ones to the left. Their relative lengths (not drawn to scale) indicate that the tendency for the hydronium ion to unite with the basic ion when they collide is extremely small. We might equally well say that the HCl, HNO_3, and H_2SO_4 molecules have a very strong tendency to donate protons, so much so that there are practically no undissociated HCl, HNO_3, or H_2SO_4 molecules in their respective solutions. It follows that these are all strong acids, for if an acid is a proton donor, the better the donor the stronger the acid. The water accepts all of the protons that the acids have to donate. It must therefore be a relatively strong base. Conversely, the bases, Cl^-, $SO_4^=$, and NO_3^-, on the right of the three equations, must be extremely weak, for they have little tendency to accept protons to become HCl, H_2SO_4, and HNO_3 molecules again. It follows also that the H_3O^+ ion must be a weaker acid than HCl, H_2SO_4, or HNO_3. We can generalize by saying that the stronger an acid is the weaker its conjugate base must be.

We should expect from this that weak acids will have small tendencies to donate protons. This is shown in Eq. 36-9 by the directions and the lengths of the long and short arrows. The result is that there are relatively few H_3O^+ and $C_2H_3O_2^-$ ions in the solution. Looking at it another way, we might say that the hydronium and acetate ions have stronger tendencies to donate and accept protons than do the acetic acid and water molecules. Thus, the latter are predominant in the solution. It follows, then, that hydronium ion is a stronger acid than acetic acid, and that acetate ion is a stronger base than water. Since the same situation exists for all weak acids, we can generalize by saying that the weaker an acid is, the stronger its conjugate base. If we consider the relative proton-donating and the relative proton-accepting properties of acids and bases, then we can see that, in Eq. 36-10, if $acid_2$ is weaker than $acid_1$, then $base_1$ must also be weaker than $base_2$. Conversely, if $acid_2$ is stronger than $acid_1$, then $base_1$ must be stronger than $base_2$.

Applying this to Eq. 36-5, we can say that water is a very weak acid because its conjugate base, the OH^- ion, is very strong; and that water is a weak base because its conjugate acid, the H_3O^+ ion, is strong. It should be apparent by this time that the terms "acid" and "base" are relative terms, for water according to the Brønsted concept may act as either an acid or a base (p. 511) depending upon the reaction. (Compare Eqs. 36-10, 36-11, 36-12.) It is therefore said to be amphiprotic (meaning that it can either accept or donate protons).

LEVELING EFFECT

All strong acids—e.g., $HClO_4$ (perchloric acid), HI, HBr, HNO_3, HCl—when dissolved in water, appear to have exactly equal strengths, although in solvents less basic than water, their strengths decrease in the order listed. A glance at Eqs. 36-4, 36-7, and 36-8 shows why; all react with water to form hydronium ion. The apparent acidity of all has been reduced to that of the hydronium ion. This is called the leveling effect. Hydronium ion is therefore the strongest acid that can exist in appreciable concentration in a water solution.

NEUTRALIZATION

In our discussion of Equation 36-5 we have seen that the H_3O^+ and OH^- ions have a considerable tendency to unite to form water, so much so that water is extremely slightly dissociated into ions. We should not be surprised, therefore, that if these two ions from separate sources are brought into contact with each other, they should combine to form water molecules. Thus, when the strong base, OH^- ion, is added to the strong acid, H_3O^+ ion, water is formed.

$$H_3O^+ + OH^- \rightleftharpoons H_2O + H_2O$$
$$\text{acid}_1 \quad\quad \text{base}_2 \quad\quad\quad \text{acid}_2 \quad\quad \text{base}_1$$

(Eq. 36-11)

This process is called neutralization, for by the disappearance of the two kinds of ions, the effects of one kind appears to neutralize the effects of the other kind. We cannot, of course, simply add these two ions together, for each always occurs with at least one other ion. Thus, if we add a water solution of HCl to a water solution of $NaOH$, we may write ionically,

$$H_3O^+ + Cl^- + Na^+ + OH^- \rightarrow$$
$$\text{acid}_1 \qquad\qquad\qquad \text{base}_2$$

$$H_2O + H_2O + Na^+ + Cl^- \quad \text{(Eq. 36-12)}$$
$$\text{acid}_2 \quad \text{base}_1$$

Eliminating the ions that occur on both sides (the so-called spectator ions), we have Eq. 36-11. Note that this equation is the same as Eq. 36-5, except that it is written in reverse. Thus, the reaction between an acid and a base tends towards the production of the weakest possible acid and the weakest possible base.

It should be obvious from Eq. 36-11 that it takes one OH^- ion to neutralize one H_3O^+ ions. Therefore, one liter of a normal solution of any acid that will form one H_3O^+ ion per molecule of acid will neutralize one liter of a normal solution of any monovalent base, i.e., one liter of a normal solution of HCl, HNO_3, HBr, or $HC_2H_3O_2$ will be neutralized by exactly one liter of a normal solution of NaOH, KOH, LiOH, etc.

The Brønsted concept of acids and bases leads to the concept of conjugate acids and bases, and this concept in turn leads to a better understanding of the phenomena that take place in water solutions of acids and bases. Chief among these phenomena are the processes of neutralization (just described), the process of hydrolysis (which we will not describe here, except to say that it may be regarded as the reverse of neutralization), and the processes involved in many of the reactions of organic chemistry.

SUMMARY

Acids are covalent electrolytes. This means that pure acids cannot conduct electric cur-rents but their water solutions can—that acids become ionic in water. This led Arrhenius to believe that water created the ions in all ionic solutions. The Brønsted concept of acids as proton donors and bases as proton acceptors was advanced as a more satisfying theory. It postulates that hydronium ions are formed when a pure acid is put in water, and that these ions are responsible for the acid properties of water. Moreover, the terms acid and base are relative terms according to Brønsted. Water, e.g., is amphiprotic, i.e., it can act as an acid under some circumstances, as a base under others. When an acid reacts with a base, a weaker acid and a weaker base are formed.

Strong acids and bases completely ionize in water, weak acids and bases do not. Since H_3O^+ ions form whenever an acid is put in water, and since the acid properties of water are due to this ion, it follows that the strongest acid that can exist in water solution is H_3O^+ ion. Also, all acids that dissociate completely in water are reduced to the same strength, that of the H_3O^+ ion. This is the leveling effect.

Under the Brønsted concept neutralization is considered to be a normal acid–base reaction in which a weaker acid and a weaker base are produced, even though water is both the acid and the base.

EXERCISES

I. TERMS AND CONCEPTS

Acid

Base

Hydronium ion

Proton donor

Proton acceptor

Brønsted concept of acids and bases

Neutralization

Conjugate acid and base

Leveling effect

II. PROBLEMS

1. Which of the following will form acids, and which bases? Sodium, chlorine,

phosphorus, magnesium, bromine, calcium, iodine, copper.

2. Write formulas for acids or bases that include the above elements.

3. Which of the metals in the list would you expect to be least affected if placed in an acid? (See Table 32-1.)

4. Write an equation that indicates what happens when pure H_3PO_4 is placed in water.

5. In the above reaction is water considered (Brønsted concept) an acid or a base? Is the phosphate ion an acid or a base?

6. Name a base that does not include a metal.

7. What element is commonly (but not always) found in both acids and bases?

8. Write the equation for the neutralization of HNO_3 by KOH. Do the same for H_3PO_4 by NaOH. (Be sure the equations are balanced.)

9. Metallic oxides that dissolve in water form bases, whereas nonmetallic oxides form acids. Write the equations to show this for SO_3, CaO, Na_2O, CO_2, K_2O, NO_2.

10. Is HCl a stronger or a weaker acid than $HC_2H_3O_2$? How could you tell?

11. You have one liter of a molar solution of HCl and one of $HC_2H_3O_2$. Would it take more, less, or the same amount, of a molar solution of NaOH to neutralize the HCl than it would the $HC_2H_3O_2$? Explain.

12. What is meant by the leveling effect?

CHAPTER XXXVII

Chemical Energy, Reaction Rates, Chemical Equilibrium

[Science is] an essentially artistic enterprise, stimulated largely by curiosity, served largely by disciplined imagination, and based largely on faith in the reasonableness, order and beauty of the universe of which man is a part.—WARREN WEAVER

EXOTHERMIC AND ENDOTHERMIC REACTIONS

That energy is released in many chemical reactions is apparent every time we burn a substance. This energy is observable in most cases as kinetic energy, heat, or light. Mix cold concentrated HCl and NaOH in a test tube and there will be a violent boiling with much heat radiated. The chemical union of the molecules that compose gasoline with oxygen in the cylinders of our cars generates so much heat that we are forced to have a cooling system. The combining of the metal magnesium with oxygen in a flash bulb produces brilliant light as well as heat; so does the union of

sodium with chlorine. All such reactions are said to be exothermic for heat energy is released when they take place.

What is the source of this energy? The answer is supplied by our electronic theory of chemical bonding. We have seen that in most chemical reactions there is a rearrangement of the electrons, either by transfer or by sharing, or some combination of the two.[1] If this is the essence of the chemical reaction, and energy is liberated during the reaction, it follows that, for exothermic reactions, the valence electrons should have less potential energy in the new arrangement than they had in the old. The excess appears as heat, light, or kinetic energy. In most reactions most of the radiant energy is emitted in the frequencies that lie in the infrared part of the spectrum, and so appears as heat. If higher frequencies are emitted in great enough intensity some light is emitted as well. That such electromagnetic energy is being emitted indicates that electrons in the atoms concerned are making transitions from higher energy orbits to lower energy orbits.

Carefully controlled experiments reveal that if equal numbers of molecules are involved in a particular reaction, the amount of energy given off is the same every time that reaction takes place. Thus, every time two moles of sodium react with one mole of chlorine, 196,800 calories of heat are liberated. Thus, we may write,

$$2Na + Cl_2 \rightarrow 2NaCl + 196,800 \text{ calories}$$
2 moles   1 mole   2 moles

(Eq. 37-1)

From the Law of Conservation of Energy we might conclude that it will take 196,800

---

[1] In acid–base reactions protons are transferred rather than electrons.

calories to break up two moles of NaCl. The electrolysis of molten NaCl proves that this is so; it takes 96,500 coulombs/mole.

This electrolytic reaction absorbs energy instead of liberating it. It is therefore said to be endothermic. We may write it thus:

$$2NaCl + 196,800 \text{ calories} \rightarrow 2Na + Cl_2$$
2 moles   2 moles   1 mole

(Eq. 37-2)

Another example is the formation of NO from N_2 and O_2, which is moderately endothermic. (If it were not endothermic there would be no oxygen left in the atmosphere.) The reaction may be written

$$N_2 + O_2 + 44,000 \text{ calories} \rightarrow 2NO$$
1 mole   1 mole   2 moles

(Eq. 37-3)

This absorbed heat does not raise the temperature of the NO formed above that of the N_2 and the O_2. Instead, a cooling results, for the absorbed heat must come from the surroundings. It follows that once the source of the added heat energy is removed, the reaction stops. We remind you again that this absorbed heat does not raise the temperature of the products formed. Instead, they are cooled.

The electronic theory of chemical binding gives us the explanation. New arrangements of the valence electrons in the products formed involve higher energy levels than the old, energy that must be supplied from the outside. In terms of the modified Bohr theory, the electrons must be supplied with energy to enable them to attain higher energy orbits, orbits that they must occupy if the particles (atoms, ions, molecules) are to exist in this new state. These transitions to outer orbits increase the potential energy of the valence elec-

trons because work must be done *against* the attractive forces of the nuclei to shift them into these more distant orbits. Their potential energy is higher because they are farther from the oppositely charged nuclei.

Many salts when dissolved in water absorb energy from their surroundings, chiefly from the water itself, thus cooling it. This process is therefore an endothermic one. An example is potassium nitrate, KNO_3 (in aqueous solution).

$$K^+NO_3^- + 8500 \text{ calories} \rightarrow K^+ + NO_3^-$$
1 mole   1 mole   1 mole

(Eq. 37-4)

Applying the Law of Conservation of Energy, we conclude that if this solution is evaporated to regain the dry KNO_3 in crystal form again, 8500 calories will be released per mole of KNO_3 crystals. Reasoning further, and remembering that salts are ionic in the solid state, we conclude that the potential energy due to the attractive forces between the ions is less in the crystalline (solid) state than it is between the ions in solution. This is so because the energy that is needed to pull the ions out of the crystal lattice is conserved as potential energy in the ions in solution. The fact that the dissolving of such salts cools the solution is another application of the Law of Conservation of Energy.

In those reactions that are reversible to a significant degree (p. 522) we may conclude, from the discussion of exothermic and endothermic reactions, that if the forward reaction is exothermic, the reverse one must be endothermic, and vice versa. This has already been discussed in the formation of NaCl (forward reaction) and its dissociation by electrolysis (reverse reaction).

FACTORS AFFECTING REACTION RATES

The electronic theory of chemical binding, if it is to be considered valid, should be able to explain how certain factors affect the rates at which chemical reactions take place. Observation and experiment have shown these factors to be five in number, as follows:

1. Nature of the reactants.
2. Temperature.
3. Concentration.
4. State of subdivision (in the case of solids).
5. Catalysts.

Nature of Reactants

Since the fundamental change that takes place in a chemical reaction is the breaking of chemical bonds and the formation of new ones, i.e., there is a reshuffling of the chemical bonds, it is reasonable to expect that the rate would depend on the specific kinds of bonds involved. We have already seen that where both reactants are ionic and in solution, the rate, in many cases at least, is instantaneous. For example, if we add ferrous ion, Fe^{++} to permanganate ion, MnO_4^-, the reduction of the latter to manganous ion, Mn^{++}, is instantaneous in a well-mixed solution, as is readily observed by the disappearance of the deep purple color.

Oxalic acid, $H_2C_2O_4$, will also reduce permanganate ion, but not instantaneously. The purple color persists for quite some time after mixing. That it is the nature of the reducing agent that accounts for the difference is proved by the fact that everything else is identical. The difference is that in the first case both the reactants are ionic, i.e., both ions are already present before the two solutions are mixed, whereas in the second case oxalic acid is covalent. True, it ionizes in water solution, but only slightly since it is a weak acid. More acid ions are formed as the ions formed earlier are used up in the reduction of the permanganate ion, and this continues as long as the reaction proceeds. The reduction is therefore not instantaneous, for two reactions must take place instead of one. Also instantaneous is the neutralization of a strong acid by a strong base.

On the other hand, many of the important reactions in organic chemistry, including those involved in the digestion of food, are so slow that they take hours. Others, as in certain reactions that take place in solids, e.g., those that accompany certain geological processes such as weathering and metamorphism (p. 562), may take years, thousands of years, or even millions of years to accomplish. Eventually, all reactions either become practically complete, or they reach a condition of equilibrium in which the rate of the reverse reaction is exactly equal to the rate of the forward reaction. Our information is gained chiefly from those reactions in which the rate is moderate.

Temperature

It is reasonable to expect that if there is to be a reshuffling of the bonds, particles—be they atoms, ions, or molecules—must collide. Electrons can neither be transferred nor shared except on close contact. Thus, any factor that increases the probability of collision will *tend* to increase the reaction rate. Chief among these factors is increased temperatures.[2] When sub-

---

[2] If this were not so, our need for refrigerators would greatly decrease.

stances are heated, the average kinetic energies of their molecules are increased. This means not only more collisions per second but more energetic collisions. The magnitude of the increase in the reaction rate with a given rise in temperature varies widely, not only from one reaction to another, but also from one temperature range to another. No simple generalization is possible.

Concentration

If the collision concept is valid, it is apparent why an increase in concentration of one or both [3] of the reactants increases the rate of reaction. The greater the number of dancers on the floor the greater the likelihood of collisions.

State of Subdivision

Thus, the state of subdivision becomes important, for reactions can take place only at the surfaces at which they come in contact. The more finely divided a solid is, the greater the total area of contact per unit mass. The rate of reaction is proportional to the area of contact between a solid and a liquid or gas. This means that the smaller the solid particles, the faster the rate. Thus, a wet mass of steel wool will completely rust away far faster than will a wet cubical bar of iron of equal mass.

Some potential reactants, even if ground as finely as flour, may remain in contact for years without reacting as long as they are kept perfectly dry. An example is ordinary baking powder, which is a mixture of solids. When water is added, there is a moderately violent reaction in which CO_2

[3] We are, have been, and will continue to assume that only two reactants are involved. This is commonly the case, but there may be three, four, or even more in rare cases.

is liberated. The role of the water with respect to potential solid reactants is to dissolve the solids; this brings the state of subdivision down to that of discrete particles (atoms, ions, molecules). This increases the surface area to the maximum possible. Thus, many reactions will take place in water (or other solvent) that will not take place otherwise.

Catalysts

Some substances have been found to speed up chemical reactions even though they themselves remain unchanged. These are called catalysts. Small amounts of catalysts are able to influence the reaction of enormously large amounts of reactants. This is not surprising if the catalyst undergoes no net change. Catalysts are equally effective in the forward and reverse directions of reversible (equilibrium) reactions. Thus, the only effect that a catalyst can have in an equilibrium reaction is to speed up the attainment of the equilibrium. Important as catalysts in biochemical reactions are the enzymes (p. 547). Chlorophyll acts as a catalyst in the most fundamental of all reactions in green plants (p. 545).

Just how catalysts increase the reaction rate is not completely understood. In some cases one reactant may react with the catalyst, with the product formed immediately reacting with the second reactant in such a way as to restore the catalyst to its original condition.

ACTIVATION ENERGY

If 22.4 liters (one gram molecular volume) of O_2 and 22.4 liters of N_2 are mixed, and are kept at standard temperature and pressure, the number of collisions between the molecules will be greater than 10^{30} per second. Yet the two gases will not unite to form any of the oxides of nitrogen under those conditions. Neither will the paper forming the pages of this book unite with oxygen under normal conditions, despite the innumerable impacts of the oxygen molecules against the pages. These facts prove that more than mere collision is necessary to initiate many reactions. Again we call on our electronic theory of chemical reactions for an answer.

Each atom, ion, or molecule, has an electron cloud (Fig. 37-1) surrounding it. These electron clouds, being similarly charged, repel one another. As a result the reactant particles do not normally get close enough together to react in the collisions that take place under average conditions. To react, at least one of two colliding particles must exist in an activated state, i.e., possesses sufficient energy to penetrate the electron clouds of the other particle.

Ions may be regarded as activated particles, for if both reactants are in the ionic state before mixing, the reaction is instantaneous. Mixing solutions of NaCl and $AgNO_3$, both ionic, produce an instantaneous precipitate. Mixing equivalent quantities of strong acids and bases in water solution, both ionic, produce an instantaneous neutralization. Electrically neutral atoms and molecules must, on the other hand, be activated in most cases before they will react. To become activated such neutral particles must receive kinetic energy from some outside source, e.g., collisions with swifter moving particles, or, more commonly, from the application of heat. Oxygen molecules in the atmosphere are not activated until the covalent bonds that hold the pairs of atoms together are broken. A slight increase, say 10 per cent, in the temperature

will sometimes increase the number of activated molecules so greatly that the reaction rate may be increased several hundred or even thousand per cent.

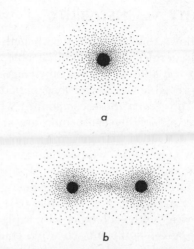

Fig. 37-1. The electron cloud concept of an atom and a molecule. The electron, with its negative charge, creates a disturbance in the positive electric field of a nucleus. In a molecule (**b**), the electrons spend more of their time between the nuclei than elsewhere; hence the disturbance is greater there. In atoms with many electrons moving about a nucleus or in molecules composed of such atoms, the "cloud" effect will be more enhanced than in a simple atom or molecule.

If all particles that are capable of reacting with one another were in an activated state at normal temperatures, pressures, concentrations, etc., our world would be so different that we would not be here to contemplate it. Everything that is combustible in oxygen would burn up. Substances with low activation energies are highly flammable. Some with extremely low activation energies are used as explosives, and are dangerous to handle, e.g., nitroglycerine, which may need only a slight jar to activate it.

STABILITY vs. INSTABILITY

It follows that substances with high activation energies are chemically stable, i.e., they are capable of existing unchanged to any appreciable degree for long periods of time. Thus, even those compounds whose reactions are highly exothermic are stable if their activation energies are sufficiently high. Compounds whose reactions are strongly endothermic are almost always stable, for it takes considerable energy to decompose them. For example, H_2 and O_2 will react with each other with explosive violence, given sufficient activation energy, liberating 116,800 calories per mole of O_2. The resulting water is highly stable. Similarly, the carbon and hydrogen of wood, coal, oil, paper, etc., unite with oxygen with the evolution of much heat to form the more stable CO_2 and H_2O.

Stability is, however, a relative concept. A substance that is stable in one environment may be unstable in another. Carbonic acid, H_2CO_3, is stable under high pressures but not at low ones. Milk is more stable in the refrigerator than out of it. All compounds become unstable at the temperatures found in stars. Minerals formed at considerable depths in the crust of the earth become unstable when exposed to the atmosphere by the erosion of the overlying rocks.

The concept of stability also involves time. Many substances that appear to remain unchanged during a person's lifetime eventually decay and crumble as they slowly react with the water, carbon dioxide, and oxygen of the earth's atmosphere. Man can prolong or permanently forestall such changes by creating an artificial environment in which little or no chemical reaction is possible. In nature, however, given time enough, all matter is reduced to the lowest energy state possible in the environment in which it finds itself. Once in that state it will remain stable as long as the environment does not change.

CHEMICAL EQUILIBRIUM

Actual experiments show that most chemical reactions do not reach completion no matter how long the reaction is allowed to continue. In other words, the reactants are rarely completely changed to products. As the reaction proceeds the concentrations of the reactants decrease and that of the products increase. Sooner or later all concentrations level off and remain constant as long as the temperature does not change. Chemical equilibrium has been reached.

Chemical equilibrium implies that the reactions involved are reversible, i.e., there is a forward reaction between two reactants, A and B, to form products C and D, and a reverse reaction in which C and D are reacting to form A and B. The reaction

$$A + B \rightleftarrows C + D \quad \text{(Eq. 37-5)}$$

does not simply proceed to a certain point and then stop. At first the reaction consists entirely of A and B reacting to form C and D, but as the concentrations of C and D become appreciable, they begin to react to form A and B, more slowly, however, than the forward reaction. The result is that the concentrations of C and D are increasing, and with this increase, the rate of the reaction between C and D increases. Meanwhile, the concentrations of both A and B are decreasing, so that the rate of the reaction also decreases.

A point in time is finally reached when the decreasing rate of the reaction between A and B is equaled by the increasing rate of the reaction between C and D. When this point is reached, both reactions continue at the same rate as long as the temperature does not change. The system is now at equilibrium.

Summarizing, we may say that the concentrations of A and B decrease relatively rapidly at first while those of C and D increase just as rapidly. When equilibrium is reached, the concentrations of all four remain constant as long as the temperature does not change. How long it takes to reach this equilibrium state varies from almost instantaneously to an indefinitely long time. Once established it persists forever if left undisturbed.

We see, therefore, that the concept of chemical equilibrium is analogous to mechanical equilibrium; it is a state of balance between two opposing actions. No *net* change is produced because the two opposing actions cancel each other. We have encountered equilibria in mechanical situations before, one being in Millikan's oil drop experiment, where the electrical force, Eq, was balanced by the gravitational force, mg. We also encountered an equilibrium situation in saturated solutions, where, with an excess of the solute, the number of molecules going into solution equaled the number passing out of solution.

Equilibrium Constant

In Eq. 37-5 A and B represent two reactants, and C and D the resulting products. If we vary the concentrations of A and B, the concentrations of C and D will also vary. Let us suppose that for a particular series of experiments at a constant temperature we vary the concentrations of A and B, and then measure the concentrations of A, B, C and D at the end of each experiment. The results are expressed in Table 37-1.

All concentrations are expressed in moles per liter. The expression $[A]$ is to read "concentration of A." $[A][B]$ is the concentration of A multiplied by the concentration of B; $[C][D]$ is the concentration of C multiplied by the concentration of D; and $[C][D]/[A][B]$ is the product of $[C][D]$ divided by the product of $[A][B]$.

An examination of the table shows that $[C][D]/[A][B]$ is a constant, K, just so long as we do not change the temperature. If we do, we will need to determine a new

TABLE 37-1

EQUILIBRIUM CONCENTRATIONS (AT CONSTANT TEMPERATURE)

Experiment	$[A]$	$[B]$	$[C]$	$[D]$	$[A][B]$	$[C][D]$	$\dfrac{[C][D]}{[A][B]}$
1	3.00	2.00	1.00	1.00	6	1	$\frac{1}{6}$
2	9.60	10.00	4.00	4.00	96	16	$\frac{1}{6}$
3	0.50	3.00	.50	.50	1.5	.25	$\frac{1}{6}$
4	21.90	1.22	2.11	2.11	26.72	4.45	$\frac{1}{6}$

constant. Experiment shows that this equation,

$$\frac{[C][D]}{[A][B]} = K \qquad \text{(Eq. 37-6)}$$

holds for all reversible reactions of the type $A + B \leftrightarrows C + D$ at equilibrium. For the reaction between H_2 and I_2 to form $2HI$, we may write [4]

$$H_2 + I_2 \rightleftarrows HI + HI \qquad \text{(Eq. 37-7)}$$

$$\frac{[HI][HI]}{[H_2][I_2]} = K$$

Let us now use specific concentrations of H_2 and I_2 in an experiment. If we put 1 mole of H_2 and 1 mole of I_2 into a gas-tight container of 1 liter volume and keep the temperature at $490°$ C (at which temperature I_2 is a gas), the two will react to form HI in accordance with Eq. 37-7. After equilibrium is attained, we find by analysis the following concentrations of H_2, I_2, and HI in the container.

$$[H_2] = 0.228 \text{ mole/liter}$$

$$[I_2] = 0.228 \text{ mole/liter}$$

$$[HI] = 1.544 \text{ mole/liter}$$

Substituting in Eq. 37-7,

$$\frac{1.544 \times 1.544}{0.228 \times 0.228} = 45.9$$

Suppose, now, that we put 2 moles of HI (instead of 1 mole of H_2 and 1 mole of I_2) into a container of the same size, keeping

[4] For each molecule (or mole) of H_2 and each molecule (or mole) of I_2 that enter into combination two molecules (or moles) of HI appear. Therefore, HI appears twice on the right, for if we double the number of molecules in our container, we will double the number of collisions, and so double the number of HI molecules that break down to form H_2 and I_2 molecules.

the temperature at $490°$ C. Since the reaction (Eq. 37-7) is a reversible one, we should expect that some of the HI would dissociate into H_2 and I_2. Analysis after equilibrium has been attained would show the contents of the container to be:

$$[H_2] = 0.228 \text{ mole/liter}$$

$$[I_2] = 0.228 \text{ mole/liter}$$

$$[HI] = 1.544 \text{ mole/liter}$$

We should not be surprised that these final concentrations are the same as in the preceding case, or that the equilibrium constant is the same as before, so long as the temperature remains the same.

Le Châtelier's Principle

Le Châtelier, a French chemist, announced an important principle concerning chemical equilibrium in 1888. It is now known as Le Châtelier's principle:

A system in equilibrium will stay that way indefinitely if the factors on which that equilibrium depends remain unchanged; if these factors are changed, then a change will take place in the system that tends to restore the original equilibrium. This statement of the principle may seem a bit long, but if it is understood, one can state it in any one of many different ways. Above all, it should be remembered that *it applies only to systems that are already in equilibrium.*

The practical use of the concept of equilibrium may be illustrated by the synthesis of ammonia gas (NH_3) from N_2 and H_2. The reaction may be written

$$3H_2 + N_2 \rightleftarrows$$

$$2NH_3 + 26,740 \text{ calories}(400° \text{ C, 100 atm})$$

$$\text{(Eq. 37-8)}$$

This reaction is still of great industrial importance but in World War I it was crucial because at that time ammonia was absolutely essential in the manufacture of certain explosives and fertilizers. Without the development of a method of synthesizing ammonia by Haber in 1913, Germany could scarcely have survived a year of war, for her supply of nitrates from Chile were effectively cut off by the British blockade. Moreover, when the United States entered the war, our supply of Chilean nitrates was greatly diminished by the German submarine blockade. The Haber method now makes us independent of the Chilean deposits.

NH_3, N_2, and H_2 are all gases, and in gaseous reactions pressure is important, for it determines the concentration of the gas by controlling the number of molecules per unit volume at fixed temperatures. This in turn determines the collision rates. The reaction between N_2 and H_2 is almost nil at ordinary temperatures, for the activation energy is high. If the temperature is raised to 500° to 700° C, the rate of conversion to ammonia is increased, for reaction rates are always increased by an increase in temperature. However, this is a reversible reaction, so the rate of the reverse reaction is also increased, in fact, it is increased more than the forward rate so that the equilibrium point is shifted to the left, actually decreasing the yield of ammonia. This failure of an increase in temperature to produce a greater yield can be predicted by the use of Le Châtelier's principle.

The reaction is exothermic, i.e., it gives off heat, so an increase of temperature (in an effort to increase the yield) appreciably above that needed to start the reaction would tend to drive it to the left so as to reduce the temperature. We want it to proceed to the right. Catalysts were sought and found, but none was good enough to make the yield satisfactory. The percentage yield at 500° C and a pressure of 1 atmosphere was only 0.13 per cent. At 800° C (and the same pressure) it was reduced to 0.01 per cent. Changes in the concentrations were of no avail. Some other stress had to be applied.

There was only one remaining—an increase in pressure. Increase of pressure forces the molecules of both reactants and products closer together and so increases the probability of collision.

Let us consider Eq. 37-8. Here we have four molecules on the left and two on the right. Translating this into volumes, we see that if one volume of N_2 were to combine *completely* with three volumes of H_2, there would result two volumes of NH_3. This follows from Avogadro's Law: equal volumes of gases under the same conditions of temperature and pressure contain the same number of molecules. Therefore, if we have half as many molecules, we have half as many volumes at the same temperature and pressure. Or we can say that the pressure would be halved if the size of the container remains unchanged—as here. Of course, the reaction does not go anywhere near completion; in fact even at best the equilibrium point is much too far to the left. However, if pressure is put on the system, the reaction shifts appreciably to the right because the formation of NH_3 reduces the pressure (by conversion of four volumes of gas into two volumes). The result is that at a pressure of 200 atmospheres and 500° C, the yield rises from 0.13 per cent (at one atmosphere) to 17.6 per cent, over 135 times as great.

You might well ask how this NH_3 is separated from the uncombined H_2 and N_2.

Ammonia gas is highly soluble in water,[5] far more so than are either N_2 or H_2. Hence water sprayed from the top of the tank dissolves the ammonia, leaving most of the H_2 and N_2 behind to be used again. The reaction between N_2 and H_2 is a classical example of the use of Le Châtelier's principle to obtain conditions favoring a desired chemical reaction. There are hundreds of similar examples. Knowledge of the principle saves untold time and money over the only alternative, trial and error.

One must not conclude that every reaction that involves gases is favored in the manner of the N_2 and H_2 reaction by an increase in pressure. Consider the reaction,

$$H_2 + I_2 \rightleftarrows 2HI$$

Increase of pressure is ineffective in pushing the reaction either way, for there are the same number of molecules in the container regardless of whether the hydrogen and iodine exist as molecules of H_2 and I_2 or as molecules of HI. It is only when the number of volumes of gaseous products is less than the number of volumes of gaseous reactants that pressure drives the reaction to the right.

Common Ion Effect

Le Châtelier's principle may also be used to explain the common ion effect. Suppose we add to a solution of acetic acid an ionic solution that contains the negative acetate ion but not the positive hydrogen ion. For example, let us add a sufficient quantity of sodium acetate. A check with an indicator of some kind will show that the acidity of the solution is greatly re-

---

[5] Ordinary household ammonia is a solution of NH_3 in water.

duced. The application of Le Châtelier's principle will explain why. The ionization of acetic acid may be written without the water, as follows:

$$\underset{\substack{\text{acetic acid}\\\text{molecules}}}{HC_2H_3O_2} \rightleftarrows \underset{}{H^+} + \underset{\text{acetate ion}}{C_2H_3O_2^-}$$

Addition of $C_2H_3O_2^-$ from any source will drive the reaction to the left to form more acetic acid molecules, thus removing H^+ ions from the solution, and so reducing the acidity. The acidity of any weak acid may be reduced by adding a salt that has an ion in common with the acid.

Likewise, the solubility of one salt may be decreased by the addition of another salt with which it has an ion in common. Consider a saturated solution of $PbCl_2$. Addition of any chloride will cause some $PbCl_2$ to be precipitated. We can predict this by the application of Le Châtelier's principle.

$$Pb^{++} + 2Cl^- \rightleftarrows PbCl_2$$

Increasing the concentration of the Cl^- ion will drive the reaction to the right, thus reducing the amount of Cl^- ion in solution. If enough Cl^- ion is added, practically all of the Pb^{++} ions will be forced out of solution.

EXTREMELY WEAK ACIDS AND BASES

No adequate discussion of these acids and bases was possible until some of the principles of the previous sections of this chapter had been developed. The pertinent concepts are those of reversibility, equilibrium, and the common ion effect. These may be used to help explain water as an extremely weak acid or an extremely weak base, pH (pronounced pee-aitch), and the phenomena of buffer solutions.

In our discussion of acids we have used the Brønsted concept, in which the acidic ion present in water solutions is the hydronium ion, H_3O^+. Many chemists still use the Arrhenius concept in which the acidic ion is considered H^+. In part this is due to convenience. Combine this with the fact that H_3O^+ is not entirely correct either,[6] and it becomes apparent why so many chemists prefer to speak and write about the hydrogen ion concentration rather than the hydronium ion concentration, particularly when dealing with low concentrations. The student should be able to handle both situations.

We may further justify speaking of the hydrogen ion concentration by considering the special case of water, which, as we have already seen, may act either as an acid or a base. We have also noted that even pure water dissociates to an extremely slight extent into ions. If we use the Arrhenius concept, these ions are the H^+ and the OH^- ions. Water, then, alone of all the innumerable chemical compounds, may be thought of as consisting solely of the ion responsible for the characteristic properties of acids, chemically combined with the ion responsible for the characteristic properties of most bases.

Thus, pure water can be considered an acid, for it is capable of forming hydrogen ions, and it can also be considered a base, because it can form hydroxide ions. It is an extremely weak acid or base, and therefore an extremely weak electrolyte, because the dissociation is so slight. The extent of dissociation is of the order of one pair of ions (H^+ and OH^-) in 555,000,000 molecules of water when the temperature is 25° C. This is to say that at 25° C there is one ten-millionth of a mole of hydrogen ions in one liter of water. An equivalent method[7] of expressing this concentration is to say that it is 1×10^{-7} mole/liter at 25° C. The concentration of OH^- ions in pure water at the same temperature must be the same.

What, then, constitutes a neutral solution? Consider the equation for the ionization of water:

$$H_2O \rightleftharpoons H^+ + OH^-$$

It is seen that the numbers of H^+ and OH^- ions must be equal. We may then define a neutral solution as one in which the $[H^+]$ and the $[OH^-]$ are the same. As long as

---

[6] A proton may be transferred to two, three, and even more water molecules. Water molecules, being highly polar, also attach themselves to other ions, Na^+ ions and Cl^- ions, which thereby become hydrated in the same manner as the H^+ ion when it forms H_3O^+. The role of this water of hydration is very unimportant in most reactions, so that we commonly omit it in our equations. When we omit it from the hydronium ion, we have the simple hydrogen ion, H^+. Another way of viewing it is that H^+ is simply an abbreviated way of writing H_3O^+.

[7] We arrive at this result as follows: A liter of water weighs 1000 gm. Its molecular weight is 18. Therefore in a liter of water there are $1000/18 = 55.5$ moles. The concentration of pure water may therefore be said to be 55.5 moles liter. One H^+ ion in 550,000,000 molecules of water is equivalent to one mole of H^+ ions in 550,000,000 moles of water. The number of moles of H^+ ion in 55.5 moles of water (one liter) at 25° C is thus,

$$55.5 \times \frac{1}{555,000,000} = \frac{55.5}{55.5 \times 10^7}$$

$$= 1 \times 10^{-7} \text{ mole/liter}$$

Since concentrations are commonly expressed in moles per liter, it follows that the concentration of H^+ in pure water is 1×10^{-7} mole per liter (at 25° C).

we have pure water, and as long as the temperature is 25° C, the concentration of either will be 1×10^{-7} mole/liter. We may therefore define a neutral solution as one in which the $[H^+]$ and the $[OH^-]$ are both 1×10^{-7} mole/liter.

An aqueous acid solution is one in which the $[H^+]$ is greater than that and an aqueous alkaline solution is one in which the $[OH^-]$ rises above 1×10^{-7} mole/liter at 25° C. The equilibrium constant of a neutral solution at 25° C is calculated as follows:

$$\frac{[H^+][OH^-]}{[H_2O]} = \frac{1 \times 10^{-7} \times 1 \times 10^{-7}}{55.5}$$

$$= 1 \times 10^{-14}$$

where 55.5 is the number of moles of water in a liter (see footnote 7).

It follows that alkaline (basic) solutions always have a few H^+ ions present and that acidic solutions always have a few OH^- ions present. The number may be very small, but it is never zero for the H^+ ion in strong basic solutions or for the OH^- ion in strong acidic solutions. From the concept of the equilibrium constant, it follows that as $[H^+]$ goes up, $[OH^-]$ must go down a corresponding amount. Thus, if $[H^+]$ is increased to 1×10^{-6} mole/liter (at 25° C), the $[OH^-]$ is decreased to 1×10^{-8} mole/liter.

pH

In the fields of analytical chemistry and biochemistry minute changes in the $[H^+]$ and $[OH^-]$ may have significant consequences. The chemist and the biologist both find it awkward to express the $[H^+]$ and $[OH^-]$ in the negative powers of 10.

To simplify matters a scale called the pH scale has been devised.[8] It simply takes the negative power of 10, changes the sign, and uses it all alone.[9] Thus, instead of saying that the $[H^+]$ in a solution containing 0.0000001 mole/liter is 1×10^{-7}, we simply say its pH is 7. Numbers higher than 7 indicate alkaline solutions, and those lower than 7 indicate acidic solutions.

This discussion should help make the concept of neutralization clearer. Neutralization consists of the reaction between H^+ and OH^- to form H_2O. The net result of the reaction (at 25° C) is that both the $[H^+]$ and $[OH^-]$ reach 1×10^{-7}. In other words, when H^+ and OH^- are brought together in an aqueous solution in equal numbers, the *product* of the two concentrations cannot long exceed 1×10^{-14}. The reaction between a strong acid and a strong base must proceed almost to completion,

$$Na^+ + OH^- + H^+ + Cl^- \rightleftharpoons$$

$$H_2O + Na^+ + Cl^-$$

to produce a solution whose pH is 7 (neutral).

[8] The term pH refers to the potential of a hydrogen electrode, because the most accurate method of determining $[H^+]$ makes use of the hydrogen electrode.

[9] More mathematically expressed, pH is the logarithm of the $[H^+]$ with the sign reversed. When $[H^+]$ cannot be expressed as 1 multiplied by some integral power of 10, one must refer to a table of logarithms to determine the pH value. Thus, for a solution with an $[H^+]$ of 0.04 mole/liter (4×10^{-2} mole/liter), we proceed as follows:

$$\log 0.04 = \log (4 \times 10^{-2}) = \log 4 + \log 10^{-2}$$

$$= 0.6 - 2.0 = -1.4$$

Reversing the sign,

$$pH = 1.4$$

INDICATORS

Accurate measurement of the pH of a solution involves considerable difficulty, in part experimental, in part theoretical. The approximate pH may be determined by the use of certain indicators, the colors of which change as the $[H^+]$ changes. These indicators are always either slightly acidic or slightly basic (alkaline) themselves. The equilibrium existing in such a solution of an indicator in water may be written,

$$\text{HIn} \underset{\text{acidic}}{\overset{\text{basic}}{\rightleftharpoons}} H^+ + \text{In}^-$$

color *A*   color *B*
(in the non-   (in the ion-
ionizable form)   izable form)

where In is the indicator. Since the color of an indicator changes with the concentration of the H^+ ion (or with the pH), it can be seen from the equation that the addition of acid to a neutral solution containing the indicator will push the equilibrium to the left, giving us color *A*; the addition of a base will push it to the right giving us color *B*. Various indicators have different sensitivity ranges, some changing color while still faintly acid, others while still faintly basic. Any indicator whose color change falls in the pH range of 4 to 10 may be used to determine the neutralization point of a strong base and a strong acid. For other combinations of strong and weak bases with strong and weak acids, the chemist can determine his choice of indicator from his knowledge of the equilibrium constants.

BUFFER SOLUTIONS

The H^+ ion and OH^- ion concentrations of the solutions we have been dealing with are astonishingly small. A solution with a pH of 5.0 corresponds to the degree of acidity produced by adding a single drop of concentrated HCl to 20 gallons of water. A pH of 9.0 corresponds to the degree of alkalinity produced by adding one drop of concentrated NaOH to the same quantity of water. Such faintly acid or faintly alkaline solutions are difficult to preserve with a definite pH. Faintly acid solutions may be neutralized in time by alkali dissolved from the glass of the container. Faintly alkaline solutions may be neutralized or even made faintly acid by H_2CO_3 derived from the atmosphere ($H_2O + CO_2 \rightleftharpoons H_2CO_3$). Thus, the pH of distilled water on exposure to the atmosphere changes from 7.0 to 6.0 or even to 5.0.

The remedy, if a constant pH is desired, is to add to the faintly acid or faintly alkaline solution a salt or a mixture of salts that have been derived from *weak acids and strong bases*, or from *strong acids and weak bases*. The resulting solution will maintain a nearly constant pH even if moderate amounts of additional acid or alkali are added. Consider a solution of acetic acid in water:

$$HC_2H_3O_2 + H_2O \rightleftharpoons H_3O^+ + C_2H_3O_2^-$$
acetic acid   acetate
molecules   ions

Now let us add an acetate salt to this solution, say sodium acetate ($NaC_2H_3O_2$). This salt is composed of Na^+ and $C_2H_3O_2^-$ ions. Adding the sodium acetate greatly increases the number of acetate ions present in the solution, constituting a reserve supply, with no corresponding increase of hydronium ions. Since acetic acid ionizes so sparingly in water, there is also a reserve supply of acetic acid molecules. We will suppose that this water solution of acetic acid and sodium acetate is in equilibrium.

If we now add a little alkali, say NaOH, to it, the OH^- ions will neutralize an equivalent number of H_3O^+ ions, thus tending to reduce the acidity. However, the loss of acid ions is immediately made good by the dissociation of more acetic acid molecules from the reserve supply into H_3O^+ and $C_2H_3O_2^-$ ions. That is, in accordance with Le Châtelier's principle, upsetting the equilibrium by addition of alkali pushes the reaction to the right to create more H_3O^+ ions to restore the equilibrium. Thus, the pH remains constant—provided not too much alkali is added.

If, instead, a small amount of acid is added to the solution, the equilibrium is again upset, pushing the reaction to the left. The H_3O^+ ions from the added acid and $C_2H_3O_2^-$ ions from the reserve supply recombine to reduce the H_3O^+ population, thus preserving the pH of the solution. The pH of a weak acidic solution is buffered [10] with an acetate salt against the addition of moderate amounts of either acid or alkali. Similarly, a weak basic solution may be buffered against an acid by adding the salt of a strong acid and a weak base, e.g., NH_4Cl.

Buffer salts play an important role both in nature and industry. Our blood is buffered to maintain a faint alkalinity (pH of 7.33) that cannot vary except within very narrow limits if we are to maintain our health. Milk stays sweet longer than it would if it were not naturally buffered to a faint alkalinity. Juices of fruits and vegetables are naturally buffered to maintain a slight acidity. In fact, all of the processes of life take place in solutions that are buffered to the hydrogen ion concentration that is most effective for the particular chemical changes that constitute each process. Soils are or can be buffered by certain salts so as to maintain the proper pH for efficient production of different types of crops.

SUMMARY

All chemical changes that take place in nature, except some of those involving life processes, are exothermic, i.e., energy of one sort or another is released during the reaction. Experiments show that the amount of energy released in any particular reaction is always the same if the number of atoms, ions, or molecules involved is the same. Endothermic reactions absorb energy; the reaction ceases if the source of the energy is removed. The energy given off by the union of two atoms to form a compound is equal to the energy needed to decompose the compound into its original components.

The rate of a chemical reaction is dependent to a very large degree upon those factors that increase the probability of collisions between reactant particles (atoms, ions, or molecules). Other factors have to do with the nature of the bond and with catalysts. The latter increase the reaction rate, presumably by somehow making collisions more probable, but the way they do this is not yet entirely understood.

Most exothermic reactions do not take place spontaneously, but need a certain amount of activation energy to get them started. Ionic reactions take place instantly because ions are activated particles. Nonionic atoms or molecules must be activated, usually by some outside source such as heat. Substances with high activation energies are chemically stable,

[10] The concept here is much the same as that of a buffer state in international politics. Just as a series of small states surrounding a major state may protect the latter to some extent from direct aggression, so a buffer solution is protected from the effects of small additional quantities of acid or base.

whereas those with very low activation energies are dangerous to handle, at least in bulk.

The concept of chemical equilibrium arises from the fact that a great many reactions are reversible and so do not go to completion. An equilibrium situation is reached in which the forward and the reverse reactions proceed at the same rate. The equilibrium point may be shifted one way or the other if any of the factors that control the equilibrium are changed. These factors are temperature and concentration, and in certain gaseous reactions, pressure. The shift in the equilibrium point brought about by a change in one of these factors is always such as to nullify or reduce the factor that upset the equilibrium. The principle involved here is that of Le Châtelier.

For any one temperature in a reaction involving two reactants and two products, the product of the concentrations of the products (measured in moles per liter) divided by the product of the concentrations of the reactants (similarly measured) is a constant, called the equilibrium constant. Knowledge of equilibria in chemical reactions and how they may be shifted one way or the other is of great importance industrially. A case in point is the synthesis of ammonia from N_2 and H_2. Applications of the equilibrium concept are found in the common ion effect, the definition of a neutral solution, the explanation of color changes in indicators, and in the use of pH.

EXERCISES

I. TERMS AND CONCEPTS

Exothermic	Chemical equilibrium
Endothermic	
Activation energy	Equilibrium constant
Reaction rate	
Catalyst	Le Châtelier's principle
Stability	
Reversibility	Stress

II. PROBLEMS

1. Which of the following reactions are exothermic, which endothermic? Justify your answer for each.
   a. The union of carbon with oxygen.
   b. Your digestive processes.
   c. The rusting of iron.
   d. The electrolysis of water.

2. Are the valence electrons of the products of an exothermic chemical reaction at higher or lower energy levels than those of the reactants before the reaction? Explain.

3. Suppose the above were an endothermic reaction.

4. In the process of photosynthesis in plants CO_2 and H_2O are combined to make a sugar. Is this an exothermic or an endothermic process? Make your reasoning clear.

5. Explain the role of temperature, concentration, and state of subdivision in governing the rate at which chemical reactions take place.

6. What is meant by activation energy? Describe its role in exothermic reactions. In endothermic reactions.

7. What is an activated particle? How does it differ from an unactivated particle?

8. Which takes place most rapidly, reactions between ionic substances or those between nonionic substances? Explain in terms of activation energies.

9. Which are most stable, compounds formed by exothermic reactions or those formed by endothermic reactions? Explain.

10. What general class of substances have low activation energies?

11. How would you explain the fact that coal dust densely suspended in the atmosphere may be highly explosive even though coal itself burns slowly?

12. Which is more active chemically, oxygen atoms or oxygen molecules? Explain. Relate this to the activation energy needed to start normal combustion.

13. Define a saturated solution in terms of chemical equilibrium.

14. Would the concept of chemical equi-

librium apply to a wholly nonreversible reaction? Explain.

15. Name some reactions that you, for all practical purposes, would consider nonreversible.

16. What is meant by the equilibrium constant of a particular reaction?

17. State Le Châtelier's principle.

18. Consider Eq. 37-8. What effect would pressure have on the equilibrium point, and why?

19. The gases H_2, O_2, and H_2O are all in equilibrium at about 2000° C. Write the equations to indicate this. What effect would increasing the pressure have on the equilibrium point? Why?

20. Consider the equilibrium equation, $H_2O + CO_2 \rightleftharpoons H_2CO_3$. The materials are in a closed container. What effect would add-ing more CO_2 have on the equilibrium point? What effect would leaving the container open have? Explain.

21. Consider the equilibrium reaction,

$$NH_3 + H_2O \rightleftharpoons NH_4^+ + OH^-$$

What effect would adding NaOH solution have on the equilibrium point? Explain.

22. What is a neutral solution? (Merely to state that it is one which is neither acidic or basic is insufficient.)

23. Define pH. Of what use is the concept?

24. What are buffer solutions? Of what use are they?

25. What common principle is used to explain the common ion effect, pH, buffer solutions, indicators, neutral solutions?

CHAPTER XXXVIII

The Chemistry of Carbon

Another interesting conclusion is, that the animal frame, though destined to fulfill so many other ends, is as a machine more perfect than the best contrived steam engine—that is, is capable of more work with the same expenditure of fuel.

—J. P. JOULE (1847)

Carbon is one of the minor constituents of the earth, forming not much more than 0.03 per cent of the outer few miles of the earth and presumably none of its deep interior. Yet there is an inexhaustible supply of carbon in the carbonate rocks, chiefly limestones and marbles, found on all continents. The coal, peat, graphite, and petroleum deposits of the world all contain large amounts of carbon. All organic matter, from wood to bones and shells, and even flesh contain large amounts. The atmosphere contains billions of tons of it, and still greater quantities are dissolved in the waters of the oceans. Carbon passes through a definite cycle in nature. Carbon dioxide is extracted from the atmosphere by plants to form living matter, part of which in times past has gone to form peat, coal, and petroleum. The burning of these fuels returns carbon dioxide to the atmosphere. Living matter dies and decays; again the carbon dioxide is returned to the atmosphere.

CRYSTALLINE CARBON

Carbon occurs in nature in two forms that are about as different from each other as two substances could be insofar as their physical properties are concerned. Graphite, by far the most common, is a soft, black, flaky, and slippery compound that is a good conductor of electricity. The diamond is the hardest substance known, colorless and transparent, and a nonconductor of electricity. Yet both are solely composed of carbon atoms and there is not one bit of difference between the carbon atom in graphite and the carbon atom in the diamond. The difference must lie in the arrangement of the carbon atoms, i.e., in the crystalline structure of graphite and the diamond; X-ray diffraction patterns confirm this.

We have already learned that carbon forms covalent bonds not only with other elements but with itself. Carbon has a valence of four, so each atom can share four pairs of electrons with four neighboring carbon atoms. If these four neighbors are symmetrically arranged about a fifth atom, they form a tetrahedral pattern. Each carbon atom is at the center of a tetrahedron (Fig. 33-3), and forms the corner of some other tetrahedron. The four covalent bonds might be pictured as radiating from the kernel of the atom in the directions of the corners of the tetrahedron where they meet the bonds of other carbon atoms similarly arranged. This arrangement, repeated indefinitely, makes each diamond crystal one giant molecule. Since the valence of carbon is four, each carbon atom is held to four other atoms by nonpolar covalent bonds. This accounts for the hardness of the diamond, its high melting point (3500° C), and its nonconductance.

In graphite the carbon atoms are arranged in the form of hexagonal rings, as in Fig. 33-4. Each carbon atom is bonded to three others that lie in the same plane, so each forms a part of three hexagons (*a* in Fig. 33-4). These hexagons, extended in all directions within a plane, are responsible for the flaky property of graphite. The fourth bond is with another carbon atom in another plane, some with the plane above, some with the plane below. The distances between the planes is much greater than the distance between atoms in the same plane. Thus, the number of bonds between planes is not more than one-sixth the number within a plane. Moreover, some of these electrons that form bonds between planes are free to move, much as are the valence electrons of metals. This explains the electrical conductivity of graphite. The relative weakness of the bonds between plates allows the plates to easily slide over one another, and so the slippery feel of graphite is accounted for. The hexagonal platy arrangement of the atoms is reflected in the six-sided tabular crystals that occur in some deposits of graphite.

Apparently noncrystalline forms of carbon occur in coal, charcoal, and coke. We say apparently, for X-rays reveal that these materials consist of submicroscopic crystals of graphite mingled with more or less other materials. Boneblack, lampblack, and carbonblack are other forms of pure carbon composed of the tiny crystals of graphite.

CARBON AS A KEY ELEMENT IN LIFE PROCESSES

It is commonly stated that carbon is a constituent of more compounds than any other element. This, however, is not true, for that honor belongs to hydrogen. Almost all compounds of carbon also contain hydrogen. There are also a considerable number of compounds of hydrogen that do not contain carbon, whereas the number that contain carbon but no hydrogen is somewhat smaller. Nevertheless, carbon and not hydrogen, is the key element in what has been called organic chemistry. It is the ability of carbon to form long chains and rings with itself that accounts for the extremely large number of its compounds. No other atoms can do this to anything like the extent that carbon can. Furthermore, the bonds between the carbon atoms are strong, so strong that the chains and rings can go through many chemical reactions without breaking. However, the readiness of carbon atoms to combine with hydrogen and oxygen make organic compounds subject to slow oxidation in air. Thus, all organic materials slowly decay at ordinary temperatures, and rapidly at higher temperatures.

The very large numbers of carbon compounds is justification enough for treating the chemistry of carbon in a separate chapter. The fact that carbon is the key element in organic matter is additional justification, and is responsible for the division of chemistry into organic and inorganic by the early chemists. The basis of the division was the belief that, except for the oxides, the carbonates, the sulfides, and a few others, the compounds of carbon could be produced only by plants and animals through the action of some "vital living force." The nature of this force was presumably similar to those other "imponderables" like phlogiston, caloric, and the ether. This concept was blasted about 1830 when the first organic compounds were synthesized in the laboratory. Others quickly followed, until today the number of organic compounds runs into the hundreds of thousands, with hundreds of new ones being added to the list every year. With the exception of the proteins, most of the compounds in living matter have been synthesized. Man has not, however, learned to synthesize carbon compounds from CO_2 and H_2O, something that is done by even the simplest of the green plants. A great many synthetic compounds have been created in the laboratory that have no counterparts in nature. Most of the modern chemical industry is based on the chemistry of carbon.

HYDROCARBONS OF THE PARAFFIN SERIES

Hydrocarbons are compounds of carbon and hydrogen only. They are simple in composition, but nevertheless exist in astonishing variety. Petroleum is a mixture of large numbers of the hydrocarbons of the paraffin (or methane) series, all in mutual solution with one another. The members of this series have a composition that conforms to the formula C_nH_{2n+2}. This means that the number of hydrogen atoms is always two more than twice the number of carbon atoms.

The simplest member of the series is methane (the chief constituent of common cooking gas) whose composition is CH_4. A methane molecule has its atoms arranged in the form of a tetrahedron with the carbon atom at the center and the four hydrogen atoms at the four corners. The next simplest are C_2H_6 (ethane), C_3H_8 (propane), C_4H_{10} (butane), etc. These four are gases. The next twelve are liquids whose volatility decrease with increasing numbers of carbon atoms (and increasing molecular weight). Included in these liquids are such fuels as gasoline and kerosene. Still higher members of the series are the semisolids that form the heavy lubricating oils, greases, and petroleum jelly (vaseline). The rest are solids like paraffin, which is a mixture of hydrocarbons ranging from $C_{23}H_{48}$ to $C_{29}H_{60}$.

Separating these mixtures of hydrocarbons from one another to obtain the pure compounds is difficult and expensive. Fortunately, for ordinary commercial purposes a complete separation is neither necessary nor particularly desirable. Natural gas is a mixture of the first four members of the series, methane through butane. Since the boiling points increase from $1°$ C for butane to above $200°$ C for some of the hydrocarbons in kerosene, the boiling point of a mixture will rise as the hydrocarbons with the lower boiling points are boiled off. Thus, by collecting different fractions of the vapors, the separation into groups of compounds is attained. The first fraction derived from the crude petroleum is a mixture of the lighter liquids, largely C_5H_{12} and C_6H_{14}, which is sold (in the United States) as naphtha. The next fraction is gasoline, which is a mixture of liquids with a composition ranging from C_6H_{14} to about $C_{10}H_{22}$. A third fraction is kerosene, etc. The whole process of separation is called fractional distillation.

In this age of motor cars and airplanes the most valuable of the fractions is gasoline. Unfortunately the size of the gasoline fraction is small, so small that to provide us with enough gasoline would not only use up our supplies of petroleum at a prodigious rate, but would also literally swamp us with the other fractions. The chemists have learned how to increase the gasoline fraction in two ways. One is to *crack* the larger molecules into the smaller ones of gasoline by heating under pressure in the presence of a catalyst. The other is to combine the smaller molecules into the larger ones of gasoline. The yield of gasoline per barrel of crude oil has been increased enormously by this process of cracking. Not all crude oils are alike; some have a much larger proportion of the light hydrocarbons than others.

The molecules of hydrocarbons are nonpolar, as we might suspect from the symmetrical arrangement of their atoms, and so are, in general, insoluble in water. They are generally rather unreactive at room temperature. They will react more or less violently with oxygen at temperatures of a few hundred degrees, and so are valuable as fuels. They are not affected by prolonged boiling in concentrated NaOH or H_2SO_4, and are only slightly affected by vigorous oxidizing agents. Chlorine and bromine are almost the only substances that will react with them at room temperatures.

STRUCTURAL FORMULAS

The formulas that we have dealt with so far are called molecular formulas since they simply indicate the number of each kind of atoms in the compound, e.g., H_2O, H_2SO_4, $CaCO_3$, etc. There is nothing in these formulas that directly tells us how the atoms are arranged, and for most purposes it has not greatly mattered. The compounds of carbon present us with another problem. If you were to ask a chemist for some C_2H_6O, he might ask you, "Which C_2H_6O?" for there are two compounds with very different properties that have this composition. One is common grain alcohol, the other is an ether. The difference is made apparent by their structural formulas:

$$
\begin{array}{cc}
\begin{array}{c}
\quad\text{H}\ \ \text{H} \\
\quad|\quad | \\
\text{H—C—C—O—H} \\
\quad|\quad | \\
\quad\text{H}\ \ \text{H}
\end{array}
&
\begin{array}{c}
\quad\text{H}\qquad\text{H} \\
\quad|\qquad| \\
\text{H—C—O—C—H} \\
\quad|\qquad| \\
\quad\text{H}\qquad\text{H}
\end{array}
\\
\text{ethyl alcohol} & \text{dimethyl ether}
\end{array}
$$

Note that the difference is in the way the oxygen atom is connected. In the alcohol (and this is true of all alcohols) the oxygen lies between a carbon and a hydrogen atom, whereas in the ether (and this is true of all ethers) it lies between two carbon atoms. We might have used the dot system, as many chemists do.

$$
\begin{array}{cc}
\begin{array}{c}
\text{H H} \\
\text{H}\!:\!\ddot{\text{C}}\!:\!\ddot{\text{C}}\!:\!\ddot{\text{O}}\!:\!\text{H} \\
\text{H H}
\end{array}
&
\begin{array}{c}
\text{H}\qquad\text{H} \\
\text{H}\!:\!\ddot{\text{C}}\!:\!\ddot{\text{O}}\!:\!\ddot{\text{C}}\!:\!\text{H} \\
\text{H}\qquad\text{H}
\end{array}
\end{array}
$$

The dash system is quicker and easier, and serves our purposes better. One must, however, *never fail* to count the number of dashes (which we will call bonds) about each atom. This number *must always* be equal to the valence. There are therefore four bonds about each carbon atom, two about each oxygen atom, and one about each hydrogen atom. Count them in the two structural formulas given above.

ISOMERISM

Compounds with the same molecular formula but with different structural formulas are called isomers.[1] Thus, dimethyl ether is an isomer of ethyl alcohol, or vice versa. These two examples were chosen because alcohol and ether are familiar compounds. Isomerism is, however, of great importance in the paraffin series itself. Consider the following structural formulas:

$$
\begin{array}{ccc}
\underset{\text{methane}}{\begin{array}{c} H \\ | \\ H-C-H \\ | \\ H \end{array}} &
\underset{\text{ethane}}{\begin{array}{c} H\ \ H \\ |\ \ \ | \\ H-C-C-H \\ |\ \ \ | \\ H\ \ H \end{array}} &
\underset{\text{propane}}{\begin{array}{c} H\ \ H\ \ H \\ |\ \ \ |\ \ \ | \\ H-C-C-C-H \\ |\ \ \ |\ \ \ | \\ H\ \ H\ \ H \end{array}}
\end{array}
$$

$$
\underset{\text{butane}}{\begin{array}{c} H\ \ H\ \ H\ \ H \\ |\ \ \ |\ \ \ |\ \ \ | \\ H-C-C-C-C-H \\ |\ \ \ |\ \ \ |\ \ \ | \\ H\ \ H\ \ H\ \ H \end{array}}
$$

$$
\underset{\text{pentane}}{\begin{array}{c} H\ \ H\ \ H\ \ H\ \ H \\ |\ \ \ |\ \ \ |\ \ \ |\ \ \ | \\ H-C-C-C-C-C-H \\ |\ \ \ |\ \ \ |\ \ \ |\ \ \ | \\ H\ \ H\ \ H\ \ H\ \ H \end{array}}
$$

These all form straight chains of carbon atoms. No matter how you arrange the atoms of the first three, remembering to count the bonds, you will come up with the same essential arrangement. There are, therefore, no isomers of these three hydrocarbons. When the number of carbon atoms rises to four, two arrangements are possible, the one given above, and the following:

$$
\underset{\text{isobutane}}{\begin{array}{c} H \\ | \\ H-C-H \\ H\ \ \ |\ \ \ H \\ \ \ \ \ C-C-C \\ H\ \ \ |\ \ \ H \\ H\ \ H\ \ H \end{array}}
$$

Note that one carbon atom is now attached to the middle one of the other three. Thus, we do not have a straight chain of carbon atoms but a branching one (or at least the beginning of a branch).[2] The properties of isobutane are similar to, but not identical with, those of butane.

When the number of carbons rises to five, as in pentane, three isomers are possible. One is given above. The other two are as follows:

$$
\underset{\text{isopentane}}{\begin{array}{c} H \\ H\ \ |\ \ H \\ \ \ C \\ H\ H\ |\ \ H \\ |\ \ |\ \ |\ \ | \\ H-C-C-C-C-H \\ |\ \ |\ \ |\ \ | \\ H\ H\ H\ H \end{array}}
\qquad
\underset{\text{neopentane}}{\begin{array}{c} -C- \\ |\ \ \ \ \ | \\ -C-C-C- \\ |\ \ \ \ \ | \\ -C- \\ | \end{array}}
$$

Isopentane is similar in structure to isobutane except that there is another CH_2 unit. Shifting the branching carbon to the carbon atom to its left would not make any significant change in the structure. In neopentane we have omitted writing in the hydrogen atoms in order to make the pattern of the carbon atoms a bit clearer. One

[1] One cannot speak of a single isomer any more than one can speak of a single twin. We may refer to one of two or more isomers just as we refer to one of a pair of twins, etc.

[2] Shifting this branching carbon to either end carbon in the chain does not make it a branching chain but merely a bent chain. Hence we would have no isomer.

must, however, always count the bonds. Note that there are three carbon atoms in each chain. Shifting the carbon atom from a position below the horizontal chain to one above would not create a new isomer.

As the number of carbon atoms increases, the number of possible isomers increases fantastically. For example, 35 different isomers of C_9H_{20} are known, and the theoretical number for $C_{40}H_{82}$ is 69,491,178, 805,831! You should now understand why we use structural formulas rather than molecular formulas for so many carbon compounds.

The question might fairly be asked about isomers, "How do we know which formula belongs to which isomer?" To answer this question let us return to the examples we gave on p. 536, ethyl alcohol and dimethyl ether. Sodium will not react with the ether but it will with alcohol, forming sodium acetate and liberating hydrogen. This suggests that in alcohol one hydrogen must be bonded differently than the others. Furthermore, sodium will liberate only one-sixth the total amount of hydrogen present. Alcohol will also react with other compounds in a similar manner. With HCl water is a product, the H of the HCl combining with an OH. This practically demands that the OH be present in the alcohol. We scarcely need more evidence.

SATURATED vs. UNSATURATED HYDROCARBONS

The hydrocarbons so far discussed have all had single bonds between the carbon atoms, i.e., each carbon atom shares not more than one pair of valence electrons with any other carbon atom. Such valences are said to be saturated. If more

than one bond exists between two carbon atoms, i.e., if the two atoms share two or three pairs of valence electrons, the valences are said to be unsaturated. There are two such unsaturated series, one of which is called the ethylene series, the other the acetylene series.

ETHYLENE SERIES

The general formula for this series is C_nH_{2n}. Since the valence of carbon is four, no such compound as CH_2 can exist. The simplest of the series is, therefore, C_2H_4, known as ethylene. Its structural formula is

$$\begin{array}{cc} H & H \\ | & | \\ H-C=C-H \end{array}$$

Other members of the series are

propylene   butylene

The first two have no isomers; butylene and higher members do. Members of the ethylene series are produced in quantities during the cracking of petroleum hydrocarbons.

The members of the ethylene series are more reactive than those of the saturated series. The reason is that the double bonds are rather easily broken and converted into single bonds by the addition of other molecules. Thus,

$$\begin{array}{cc} H & H \\ | & | \\ H-C=C-H + Br_2 \rightarrow Br-C-C-Br \\ | & | \\ H & H \end{array}$$

ethylene   ethylene bromide

Also,

$$H-\underset{\underset{H}{|}}{\overset{\overset{H}{|}}{C}}=\underset{\underset{H}{|}}{\overset{\overset{H}{|}}{C}}-H + H_2O \rightarrow \qquad H-\underset{\underset{H}{|}}{\overset{\overset{H}{|}}{C}}-\underset{\underset{H}{|}}{\overset{\overset{H}{|}}{C}}-OH$$

ethylene   ethyl alcohol

There are other hydrocarbons with several, sometimes scores, of double bonds in the same molecule. Some of their derivatives are abundant in food, e.g., one forms the red coloring matter of tomatoes, another the yellow coloring matter of carrots and butter, etc. Vitamin A ($C_{20}H_{29}OH$) has double bonds between five pairs of carbon atoms.

ACETYLENE SERIES

This series has three bonds between two carbon atoms, and so the general formula is C_nH_{2n-2}. The simplest is acetylene, C_2H_2 or, $H-C \equiv C-H$. It burns with a very hot flame (up to 2800° C in pure oxygen) and is used in welding and cutting metals. It is produced from calcium carbide and water, or by the dehydrogenation of natural gas.

HYDROCARBON RING STRUCTURES

The hydrocarbons discussed so far have been those with either straight or branching chains. Another somewhat different class of hydrocarbons has all or many of the carbon atoms arranged in rings, six carbon atoms to a ring with one hydrogen atom attached to each carbon atom in the ring. The simplest of these compounds is benzene, discovered by Michael Faraday. Its composition is C_6H_6. When it became customary to write structural formulas for

hydrocarbons, chemists at first found it impossible to write one for benzene that would have four bonds about each carbon atom. Eventually Kekulé, a German chemist, had the inspiration to try writing the formula as a ring in which every other bond was a double one:

Today chemists often write the ring as a simple hexagon, omitting the hydrogen atoms at each corner of each hexagon as follows:

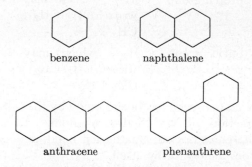

benzene   naphthalene

anthracene   phenanthrene

Benzene and others of the group have long been derived from coal tar, a by-product of the heating of bituminous coal in the absence of air to produce coke. From the coal tar, which is an ugly, black, evil-smelling residue, the chemist produces choice perfumes and flavors, dyes of delicate shades, solvents, lacquers, drugs, insecticides, powerful explosives, and a host of other products.

DERIVATIVES OF THE HYDROCARBONS

Every organic compound may be considered to have been derived from some one of the three groups of hydrocarbons mentioned above by substituting another atom or a group of atoms for one or more of the hydrogen atoms, i.e., by substituting certain *reactive functional atoms or groups* for the hydrogen atoms. The compounds derived in this way are called derivatives of the hydrocarbons.

The study of organic chemistry is primarily a study of the hydrocarbons and their derivatives. The study may be best started by first considering a few of the alkyl groups of the saturated hydrocarbons.[3]

methyl group CH_3—

ethyl group C_2H_5—, which may be written $CH_3 \cdot CH_2$—

propyl group C_3H_7—, which may be written $CH_3 \cdot CH_2 \cdot CH_2$—

butyl group C_4H_9—, which may be written $CH_3 \cdot CH_2 \cdot CH_2 \cdot CH_2$—

Note that each has been formed by the subtraction of one hydrogen atom. Each therefore has one unattached bond, and so does not exist by itself.

Consider the methyl group. If we add a chlorine atom, we have, in effect, substituted a chlorine atom for a hydrogen atom to give us CH_3Cl (methyl chloride). If we substitute another chlorine atom for a second hydrogen atom, we have CH_2Cl_2 (dichlormethane). Substitution of a third chlorine atom will give us $CHCl_3$ (chloroform) and of a fourth, CCl_4 (carbon tetra-

[3] These four alkyl groups should be memorized.

chloride). The same substitutions may be made in the other groups, and other atoms may be used in place of chlorine.

Alcohols

Of much more interest is the substitution of the various functional groups listed in Table 38-1. If we add an —OH to any of the alkyl groups we get an alcohol.

methyl alcohol (methanol)   ethyl alcohol (ethanol)

propyl alcohol   butyl alcohol

If we let R stand for an alkyl group, then the general formula of these monohydric alcohols is R—OH. If we remove a second hydrogen atom that is attached to some *other* carbon atom, we get a dihydric alcohol. The simplest and best known is ethylene glycol which is used extensively as an antifreeze. Its structural formula is

If a third hydrogen atom is removed from still another carbon atom, we have glycerol (glycerine). Its structural formula is

TABLE 38-1 *

Characteristic Group	Type Formula	Class of Compound	Formula of Example	Name
—OH	R—OH	Alcohol	C_2H_5OH	Ethyl alcohol (ethanol)
—OR	R—O—R′	Ether	$C_2H_5 \cdot O \cdot C_2H_5$	Diethyl ether
$-\overset{\overset{O}{\|\|}}{C}-H$	$R-\overset{\overset{O}{\|\|}}{C}-H$	Aldehyde	$CH_3-\overset{\overset{O}{\|\|}}{C}-H$	Acetaldehyde
$-\overset{\overset{O}{\|\|}}{C}-$	$R-\overset{\overset{O}{\|\|}}{C}-R'$	Ketone	$CH_3-\overset{\overset{O}{\|\|}}{C}-CH_3$	Acetone
$-\overset{\overset{O}{\|\|}}{C}-OH$	$R-\overset{\overset{O}{\|\|}}{C}-OH$	Acid	$CH_3-\overset{\overset{O}{\|\|}}{C}-OH$	Acetic acid
$-\overset{\overset{O}{\|\|}}{C}-OR$	$R-\overset{\overset{O}{\|\|}}{C}-OR'$	Ester	$CH_3-\overset{\overset{O}{\|\|}}{C}-C_2H_5$	Ethyl acetate
—NH₂	R—NH₂	Primary amine	CH_3-NH_2	Methyl amine
$-\overset{\overset{O}{\|\|}}{C}-NH_2$	$R-\overset{\overset{O}{\|\|}}{C}-NH_2$	Amide	$CH_3-\overset{\overset{O}{\|\|}}{C}-NH_2$	Acetamide

* From Sisler, Vander Werf, Davidson, *General Chemistry*, Macmillan, New York, 1949.

Ethers

If we take two of the alkyl groups and link them together by means of an oxygen atom between them, we have an ether.

CH₃·O·CH₃
dimethyl ether

CH₃·O·C₂H₅
methyl ethyl ether

C₂H₅·O·C₂H₅
dimethyl ether

The last is the well-known anesthetic. Again letting R stand for an alkyl group and letting R′ be the same as R or another alkyl group, the general formula of an ether is R—O—R′.

Aldehydes

If we start with an alkyl group, e.g., C₂H₅—, remove a second carbon atom, and substitute a double-bonded oxygen, we have an aldehyde, e.g.,

CH₂O   CH₃CHO

formaldehyde   acetaldehyde

The general formula for an aldehyde is

$$R—\overset{\displaystyle O}{\overset{\|}{C}}—H$$

where R is either H or an alkyl group. Formaldehyde is used as a preservative for biological specimens, as a fumigant, and in the production of the plastic bakelite. Acetaldehyde is used as a starting point for the synthesis of many organic compounds.

Ketones

Let us start with the propyl group, $C_3H_7—$, which may be written structurally as

$$H—\overset{\overset{\displaystyle H}{|}}{\underset{\underset{\displaystyle H}{|}}{C}}—\overset{\overset{\displaystyle H}{|}}{\underset{\underset{\displaystyle H}{|}}{C}}—\overset{\overset{\displaystyle H}{|}}{\underset{\underset{\displaystyle H}{|}}{C}}—H$$

We now remove the one remaining hydrogen attached to the middle carbon and add a double-bonded oxygen. We then have acetone, which is the simplest ketone.

$$H—\overset{\overset{\displaystyle H}{|}}{\underset{\underset{\displaystyle H}{|}}{C}}—\overset{\displaystyle O}{\overset{\|}{C}}—\overset{\overset{\displaystyle H}{|}}{\underset{\underset{\displaystyle H}{|}}{C}}—H$$

Note that both aldehydes and ketones have the double-bonded oxygen. The difference is that in the aldehydes it is always attached to a carbon atom at the end of a chain, whereas in the ketone it is always attached to a carbon *not* at the end of a chain. The general formula for a ketone is

$$R—\overset{\displaystyle O}{\overset{\|}{C}}—R'$$

Both the aldehydes and the ketones may be considered partially oxidized alcohols.

Organic (Fatty) Acids

The aldehyde group (CHO—) may be further oxidized to form the carboxyl group–COOH, the characteristic group of the fatty acids. Its general formula is RCOOH, where R is hydrogen in the simplest of this large group, and an alkyl group in any of the others. Structurally they are written

$$R—\overset{\displaystyle O}{\overset{\|}{C}}—OH$$

The simplest is formic acid, HCOOH. Next simplest is acetic acid which we have heretofore written as $HC_2H_3O_2$, but which we will write here as CH_3COOH. Others are butyric acid, C_3H_7COOH (found in rancid butter and limburger cheese), palmitic acid, $CH_3\cdot(CH_2)_{14}COOH$ (derived from vegetable oils) and stearic acid, $CH_3\cdot(CH_2)_{16}COOH$ (derived from animal fats). Palmitic and stearic acids when chemically combined with glycerol are the common vegetable oils and animal fats. These two acids find their chief use in soap-making.

Esters

Organic acids and alcohols slowly react to form esters. In the process a molecule of water is eliminated.

$$CH_3COOH + C_2H_5OH \rightarrow$$
acetic acid   ethyl alcohol

$$CH_3COOC_2H_5 + H_2O$$
ethyl acetate

The general formula for an ester is

$$R—\overset{\displaystyle O}{\overset{\|}{C}}—O—R'$$

Thus, an ester might be considered to be two alkyl groups linked together by the —COO— group, which might be called an ester linkage. Esters have pleasant flower- and fruitlike odors; in fact the natural odors of fruits and flowers are due to esters. They are therefore used as artificial flavors and in perfumes.

Amines

Amines may be considered either as alkyl groups to which the amino group, —NH$_2$, is attached, or as derived from ammonia by substituting an alkyl group for one or more hydrogen atoms.

$$
\begin{array}{ccc}
\text{H} & \text{H} & \text{CH}_3 \\
| & | & | \\
\text{N—H} & \text{N—CH}_3 & \text{N—CH}_3 \\
| & | & | \\
\text{H} & \text{H} & \text{H} \\
\text{ammonia} & \text{methylamine} & \text{dimethylamine}
\end{array}
$$

Amides

The amides are similar to the fatty acids whose general formula is

$$
\begin{array}{c}
\text{O} \\
\|\\
\text{R—C—OH}
\end{array}
$$

If we substitute an —NH$_2$ group for the —OH, we have the general formula for an amide,

$$
\begin{array}{c}
\text{O} \\
\|\\
\text{R—C—NH}_2
\end{array}
$$

Nylon and silk are complex polyamides.

Amino Acids

Amino acids contain both the carboxyl (—COOH) and the amino (—NH$_2$) groups. The simplest is

$$
\begin{array}{c}
\text{O} \\
\|\\
\text{NH}_2\text{—CH}_2\text{—C—OH}
\end{array}
$$
glycine

Amino acids combine with one another to form proteins. They are discussed further under that heading.

Benzene Rings

The benzene ring can act as the basic structure in which other atoms or groups of atoms may be substituted for one or more of the hydrogen.

toluene   phenol   *ortho*-cresol   chloro-benzine

TNT

GIANT MOLECULES

All of the organic materials that possess the properties of elasticity, resiliency, high tensile strength, and pliability are made of "giant" molecules, molecules whose atomic weights run up into the thousands, tens of thousands, hundreds of thousands or even millions. Such organic materials include cotton, wool, silk, wood, rubber, and resins among the natural products, and the plastics and synthetic fibers and rubbers among the artificially made products. These giant molecules are made up of groups of atoms that are repeated over and over in a regular order, sometimes thousands of times to form single huge molecules. The process of joining them together is called *polymerization;* the products are called *polymers,* and the atom groups are called *monomers.* The architecture of these giant molecules has been worked out largely since 1925, much of it since World War II.

An excellent example of a polymer in which the monomers are simply "added" together is polyethylene. Such polymers are called addition polymers; they can form only from the unsaturated hydrocarbons. The monomer of polyethylene is ethylene,

$$
\begin{array}{cc}
\text{H} & \text{H} \\
| & | \\
\text{C} & = \text{C} \\
| & | \\
\text{H} & \text{H}
\end{array}
$$

If we break the double bond we can write it:

$$
\begin{array}{cc}
\text{H} & \text{H} \\
| & | \\
-\text{C} & -\text{C}- \\
| & | \\
\text{H} & \text{H}
\end{array}
$$

We can now break the double bond of other ethylene molecules, and add one on the right and one on the left.

$$
\begin{array}{ccccc}
\text{H} & \text{H} & \text{H} & \text{H} & \text{H} \\
| & | & | & | & | \\
-\text{C} & -\text{C} & -\text{C} & -\text{C} & -\text{C}- \\
| & | & | & | & | \\
\text{H} & \text{H} & \text{H} & \text{H} & \text{H}
\end{array}
$$

Since we still have a vacant bond at each end, we can add other monomers, and so on indefinitely.

Natural rubber is made of giant molecules in the form of long coiled chains. The coils unroll when the rubber is stretched and roll up again when released. The monomer of natural rubber is isoprene,

$$
\begin{array}{c}
\text{CH}_3 \\
| \\
\text{CH}_2=\text{C}-\text{CH}=\text{CH}_2
\end{array}
$$

During polymerization one of the double bonds is broken so that monomeric unit after monomeric unit can join together.

$$
\begin{array}{cccc}
\text{H} & \text{CH}_3\ \text{H} & \text{H} \\
| & |\qquad | & | \\
-\text{C} & -\text{C}=\text{C} & -\text{C}- \\
| & \qquad | & | \\
\text{H} & \quad\ \text{H} & \uparrow\text{H}
\end{array}
$$

connecting bond

Many rubber substitutes (popularly known as synthetic rubbers) with compositions quite different than that of natural rubber have been made. Man has never been able to synthesize natural rubber. One of the substitutes may be superior to natural rubber in one way, some in another.

The synthetic fibers, rayon, nylon, dacron, orlon, etc., are all polymers of one sort or another. So are the plastics, which today exist in a bewildering array. Some of these polymers are made of alternately repeating units of two monomers. They are known as copolymers. Some are condensation polymers, in which a water molecule is "condensed out" when two monomeric units combine. Proteins are condensation polymers.

CHEMISTRY OF FOOD

The diet of a healthy person must include carbohydrates, fats, proteins, vitamins, and certain so-called minerals.[4] All

---

[4] They are not minerals in the geological sense. They are simply compounds containing metals that are essential to health.

but the last are organic, and all living matter contains them in varying proportions.

Carbohydrates

In plants the carbohydrates are most important, for from them are derived the other foods. Plants, using the energy of sunlight, and with chlorophyll as a catalyst, synthesize carbohydrates from CO_2 abstracted from the atmosphere and H_2O from the soil. The reaction is as follows:

$$6CO_2 + 6H_2O \rightarrow C_6H_{12}O_6 + 6O_2$$

glucose

This is a reaction in which the energy of the valence electrons in the products are at higher levels than they were in the reactants; energy is absorbed in the process. The energy needed is one photon for each molecule of reacting substance. Photons, each with energy equal to hf, can be absorbed only by some colored substance (for there are no photons of white light, but only photons of red, orange, yellow, green, blue, and violet); in the process of absorption molecules of H_2O and CO_2 become activated. Thus, the radiant energy of the sun is stored in plants as chemical energy.

The simpler carbohydrates are the sugars; the more complex ones are starch, glycogen, and cellulose, which consist of very large molecules. The general formula is $C_x(H_2O)_y$, from which it may be seen that the process of photosynthesis consists essentially of combining carbon with water. Also it is seen that the ratio of hydrogen to oxygen is 2 to 1.

Sugars

Glucose and fructose are isomers; they are the most important simple sugars. Glucose (sometimes called dextrose, grape sugar, corn sugar) is found uncombined in leaves, sap, flowers, honey, and fruits. As noted in the above equation it is glucose, or its isomer fructose, that is made during photosynthesis. Fructose is the sweetest of all the sugars.

Cane sugar ($C_{12}H_{22}O_{11}$) may be considered to have been formed by the union of a molecule of glucose with one of fructose, with the elimination of a molecule of water.

$$C_6H_{12}O_6 + C_6H_{12}O_6 \rightarrow C_{12}H_{22}O_{11} + H_2O$$

Two isomers of cane sugar (sucrose) are malt sugar (maltose) and lactose (milk sugar). In the digestive process all of these sugars combine with water again to form the original simpler sugars; they are said to have been hydrolyzed. The glucose so formed is absorbed directly through the intestinal walls to serve as a source of energy.

Starch

Starch is a noncrystalline insoluble substance that forms the reserve supply of food in tubers and seeds of plants. Its empirical formula is $(C_6H_{10}O_5)_x \cdot H_2O$, where x may have varying values up to 3000. It probably consists of long branching chains of glucose units as monomers, any pair of which are linked together with the loss of a molecule of water. Starch is therefore a condensation polymer of glucose. During digestion, which for starch begins with the saliva in the mouth, the monomeric units are separated and recombined with water (hydrolyzed) to form glucose. Glycogen, an isomer of starch and very similar to it, is stored in the liver of animals as a reserve supply of readily available food; whenever the concentration of glucose in the blood falls below a certain level, glycogen is rapidly hydrolyzed into glucose.

Cellulose

The molecular formula for cellulose is like that of starch in that it is made up of large numbers of monomeric units of glucose, but structurally it is sufficiently different to be indigestible to man. It is the most abundant of the carbohydrates, since it constitutes the skeletal material in all kinds of plants. Some animals have digestive systems that can hydrolyze it to glucose.

Proteins

Proteins are constituents of all living cells, and so are essential to life processes. In part they serve as the structural materials for animals except for bones and shells. Skin, tendons, muscle fibers, hair, wool, feathers, nails and hoofs are largely made of proteins. The blood contains many kinds of protein molecules. In all, the human body contains several hundreds, possibly thousands of them, each having special structures that allow them to carry out specific tasks. In the human diet proteins are obtained chiefly from lean meat, eggs, fish, cheese, milk, and cereals. The function of proteins is to build body tissues and to repair them.

All proteins contain approximately 16 per cent nitrogen, combined with carbon, hydrogen, oxygen, and sometimes iron, phosphorus, sulfur, and copper. The digestive juices of man hydrolyze them, breaking them down into a number of amino acids. Actually proteins are condensation polymers in which the monomers are amino acids. There are about 25 amino acids known, 19 of them in the human body. By varying the combinations of amino acids and with the elimination of a water molecule from each pair, tens of thousands of different proteins are made possible. The number of monomeric units in proteins is sufficiently large to give their molecules an atomic weight of about 40,000 (for egg albumin) to 2,000,000,000 (for vaccinia virus).

Consider the simplest amino acid, glycine, which can be written as follows:

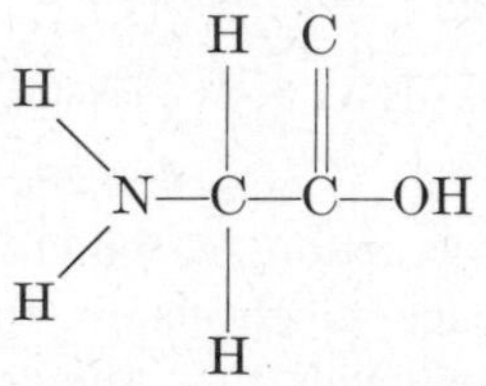

Let us suppose that two molecules of it combine. The —COOH end of one molecule combines with the —NH$_2$ end of the other, eliminating a water molecule. Thus,

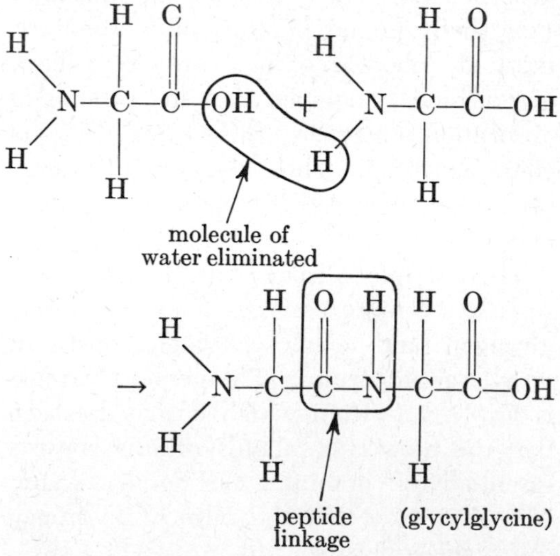

molecule of
water eliminated

peptide   (glycylglycine)
linkage

from —COOH and —NH$_2$ we have four atoms left over, C, O, N, and H. These are bonded together as shown on the right in the above reaction. Together they form a link between what is left of each of the two glycine molecules. This link is called a *peptide linkage*. A third glycine molecule can be linked in the same manner to the right end and a fourth to the left end of the product in the equation above, and so on almost ad infinitum. Different amino acids, all of them more complex than glycine, may appear as monomers in the same protein. They are, however, all linked together by the peptide linkage.

Amino acids are water soluble, so that they can be carried by the blood to the cells of the body, where the acids are synthesized by the cells into the particular kind or kinds of protein the cell needs. This is a remarkable feat, considering the fact that man has never been able to synthesize as much as a single protein in the laboratory. Proteins are also a source of energy for the body.

Enzymes

Most of the chemical reactions of the human body (as well as in all other animals) take place at a slow rate. The surprising thing is that they take place fast enough to furnish the energy needed, for at body temperatures outside the body the rate is far slower than in the body. The answer is found in enzymes, which act as catalysts to speed up the various physiological reactions. The importance of enzymes is beyond estimation. The human body contains thousands of them, each specific in its action. They are all proteins themselves.

Fats and Oils

We have already stated that fats and organic oils are esters of the large molecule fatty acids such as palmitic acid, stearic acid, oleic acid, etc., and the trihydric alcohol, glycerol. Fats and oils are easily decomposed by boiling them with strong alkali, usually NaOH. The products are glycerol and the sodium salts of the fatty acids—sodium palmitate, sodium stearate, and sodium oleate—otherwise known as soap. If KOH is used, the resulting salts constitute soft soap.

The vegetable oils are generally liquid at normal temperatures. They are composed of chains with double bonds between some of the carbon atoms, i.e., they are unsaturated. Because of the double bonds they are more reactive than the saturated fats and so spoil more quickly. They may, however, be converted to solid fats by breaking the double bonds and adding hydrogen. Crisco, Spry and many other vegetable shortenings are produced in this way. Fats are, of course, a source of energy for the body. They also serve other purposes, which we will not discuss here.

SUMMARY

Carbon exists in two forms, graphite and the diamond, that are about as different as two substances can be. The difference is due to the way the carbon atoms are bonded together. Although there are more compounds of hydrogen than there are of any other element, carbon, ranking second, is the key element in all life processes. The reason is that its atoms are the only ones that can form long straight or branching chains by forming bonds with other carbon atoms.

The simpler hydrocarbons are those that form petroleum. Petroleum is a mixture of large numbers of these hydrocarbons in mutual solution with one another. They form the paraffin (or methane) series. They have the general formula C_nH_{2n+2}. Other series are the ethylene series, C_nH_{2n}, and the acetylene series, C_nH_{2n-2}. The latter two series are unsaturated, and so are more reactive than the saturated paraffin series.

Structural formulas are commonly used in preference to molecular formulas for several reasons. The chief one is that for all but the simpler hydrocarbons there are many isomers, the potential number increasing prodigiously with the number of carbon atoms present.

Every organic compound may be considered to have been derived from some one of the three hydrocarbon series by substituting another atom or group of atoms for one or more hydrogen atoms. Thus, the study of the derivatives of the hydrocarbons is largely the science of organic chemistry. The chief derivatives considered here are the alcohols, the ethers, the aldehydes, the ketones, the organic acids, the esters, the amines, the amides, and the amino acids.

Polymers, copolymers and monomers are considered with the process of polymerization. Polymers may be of the additive type or of the condensation type. In the first no other product is involved; in the second a molecule of water is eliminated for each two monomers joined. Proteins are condensation polymers of the various amino acids. The sizes of the individual molecules of proteins are the largest known, ranging from a molecular weight of 40,000 up to 2,000,000,000 for the vaccinia virus.

EXERCISES

I. TERMS AND CONCEPTS

Hydrocarbon	Branching chain
Saturated series	Benzene ring
Unsaturated series	Molecular formula
Paraffin (methane) series	Structural formula
	Isomer
Ethylene series	Hydrocarbon de-
Acetylene series	rivative
Straight chain	

Double-bonded oxygen	Amide
	Amino acid
Carboxyl group	Fat
Alkyl group	Carbohydrate
Amino group	Protein
Peptide linkage	Polymer
Enzyme	Copolymer
Alcohol	Monomer
Ether	Addition polymer
Aldehyde	
Ketone	Condensation polymer
Organic acid	
Ester	Polymeriza-
Amine	tion

II. PROBLEMS

1. Using the general formulas, C_nH_{2n+2}, C_nH_{2n}, C_nH_{2n-2}, write specific formulas, molecular and structural, for the first three members of each group.

2. Write the structural formulas for three of the isomers of C_7H_{16}.

3. How do saturated carbon compounds differ from unsaturated? Which of the compounds that you listed in your answer to problem 1 are saturated and which unsaturated?

4. Which of the hydrocarbons occur as such in nature? How do we obtain the others?

5. In the plant and animal world there is a vast host of compounds containing carbon. Are these hydrocarbons, derivatives of the hydrocarbons, or both?

6. Would you expect any difference in the polarity of CCl_4 and $CHCl_3$ (chloroform)? Explain.

7. Name eight different kinds of hydrocarbon derivatives.

8. Classify the following compounds as completely as you can.

C_4H_9OH	C_4H_9Cl
C_4H_9COOH	$C_{15}H_{32}$
$C_4H_9 \cdot O \cdot C_2H_5$	$C_4H_9COOCH_3$
C_6H_6	$C_3H_7(OH)_3$
NH_2CH_2COOH	$C_4H_9NH_2$

$$O$$
$$\|$$
$$C_4H_9—CH \qquad C_{12}H_{24}$$

$$O$$
$$\|$$
$$C_4H_9—C—CH_3 \qquad C_{16}H_{33}COONa$$

9. You should be able to supply the names (common or otherwise) of at least six of the above compounds. Do so.

10. Try to write the hydrocarbon C_6H_6 as a chain, either straight or branching, remembering to count to four for the bonds of each carbon atom. You should then be able to appreciate the problem of Kekulé. How did he solve it?

11. What is coal tar? Of what use is it?

12. Wine, if left exposed to the atmosphere for a time will go sour (turn to vinegar) by oxidation of the alcohol. Explain why this is possible.

13. Distinguish between polymers, co-polymers, and monomers.

14. Distinguish between addition polymers and condensation polymers.

15. What sorts of hydrocarbons form addition polymers?

16. Show by structural formulas how C_3H_6 can act as a monomer to form a simple additive polymer.

17. Explain the process of photosynthesis.

18. What are amino acids? Name the simplest one. About how many are known?

19. The next simplest amino acid is valine. It contains one more carbon atom than glycine, and the amino group is attached to the middle carbon. Write the structural formula for it.

20. What do amino acids form when they polymerize?

21. What is the peptide linkage?

22. Are proteins addition or condensation polymers? What is a "simple" protein?

23. A third amino acid is phenylalanine. Its structural formula is

Show, by a structural diagram, how two such molecules may polymerize. Is the resulting product a protein? Explain.

24. Distinguish as simply yet as meaningful as you can between fats, carbohydrates, and proteins. What one property do they have in common?

25. What happens to proteins during the digestive process? Could you use amino acids for food directly? What does your body do with amino acids once they are formed?

MATTER AND ENERGY IN THE STUDY OF THE EARTH

We started this book by a general consideration of matter in chunks of planetary size, but we learned little about what matter really was until we took up the study of matter in microscopic and submicroscopic pieces. This led us into the structure of the atom, knowledge of which gave us an understanding of the chemical and physical properties of matter. None of this has given us much of an insight as to how matter occurs in nature. Any discourse on matter and energy that fails to take into account how they occur in nature, or to consider the processes involved with both in the ordinary everyday life of each of us would be woefully incomplete.

It is rather surprising that more than 98 per cent of the outer few miles of the solid part of the earth is made up of eight elements, and that the one of them that is almost as abundant as all other eight put together is a gas when in the elemental state at any natural temperature. The study of matter in the crust therefore is resolved largely into a study of how these eight elements combine to form the great variety of rocks and minerals. We say largely, not wholly, for the less than 2 per cent of other elements include many that are important to man.

The natural manifestations of energy in our inorganic world have sources that are either internal or external. Those that are of internal origin may be at times spectacular and mysterious, e.g., volcanic eruptions and earthquakes, and so excite wonder. Those that are of external origin and whose source is the sun are so commonplace that they are taken for granted. These represent transformations of energy on a gigantic scale which affect our daily lives in a multitude of ways. The energy cycle involved is not at all simple, but complex and varied to a degree that is even yet not thoroughly understood.

In these new investigations into matter and energy, we pass from experimental science where our conclusions are constantly checked in the laboratory, to natural physical science where the limitations of space and time so frequently make laboratory investigations impossible. For example, the processes that result in the folding of rock layers, their intrusion by great masses of molten material, and their elevation into great mountain ranges operate so slowly that a lifetime of observation may not reveal that they are taking place. A net elevation of a region by a foot a century would pass unnoticed in most places, yet if continued for a million years would result in the area being uplifted nearly two miles. In man's attempts to understand these processes (and many others), he is therefore forced to work with the results of natural processes that have operated in the remote past. He has therefore had to devise new techniques of obtaining information, and new methods of reasoning in which deduction plays an important role. Throughout it all the method of progressing from the known to the unknown, from the simple to the complex, is followed as it has been in all other branches of science.

CHAPTER XXXIX

Matter of the Earth: Rocks and Minerals

One of the marvels of creation is the infinite capacity of the human brain to withstand the introduction of knowledge.—THEODORE ROOSEVELT

Silicon, a member of the same family as carbon, occupies the same relative position in the inorganic world that carbon occupies in the organic world. All of us are familiar with carbon; we have all of us seen it in the pure state (diamond, graphite, lampblack, etc.) and in the impure state (in charcoal, coal, etc.) but few, if any, of you, have ever seen silicon. Yet in the outer part of the earth there are about 10,000 atoms of silicon for every 27 atoms of carbon; if we include the whole earth, the ratio is even larger.

Silicon is much more active chemically than carbon, which is why we never see it in the free (native) state in nature. Silicon constitutes about 25 per cent of the crust of the earth. Oxygen constitutes about 50 per cent of the average rock, so that together they make up nearly 75 per cent of the earth's crust. The two combined together to form crystals constitute the mineral quartz (SiO_2). Most of the

SiO_2 is, however, combined with various metals to form a group of minerals called silicates.

Considering the abundance of SiO_2 in the crust of the earth, it inevitably follows that the chief rock-forming minerals are silicates.[1] Quantitatively, they make up about 98 per cent of the crust of the earth. These silicate minerals fall into three groups, the framework minerals (with properties somewhat similar to quartz), the layer minerals (such as the micas), and the fibrous minerals (such as chrysolite, more popularly known by its trade name Asbestos). These groups will be discussed shortly.

Silicon, atomic number 14, is directly beneath carbon in the periodic table. We should therefore expect it to have properties similar to those of carbon. Chief among them are its valence of 4 and the ability to combine with other atoms only by sharing four pairs of electrons.

One of the important differences is in the sizes of the two atoms. Not more than three oxygen atoms (as in $-CO_3$) can fit about the small carbon atom. Even with two (as in CO_2), the oxygen atoms are warped. Four oxygen atoms can cluster about the larger silicon atom without warping. Silicon is more metallic than carbon, enough so that one form of it has the lustrous sheen of a metal, but not enough to form positive ions. It has little tendency to form chains of silicon atoms in the manner of carbon, but it will form chains of

---

[1] Quartz should be considered a silicate, even though no metal appears in its composition, for the structure of quartz is fundamental to the structure of the silicates. Silicon dioxide is better known as silica. The chief crystalline form of silica is quartz, but the two words are not interchangeable, e.g., molten SiO_2 is silica but not quartz.

alternating silicon and oxygen atoms. These are arranged in tetrahedral structures as in the diamond (Fig. 33-3); the silicon atom is at the center of the tetrahedron with an oxygen atom at each of the corners. The tetrahedra are therefore SiO_4, with each oxygen atom serving as the corner of two tetrahedra. Since each silicon atom has four electrons to share and each oxygen atom has two, there are four pairs of shared electrons in the SiO_4 tetrahedron and four open bonds, one for each oxygen atom. Since the valence of oxygen is negative, this leaves a net charge of -4 on each tetrahedron. In some minerals this charge is neutralized by four positive charges on metallic ions, e.g., in $(Fe, Mg)SiO_4$ (which is the mineral olivine).

The mineral quartz is composed of nothing but SiO_4 tetrahedra. Since each silicon atom is surrounded by four oxygen atoms, and each oxygen atom serves as a neighbor to two silicon atoms, the ratio of silicon to oxygen is 1:2. The formula of a crystal of quartz is therefore SiO_2, but it should be understood that there is only one molecule per crystal even though some such natural crystals weigh a ton or more. The formula merely expresses the ratio of silicon atoms to oxygen atoms. A two-dimensional representation of the way these two elements are linked together in quartz is

$$
\begin{array}{c}
| \\
-\text{Si}- \\
| \\
\text{O} \\
| \quad\quad\quad | \quad\quad\quad | \\
-\text{Si}-\text{O}-\text{Si}-\text{O}-\text{Si}- \\
| \quad\quad\quad | \quad\quad\quad | \\
\text{O} \\
| \\
-\text{Si}- \\
|
\end{array}
$$

Other oxygen atoms are attached to the open bonds of silicon, and so on to form giant molecules. These molecules are among the largest in nature. The Si—O bonds are covalent, as in the diamond, and to break or melt a quartz crystal (which is one giant molecule) many of these bonds must be broken. The crystal is therefore very hard and has a high melting point ($1600°$ C), but it is not as hard as the diamond.

In most silicate minerals, the -4 negative charge on an SiO_4 tetrahedron is not neutralized by positive metallic ions in the simple way described in a previous paragraph. Instead two or more tetrahedra may combine to form larger ions of *definite* extent. Among the more common are $Si_2O_7^{-6}$, $Si_4O_{12}^{-8}$, $Si_3O_9^{-6}$, and $Si_6O_{18}^{-12}$ (Fig. 39-1a). Note that by combining tetrahedra, the ratio of the number of positive charges to the number of Si atoms needed to neutralize those charges has been reduced from the ratio in SiO_4^{-4}. These negative ions (and other silicate ions) together with interspersed positive ions of metals, and arranged in various patterns, form the framework, layer, and fibrous minerals that have been mentioned. The metallic ions are almost exclusively those of aluminum, potassium, sodium, iron, calcium, and magnesium. These six elements, along with silicon and oxygen make up more than 98 per cent of the earth's crust, leaving less than 2 per cent for all of the other 80-odd elements.

FRAMEWORK MINERALS

We have already described the tetrahedral structure of quartz, with an Si atom at the center of each tetrahedron and oxygen atoms at the corners, where each is joined to another Si atom at the center of another tetrahedron. These tetrahedra, repeated almost endlessly, give a tetrahedral framework structure. Aluminum atoms can substitute for silicon in some tetrahedra, most commonly in the ratio of 1:3, i.e., in the framework every fourth tetrahedron will have an aluminum atom at the center; these are AlO_4 tetrahedra. Aluminum adjoins Si in the periodic chart; it is slightly larger, but not enough to alter the structure of the crystal significantly. However, it has a valence of 3 only, and so another positive ion must be present to preserve electrical neutrality in the crystal.

The common positive ions are K^+ and Na^+. The resulting minerals are the light-colored feldspars, chiefly orthoclase ($KAlSi_3O_8$) and albite ($NaAlSi_3O_8$). If every second tetrahedron is an AlO_4 tetrahedron, then a doubly charged positive ion, commonly calcium, must be present to preserve electric neutrality. The resulting mineral is a very dark-colored feldspar, anorthite ($CaAl_2Si_2O_8$). This dark feldspar and the light soda feldspar albite may have their tetrahedra mixed in all proportions; they (the atoms of sodium and calcium) are almost the same size. When they are mixed about half and half, the resulting feldspar is the common dark feldspar called labradorite.

The potassium atom is considerably bigger (Fig. 30-2) than either the sodium or the calcium atom so that the tetrahedra to which they are attached do not fit into the same framework as those of sodium and calcium; instead they form the potash feldspars, orthoclase and microcline. There are many other framework minerals, but these, together with quartz, form the great bulk of the rocks of the earth's crust. The feldspars alone outbulk all of the other minerals of all kinds in the crust of the earth. Ground-up feldspar, together with a white clay mineral and quartz, forms the porcelain of our kitchens and bathrooms, and the glaze on our dishes.

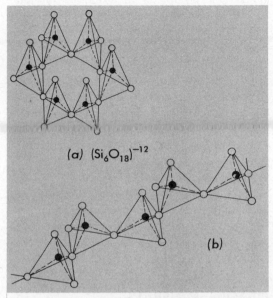

Fig. 39-1. Silicates Structures. **(a)** A complex silicate ion showing how the tetrahedra are joined. There is a net negative charge of -12 which is neutralized by the positive charges of metallic ions. **(b)** Long chains of tetrahedra are present in fibrous minerals such as asbestos.

LAYER MINERALS

The layer minerals include such well-known minerals as the micas and talc. Others less well known but more important are the clay minerals, which are abundant constituents of all good soils. These layer minerals are characterized, from the compositional viewpoint, by the presence of OH groups. They may therefore be considered hydrated silicates, e.g., the clay minerals are hydrous aluminous silicates, the micas are hydrous aluminous silicates with either potassium ions (light-colored mica) or with iron and magnesium ions (dark-colored mica) in addition, and talc is a hydrous silicate with magnesium ions.

Structurally, the layer minerals are composed of SiO_4 and/or AlO_4 tetrahedra arranged in the form of continuous layers. In the micas the metallic (positive) ions lie between the layers. Their attraction for the negative ions forming the layers binds the layers together. These attractions are not nearly so great as those between the Si and O ions in the layers. Thus, the layers can be split apart, i.e., cleaved, readily. In talc and the clay minerals the layers are electrically neutral and are loosely superimposed on one another. They slip over one another easily; this accounts for their softness, ready cleavage, and soapy feel.

FIBROUS MINERALS

In these minerals the tetrahedra are arranged in long chains. In the pyroxene group, the chains are single, in the amphibole group they are double (Fig. 39-1*b*). In both there are numerous Ca^{++}, Mg^{++}, or Fe^{++} ions (and sometimes others) to hold the chains together, so that the fibrous character is not at all evident in most species. In the asbestos minerals the OH group is also present. The chains of tetrahedra are held together only loosely by the metallic ions (Ca^{++}, Mg^{++}) so that the fibers can be easily pulled apart.

DEFINITION OF A MINERAL

So far we have been using the term without formally defining it. Minerals are nat-urally occurring inorganic substances having a characteristic range of physical and chemical properties and a characteristic internal structure. A careful inspection of this definition will show that many things called minerals are not true minerals. Thus, coal is not a mineral; neither are most metals. The significance of the characteristic internal structure requirement is easily seen by comparing the diamond with graphite.

NONSILICATE MINERALS

There are some two thousand known minerals, most of which are rare and unimportant either as a constituent of the earth or to man. Not many of the minerals important as rock-formers are of great direct importance to man. None have the importance that a few of the nonsilicate minerals have played in the development of our civilization, e.g., the iron minerals, magnetite (Fe_3O_4), hematite (Fe_2O_3), limonite ($Fe_2O_3 \cdot xH_2O$). The first two are oxides, the third a hydrated oxide (of which common iron rust is an example). Other minerals that occur as oxides and are of great importance to man are those of copper, tin, aluminum, and manganese. Another important group are the sulfides; of greatest importance to man are those of lead, zinc, copper, silver, mercury, nickel, etc. Among the chlorides are those of sodium and potassium; among the carbonates are those of calcium, magnesium, zinc, lead, and copper. Only gold and platinum are important as native metals, although there have been (and are) some important deposits of copper and silver in the native state. There are a score or two groups of lesser importance.

These nonsilicate minerals occur as ores,

i.e., they occur as parts of mineral aggregates from which one or more metals may be extracted at a profit. There are many low-grade deposits of them which contain enormous quantities of the metals, but not in sufficiently high concentrations to make them minable at a profit. Whatever concentrations there are in nature that are profitable were made by one or more of a variety of natural processes. The study of ore deposits is therefore largely a study of the various natural methods of concentration. We will not discuss them here, except to say that if no such natural methods existed, man would still be in the stone age.

ROCKS

A rock is a very difficult thing to define in satisfying terms. To say that it is anything that naturally forms a significant portion of the earth's crust is scarcely satisfying, yet it is the only all-inclusive definition that we can give. Most rocks are aggregates of minerals, but there are a few with no minerals, e.g., the volcanic glasses (obsidian, pumice, scoria) and the coals (which are commonly called minerals). To the geologist minerals are not rocks. To think they are is somewhat analogous to calling a piece of cloth a dress.

Classification of Rocks

We might suspect from the definition of a rock that they would be difficult to classify. Basing a system on definite substances like elements and minerals has its problems in any classification scheme. Any scheme based on chemical composition breaks down so completely that it is entirely unusable, because rocks of very different origins, even different mineralogical compositions, may have closely similar chemical compositions. Systems based on mineralogical compositions run into similar difficulties that are nearly as great. A usable one is based on origin, although there are some rocks whose origin is in dispute. The major rocks, however, have origins agreed on by all geologists.

On this basis rocks are classified as igneous, sedimentary or metamorphic. The igneous rocks are those that have solidified from a once molten state. They are sometime referred to as the primary rocks, for if we go back far enough in time, all rocks were igneous (since the whole earth was once molten). From the products of destruction of these original igneous rocks through the processes of weathering and erosion, the first sedimentary rocks were formed. In the course of vast periods of time other processes (vulcanism and diastrophism) caused these sedimentary and igneous rocks to be changed in various ways, sometimes in chemical composition, sometimes in mineralogical composition, sometimes in the way the crystals were arranged, or even all three. If these changes are great enough, we call the resulting product a metamorphic rock. Obviously, there are all sorts of gradations between sedimentary and metamorphic rocks on the one hand, and between igneous and metamorphic rocks on the other. There are even metamorphic rocks that have a mixed origin, and some whose ancestry is uncertain.

IGNEOUS ROCKS AND THEIR MINERALS

Magmas and molten lavas are heterogeneous liquids that have high freezing points—1000° C or higher. They *might be* considered to consist almost wholly of various silicate ions, e.g., SiO_4^{-4}, SiO_3^{-2}, $Si_2O_7^{-2}$, $Si_3O_9^{-6}$, $Si_6O_{18}^{-12}$, etc., all negatively charged, and the positively charged metallic ions, Al^{+3}, Fe^{+2}, Ca^{+2}, K^+, Na^+, Mg^{+2} ions, all in mutual solution with one another. As long as the temperature is high enough, the kinetic energy of the ions is great enough to prevent the attractive forces between negative and positive ions from forming bonds. Thus, no minerals are formed; the whole mass remains a liquid. If the temperature drops far enough and slowly enough, the whole mass becomes solid by the process of crystallization of various minerals. The reason is as follows:

Minerals are solid substances in which the ions are arranged in characteristic patterns, more commonly called crystal lattices. To form these lattices, the temperature must slowly drop to the point where the attractive forces between the ions begin to overcome the kinetic forces. Until this point is reached the ions will not occupy the lattice points. Furthermore, if crystals large enough to be visible to the naked eye are to form, the temperature must remain nearly constant for a long time. This allows the ions to still have some freedom of movement, enough freedom to find and occupy lattice points, but once in the lattice, not enough freedom to move out against the attractive forces. If these conditions prevail, ion after ion occupies the lattice points, slowly building up solid mineral crystals or grains, neutral with respect to electric charge. The temperature at which the ions *begin* to form the crystal lattice of any particular mineral is highly variable. For olivine it is about 1500° C; for quartz it is less than 800° C. The following diagram, called Bowen's reaction series, illustrates the order of crystallization, i.e., the order in which the various minerals formed.

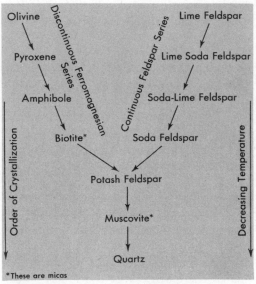

Fig. 39-2. Bowen's Reaction Series: Not all of the minerals in the series ever appear in the same rock.

The ferromagnesian series progresses from the simpler ionic-like bonding of olivine through increasing numbers (1, 2, and 3) of directions of connections among tetrahedra. This is because the decreasing kinetic energy of the ions as the temperature drops permits the formation of more complicated linkages among the tetrahedra. The ferromagnesian series is said to be discontinuous because each successive mineral formed has a different crystal lattice, and therefore is a distinct mineral species.

The feldspar series is said to be continuous because once feldspar formation begins, it continues throughout the crystallization of the molten mass by *continuously* changing composition *without* changing the crystal lattice. The lime feldspar forms first because the Ca^{++} ion has a double charge whereas the Na^+ ion has only a single charge. The former is therefore more strongly attracted into the crystal lattice. This early formed lime feldspar reacts continuously with Na^+ ions, assimilating more and more as long as any remain in the magma. The final result is a single species of lime-soda or soda-lime feldspar rather than a lime feldspar *and* a soda feldspar. The actual composition of this type of feldspar will depend upon the relative proportions of Ca^{++} and N^+ in the magma. If Ca^{++} is high and Na^+ low, a nearly pure lime feldspar will form; if Na^+ is high and Ca^{++} low, a pure or nearly pure soda feldspar will result. Ca^{++} ion can substitute easily for Na^+ ion, or vice versa, in the crystal lattice because their atomic radii are nearly the same. The higher valence of Ca^{++} is taken care of by slightly different linkages among the tetrahedra.

The potash feldspar crystallizes separately in a crystal lattice of its own rather than participating in the formation of the lime-soda, etc., feldspars. This is because the atomic radius of K^+ is too great for it to substitute for either Ca^{++} or Na^+ without changing the structure of the lattice. These facts about substitution can easily be understood by an analogy: A bricklayer can substitute one kind of brick for another without changing the shape of his structure only as long as the substituted bricks are all close to the same size as the original bricks.

The sizes of the individual crystals (also called grains) in the resulting rock clearly depends upon the length of time that the temperature of the magma remains within the range where the ions can occupy the lattice points and *stay there*. The greater the number of ions in a particular lattice the larger the size of the crystal. Slow cooling, then promotes large grain size, sizes large enough to be easily seen with the naked eye. Thus, the coarse-grained igneous rocks, e.g., granite, are formed. Conversely, rapid cooling promotes small grain size, sizes too small to be seen with the naked eye. Thus the fine-grained igneous rocks, e.g., basalt, are formed. In some cases the cooling may be so rapid— as when lava is poured out on the surface to form a thin sheet—that few or no ions manage to occupy lattice points. The result is a rock with no grains, a rock we call a volcanic glass because, like glass, it has a noncrystalline structure. Such rocks either have a glassy appearance, e.g., obsidian, or are full of holes formed by bubbles of expanding gases as the pressure on the lava is relieved by escape to the surface; scoria and pumice are examples of this type.

The rate of cooling of a molten mass varies enormously with depth and with thickness. For example, it has been estimated that a 3-ft layer of lava on the surface at a temperature of $1100°$ C ($2000°$ F) would cool to $750°$ C ($1400°$ F) in about 12 days, whereas the deep interior of a layer 30,000 ft thick (about 6 mi) would take about 3,000,000 years to cool from $1100°$ C to $750°$ C. Of course, no layer of lava is ever anything like that thick. It follows that an intrusive 30,000 ft thick whose top is several *miles* below the surface would take far more than 3,000,000 years to cool from $1100°$ C to $750°$ C. This is in part because rocks are notoriously slow conductors of heat.

The minerals that form from lavas and magmas are obviously dependent upon the kinds and proportions of ions that compose the molten matter. Most magmas are high silica magmas, composed largely of silicate ions, up to 75 per cent or even more. Metallic ions, chiefly Al^{+++}, Na^+ and K^+, make up the remaining 25 per cent. The lattices that form are thus those that use large amounts of silica. The resulting minerals are chiefly the light-colored sodic and/or potassic feldspars. What little Fe^{++} or Mg^{++} there is usually goes into the biotite (black mica) lattice. If Ca^{++} ions are present in significant amounts, amphibole may form in place of biotite. Any excess iron may crystallize as tiny crystals of magnetite.

In these high silica magmas there is always an excess of silicate ions after all of the metallic ions have entered into the lattices. These excess silicate ions break up into SiO_4^{-4} and $Si_4O_2^{-8}$ ions, which then arrange themselves in the quartz crystal lattice in the ratio of two oxygen ions to one silicate ion. Thus, quartz in an igneous rock is an indication that the magma from which it formed was a high silica magma. Furthermore, since the great bulk of the minerals formed are the light-colored feldspars and quartz, the resulting rock will be light-colored. Most commonly the rock formed, if coarse-grained, is *granite*.

In low silica magmas silicate ions compose about 50 per cent of the mass; metallic ions form the other 50 per cent. Thus, the proportion of the latter is doubled, the increase being chiefly in Fe^{++}, Mg^{++} and Ca^{++} ions. Hence, crystal lattices form that use more of these ions and fewer silicate ions. Minerals with such lattices as these are the ferromagnesians, olivine, pyroxene, and amphibole, and the dark-colored calcic feldspar (or lime-soda feldspar). Obviously there are no silicate ions

left over to form quartz. The resulting rocks are therefore dark-colored with *no* quartz. The feldspar will always be the one that is most sparing in the use of silica, i.e., dark-colored lime feldspar. The most common fine-grained low silica rock is basalt.

It is well worth noting that color is an extremely useful property in igneous rock identification. One should no more think of hunting for quartz and light-colored feldspars in a dark-colored rock than one should think of hunting lions in Greenland. There are, of course, exceptions to every rule, but let us not concern ourselves here with them.

SEDIMENTARY ROCKS AND THEIR MINERALS

The chief sedimentary rocks are conglomerate, sandstone, shale, and limestone. They are formed chiefly by the consolidation of the products of weathering and erosion of previously existing rocks. Some are formed from accumulations of organic debris. The coals are examples of the latter; we will omit them from the following discussion because they are not typical sedimentary rocks.

The products of weathering and erosion are for the most part sediments—gravels, sands, clay muds, and lime muds. In time these sediments usually become consolidated into solid rock either by compaction (of the muds) or by cementation (of the gravels and sands). Compaction is accomplished by sheer weight of the sediments as layer is piled upon layer. Compaction is effective only in fine-grained sediments, for it is obvious that coarse sands and gravels cannot be made to stick together by pressure alone.

Cementation involves the introduction of cements between the pebbles or sand grains by percolating ground waters. The chief cements are silica, calcium carbonate, and the iron oxides, limonite and hematite. Cementation is not effective in the muds because the pore spaces are too small for the cement-carrying waters to freely pass through them. As previously stated, the color of the cement commonly determines the color of the rock. Thus, sandstones cemented with either silica or calcium carbonate are commonly white or gray, those cemented with hematite are red or reddish-brown, and those cemented with limonite are yellow or yellow-brown.

On consolidation by compaction or cementation the gravels become conglomerates, the sands become sandstones, clay muds become shales, and the lime muds become limestones. The first three—conglomerates, sandstones, shales—are called the clastic rocks because they are formed from fragments of minerals. These fragments are *either* original minerals, e.g., quartz, that were not affected by chemical weathering or they are the insoluble products of chemical weathering, e.g., the clay minerals. They are transported by one or the other of the agents of erosion—of which streams are by far the most important— and eventually deposited mechanically in some low place to form the clastic rocks.

The lime muds which eventualy form limestones are called precipitates because they were precipitated from solution. During the chemical weathering of the minerals in igneous rocks, some of the minerals are changed into new minerals by chemical reactions with moisture and air. A small fraction of these new minerals are water soluble and so are dissolved out of the weathered material by rainwater. Much of this water finds its way to seas or lakes where the dissolved material is precipitated if conditions are right. Limestone, made of calcium carbonate (calcite) is by far the most common precipitate. Two others are halite ($NaCl$) and gypsum ($CaSO_4 \cdot 2H_2O$).

Most sedimentary rocks are chiefly accumulations of clay, quartz, and calcite, either alone or in various combinations. Most sandstones are made essentially of quartz because quartz, an original constituent of most igneous rocks, is not only immune to change by chemical weathering but is also insoluble in water. Sandstones may sometimes contain feldspar and mica grains as well as many other resistant minerals in small quantities. A few sandstones with little or no quartz do exist, but none extensively.

The clay minerals form a group we will refer to as kaolin. The chief source of clay is the feldspars, from which it is derived by the processes of chemical weathering, as follows:

$$2K(AlSi_3O_8) + CO_2 + 2H_2O \rightarrow$$
potash feldspar

$$Al_2Si_2O_5(OH)_4 + K_2CO_3 + 4SiO_2$$
clay mineral   potassium   silica
carbonate

From this reaction it is readily seen that if most of the mass of an igneous rock is feldspar (which it is), far more clay than anything else is produced when that rock is chemically weathered. It follows that the rock that forms from this clay, i.e., shale, should be the most abundant of the sedimentary rocks.

The clastic sediments, gravels, sands, and clay muds, are washed into the streams by rain or other processes of masswasting. The streams carry them in suspension to their more or less "final" resting place. Loss of velocity causes the stream to deposit, the coarsest first, the finer later. The result is a succession of layers or strata. This stratification is the most characteristic feature of sedimentary rocks.

METAMORPHIC ROCKS AND THEIR MINERALS

Rocks, like living things, adjust themselves to changes in their environment. When rocks are subjected to greatly increased pressure or temperature, or a combination of them, metamorphism may result. The degree or "grade" of metamorphism depends on the intensity of these factors and the duration of their action. The heat is in part derived from igneous activity and the pressure is derived chiefly from diastrophic activity. This heat and pressure, if great enough, imposes a new set of characters—minerals, structures, textures—on the original rocks, metamorphosing them.

Pressures of 40,000 to 60,000 lb/sq in. are great enough to cause rocks to flow plastically. These pressures combined with the horizontal pressures that cause rocks in *some* areas to bend and fold are capable of bringing about metamorphism. It should be obvious from this that rocks at or near the surface can never be metamorphosed. Where metamorphic rocks are exposed at the surface today, it is because erosion to considerable depths have exposed them.

Heat is a necessary agent of metamorphism because it increases the average kinetic energy of the atoms in the minerals, and so weakens the bonds between them. This accelerates the rate at which chemical reactions take place. Obviously, the higher the temperature, the faster the rate. As previously stated, part of the heat is derived from igneous activity (in those areas where there is igneous activity), and in part it is derived from friction in areas where folding and/or faulting on a large scale have taken place. Both igneous activity and folding are associated with mountain building. Therefore, metamorphic rocks are confined to those regions where complex mountains, past or present, have been formed. The rocks of New York City and at shallow depths in adjoining regions on Long Island are highly metamorphosed rocks. Therefore, a great complex mountain range once occupied these areas; only the roots remain.

Since igneous rocks were formed under conditions of high temperature, and, in the case of intrusive igneous rocks, under high pressure, it follows that such rocks are difficult to metamorphose. Sedimentary rocks, on the other hand, were formed at the surface of the earth under conditions of low temperature and low pressure. It is therefore expected that they would metamorphose most easily. It also follows that metamorphic rocks would resemble igneous rocks more than they would sedimentary rocks, because the conditions under which they formed resemble those under which igneous rocks formed. In fact, the most abundant minerals in metamorphic rocks formed from either igneous rocks or the *clastic* sedimentary rocks are those most abundant in igneous rocks—feldspars, micas, amphibole, quartz. Much of the quartz, however, is reconstituted quartz of the sedimentary rocks. Thus, a quartz sandstone becomes a quartzite by recrystallization of the grains so that their rounded discrete character is lost. The result is a tougher rock, one that breaks right through the grains rather than around them as in sandstones. If the sedimentary rock is a limestone, the calcium carbonate is recrystallized into larger grains, forming a marble. The size of the grains depends upon the intensity of the metamorphism and its duration; they vary from those barely visible to those a quarter of an inch or more across.

The density of metamorphic rocks is, on the average, greater than that of their sedimentary antecedents. In part this is due to reduction of pore spaces, and in part to the application of Le Châtelier's principle: When a system is in equilibrium and one of the factors which determine the equilibrium is altered, the system always reacts in such a way as *to tend* to counteract the original alteration. The factor in question here is pressure. At the start of metamorphism the pressure is increased. New minerals which are denser than the original ones may form, or many small grains may unite to form fewer larger ones. In either case space is saved as the system reacts to counteract the increase in pressure.

Some metamorphic rocks are foliated, e.g., slate, schist, and gneiss; and some are nonfoliated or massive, e.g., quartzite, marble, and hornfels. In the foliated rocks pressure has been an important factor. If the composition of the original rock allows platy minerals like mica or elongate minerals like amphibole to form, these minerals form in layers that to the uninitiated look like stratification but which is called foliation by geologists. The trend of the layers is at right angles to the pressure causing the folding. Marbles and quartzites are not foliated because their minerals, calcite and quartz, respectively, are neither platy nor elongate but equidimensional. There is nothing to line up. Hornfels is not foliated because it does not form where there is any orienting stress; it is the product of heat (thermal) metamorphism only.

SUMMARY

The differences between carbon and silicon, both members of the same family of elements, are due in large part to their differences in size. Silicon is a major component of most rocks; it is the second most abundant element in the outer part of the earth. It combines with oxygen to form SiO_4 tetrahedra. AlO_4 tetrahedra may substitute for some SiO_4 tetrahedra. These tetrahedra are joined together, sometimes with metallic ions, sometimes without, to form the various silicates that make up igneous rocks. These silicates consist of three main groups, the framework minerals, the layer minerals, and the fibrous minerals, depending upon the way the tetrahedra are linked together.

Other minerals include metallic oxides, sulfides, carbonates, etc. Many of them are ores when they occur in large enough natural concentrations. Whether or not an aggregate of minerals is an ore or not depends upon the possibility of extracting ore or metals from them at a profit.

Most rocks are aggregates of minerals, although a few contain no minerals, e.g., obsidian and pumice. Rocks are classified as igneous, sedimentary, or metamorphic. The formation of igneous rocks is essentially a problem in physical chemistry. The formation of sedimentary rocks involves the processes of chemical and physical weathering, masswasting, erosion, and deposition (or sedimentation). The formation of metamorphic rocks is, like that of igneous rocks, essentially a problem in physical chemistry.

EXERCISES

I. TERMS AND CONCEPTS

Mineral

Framework minerals

Layer minerals

Fibrous minerals

Silica

Quartz

Feldspar

Mica

Amphibole

Pyroxene

Granite

Basalt

Calcite

Kaolin

SiO_4 tetrahedra

AlO_4 tetrahedra

Silicate mineral

Ore

Rock

Classes of rocks

Crystallization of a magna

Grains

Low silica magma

High silica magma

Cementation

Compaction

Metamorphism

II. PROBLEMS

1. Name the eight most abundant elements forming the crust of the earth. Name the first four in order of abundance.

2. Which of the above elements occur as elements in the outer part of the earth? Why it, or them, and not the others?

3. What is a magma composed of? (Make your answer significant.)

4. Which can crowd around a carbon atom more easily, four oxygen atoms or four other carbon atoms? Explain.

5. It is incorrect to speak of a molecule of SiO_2. Why? Would it be incorrect to speak of a molecule of quartz? Explain.

6. Some fibrous minerals are amazingly fibrous whereas others are not at all obviously fibrous. Why the difference?

7. Why is coal not considered a mineral in the scientific sense?

8. Distinguish between a rock and a mineral.

9. Define each of the three great classes of rocks.

10. What is a grain? Where is the boundary line between fine-grained and coarse-grained rocks drawn? What factors determine grain size?

11. What is a glassy rock? What conditions produce them?

12. What is the most abundant mineral group in most igneous rocks?

13. Under what conditions will quartz form in an igneous rock?

14. Why should rocks from low silica magmas be darker in color than those formed from high silica magmas?

15. What is by far the most common coarse-grained igneous rock? The most common fine-grained igneous rock.

16. Name the essential minerals that, in general, are found in igneous rocks.

17. Distinguish between the minerals of a granite and those of a basalt.

18. How do sediments differ from sedimentary rocks? What processes can convert the former into the latter?

19. What are the chief cements in sedimentary rocks?

20. Cementation is far more important in sandstones than in shales. Why?

21. What is the role of weathering in the formation of sediments?

22. Why should any rock undergo metamorphosis?

23. Which would you expect to undergo metamorphosis most easily, a sedimentary or an igneous rock? Explain.

24. Name the common metamorphic rocks and state the kind they may have been before metamorphosis.

25. Name the essential minerals in each of the following: a sandstone, a shale, a limestone, a quartzite, a slate, and a marble.

CHAPTER XL

A General View of the Earth

*The earth was made so various, that the mind
Of desultory man, studious of change
And pleased with novelty, might be indulged.*
—WILLIAM COWPER

Before continuing our discussion of matter and energy in and on the earth, it is highly desirable to take a general view of the earth as a whole. If we do, the later discussions will be much more meaningful. We will start with the surface of the earth.

CONTINENTS AND OCEAN BASINS

The outstanding feature of the earth's surface is its division into continents and ocean basins. The latter are much the larger; they occupy about 70 per cent of the earth's surface, leaving only 30 per cent for the land areas. The average depth of the oceans is a little over 2 mi below sea level and the average height of the continents is about ½ mi above. The greatest depth in the oceans is about 37,000 ft below sea level, the greatest height above is a bit over 29,000 ft. This makes the difference between the highest mountain top and the greatest depth of the sea about 65,000 ft (12.5 mi).[1]

How did the earth's surface get that way? The origin of continents and ocean basins is never asked by the average person in the Western world; he takes them for granted, perhaps because he believes the earth was created that way. If we all believed that, there would be no science of geology, for the answers to all our questions would be the same: Things are as they are because they were created that way.

Our basic question is this, "Why is the earth not covered with a universal ocean two miles deep?" This is the way it should be if we removed the water, shoveled the continents into the basins to make a uniform surface, and then let the water return. No direct evidence of any sort has been found that would indicate how the land and water became divided, and no widely accepted theory has ever been formulated, although the one that will be presented here is gaining in favor.

As far as the evidence goes, the continents have always been continents and the ocean basins have always been ocean basins as far back in geologic history as we can probe. Radioactive age determinations seem to indicate that in general the central parts of shield areas (Fig. 40-1) of each continent are made of the oldest rocks of that continent, and that as we go outward from these centers the rocks become younger. Perhaps the formation of continents is related to the fact that mountain-building has always been concentrated in narrow strips called mobile belts, i.e., belts

---

[1] This is called the relief of the earth. Relief is defined as the difference in elevation between the highest and the lowest points *in the area under consideration.*

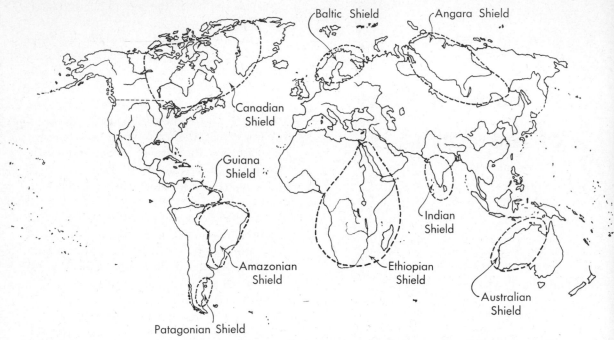

Fig. 40-1. The Canadian Shield. Typical shield rocks are shown in the stippled region. Blank areas within the dashed line are covered with water or ice, or are areas where typical shield rocks are interspersed with sedimentary rocks. Typical shield rocks are igneous (largely granitic) and highly metamorphosed rocks, e.g., gneisses and schists.

in which the earth's crust has been subject to movements of one sort or another. Two such belts exist today, one extending from Antarctica up the west coasts of South and North America to the Aleutians, where it swings westward and then southward along the Kuriles, Japan, Philippines, and Indonesia; and the other includes the Atlas, Alpine, Turkish, Persian, Himalayan, and Burmese mountains and the island chains of Indonesia, New Guinea, the Solomons, New Hebrides, and New Zealand (Fig. 40-1).

Along these belts are all of the world's youngest mountains, most of its active and recently extinct volcanoes, and most earthquake epicenters. Chief among the features of these mobile belts are the island arcs and the associated deep sea trenches. The island arcs contain all of the world's volcanoes that erupt silicic lavas and all of the young silicic intrusive rocks.

Perhaps the earth was once covered by a universal ocean early in its history. Then vulcanism started as a consequence of fracturing of certain parts of the solid crust beneath the waters; great volumes of molten materials were poured out. If the fractures were arcuate, then the piles of volcanic materials that were eventually built up above the ocean levels would be arcuate also. Thus, the first island arcs would have been formed somewhat more than 3 billions of years ago. In time other island arcs might have developed more or less parallel to the first ones and adjacent to them.

According to J. Tuzo Wilson of the University of Toronto these arcs went through a series of stages, much too complicated to be presented here. When the final stages were completed, an embryonic continent had come into existence. The final stages of the adjacent island arcs allowed them and their associated features to be added to the first. Thus, the continents grew by accretion, i.e., by the addition of more island arcs. The process may not yet be ended. This process of accretion would explain why the rocks get younger outward from the centers of the shield areas. The ejection of volcanic materials in such enormous amounts would have made it necessary for other areas to sink as material (at relatively shallow depth in the crust) moved inward towards the arc to replace the ejected material. Thus, the continents and the ocean basins may have come into being.

This is, of course, only a sketch of the hypothesis, and a greatly oversimplified one at that.[2] It is, however, the only hypothesis of the origin of continents that has shown any promise.

STRUCTURE OF CONTINENTS

The structure of a continent, i.e., the arrangement of its major relief features, is not haphazard. Each continent has a shield area (Fig. 40-2). These are vast areas (about 2,000,000 sq mi for the Canadian

[2] For more details, see Russell Jacobs and Wilson, *Physics and Geology*, New York, McGraw-Hill, 1959, Chapters 14 and 15.

Shield) of ancient igneous and intensely metamorphosed (for the most part) sedimentary rocks, which form the "cores" of their respective continents. Their rocks represent the roots of complexly folded (Fig. 40-3) mountain ranges, which have been deeply eroded, re-elevated, and eroded again and again. They stand an average of a few hundreds of feet above sea level at present. They are the most stable areas of the continents and have been so for the last half billion years. If we could remove from each of the continents all rocks younger than about one-half billion years, then the rocks exposed would be the ones like those in the shield areas. The younger rocks are chiefly sedimentary, with interbedded lava flows in some areas. Some, however, have been metamorphosed and in some areas igneous material has been forcibly injected into them.

Each continent has a number of mountain systems that more or less parallel the continental borders. In the United States the Appalachians parallel the east coast, the Rockies, the Sierra Nevada, the Cascades and the Coast Ranges parallel the west coast. None is more than a quarter of a billion years old. In general, igneous and metamorphic rocks form the cores of at least the older of these mountains, and folded sedimentary rocks are exposed on the flanks (Fig. 40-4). In the northern Appalachians erosion has not yet cut deep enough to expose the core, even though they have been nearly leveled by erosion and re-elevated at least three times.

In contrast to the folded character of most mountain ranges, the plains and plateaus are composed of essentially flat-lying sedimentary rocks, or, exceptionally, of flat-lying lava flows (Fig. 40-4). These

Fig. 40-2. Shield Areas of the World. The oldest exposed rocks of each continent are found in the areas enclosed within the dashed lines. Very largely they are igneous and metamorphic rocks. The dotted lines indicate the approximate positions of the earth's two chief mobile belts.

rocks may be a few hundred or at most a few thousand feet thick (in contrast to the tens of thousands of feet of originally sedimentary rocks in folded mountain chains). Below the horizontal rocks there are always deformed (tilted or folded) sedimentary, metamorphic, or igneous rocks (Fig. 40-4), or all three. These plains or plateaus typically lie between the mountain ranges. Thus, the Appalachian plateaus (Cumberland, Allegheny, Catskill), the Interior Lowlands (plains), and the Great Plains lie between the Appalachians and the Rockies, the Colorado Plateau lies between the southern Rockies and the Sierras, and the Columbia Plateau (a lava plateau) lies between the northern Rockies and the Cascades (see inside of back cover).

The coastal plains represent an exception to what we have just said. When present they typically lie on the ocean sides of mountain ranges, e.g., the Atlantic Coastal Plain. The rocks are always sedimentary and have a slight seaward dip. There is no Pacific coastal plain; the Coast Ranges there come right down to the sea in most places.

CONTINENTAL SHELVES

Every continent is surrounded by a continental shelf that extends outward beneath the ocean waters for a few miles, in some places as much as a hundred miles or more. Off the east coast of the United States the shelf is over 100 mi wide off New England; it narrows to less than 60 mi off Florida. They are narrowest on the sides of continents having the youngest mountains. Hence on the Pacific Coast of the United States they are less than 10 mi wide. The slope of the shelves may be as little as 5 or 6 ft/mile (0.071°). Southeastward from Long Island the 300-ft depth contour is not reached until in the neighborhood of 85 mi seaward, and the 600-ft contour is reached at about 100 mi. At the edge of the shelf the water deepens rapidly, for the 6000-ft contour is reached at about 125 mi.

From the geologic viewpoint these are best considered as parts of the continents rather than as parts of the ocean basins. The ocean basins are a bit overfull today so that the sea waters spill over the edges of the continent, forming the shelves. In past geologic time the ocean basins have been a bit more overfull, thus flooding large parts of the continents. At times the ocean basins have been a bit less than full, thus allowing the shelves to be exposed. The Hudson Canyon, which extends from New York Bay out to the edge of the shelf,

was cut at a time when the shelf was exposed.

If the ocean basins were a bit more overfull, Long Island and other large parts of the Atlantic and Gulf Coastal Plains would be under water. These submerged regions

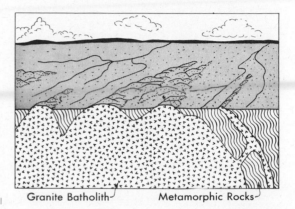

Granite Batholith⌐   Metamorphic Rocks⌐

Fig. 40-3. Roots of a Complexly Folded Mountain Range. Previously existing rocks were complexly folded, metamorphosed, and intruded by molten magma to form a great mountain range. The processes of weathering, masswasting and erosion through countless millions of years have removed several miles of rock so that only the mountain roots remain.

would, however, still be parts of the continents. In fact, if we go back far enough in geologic history, we would find that at one time or another the waters of the sea have covered every part of the continents (but never all at once). We have positive evidence for about 75 per cent of the land surface. For many reasons geologists infer that the sea has covered the other 25 per cent at one time or another. There is no place on earth about which the geologist

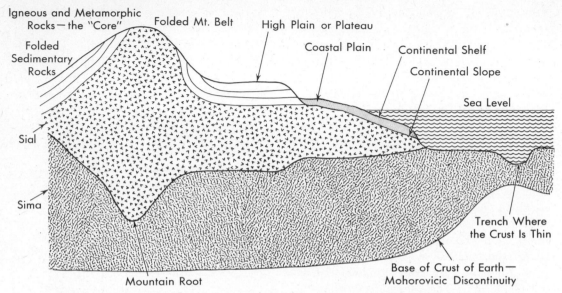

Fig. 40-4. Generalized Section across a Continent. The vertical scale is greatly exaggerated with respect to the horizontal. The continental block, composed of sialic rocks, rests on simatic rocks. Note that sialic rocks are thickest beneath the mountain ranges, and generally absent from the ocean basins. Note also that the crust is thinnest in the deep sea trenches that always lie relatively close to the continents.

can definitely say, "The sea was never here." Yet, as we have said before, so far as we know the ocean basins have always been ocean basins and the continents have always been continents.

Despite all we have said, neither the Alps nor any other great mountain range, even though they are largely made of marine-deposited strata containing marine fossils, were ever beneath the sea. *When the sea covered the areas where the mountains now stand, the mountains had not yet been formed.* The mountains were made essentially by compression and uplift of a few tens of thousands of feet of sediments, much of which was deposited in shallow seas covering the area. The water in these seas was probably never more than a few hundred feet deep. How such great thick-

nesses could accumulate in such shallow water will be explained later.

The continental shelves are the great repositories of the sediments eroded from the lands. There are thousands of feet of sediments below the surface of the Atlantic continental shelf. The sedimentary rocks of the coastal plains form a part of these sediments as they dip beneath the waters of the oceans.

CONTINENTAL SLOPES AND THE OCEAN BASINS

At the seaward edge of the shelf the slope of the bottom increases with some abruptness to 300 to 400 ft/mi (about 4°). Generally this change in slope takes place at a depth of about 600 ft. The continental slopes may be thought of as forming the sides of the ocean basins, whose average depth is about 12,000 ft. They were once thought to be more or less featureless from a topographic viewpoint. This has all been changed due to sonic methods of mapping the sea floor—methods hundreds' of times faster than the old "lead and line" method. The new information, mostly gained since World War II, shows that in addition to the long narrow elevated regions that we call *ridges* (Mid-Atlantic Ridge, etc.), there are broader and larger tracts called *rises*, small flat-topped steep-sided elevations called *sea mounts*, and shallower and broader flat-topped elevations called *banks* (Fig. 40-5).

TRENCHES (OR DEEPS)

These trenches are areas that are greater than about 23,000 ft deep. They are never found out in the middle of the basins far from land, but always relatively near the continents where active mountain making is still going on or is very recent. Most of the great trenches are in the Pacific where the most active mountain making of the present is going on. Most are on the convex side of island arcs (archipelagoes), e.g.,

the Aleutians, the Japanese Islands, and the Philippine Islands in the Pacific, and the Antillean Arc in the Atlantic. The greatest deep is in the Japanese Trench; its depth is about 37,000 ft. The greatest depth in the Atlantic is off the coast of Puerto Rico, where it is a bit over 27,000 ft. There is evidence that the Japanese Trench has recently been deepened by a further dropping down of this part of the ocean floor.

CONCEPT OF ISOSTASY

Consideration of the above observations can lead to a number of questions. We will not attempt to ask all of them but will concern ourselves only with the following: "Why are the continental masses able to stand so high above the ocean floors?"

We can probably understand this question better if we first take only one phase of it, namely, "How can the earth's crust support a great mountain range like the Himalayas?" Is it because the rocks at the base of the range are strong enough to do so? Now we know rather accurately the crushing strength of rocks under various conditions, and we also know with reasonable accuracy the weight per unit area the rocks beneath the Himalayas have to sup-

Fig. 40-5. Seamounts in the Gulf of Alaska. They are interpreted as extinct volcanoes whose tops were truncated by wave action at or near sea level, and which were then submerged by subsidence of the ocean floor. Vertical scale greatly exaggerated. (After H. W. Menard and R. S. Dietz.)

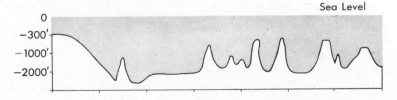

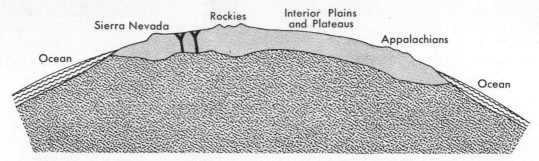

Fig. 40-6. Profile of a Continent. The sialic rocks (stippled area) average 10 per cent lower density than the simatic rocks below the ocean basins. The continents therefore stand higher than the ocean basins. The base of the sima is not shown.

port. These figures show that the rocks are not anywhere near strong enough; they should spread out underneath their own weight, thus lowering the height of the mountains to a point where the strength of the rocks is sufficient to support the mountains. Now it is perfectly apparent that the rocks do not spread out in this way, the mountains *are supported,* and so there must be some way to support them. What other way is possible? There are two.

The first is by the compressional forces that originally formed the mountains, and which may still be operating to hold them up. However, although in some areas there is evidence of this, in many there is none. This leaves us the other possibility, one that seems to tie in well with all of the evidence. This is that the mountains are supported by roots that penetrate deeply into underlying *denser* rocks (Fig. 40-4) so that they are literally supported (buoyed up) by them. These denser rocks are at such depths that they are under tremendous pressures and at high temperatures. Under these conditions the rocks are plastic, and have the property of liquids that enables them to buoy up bodies of

lesser density, just as water buoys up an iceberg.[3] The mountains are thus in balance with the rocks into which their roots are submerged. This condition of balance is called isostasy. Just as the higher an iceberg is above water, the deeper the bottom of it is in the water, so the higher the mountains, the deeper its roots.

The inevitable conclusion is that the continents stand higher than the ocean basins because they are composed of lighter rock (Fig. 40-6). It is an established fact that they are composed essentially of granite, whereas, the ocean basins are composed essentially of basalt, a rock about 10 per cent heavier than granite, volume for volume.

Suppose the earth divided into a number of huge blocks, each of the mountain ranges representing a block, each of the great plateaus, plains, coastal plains, etc., representing other blocks. The continental rocks

[3] If you stood on a scale to weigh yourself while both you and the scale were completely submerged in water, you would find that you weighed only a few pounds. This weight would represent the difference in your weight outside the water and the weight of the water you displace. If your density were exactly that of water, the scale would register zero. Your body would be entirely supported (buoyed up) by the water.

everywhere have much the same density, except for local variations. The difference is in the lengths of the blocks. Thus, the short blocks—the coastal plains and the low interior plains—neither rise high nor sink low in the substratum. The high plateaus and the various mountain systems, being longer, rise higher and sink lower than the low blocks. Each block, according to the concept of isostasy, stands at an elevation that places it in equilibrium with the other blocks. Gravity determinations and plumb-bob deflections do show a lesser average density for higher blocks. The behavior of earthquake waves (not explainable here) suggests that the higher blocks also extend deeper than the lower blocks into the denser plastic substratum.

Like any other theory this one must not be pushed too far. It does not explain how the continents came to be continents. It does not explain how mountains came into being. It does not apply to small blocks of the earth's crust. Neither is isostatic adjustment perfect, because the rocks do have considerable strength and can stand a very considerable imbalance (caused by erosion and deposition) before adjustment (by diastrophism) takes place.

This adjustment explains the re-elevation of mountain areas after they have been reduced by gradational processes. Erosion of material from the high blocks lightens them and deposition on a low block (e.g., the continental shelves) makes them heavier. Eventually the lighter block rises and the heavier one sinks as the plastic substratum flows out from beneath the subsiding block to the region beneath the rising block.

Two additional facts support the concept: (1) Lavas from oceanic volcanoes, i.e., volcanoes that rise from the true ocean floors, have a higher specific gravity than most lavas from continental volcanoes. (2) The acceleration due to gravity, i.e., the value of g, averages slightly greater over the oceans than over the continents. If the continents did *not* stand higher than the ocean basins, then we really would be puzzled.

INTERIOR OF THE EARTH

The solid part of the earth is easily divided into three parts, crust, mantle, and core. The core has a diameter of about 2100 mi and is surrounded by a mantle which is about 1800 mi thick. The mantle is, in turn, covered by a crust which varies from a few miles (beneath the ocean basins) to as much as 50 mi in thickness (beneath the great continental mountain ranges).

At the present time ideas about the interior of the earth are changing. A few years ago we could not have written so confidently, and a few years hence the newer concepts will probably have been sorted out and tested. For the present we will choose those concepts that appear to be soundest and in best accord with the facts, and we will use them as a framework for describing that part of the crust not visible in any way to man, and for describing the mantle and the core.

The evidence for the properties of the material forming the deeper parts of the crust, the whole of the mantle, and the core, comes from the behavior of earthquake waves as they pass through the earth. Earthquakes, the causes and characteristics of which we will postpone until later, imply the earth quakes, and that it does so because vibrations (mechanical waves) are propagated which travel through the earth. There are several types of waves, but we will be concerned with only the primary (longitudinal) and the secondary (transverse) waves.

The primary (P) waves travel about one and two-thirds times as fast as the secondary (S) waves. The speeds of these waves increase as the rigidity of the rocks through which they pass increases, and decrease as the density increases. Both the rigidity and the density increase with depth, but the effect due to increase of rigidity is greater than the effect due to increase of density; therefore the speeds of both types of waves increase with depth. This rate of increase should be constant, other things being equal. *If at any particular depth there should be an abrupt increase or decrease, then some other factor should play a part, e.g., composition.*

The first concrete evidence that the earth's crust had a natural lower boundary came in 1909 when Mohorovicic, a Yugoslav seismologist, attempted to explain a peculiarity in certain seismograms.[4] At depths that ranged from 25 to 50 mi beneath the great mountain systems, and from 18 to 25 mi elsewhere beneath the continents, and as little as 2 to 3 mi beneath the ocean basins proper, these seismograms showed an abrupt increase in wave velocities. This zone of abrupt increase is now called the Mohorovicic Discontinuity, recently abbreviated to Moho, and the crust is now defined as that part of the earth which lies above this discontinuity.

Further seismographic research has indicated that the crust itself can be divided into two parts. The upper part, where

---

[4] Seismograms are the records of the vibrations made by an earthquake on a seismograph.

the wave speeds are slower, consists of rocks whose chemical composition averages that of granite, and is, in fact, largely granite. It is called the *sial*, a mnemonic term coined from the chemical symbols for silicon and aluminum. The density of the sialic rocks averages about 2.7. The lower part, where the wave speeds are faster, consists of rocks whose composition is that of an olivine basalt. It is called the *sima*, coined from silica and magnesium. Its density averages about 3.0 or a bit higher. The sima forms the lower part of the crust of the continents, and essentially the whole of the crust of the ocean basins proper (Fig. 40-4). Thus, we have the evidence to support the statement made previously (under isostasy) that the continents stand higher than the ocean basins because they are composed of less dense rock.

That part of the earth between the crust and the core is called the mantle. Since the wave speeds increase abruptly (from 7.0 and 3.8 km/sec to 8.15 and 4.7 km/sec, respectively, for the P and S waves) at the Mohorovicic Discontinuity, a compositional change in the rock is postulated. The change is from a feldspar-pyroxene basalt with some olivine to a rock composed chiefly of pyroxene and olivine. The latter would satisfy the density and rigidity requirements. At about the 275-mi depth there occurs another discontinuity in wave speeds. This minor discontinuity may be accounted for by an increase in the amount of iron in the olivine. (Olivine is an iron-magnesium silicate in which the ratio of Mg to Fe may vary from 16:1 to 2:1.)

At a depth of about 1800 mi the greatest change of all takes place, not only in amount but also in kind. For here the speeds of the P waves *decrease abruptly* from 13.6 to 8.1 km/sec, and the S waves *disappear*, never to be heard from again.

CORE

Long before these changes in speeds had been worked out, it was known that the earth had a core. Whenever an earthquake was sufficiently strong to be recorded on seismographs on the opposite side of the earth, it was noted that there was a belt about 40° wide encircling the earth in which seismograph stations received no record. This belt lies between 102° and 145°, approximately, from the epicenter. Stations at a greater distance than 145° received the P waves strongly but no S waves. This belt has been termed the shadow zone (Fig. 40-7).

The explanation of the shadow zone is as follows: Waves are refracted as they pass through media of differing rigidities. Therefore their paths are curved. Those that penetrate the crust and the mantle only, i.e., penetrate no deeper than 1800 mi, follow normal curved paths, eventually reaching all stations not more than 102° (7000 mi, since 1° = 70 mi) distant from the epicenter. Waves that penetrate deeper enter a different material with a greatly different rigidity, and so are **strongly** refracted towards the medium of lesser rigidity. This means that the P waves are bent so that they penetrate deeper into the earth. Eventually they re-enter the mantle and emerge at stations 143° to 180° (10,000 to 12,500 mi) distant from the epicenter.

This great ball of material with a rigidity less than that of the base of the mantle is called the core. Another piece of evidence for the core consists of the difference between the predicted arrival time of the P waves at stations near 180° from the epicenter and their actual arrival time. Enough information had been obtained so

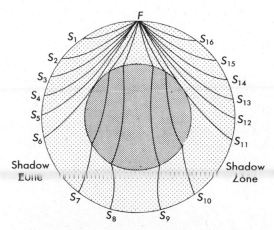

Fig. 40-7. Cross-section through the Earth. The core is shown surrounded by the mantle. F is the focus of an earthquake. Primary and secondary waves from it are received at seismographic stations S_1 through S_6 and S_{11} through S_{16}. Note that none of these waves strikes the core. Only the primary waves are received at stations S_7 through S_{10}. The secondary waves are of a kind that cannot pass through liquids; the core is therefore inferred to be liquid. The inner solid core is not shown. The primary waves travel faster through solids than through liquids. The time interval between a quake at F and its arrival at S_7, S_8, S_9, or S_{10} is too great for us to assume that the core is entirely solid, but too small for us to assume that it is entirely liquid. Therefore a liquid core with an inner solid core is postulated.

that the arrival time at stations up to 102° distant could be predicted within a few seconds if the time the quake took place was known. If the assumption were made that there was no core, that the mantle extended clear to the center, then a *P* wave that went straight through should arrive at a station directly opposite the epicenter in 16 minutes. Actually it arrived in 20 minutes, *4 minutes late.* This meant that it had been slowed down by passing either through less rigid material, or material of greater density, or both.

For a time the state of the matter in the core was uncertain. If it were liquid, then S waves could not pass through it. (Mechanical transverse waves can traverse solids only.) The uncertainty arose from the fact that the wave record is much more complex than we have led you to believe. At every boundary surface new waves are set up, some reflected, some refracted, and all with less energy than the new wave. Therefore the seismogram recorded a complex of waves that took long study to sort out. Some observers thought that the S waves came through feebly. If they did, the core was solid. Eventually better seismographs and more knowledge solved the problem in favor of a liquid core—or at least part liquid. Assumption of a completely liquid core raised problems with wave speeds also, but we will not analyze them here. These were resolved by assuming the presence of an inner solid core 1500 mi in diameter surrounded by a layer of liquid 250 mi thick. We will defer discussion of the composition of the core until we have discussed density distribution in the earth.

The range of choice for the material of the mantle and core is limited, in part for seismic velocity reasons, in part for density reasons, and in part for other reasons. The possibilities for the mantle are peridotite (chiefly pyroxene and olivine), dunite (chiefly olivine), and eclogite (a garnet-pyroxene rock). The last could be present only in the upper part of the mantle. Most authorities in the field favor dunite for the lower part of the mantle. The composition of the core is limited by density considerations.

The density of the earth as a whole is 5.5 and that of the surface rocks is 2.7. The inner core must have a density of 11 or 12 or possibly even more to give an average density of 5.5. By analogy with meteorites the core is assumed to be made up largely of iron with a few per cent nickel. It is reasonable to assume that the core is made of a material reasonably abundant in the crust. Whether it is or not, the existence of a liquid core having a density several times that of silicate rocks is now accepted. The situation is very similar to that of a blast furnace. In its solidification from a wholly liquid earth, the iron sank to the center, with a "slag" of heavy iron and iron-magnesium silicates forming around the free iron phase (which is immiscible with the iron silicate phase), and a "slag" of lighter silicates forming the outer part.

One cannot be too dogmatic about the constitution of the interior of the earth, nor yet too free with one's imagination concerning it. Solution of the problem calls for expert knowledge; the speculations of the ignorant or of those with a little knowledge are useless.

We can now turn our attention to the three fundamental processes that are operating to alter the face of the earth, vulcanism, diastrophism, and gradation. The first two involve energy from a source within the earth; the third involves energy from a source outside the earth, i.e., energy from the sun.

SUMMARY

The main relief features of the earth are the continents and the ocean basins. Their origin goes back farther in geologic time than we can probe at the present time. There is no agreement as to how they originated. Each continent has a shield area of ancient rocks. Both the continents and mountain ranges are younger away from the center of the shield area. The mountain ranges are formed by folding, faulting, and igneous intrusion. Their general orientation is parallel to the continental margins. Between the ranges are horizontal strata forming plains and plateaus.

The continental shelves are considered parts of the continents rather than parts of the ocean basins. The ocean basins are a bit overfull, and so spill onto the edges of the continents. In times past they have spilled up even farther. The bottoms of the ocean basins are not as smooth as they were once considered to be. Their topographic features include mountain ranges, sea mounts, and the deep trenches. The last lie near island arcs that lie offshore from the continental borders.

The continents with their mountains and high plateaus stand higher than the ocean basins because the average density of the rocks composing them is less than the density of rocks beneath the ocean basins. These lighter rocks are supported by denser rocks below, just as an iceberg, which is less dense than water, is supported by the denser water.

The earth has a concentric zonal structure, consisting of the crust, the mantle, and the core. The differentiation is made by a study of the behavior of earthquake waves. The outer core is believed to be molten because the transverse (secondary) waves of earthquakes do not pass through it. The inner part of the core is assumed to be solid in order to account for the time it takes the primary waves to pass through it.

EXERCISES

I. TERMS AND CONCEPTS

Continents	Isostasy
Continental shelf	Crust
Continental slope	Sial
Deep sea trench	Sima
Sea mount	Mantle
Plain	Primary wave
Plateau	Secondary wave
Relief	Mohorovicic Dis-
Island arc	continuity
Shield	Core of the earth

II. PROBLEMS

1. What is meant by the relief of an area? What is the relief of the earth?

2. What is a shield area?

3. What is a mobile belt? What two features are associated with present mobile belts?

4. Where are most mountain ranges situated with respect to the continents?

5. Name the major mountain ranges from east to west in the United States. Which is the oldest? Which the youngest?

6. What structure do the rocks have in the great mountain ranges? In the plains and plateaus?

7. What sorts of rocks do you always encounter if you drill deep enough everywhere?

8. Why are the continental shelves best considered as parts of the continents?

9. The rock strata on the tops of many mountains are marine-deposited rocks containing marine fossils. Yet these mountains were never beneath the sea. Explain.

10. Where are the deep sea trenches located with respect to continental margins?

11. What is the concept of isostasy?

12. How does it explain the major relief of the earth?

13. Can the concept be invoked to ex-

plain minor relief features, e.g., why the tops of hills stand higher than the valleys? Explain.

14. How does sial differ from sima?

15. What is the evidence that the earth has a natural lower boundary?

16. Differentiate between primary and secondary waves.

17. What two factors govern the speed of primary and secondary waves?

18. In what part of the earth do the waves travel fastest? Why?

19. What happens to the transverse wave when it strikes the core? How do we know? What happens to the longitudinal waves?

20. Why are the paths of P and S earthquake waves curved?

21. What is the average density of the earth as a whole? Of the crustal rocks? Of the core?

22. What is the volume of the core with respect to the total volume of the earth?

23. List the evidence for the composition of the core.

24. Suppose that someone postulates that the core of the earth is made of an element that has not yet been discovered here on earth. Considering all that you have so far learned in this course, in particular what you have learned about the periodic chart and the structure of atoms, what are the probabilities that the postulate is correct?

25. Is the concentric zonal structure of the earth consistent with the concept of its having once passed through a molten state? Explain.

CHAPTER XLI

Energy within the Earth: Volcanism and Diastrophism

We especially need imagination in science. It is not all mathematics, nor all logic, but is somewhat beauty and poetry.—MARIA MITCHELL (1860)

The external phenomena of volcanism, displayed either by spectacular eruptions of volcanoes or the quiet bubbling of lavas in their craters, and the enormous damage done to the works of man by some earthquakes, attest to the fact that the earth has enormous stores of energy within it. The source of this energy and the manner in which it is enabled to manifest itself are not entirely clear. We will defer discussion of it until some of the observations of volcanism and diastrophism have been presented; it will be more meaningful then.

VOLCANISM: EXTRUSIVE ACTIVITY

The external phenomena of volcanism may be viewed in many parts of the earth today. Spectacular as the extrusive activities of some volcanoes may be, they are only superficial manifestations of the far

more geologically important deep-seated processes responsible for the formation and intrusion of enormous bodies of molten material into younger rocks. The composition of this molten material, called magma when deep in the crust and lava when it is extruded, has been discussed on pp.

Fig. 41-1. Frozen Lava at Kilauea, Hawaii. The lava is a type that forms relatively smooth rounded, twisted, or pleated surfaces. It solidified as it poured over a low cliff. (Courtesy United States Geological Survey.)

557–560. The difference between magma and lava is in their gaseous content. The gases—chiefly water vapor, but also CO_2, CO, H_2, sulfur vapor, and many others—are kept dissolved in the magma at depths where the pressure is high, but escape when the pressure is released as the magma comes to the surface. Lava is, therefore, magma which has lost most of its gaseous content (Fig. 41-1).

The gases are important for several reasons. One is that they are the cause of the violence of many eruptions. If magmas contained no gases, extrusive volcanic activity would be limited to the quiet extrusion of lava. Volcanic explosions are due to the extremely rapid expansion of large volumes of gases under high pressure (as are explosions of any sort). The gases may

Fig. 41-2. Lava Tubes, Craters of the Moon National Monument, Idaho. Here the lava surfaces froze but the lava continued to flow underneath, eventually draining away, leaving hollow tubes. A pencil to the left of center gives the scale. (Photograph by John Shimer. Courtesy Columbia Geographical Press.)

be so abundant that there is an explosive foaming like that in a warm bottle of soda pop that is violently shaken and then opened. This foam freezes on exposure to the atmosphere. This frozen foam we call pumice.

Volcanoes are vents (craters) in the earth's crust from which gases, liquid lava, or solid materials are ejected; the latter two form a conical hill or mountain about the crater. The cones may vary from a few tens of feet in height to more than five miles. They are cone-shaped simply because more of the ejected material falls (if solid) or solidifies (if lava) close to the crater. The solid ejecta is commonly a great cloud of volcanic "ash," chiefly the result of instantaneous freezing of a fine liquid lava spray thrown into the air, sometimes to a height of many miles. It falls as "dust" or "ash." Larger particles fall as "cinders" or lapilli. Sometimes the lava thrown out is in the form of large clots which solidify while spinning through the air; they fall as volcanic "bombs." Sometimes masses of lava previously solidified in the throat of the volcano are thrown out as solid blocks weighing a ton or more, and for a distance of as much as a half mile.

Krakatoa, in the East Indies, blew up in 1883. Over a cubic mile of rock was thrown into the air, some to a distance of 17 miles. The "dust" circled the earth and took three years to settle. The noise of the explosion was heard twenty-five hundred miles away. Monte Somma literally blew its top in A.D. 79, burying Herculaneum and Pompeii and much of their populations under a thick layer of ash. A new volcano was then built up on the inside of the remnants of Monte Somma; its name is Vesuvius. Scores of similar explosions have occurred elsewhere in the world since.

Hundreds of volcanoes are quietly active today. Our fiftieth state, Hawaii, is composed *completely* of volcanoes. The island of Hawaii is a composite of five of them, the highest of which stands nearly 14,000 ft above sea level. Their bases rise from the floor of the Pacific more than 14,000 ft below sea level. Thus, these volcanoes range up to 28,000 ft above their bases; they are the greatest volcanoes on the face of the earth. Two of the five, Mauna Loa and Kilauea, are still active. The other three are dormant or extinct. All the other Hawaiian Islands are also volcanoes. The lava erupted from all of them is low silica magma, and so is very fluid. The result is that the cones that have been built from them slope so gently that it is hard to believe that all of the people in the state of Hawaii live on the slopes of volcanoes.

The infant among volcanoes is Paricutín, two hundred miles west of Mexico City. It began its life in 1943, and became inactive nine years later. Meanwhile, it had built a cone nearly half a mile high, and devastated the countryside for miles around with deposits of volcanic ash and lava flows. It is the only volcano in history that has been intensely studied by geologists from the day of its birth. Will it become active again? Only time will tell. Some volcanoes erupt once and then become extinct. Others may lay dormant for hundreds of years, e.g., Monte Somma. Mount Lassen, in northern California, erupted last in 1915. It is the only active volcano in continental United States except for Alaska —which has several.

In addition to the extrusive activity of volcanoes there are the fissure eruptions of plateau basalts. They build no well-defined volcanoes. Instead the lava, which is always of the very fluid basaltic type and so flows readily, spreads out in great sheets forming more or less horizontal sheets of lava (Fig. 41-2). One such fissure eruption took place in Iceland in 1783. The lava welled up out of a crack in the earth's crust and spread out in a sheet 12 to 15 mi wide and 100 ft deep.

Fig. 41-3. Ancient Buried Lava Flows Exposed by Erosion. First and Second Watchung Mountains in New Jersey. The surface was level when these flows were extruded. The first flow was buried by hundreds of feet of sandstone and shale before the second flow was extruded. It in turn was buried by similar sediments. Later much of eastern United States was tilted westerly, and then deeply eroded, exposing tilted edges of the flows.

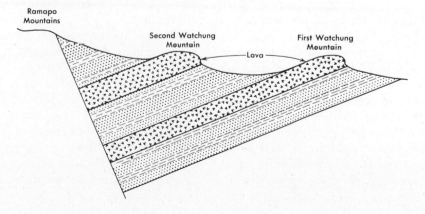

There have been great fissure eruptions in past geologic times. The lavas from one of them today form the great Columbian Plateau in Northwestern United States. Some tens of thousands of cubic miles of

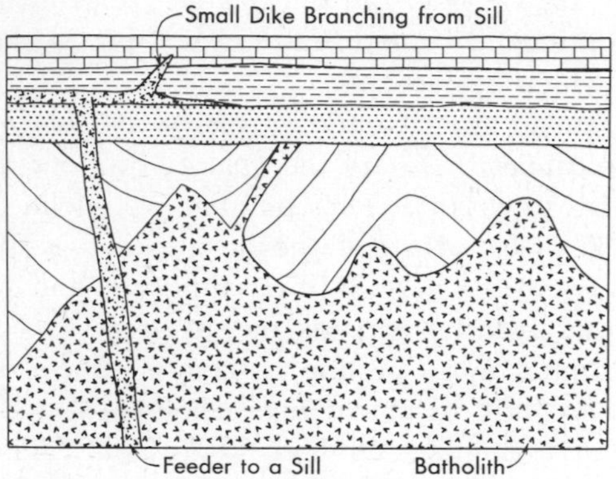

Fig. 41-4. Vertical Cross-section of a Batholith Intruded into Folded Sedimentary Rocks and a Sill into Horizontal Sedimentary Rocks. The sill cuts across the batholith and so is younger. The small dike branching from the sill proves that this igneous body is an *intrusive*, not a buried *extrusive* as in the case of the Watchung lavas (Fig. 41-3). Which is older, the batholith or the folded sedimentary rocks? How can you tell?

lava were poured out to fill the valleys and bury the hills. In northeastern New Jersey there are the remnants of two major and several minor outpourings of basaltic lava some 175,000,000 years ago. The eroded edges of the two major flows form First and Second Watchung Mountains (Fig. 41-3).

All the fissure eruptions, as well as all the lavas poured out from volcanoes rising from the floors of the true ocean basins,

consist of the low silica rock known as basalt.

VOLCANISM: INTRUSIVE ACTIVITY

We cannot, of course, directly observe intrusive activity. Moreover, we would not know anything about it if deep erosion had not taken place. Magma, once formed at depth, is under terrific pressure. Since it is a mobile liquid, it will escape to regions of lower pressure if any route is available. This region of lower pressure is always upward. Sometimes the magma reaches the surface to give us the phenomena described above. It may work its way up towards the surface until its energy is spent, without any great quantity of it reaching the surface. It may then solidify in place, forming a huge body of rock that we call a *batholith* (Fig. 40-3 and 41-4). It will have cooled and crystallized extremely slowly to give a coarse-grained rock called granite. These granitic batholiths may be as much as several hundreds of miles long, several tens of miles wide, and several miles deep. How deep we do not know, for erosion has nowhere cut deep enough to expose the rocks below a batholith. The home of the batholith is in the cores of the great mountain ranges of the earth.

At one time or another during the past three billion years, batholiths have intruded every portion of the continental areas of the earth. The vast majority of them are composed of granite. From these batholiths tongues of magma have been forcibly injected into fractures in the rocks above, the enormous pressures widening the fractures. If these tongues are tabular in shape and cut across the structures of the rock they intrude, they are called *dikes* (Figs. 41-4 and 41-5). The presence of great numbers of dikes intruded into the overlying rocks (as in the rocks of northern New York City) is evidence that a great batholith lies below.

If the magma finds it easier to spread between the layers of sedimentary rock, lifting them up if they are horizontal or nearly so, and so solidify between the layers, we call the intrusion a *sill* (Fig. 41-4). The best known sill in North America, perhaps in the world, is the one whose eroded edge now forms the Palisades of the lower Hudson River (Fig. 41-6). This great sill is some forty miles long, extending from Staten Island on the south to Haverstraw, New York, to the north. It is well over a thousand feet thick in its thickest part, and ends both in the north and the south by thinning out. How great its third (east–west) dimension originally was is unknown, but it must have extended east of the Hudson for many miles.[1] To the west it disappears beneath the intruded sandstones and shales of the Newark Series, where it either extends to the eastern base of the Ramapo Mountains where it ends against a fault, or it thins gradually to zero before reaching the fault (Fig. 41-3).

Both the sill and the intruded rocks dip 10° to 15° in a westerly direction; thus, the sill gets deeper and deeper in that direc-

[1] In the part of the Connecticut River Valley south of the Massachusetts border there is a similar sill, comparable in thickness and with all of the associated features of the Palisades Sill except that the rocks dip easterly. Were they once connected with the Palisade rocks, forming a great arch whose center has been removed? The concept is tempting but it need not have been that way—and probably was not.

tion. When this sill was intruded the Hudson River had not yet been born, and there were at least two to three miles of sandstones and shales above it. Only because

Fig. 41-5. Basalt Dike Cutting Granite, Cohasset, Massachusetts. The granite was intruded into still older rocks (not shown) in a different period of igneous activity. It extends as a great tabular sheet downward, connecting somewhere at depth with a larger body of similar rock. Both the granite and the dike are exposed only because of deep erosion. (Photograph by John Shimer. Courtesy Columbia University Press.)

of deep erosion has it become exposed. The rock composing it is a basaltic type called diabase. At both the base and the top of the sill, where it cooled fastest and so is fine-grained, it is indistinguishable from basalt. It contains the minerals dark-colored feldspar (labradorite) and pyrox-

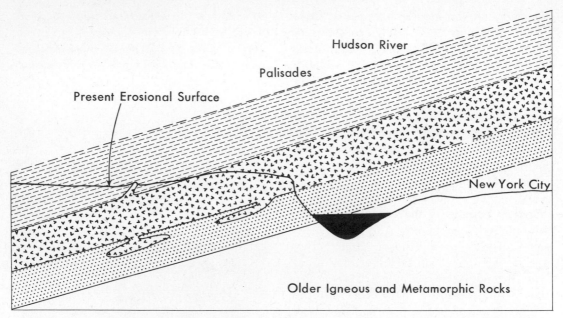

Fig. 41-6. The Palisades Sill. A sill in sedimentary rocks is intruded between the layers (strata) instead of cutting across the layers in the manner of dikes. Note carefully the position of the present erosional surface. Originally the sill extended far to the east over where New York City is now. Erosion of a minimum thickness of 3 mi of rock was necessary to produce the present topography. The Hudson River originated too late to play much part in the removal of this rock. Note the small protrusions from the sill into the sedimentary rocks in the left half; they prove intrusion, rather than extrusion followed by burial under later sediments.

ene, with lesser amounts of amphibole, biotite, and olivine.

When this great sheet of magma crystallized and cooled, it contracted. So huge a sheet could not contract as a unit; for one thing, it was welded to the rocks above and below. The stresses set up by contraction were too great for it to withstand, so a great series of fractures (called *joints*) developed. The major fractures formed perpendicular to the cooling surfaces, i.e., to the top and the bottom of the great sheet, and in a more or less hexagonal pattern (Fig. 41-7). Weathering has widened the joints on the exposed surfaces so that when the Palisades cliff is viewed from in front, it appears as a series of gigantic columns (or stakes) driven into the ground, so it looks like a palisade, hence the name.

The abundance of extrusive activity today implies that intrusive activity is still going on. Beneath all active volcanoes there must be reservoirs of magma, some of which are probably large enough to be called batholiths, that are still in the process of cooling. Such features as the geysers of Yellowstone National Park, Iceland, and New Zealand indicate that there are bodies of igneous rock at shallow depths (even less than 100 ft), so hot that water soaking down to them is heated to the boiling point and above. The evidence seems to indicate that there never has been a time in the history of the earth when some volcanic activity, intrusive or extrusive, was not taking place. Before we investigate the sources of the energy, we will briefly consider diastrophism, and then discuss causes, the problems of origin, etc., together.

DIASTROPHISM

By the time students are of college age they have read accounts of more than one disastrous earthquake somewhere on earth. Earthquakes are much more common than that, for the seismologists tell us that the earth is trembling all of the time. Almost all of these tremors are minor, do no damage to the works of man, and so do not get in the newspapers. Over one seven-year period, California averaged 75 earthquakes per month; Japan has about 4 per day.

Earthquakes represent an unusual kind of diastrophic activity in that the movements involved are sudden; they take place in a matter of seconds. These movements occur along fractures in the earth's crust, fractures that may be some miles, tens of miles, or even hundreds of miles long, and that extend downward into the earth's crust for some few miles. The fracture, together with the resulting horizontal and/or vertical displacement of the rocks on one side with respect to those on the other, is known as a *fault*. The magnitude of a single displacement may be a few inches, a few feet, or even a few tens of feet; the largest in historic times has been about 45 ft.

Fig. 41-7. Devil's Tower, Wyoming. This mass of igneous rock towers 865 ft above the surrounding countryside. Note the fluted columnar structure, called jointing, due to contraction on cooling of the original magma. The tower may have been formed by solidification of magma in the throat of a volcano, or it may have been a "finger" of magma pushed up into overlying sediments. In any case, it now stands higher than its surroundings because it is composed of rock more resistant to weathering and erosion than the rock which once enclosed it. (National Park Service Photograph.)

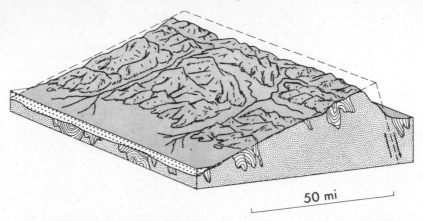

Fig. 41-8. The Sierra Nevada Fault Block. The Sierra Nevada Mountains are formed from a single great fault block 400 mi long and 80 to 100 mi wide. During a long period of faulting the western side of the block was tilted some 20 to 25 thousands of feet higher than the eastern. (See arrows right rear.) Erosion during the very long period of faulting and since has greatly reduced its height. Mt. Whitney, California, the highest mountain in the (formerly) 48 states, is in the Sierra Nevadas. The rock is largely granite, formed from a great batholith intruded into older rocks. (Modified from F. E. Matthes.)

Repeated displacements along the same fault over millions of years have resulted in total displacements of several miles. Great fault block mountain ranges like the Sierra Nevada (Fig. 41-8) and countless smaller ranges in the Basin and Range Province of Utah, Nevada, southern California, and parts of Arizona and New Mexico have been formed by repeated displacements. The continuity of many rock formations is broken and displaced (offset) by faults. Thus, rock strata, dikes, sills, coal seams, veins of gold and other valuable minerals, may end against a fault. Where they are continued on the other side may be obvious to anyone, or it may be a problem that baffles even the most astute of geologists. Many a mining venture has failed because the ore-bearing vein was lost by faulting (Fig. 41-9).

Faulting, with the resulting earthquakes, represent only one type of diastrophic activity. *Diastrophism includes all of those normally large-scale movements of the earth's crust that result from forces acting from within the earth.* In addition to faulting there are the warping movements and those due to the folding of rock strata. Warping consists of large-scale vertical uplifts or subsidences. They are called warps because the movements commonly involve large parts of continents, with the result that some parts are uplifted more than others. The Colorado Plateau includes an area of over 200,000 sq mi (four times the size of New York State), has been up-lifted considerably more than a mile above sea level in the last sixty million years.

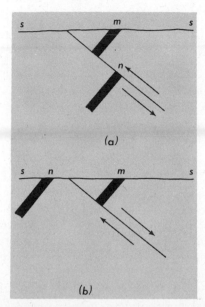

Fig. 41-9. Veins of Ore Displaced by Faults. Relative movements along the faults are shown by the arrows. The present deeply eroded surface of the earth is indicated by *ss*. Relative movements are shown by arrows. Mines at *m* run out of ore against the faults. **(a)** Search for the displaced vein must be made at a lower level because the left side has moved *down* relative to the right. **(b)** Here *n* is the continuation of the vein because the left side has moved *up* relative to the right. Somebody else is probably mining it.

Most plains and plateaus owe their present elevations to warping. The geologic history of every continent is involved with

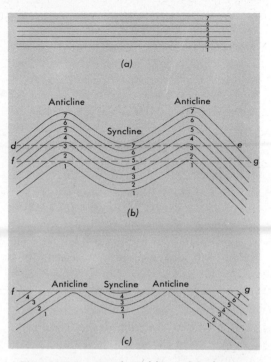

Fig. 41-10. Simple Folding of Sedimentary Rocks. **(a)** A series of sedimentary rocks have been deposited in horizontal layers in a shallow seaway. **(b)** Compressive forces have folded them into anticlines (upfolds) and synclines (downfolds). Future erosion surfaces are indicated by *de* and *fg*. **(c)** Erosion to the level of *fg* is indicated. Note that the anticlines and the syncline still exist even though the surface is level; folds are structural features of the rocks, not topographic features. Note that if a geologist were to walk across the surface shown in either **(a)** or **(b)**, he would see the top formation only, whereas in **(c)** he would see the upturned edges of the whole sequence of formations shown in **(a)** or **(b)**. Thus folding, followed by deep erosion, causes formations to be exposed at the surface that otherwise would be deeply buried.

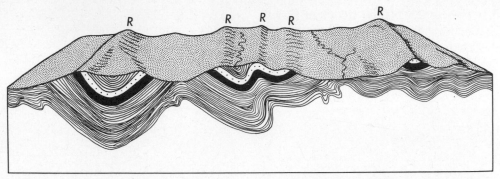

Fig. 41-11. Eroded Simple Folds in the Appalachians. Note that the position of the ridges (R) is not determined by the positions of the anticlines and synclines but by the outcrop of the dotted layer. This layer is more resistant than the others. On the right it forms a ridge even though it is in the center of a syncline. (After Keith, United States Geological Survey.)

upwarpings and downwarpings, with the emphasis on the former to offset the lowering by erosion. In general, the downwarpings have been far more local than the upwarpings.

The most conspicuous consequences of diastrophism are the great folded mountain ranges of the earth (Figs. 41-10 and 41-11). These include the Appalachians, the Rockies, the Andes, the Alps, the Himalayas, the Carpathians, the Pyrenees, and a vast number of others. The most common types of rock found in them are either sedimentary rocks or metamorphosed sedimentary rocks (Fig. 41-12). The more complex the folding the more the rocks have been metamorphosed. In some, as in the high peaks of the Front Range of the Rockies (Pikes Peak, etc.), coarse-grained igneous rocks are exposed in the core because of removal of other rocks by erosion. The sedimentary rocks often contain fossils of marine animals; in fact fossils of the various kinds of marine life are found in the rocks composing one or another of the great mountain ranges of the earth.

Although upwarpings have contributed to their dizzy heights, a theory that the mountains are caused by these uplifts is not consistent with the mountain structures and mountain patterns. For example, if the Appalachian folds were "unfolded," i.e., if the strata were stretched back into their original horizontal positions (Fig. 41-10), the mountain belt would be more than fifty miles wider than it is at present. All folded mountains (and most of the great mountain ranges are fold mountains, simple or complex) tell much the same story. All are essentially composed of sedimentary rocks, for they are the layered rocks, and only layered rocks can be truly folded (Fig. 41-13, 41-14, and 44-4). Lateral squeezing has been the cause of the buckling into anticlines and synclines, and commonly has been the cause of thrust faulting; the uplift has been, at least in part, a result of the squeezing.

We have already learned (p. 567) that mountain ranges are not haphazardly scattered over the face of the earth. Most are near and parallel to continental margins;

some are rows of oceanic islands that are near and parallel to continental margins. Moreover, the forces that have caused the folding and the thrust faulting seem to have come from the ocean basins.

This brings us back to the repeated advances and retreats of the sea over the continents (p. 569). We may view the advances as the result of ocean basins that were somewhat overfull becoming shallower, spilling the sea over the lowlands of every continent at the same time. The retreats could result from the deepening of the ocean basins, which would draw the water off the lowlands into the ocean basins proper, leaving the continents with no submerged continental shelves.

While this explains why the advances and retreats took place, it still leaves us with the problem of the cause of the alternate shallowing and deepening of the basins. As might be expected, the deepening can be correlated, in part at least, with the times of most rapid mountain-building. The problem is complicated by the fact that mountain-building has not been so exclusively confined to certain epochs as was once believed. It seems to have been going on in one place or another in every epoch, although there is little doubt that it has been more widespread and more intense in some epochs than in others.

Geologists cannot agree on any theory that can explain the forces involved. Tremendous amounts of energy are required to fold and elevate huge rock masses into high mountain ranges, amounts that the mind cannot conceive. What is the origin

Fig. 41-12. Complex Folding of Sedimentary Strata. This is the kind of folding one sees in the Alps. The dashed line represents the former extension of the limestone (marble) layer. The folding has been intense enough to metamorphose the rocks.

Fig. 41-13. Eroded Anticline, Hancock, Maryland. Only small anticlines can be shown in photographs. (Courtesy United States Geological Survey.)

of the energy? How is it applied to accomplish the compression needed to **fold**, fault, or elevate rock masses? What accounts for the intrusion of the great batholiths into the cores of the mountain ranges at one stage or another of the orogenic (mountain-building) cycle? All geologists agree that mountain-building is essentially the product of horizontal compression, which reduces the diameter and the circumference of the earth, but they cannot agree on the cause. We will briefly review one theory only, not because we believe it to be the

best, but simply because it is the easiest to understand and also an old one.

The thermal contraction theory assumes (as do any of the others) that the earth was once completely molten and that it has been cooling and contracting ever since. During the process, the solid already-cold outer part cannot shrink any more, whereas the hotter still-cooling inner part continues to shrink. The crust therefore gets too big, gravity pulls it centerward, and it eventually collapses to fit the inner part. These collapses give rise to a wedging effect (Fig. 41-15), which produces folds, faults, and upwarps.

This theory, an old one, has many adherents, for it is an extremely reasonable one. But there are a number of objections, one of which is that it fails to provide for enough shrinking of the crust to account for all the foreshortening that has actually taken place. Another is that there is considerable doubt that the earth is cooling off. The evidence from radioactivity (p. 650) suggests the crust may be heating up. The energy from radioactivity is nu-

it would be fatal to the thermal contraction theory. Equally valid objections exist for the other theories.

We have not yet answered many of the questions concerning the phenomena of volcanism. We postponed the discussion of causes until we had learned something

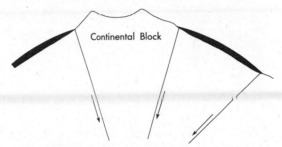

Fig. 41-15. Wedge Theory of Mountain Building. The downdropping of the oceanic areas, shown by the shaded areas, has resulted in the wedging upward of the continental block between them, and the consequent folding of the weaker belts of rocks on the continents. Compare this theory with the one given in Fig. 44-5. Note that the actual shape of an ocean basin is convex, not concave.

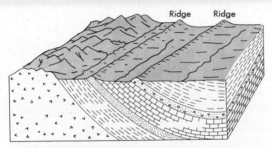

Fig. 41-14. Ridge and Valley Structure Characteristic of Fold Mountains. Only one-half of the fold and an igneous core is shown. The ridges and the rocks of the core stand higher than the valleys because of the greater resistance of the rocks to weathering and erosion. The ridges are of sandstone and conglomerate, the valleys are carved in limestone and shale. Note that the whole top of the fold has been removed, exposing the granite in the core.

clear energy. All rocks contain minute amounts of radioactive elements (uranium, thorium, actinium, potassium) which spontaneously disintegrate into other atoms, giving off energy which is converted to heat energy. If the amount of this heat has been significant throughout geologic time,

of the phenomena of diastrophism, for the two are related in more ways than one. Most of the earth's active and recently extinct volcanoes are found in two great belts, one surrounding the Pacific Ocean and the other running at right angles to it somewhat north of the equator. Oddly enough, the great majority of the epicenters of earthquakes are located in these same regions. Moreover, these are the regions that include the youngest of the fold and complex mountains of the earth, the regions where such mountain-making processes are still going on. One must not conclude that volcanism is a major cause of earthquakes, nor vice versa, even though some local quakes may be caused by the shifting of magma at depth. Both seem to be consequences of the mountain-making processes, but this does not help us much so long as we do not know how these processes operate.

Any discussion of the causes of diastrophism involves heat in one way or another, just as does discussion of the causes of volcanism. Before the study of the composition of the interior of the earth by the behavior of earthquake waves was begun, the earth was believed to consist of a crust a few tens of miles thick, below which all was molten. The source of the magma was easily explained. When the earth was found to be solid to a depth of 1800 miles, the concept that the source was from a generally molten interior collapsed. Pressures were far too great for openings to be maintained to allow the passage of magma upward from that depth. Magma must then originate by the melting of rock deep in the crust of the earth. The lower limit would not be much below the base of the crust. The melting is obviously local (Fig. 41-16), as indicated by the distribution of volcanoes.

How does the rock get hot enough to be molten in some places but not in others? Perhaps the answer is that they do not; perhaps the rocks are equally hot everywhere if the depth is the same.[2] If so, the cause of the melting is not simply temperature.

It is a fact that pressure raises the melting point of rocks. It has been estimated

that a rock that will melt at about 1250° C at the surface will melt at about 1400° C at a depth of about twenty miles. Since rocks at that depth are solid in most places, we must conclude that the temperature at that depth is not more than 1400° C. But it most probably is very near that.

Now suppose that something happens to reduce the pressure locally. It might be a fault, for faults are due to stresses that are released, in part at least, by the faulting. The reduction in the stresses (pressure) would not have to be great for the rock in the vicinity of the fault to become molten. This may explain why volcanic activity is so often evident along faults. The melting could be due to a cause other than relief of pressure. Perhaps some diastrophic movement, e.g., folding of rock strata, could add enough heat (produced by friction) to cause the melting. Or perhaps the folding reduced the pressure a bit. At any rate, once formed, the magma would tend to work its way upward towards regions of lower pressure in the manner of all fluids. It would tend to follow routes of least resistance, and the kind of volcanic activity, intrusive or extrusive, would be governed in large part by these routes.

To answer satisfactorily the questions that have been raised or implied in this discussion, we need better and more complete information. One of the great difficulties is our limited methods of investigation of the deeper parts of the crust. Perhaps the drilling of holes down to the base of the crust and into the mantle will give us some of the information needed. Preliminary work leading to the drilling of such a hole was begun in 1961. This project, called the Mohole Project, plans to drill the hole in one of the oceanic trenches (Fig. 40-4) where the crust may be as little

---

[2] This would exclude those places where the temperature has risen because of the movement of molten material upward in the crust to, or close to, the surface.

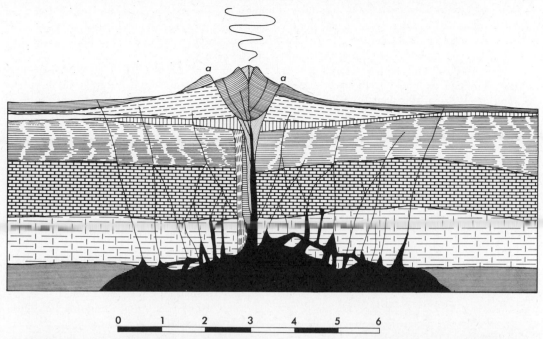

Fig. 41-16. Inferred Conditions below Vesuvius. The magmatic reservoir and the dikes extending from it are shown in black. Vesuvius has been built up inside the explosion pit (caldera) of an older volcano, Monte Somma, which "blew its top" in A.D. 79, burying Herculaneum and Pompeii in volcanic ash and cinders. Parts of the rim of Monte Somma are shown at a. A volcano is an unusual kind of mountain, formed by accumulation of debris ejected from within the earth, rather than by diastrophic processes. (After Rittman.)

as three miles thick. No one expects the successful completion of such a hole to give us all the answers. The problems may be only a little nearer solution. There is something to be said for the statement that science never solves problems; it simply advances them, raises new questions, and so on ad infinitum.

SUMMARY

The phenomena of volcanism may be divided into two parts, extrusive and intrusive.

The extrusive phenomena are superficial manifestations of far more important (geologically) phenomena taking place below the surface—the intrusive phenomena. The various intrusive igneous bodies are classified according to their form. Of particular interest are the batholiths, dikes, and sills.

Diastrophic activity, like volcanic activity, is much more prevalent in some regions of the earth than in others. The most obvious type is faulting, which gives rise to earthquakes. Of greater importance in the past have been those movements that fold rock strata and elevate continents.

Geologists cannot agree on the origin of the forces involved, even though all agree that compression on an enormous scale has taken place. Certainly heat has played a role in both diastrophism and volcanism. The thermal contraction theory postulates that the earth is cooling off and that the folding and faulting is a consequence of the solid crust adjusting itself to a shrinking interior. The evidence from radioactivity suggests, however, that the earth is not cooling off.

The melting of rock locally at depth to form batholiths may be related to release of pressure following diastrophic activity. The distribution of present-day volcanic and diastrophic effects in the same regions as those where mountains are youngest suggest a relationship that is not yet entirely understood.

EXERCISES

I. TERMS AND CONCEPTS

Extrusion	Sill
Intrusion	Joint
Crater	Fold
Volcanic ash, La-	Fault
pilli, Bombs	Warp
Fissure eruption	Folded mountain
Batholith	range
Dike	Thermal contraction

II. PROBLEMS

1. What is the direct cause of any volcanic explosion?

2. What is a fissure eruption?

3. In many active volcanoes the molten material in the crater may be observed to be "boiling." Considering what you have learned about boiling, would you expect this to be true boiling? If not, what is it? Explain.

4. Volcanic ash is the abrasive used in the common kitchen scouring powders. Precisely why should it make such a good abrasive?

5. For geysers to erupt water and steam high in the air, part of the water must be heated *above* the boiling point. What conditions must exist below the surface for this to be possible?

6. Criticize the following statement, giving your reasons: The eruption of a geyser may be considered to be a volcanic eruption in which the molten material is water instead of magma or lava.

7. Differentiate between a dike and a sill.

8. Both sills and lava flows may be horizontal or tilted sheets of igneous rock lying between beds of sedimentary rock. How is it possible to distinguish one from the other?

9. In what sorts of regions are batholiths most likely to be exposed? Give two very different reasons.

10. What kind of rock forms most batholiths? Most of the great lava flows?

11. How can you distinguish batholiths and lava flows from each other?

12. What is a fault? How are faults related to earthquakes?

13. What other types of diastrophic activity are there besides faulting? One series of horizontally deposited sedimentary rocks has been elevated by being upwarped. Another similar series has been elevated by folding. In what fundamental way would these two regions differ geologically?

14. Name two prominent folded mountain ranges in North America, and one great fault block mountain range.

15. Suppose that you lived on a low-lying sea coast. If you awoke one morning to find the waters of the sea lapping at your doorstep, you have to assume that either the land had sunk, or that sea level had actually risen. How could you find out which?

16. If you concluded (above) that the sea had actually risen, how could you explain it, considering the fact that the total volume of water on the earth is constant?

17. Changes of sea level have taken place without any diastrophic activity whatever.

For example, during the last ice age, the sea level dropped as much as 200 ft. Explain.

18. May rock at depth be at the same temperature but solid in one case and molten in the other? Explain.

19. The melting of rock at depth causes an increase in volume. The magma must therefore have a lesser density. Would this have any effect on its tendency to move upwards? Explain.

20. If a new volcano were to form in the United States, in what state do you think it would be? Justify your answer.

CHAPTER XLII

Natural Large–Scale Energy Transformations: Weather and Climate

"Some people are weatherwise, but most are otherwise."—BENJAMIN FRANKLIN

The source of all of the energy that makes life possible on earth is the sun. Without enough of its energy this would be a cold dead planet just as Jupiter, Saturn, Uranus, Neptune, and Pluto are. Solar energy evaporates enormous quantities of water from the oceans which, carried by winds over the lands, is ultimately condensed to rain and snow. Its heat makes chemical weathering possible which in turn provides the earth with its soil. Its radiant energy supplies, via photosynthesis, the earth with plants, which in their turn supply animals with their energy.

The distance of the earth from the sun is more than 10,000 times the earth's diameter. The sun's rays, therefore, are essentially parallel when they reach us. If the earth were perfectly flat with its surface at right angles to these rays, the noonday sun would appear directly overhead everywhere; every square mile of the earth would receive the same amount of solar energy each day. That the altitude of the noonday sun is not only different in different places, but varies from day to day at the same place is proof that the earth's surface is curved. It is this curvature that is a chief factor in causing the great inequality in the amount of solar energy received in various parts of the earth. Thus, temperature difference arise, giving rise to differences in air pressure, which in turn cause winds.

Winds transport the water vapor evaporated from the oceans over the lands, where it may be condensed to fall as rain or snow. Winds also transport heat from warmer to cooler regions, and return the cold air to the warmer regions to be heated again. Winds also cause ocean waves and long-shore currents which erode the shore lines. Winds start the great oceanic drifts of sea water, e.g., the Gulf Stream, and together with the configuration of continents and the rotation of the earth determine their courses, courses that change the inhabitability of continents. Winds themselves are a minor agent of erosion; their climatic functions greatly overshadow their direct geologic functions.

WEATHER vs. CLIMATE

Weather refers to the atmospheric conditions of the moment, or at best over a short period of time. The weather of any place is the sum of such atmospheric conditions as temperature, air pressure, winds, atmospheric moisture, and precipitation over a short period. Climate is sometimes said to be average weather over a longer period of time. This is not strictly true, for it fails to give proper consideration to the extremes. It is conceivable that the weather of two regions could average out the same from year to year and yet have very different climates. For example, consider the temperature factor alone. The average for New York City is 52° F and that of Seattle is 51.4° F. Yet you would have far more need of an overcoat in winter and an air-conditioning system in summer in New York than you ever would in Seattle.

MOTIONS AND ORIENTATION OF THE EARTH THAT AFFECT WEATHER AND CLIMATE

These have already been dealt with in Chapter III. The student is strongly advised to read this chapter again, especially pp. 20–35.[1] The two motions are, of course, rotation and revolution. The orientation is that of the earth on its axis with respect to the plane of the ecliptic, and the constancy of this relationship during a complete revolution.

TROPOSPHERE AND STRATOSPHERE

At an altitude of six or seven miles above sea level at the poles, and ten to eleven miles at the equator, there is a reasonably sharp boundary line between two parts of the atmosphere. The lower part, or zone, is called the *troposphere;* it carries all of the clouds, always contains dust particles, and yields all of the rain and snow. The upper part is the stratosphere; it is cloudless, almost without water vapor or dust particles, and the air is almost uniform in temperature. In contrast to lack of turbulence in the stratosphere, the troposphere is almost everywhere disturbed by vertically rising and descending air currents.

ELEMENTS OF WEATHER AND CLIMATE

1. Air Temperature

Two factors govern the amount of solar energy received at any one place at any one time. They are (1) the angle at which the sun's rays strike the earth (Fig. 2-12*a, b, c*), and (2) the relative lengths of day and night. Both are functions of the latitude of the place in question. Our summers are warmer than our winters, not only because the sun's rays are nearer the vertical, but because the days are much longer in the higher latitudes. Thus, the earth has more time to heat up during the hours the sun is above the horizon and less time to cool off at night when it is below the horizon. Conversely, winters are colder not only because the sun's rays are more slanting, but because there are fewer hours of sunlight and more hours of darkness. At 40° N latitude [2] there are about 15 hours of sunlight and 9 hours of darkness on June 21; 9 hours of sunlight and 15 hours of darkness on December 22. The same is true at 40° S latitude, but with the dates reversed.

Much of the sun's radiant energy is reflected back into outer space by clouds and by dust particles before it reaches the

---

[1] Some of the questions at the end of the chapter will be based on the assumption that you have read these pages.

[2] Latitude is defined as the distance north or south of the equator measured in degrees. One degree of latitude is equivalent to about 70 mi.

earth. The sun's energy that reaches the earth consists of wavelengths of electromagnetic radiation, most of it in the visible and infrared part of the spectrum. Only the longer wavelengths are capable of heating the atmosphere directly. The earth, however, absorbs the shorter wavelengths, is warmed by them, and reradiates part of this heat back into the atmosphere.

Since the reradiated wavelengths are longer [3] than those absorbed, they are much more effective in heating the atmosphere. They can be absorbed by the molecules that make up the atmosphere, more so by the molecules of water vapor and carbon dioxide than by those of oxygen and nitrogen. Absorption of the infrared rays makes the molecules move faster, and collisions of these faster moving molecules make other molecules move faster, and so the temperature rises. The so-called "greenhouse" effect is due to the fact that glass admits the shorter wavelengths which are absorbed by materials inside the glass enclosure. These materials reradiate the absorbed energy as longer infrared rays, which do not readily pass out through the glass. This explains why the inside of cars parked in the sun even on a cold winter day are warmer than the outside.

Water surfaces differ from land surfaces in their properties of absorption and reradiation of heat, even when they lie side by side. Each receives the same amount of insolation (solar energy), has the same thickness of air above it, and is affected by the same major wind system. Yet summer is hotter and the winter colder on the land than on the water. The reasons are several. Water reflects more of the sun's rays than the soil and rocks, and so absorbs less. Water has a specific heat (p. 170) four times that of soil and rocks, so its temperature is not raised so rapidly nor so much. Water circulates whereas the soil and rocks do not. Thus, there is a much greater thickness (depth) of water to be heated. Moreover, water constantly evaporates. Since evaporation is a cooling process, it helps to keep the water cooler than the land. But when night or winter comes, the land cools more rapidly than the water, and so the air over the land is cooler.

Temperatures are lower at high altitudes than they are at lower, other things being equal. This is in part due to greater distance from the radiating earth, and in part due to the lesser density of the atmosphere. There are fewer molecules to absorb the heat. The average decrease is about 3.3° F per 1000 ft. In deserts the air cools quickly after sundown because of the fewer molecules of water vapor in it to trap and hold the heat. In humid climates where clouds are more prevalent, they act as blankets to prevent heat from escaping.

2. Air Pressure

Pressure differences are far more significant insofar as weather and climate are concerned than the absolute pressures. There is a continuous variability of pressure at the same place from hour to hour as the temperatures rise from those of early morning to a high and then decrease with the coming of night. Pressures also change locally with the seasons. Moreover, average pressures differ in different parts of the earth; e.g., they are lower at the equator

[3] On p. 359 we saw that the hotter the radiating body the shorter the dominant wavelengths emitted. Thus, the earth, being cooler than the sun, radiates only the longer wavelengths. Reradiation must not be confused with reflection. The latter involves no absorption.

Fig. 42-1. Wind and Pressure Belts. The boundaries cannot be shown even approximately due in part to their migration with the sun and in part to the irregular distribution of land and sea. The equatorial low-pressure belt is well developed everywhere, the trade winds are well developed except in the Indian Ocean, the subtropical high-pressure belt is broken up into a series of high-pressure cells, and the westerlies are highly variable from any viewpoint. Nevertheless the student should memorize the broad features of the diagram if he wishes to have even a superficial understanding of world climates.

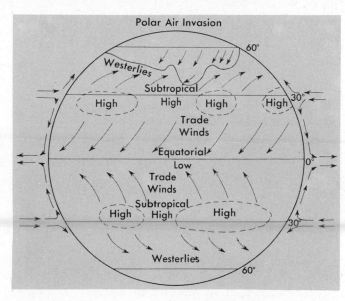

than elsewhere. All of these pressure differences arise from the fact that the earth's surface is unequally heated by the sun. Aside from the inequalities due to the earth's curvature and to the land and water differences in absorption and reradiation of heat, there are the more local causes due to differences in the absorbing and reflecting abilities of different types of land surfaces. Thus, plowed fields or stretches of barren sand absorb more heat than do forested or grass-covered areas. Since it is the reradiated rays that warm the atmosphere, the more heat that is absorbed by the earth, the faster the air above it is warmed. Warm air tends to produce low pressure in an open system where it is free to expand, and cold air tends to produce high pressure. Thus, air pressures are relatively low over the oceans in summer with respect to those over the continents. In winter the reverse is true.

One result of this tendency for warm air to create low pressure is that the region about the equator forms a belt of low pressure, called the equatorial low, or, less formally, the doldrums. Here the warm air rises, expanding as it does so; the chief air movement is upward. It is, therefore, a region (except at high elevations) of much calm; whatever winds there are, are light and variable in direction.

As might be expected the cold polar regions are regions of high pressure. In such regions the chief movement of air is downward and outward. In between the poles and the equator there are other pressure belts, the most important of which is centered between the 25° and 30° parallels on either side of the equator. These are the subtropical high-pressure belts. These belts are not continuous but are broken into a series of high-pressure cells (Fig. 42-1). As in all high-pressure areas the movement of air is downward and outward. Like the equatorial low, they are regions of much calm, and whatever winds there are, are usually light and variable. The rea-

son for the high-pressure belt at these latitudes (often called the horse latitudes) is
at present an inadequately explained effect
of the earth's rotation.

MOVEMENTS OF THE AIR: WINDS AND CURRENTS

The immediate result of pressure differences are winds and air currents. Winds
refer to horizontal movements of the air,
whereas air currents refer to vertical movements. The winds always tend to blow
from regions of higher towards regions of
lower pressure, tending to equalize the
pressure. The greater the pressure difference, the stronger the wind. A difference
equivalent to 2 in. of mercury is sufficient
to cause the violent winds of a hurricane.

While the differences in pressure govern
the general direction of the movement of
air masses, the rotation of the earth exerts
a strong influence also. The fundamental
reasons for this deflection are discussed in
connection with the Foucault pendulum
experiment in Chapter III. The practical
result is that the winds are deflected to the
right [4] in the northern hemisphere, to the
left in the southern; the trade winds which
would normally blow towards the equator
from both the north and the south are deflected so that they become the northeast
trades in the northern hemisphere and the
southeast trades in the southern (Fig. 42-1).

The trade winds are the most constant
winds on earth, both as to velocity and per-
sistence. This belt provided a splendid
route for westward travel in the days of

[4] The direction of a wind is, of course, that from
which the wind is coming. Thus, to apply this
rule (known as Ferrel's Law) one should imagine
oneself to be standing with one's back to the wind.

sailing ships. The velocity rarely rises
above 15 mi/hr. At times hurricanes (in
the western Atlantic) or typhoons (in the
western Pacific) move across them. The
trades arise in the subtropical highs; the
air to nourish them comes from the descending currents in the high-pressure cells
in the horse latitudes.

Part of these descending currents of air
in the subtropical high-pressure cells moves
northward (northern hemisphere) and is
quickly deflected to the right (east). Other
air masses move down from the polar regions (Fig. 42-1) and are deflected to the
right (west). These two types of air masses
meet and are, in general, carried along in
an easterly direction because of the earth's
rotation. *These winds are the westerlies.*
Locally the winds in the belt of the westerlies may be from any point of the compass. Nevertheless, the prevailing direction is always from the west, southwest, or
northwest, and so they are sometimes referred to as the prevailing westerlies. The
result is that in this belt the movement of
weather is from west to east. Therefore,
west coast climates in the belt of the westerlies are controlled by oceanic conditions
to the west of them, whereas east coast
climates are controlled by the continental
conditions to the west of them.

AIR MASSES AND FRONTS

A large body of air that has acquired definite characteristics, from lying over a large
uniform surface of the earth until it is in
equilibrium with the surface with respect
to temperature and moisture content, is
called an air mass. One with a source over
northwestern Canada will be cold and dry,
whereas one whose source is over the

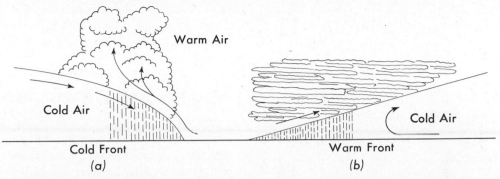

Warm Air

Cold Air

Cold Front

(a)

Warm Air

Cold Air

Warm Front

(b)

Fig. 42-2. Fronts. **(a)** A cold front. The cold air is aggressively pushing in under a mass of warm air. The rising moisture-laden warm air mass is pushed upward and cooled; part of its water vapor is condensed to fall as rain or snow. **(b)** A warm front. The warm air is aggressively moving towards a mass of cold air. Since it is less dense, it rises up over the cold air along a gently sloping front. As it does so, it is cooled; part of its water vapor is condensed to fall as rain or snow.

southwestern United States will be warm and dry, and one whose source is over the Gulf of Mexico will be warm and humid. Such air masses retain these characteristics to a large degree even after they move away from their source regions. Lower pressures in surrounding regions start them moving.

An air mass moving down from the north or northwest commonly comes in contact with an air mass moving up from the south or southwest. There is little mixing of the air between the two masses. They may move in part side by side but in different directions, or they may meet at some angle. The warmer air rises above the colder denser air. There is, therefore, a boundary surface between the air masses, a surface that always slopes upward. The line formed by the intersection of this surface with the ground is called a front (Fig. 42-2). The boundary surface is a gently sloping one, more gentle along a warm

front [5] than a cold one. If the warmer air mass is actively pushing ahead, displacing the colder air and pushing it forward as it rises above it, the front is a warm one; the temperature of the air ahead of it either remains constant or it rises. If it is the colder air mass that is actively pushing ahead, wedging itself beneath the warmer air as it displaces it by forcing it upward, the front is a cold one; the temperature ahead of the front drops. In any case, it is the air mass that is the "aggressor" that is the chief determiner of the character of the front. Since weather travels from west to east in the United States, a front with the cold mass to the west and a warm mass to the east is a cold front, and one with a cold mass to the east and a warm mass to the west is a warm front. If one front overtakes another, bringing three air masses

[5] The slope of the boundary surface may vary from 1:100, to 1:200, i.e., its rise may be 1 ft or less per 100 ft.

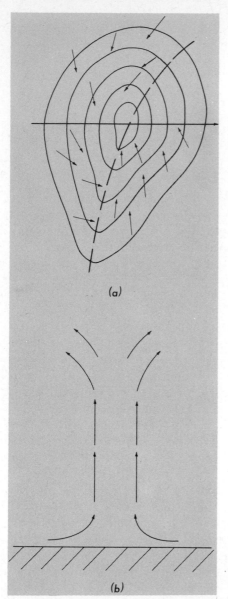

(a)

(b)

Fig. 42-3. A Cyclone. **(a)** The closed lines are isobars, lines of equal pressure. Since the lowest pressure is at the center, the air moves inward from all directions towards it, spiraling as it does so in accordance with Ferrel's Law. **(b)** At the

close together, an occluded front results. The middle air mass is warmer than the other two, and so is lifted above the cooler masses.

CYCLONES AND ANTICYCLONES

Within the belt of the westerlies large pressure systems are constantly developing as a result of the meeting of air masses with widely different characteristics of temperature, density, and moisture content. These systems vary from nearly circular to elliptical in shape, and are several hundred to a thousand or more miles long. They are the cyclones (lows) and anticyclones (highs) that are seen on every weather map of the United States. The lows are great low-pressure centers into which the air from surrounding regions of higher pressure spirals and moves upward. The spiraling is to the right in accordance with Ferrel's Law (Fig. 42-3a). The essential condition for such a low seems to be the presence of two air masses adjacent to each other, with markedly different temperatures and humidities, and moving in different directions. A "kink" in the front may be caused by a number of things, e.g., the topography. Once started it may develop into a cyclone (Fig. 42-3).

Anticyclones also start as "kinks" in fronts. They are huge centers of high pressure in which cooler descending air spreads out near the surface of the earth in all directions. In the United States and Canada they have their beginnings in surges or wedges of cold air moving southward from

center the air rises and is cooled, commonly below the dew point.

polar regions. They commonly develop along with the lows when these wedges encounter a warmer air mass.

Cyclones and anticyclones travel a generally easterly course across the United States, often following one after the other, especially in winter. So numerous are they that they form the main flow of the westerlies across the United States. They are like the eddies in a turbulent stream. The speed with which they move is highly variable but 600 mi a day is a fair average.

MODERN VIEWS ON THE PLANETARY CIRCULATION

If the earth were all water or all land of uniform topography and not rotating, the circulation of the atmosphere would be simple. Warm air rising at the equator would drift poleward at high altitudes, descend in the polar regions and move along the surface towards the equator. This would be a simple one-cell system. The rotation of the earth, combined with the distribution of land and sea, with most of the land in the northern hemisphere, breaks this idealized system up into a system so complicated that it is not yet completely understood.

Until World War II it was believed that the circulation consisted of a three-cell system in each hemisphere. The equatorial low, northeast trades, subtropical high, belt of the westerlies, polar easterlies, and polar high formed the primary wind system in the northern hemisphere. The cyclonic and anticyclonic circulation was designated a secondary system superimposed upon the primary system, and almost exclusively confined to the belt of the westerlies.

Research during and since World War

II has destroyed this reasonably simple model, chiefly by giving us more information about air movements at high elevations. The winds at high altitudes which were thought to blow in directions opposite to those on the surface in order to complete the circulation were found to be weak or absent. The cyclonic and anticyclonic circulation is now assigned a major role in the belt of the westerlies. The jet stream at high elevations in this belt flows at high speeds (up to 300 mi/hr) in the same easterly direction as do the westerlies. Much research needs to be done before present ideas are sorted out, evaluated, and classified.

PRECIPITATION AND HUMIDITY

Included under precipitation are rain, snow, hail, and sleet; included under humidity are atmospheric moisture, clouds, fog, and dew. The amount of rainfall per year varies from 450 in. or more in Assam province, India, to less than ½ in. in the Atacama Desert of northern Chile. The amount of moisture that air can contain in the form of water vapor is dependent on the temperature; warm air can hold far more than cold. The ratio between the actual amount of moisture in the air and the amount that it can hold at a given temperature is called relative humidity. Thus, the relative humidity is said to be 50 per cent if it contains just half the moisture that it is capable of holding at that temperature. If the temperature drops and the total amount of moisture in the atmosphere remains the same, the relative humidity increases. The temperature at which the relative humidity reaches 100 per cent is called the *dew point*. Further cooling results in precipitation. Since grass, leaves, etc., cool off at night more rapidly than the atmosphere, the air in contact with them may be at the dew point, whereas the air elsewhere is well above it. Dew therefore is precipitated on them.

It follows that in order to produce significant precipitation of any kind, a large air mass must be cooled below the dew point. There is only one way a large air mass can be sufficiently cooled and that is to cause it to rise to a higher altitude. There are three ways by which air masses can be forced to rise to higher altitudes; each gives rise to a particular type of precipitation, as follows:

1. Convectional Precipitation

The air, warmed to a higher temperature than the surrounding air, rises more or less vertically. As it rises, it expands and is cooled. How much cooling must take place depends upon the amount of moisture in the air and its original temperature. Large patches of plowed land or other bare ground or great stretches of concrete, brick, and stone heat up faster than green fields and woodlands. The air above them is warmed more than the air above adjacent areas. It is, therefore, less dense and so rises; cooler air from the adjacent regions moves in, is in turn warmed, and so rises. A vertical current of air is thus set up. If the rising air is cooled below the dew point, precipitation occurs. This type of precipitation is at a maximum in the equatorial low (doldrums). It is also the type that gives us our summer thunderstorms.

2. Orographic Precipitation

A moving air mass will be forced to rise if it encounters a mountain range or other high area in its path. As it rises, it expands and is cooled, possibly below the dew point. If so, the resulting precipitation is termed orographic, which means "related to mountains."

After crossing the mountains the winds descend, and are warmed. This increases the capacity of the air to hold moisture. Thus, the areas on the leeward sides of mountain ranges are commonly desert areas if the mountains are high enough. A fine example is that furnished by winds from the Pacific crossing the Sierra Nevada range along the California-Nevada boundary. In the central and northern parts of California, heavy rainfall is experienced on the western slopes of the mountains, whereas the Nevada side of the range is dry. In its general character much orographic rainfall is like that of the convectional type. The moisture-carrying trade winds do not bring rain unless mountain ranges lie across their paths, because they are blowing from a cooler region to a warmer region, i.e., they are blowing towards the equator. The same is true of the summer monsoons in southern and southeast Asia. They blow from the cooler ocean towards the warmer land, yet the heaviest rainfall anywhere in the world results when the monsoons rise to cross the towering Himalaya Range.

3. Cyclonic and Frontal Rain

We have already discussed cyclones and fronts. In a warm front the advancing warm air rises along a gently inclined slope of a wedge of cold air. Cooling by expansion takes place slowly. If the warm air is dry, little or no precipitation may result. Most generally the warm air is moist, so there is rain ahead of the advancing front. When the front passes, the weather generally clears, partly at least, and commonly there is a rise in temperature.

In a cold front warm air is being replaced by an advancing wedge of cold air which pushes in beneath the warm air. Thus, the slope of the boundary surface between the two air masses is backward instead of forward as in a warm front; it is also steeper. Most of the rain falls along the front or close to it in a zone that is much narrower than that in a warm front. After the front has passed, the weather clears, and there is usually a sharp drop in the temperature. The winds commonly change from southwesterly to northwesterly.

As we have already learned, cyclones develop along fronts. In them the air at the center is rising, expanding and being cooled. If cooled below the dew point, cyclonic rain falls. Since fronts and cyclones are so intimately related, it is difficult for us to make any distinction between cyclonic and frontal rainfall. Most of the rainfall in the wintertime in the United States is cyclonic or frontal.

Hurricanes and typhoons are violent tropical cyclones of comparatively small area. They originate over the oceans along the boundaries between the equatorial low and the trade winds. Tornadoes are the most violent of all storms. They are miniature storms, rarely much more than one-quarter of a mile wide, and never lasting more than an hour or two. They commonly occur along cold fronts.

In all violent storms a great deal of energy is expended. What is the source of this energy? If we remember that about 540 calories of heat are absorbed in evaporating 1 gm of water, and that this energy is released when condensation takes place, it is easy to account for the enormous amounts of energy expended during a violent storm.

"MIGRATION" OF THE SUN

One of the *apparent* motions of the sun is a northward advance from December 22 to June 21 and a southward advance from June 21 to December 22. Since solar energy is responsible for varying weather and climate, and the distribution of this energy is profoundly affected by the apparent migration of the sun, the temperature, pressure, wind, and rainfall belts migrate with the sun. The boundaries between these belts shift northward in the northern summer and southward in the northern winter. Regions that have alternating wet and dry seasons are located such that these shifting boundary lines cross them. Thus, southern California and the Middle East lie in the dry subtropical belt during the summer and in the more humid belt of the westerlies during a part of the winter.

OCEAN CURRENTS

A great ocean current like the North Atlantic Drift (Gulf Stream) is set in motion by winds blowing in a constant direction. Once well developed they have an enormous momentum which may carry them across wind belts where the winds are not favorable. Their courses are affected by the configurations of continents. They are great distributors of heat, some carrying warm waters far to the north, some bringing cold waters down from the north. Europe, e.g., is largely north of the United States, but much of it has average temperatures far above those of the corresponding latitudes in the United States.

SUMMARY

As a result of the unequal heating of the earth's surface by the sun, differences in temperature arise. Temperature differences give rise to rising or descending air currents and consequent differences in pressure. These in turn give rise to winds and, under certain conditions, to precipitation. Combine the above with the effects of land and water differences, mountain barriers, differences in altitude and latitude, large land masses with their semipermanent high- and low-pressure areas, ocean currents, and storms, and the many types and varieties of weather and climate are produced.

EXERCISES

I. TERMS AND CONCEPTS

Insolation
Weather
Climate
Troposphere
Stratosphere
"Greenhouse" effect
Land and water differences
Equatorial low—doldrums
Subtropical high—horse latitudes
Trade winds
Belt of the westerlies
Air currents
Ferrel's Law
Air mass
Cold front
Warm front
Cyclone
Anticyclone
Relative humidity
Dew point
Convectional rainfall
Orographic rainfall
Cyclonic or frontal rainfall
Hurricanes
Typhoons
Tornadoes
Migration of the sun
Ocean currents

II. PROBLEMS

1. Why should the amount of solar radiation (insolation) received per unit area per unit time be so much greater at your latitude than it is at the north pole on June 21?

2. What are the two great climatic functions of the winds?

3. Suppose the earth rotated once on its axis in one of our months. What do you think the climate would be like in your area? What effect would this have on life?

4. Distinguish between stratosphere and troposphere.

5. List the elements of weather and climate.

6. What two factors govern the amount of solar energy received at any one place at any one time?

7. What two constituents of the atmosphere are the best absorbers of heat? Relate this fact to the rapid cooling of desert areas after sundown.

8. Is the atmosphere heated directly by the sun? Explain.

9. Water surfaces heat up more slowly and cool off more slowly than land surfaces. Why?

10. What is the fundamental cause of differences in air pressure in different areas?

11. Warm air tends to produce low pressure and cold air to produce high pressure. Explain.

12. What is the chief movement of air in the doldrums? in the Horse latitudes?

13. What is the immediate cause of winds? The more remote cause?

14. Describe the trade winds. Where do they have their origin? What happens to the air that forms them?

15. What is Ferrel's Law as applied to winds?

16. What is the origin of the westerlies? Compare them with the trade winds.

17. What is an air mass? A front?

18. Distinguish between a warm front and a cold front.

19. Compare cyclones and anticyclones with respect to air pressure, directions of air movement, temperature, and likelihood of bringing rain.

20. It is commonly said that an easterly (northeast, east, southeast) wind brings rain in eastern and northeastern United States. Where is the storm center with respect to an area where such rain is falling, and in what general direction is it traveling?

21. In the northeastern quarter of the United States the center of a cyclonic low passes to the south of you. If it is winter, you will probably receive snow, whereas if the center passed to the north of you, you would probably receive rain. Explain.

22. What is relative humidity? Is it directly or inversely proportional to the temperature? What is the dew point?

23. Explain the three types of rainfall. What areas in the United States experience each?

24. The great deserts of the world lie in the Horse latitudes and the northern part of the trade wind belts which lie just to the south of them. Explain.

25. Many believe that if the Gulf Stream shifted its course somewhat farther north in the western Atlantic that the coastal climate of northeastern United States would be warmer. It is doubtful that there would be much temperature difference, but is reasonably certain that the east coast would experience stormier weather and more snow in the winter. Explain. (Hint: The northeastern part of the United States lies in the belt of the westerlies.)

CHAPTER XLIII

Energy Transformations on a Huge Scale: Weathering and Erosion

Nothing is constant but change.—ANON.

Here below to live is to change, and to be perfect is to have changed often.—CARDINAL NEWMAN

The processes of gradation are, in general, opposed to the processes of volcanism and diastrophism. For purposes of convenience we may call them constructional processes. Their net effect is to change the elevation of the lands with respect to the seas, to fold the enormous thicknesses of sedimentary rock strata that have been deposited in shallow troughs (Fig. 41-13) into great mountain ranges, and to elevate other areas by vertical uplift or by block faulting into plains and plateaus and fault block mountains, some of which are at present a mile or two or even more above sea level. Other areas have been downwarped or

down faulted below sea level but at present the effects of elevation are far more extensive and impressive than those of subsidence.

The net effects of gradation are to ultimately reduce these elevated land areas to surfaces of low relief. The gradational processes, which for convenience we may call destructional forces, begin long before the constructional forces have come to a halt; in fact, they begin as soon as an area is uplifted an appreciable distance above sea level, and they never cease until the area is reduced to near sea level again. Mountains, therefore, never reach their greatest potential height, for much erosion has taken place to reduce them before the mountain-building forces have completed their work.

The whole of geologic time has been a constant "struggle" between the constructional and the destructional forces. For long periods of geologic time the constructional processes have been dominant, so that mountains were formed and the continents elevated, giving the lands a considerable relief. For other long periods of time the destructional processes have been dominant, with the result that the highlands have been brought low. Intermittent briefer periods of uplift may have delayed the processes of degradation, but there have been times when whole continents were reduced to near base level (defined as the lowest level to which a stream can erode its channel). The earth has just passed through a great period of mountain-building, a period that is not yet ended. The result is that the earth is now in an exceptional stage of its history; the continents are abnormally large and at a higher average elevation than usual; the highland areas are larger and the mountains more lofty and rugged; the climate is more varied. The landscape is therefore more varied and the scenery grander than for the average of geologic time.

All in all we are living in an unusually interesting period of the earth's long history. The conclusion that the constructive processes have not yet died down is warranted by the great number of volcanoes that are still active, by the enormous number of earthquakes each year, and by the number of areas where elevation or subsidence are still taking place.

AGENTS OF GRADATION

The agents of gradation may be divided into two groups according to whether the role they play is an active or a passive one. The passive (or static) agents are the atmosphere—oxygen, carbon dioxide, and water vapor—freezing water, roots of trees, organic acids, and gravity. We might also add to the above list that part of the rain or snow which acts as a wetting agent to keep the soil and rocks moist to greatly varying distances below the surface. The active (or dynamic) agents are groundwater, streams, glaciers, ocean waves, and longshore currents.

ENERGY SOURCES AND TRANSFORMATIONS

Solar radiation creates all of these agents except gravity, either directly or indirectly. The action of the atmospheric agents, oxygen, carbon dioxide, and water vapor, and the action of the organic acids formed by decay of once living organisms, are chemical in nature. Heat speeds them up; on a sunless earth chemical activity would be at a standstill, there would be ice but no

freezing water, and there would be no roots of trees.

All of the active agents are dependent on wind; none could exist in a windless world. Streams, glaciers, and groundwater get the water or snow that forms them from water evaporated from the oceans by solar energy. Winds and air currents are needed to carry this water vapor to high altitudes, and over the lands, where it may fall as rain or snow. Most that falls as snow is melted by solar energy; that which is not becomes glaciers which move to lower altitudes or latitudes where they are eventually melted by solar energy.

Once the rain falls on the earth its further movement is governed by a number of factors. Some is evaporated and so returned to the atmosphere, the percentage depending on the temperature and humidity. Some soaks into the soil and is absorbed by the roots of plants, which use it either in photosynthesis or transpire it back into the atmosphere. Some is carried on down to a zone where the rocks and soil are saturated, to become a part of the groundwater. The percentage that does this is controlled by the amount and kind of vegetation, the porosity and permeability of the soil and rocks, and the slope of the land. Vegetation acts as a sponge to soak up water. In a flat country all of it is disposed of in one or the other of the above ways.

Where there are slopes there is some runoff into the lower places to form streams. The steeper the slopes, the greater the percentage of run-off. The energy of streams is both kinetic and potential; the higher above sea level, the greater the potential energy, and the steeper the slopes the greater the kinetic energy at any one point. The kinetic energy reaches a maximum in waterfalls. It is, of course, the kinetic energy of winds and air currents, derived from solar energy, that carried the water vapor to high elevations, thus giving it potential energy. Once the vapor is condensed, the force of gravity takes over, and under its influence much of the water finds its way back to the sea whence it came.

Ocean waves and longshore currents are both caused by winds. Winds do some gradational work of their own directly, but their indirect effects are vastly more important. It is therefore apparent that almost all the energy of the gradational agents can be traced back through a series of transformations to solar energy. This is in contrast to the energy of vulcanism and diastrophism, both of which have their sources within the earth.

PROCESSES OF GRADATION

Gradation is essentially a leveling process. The leveling can be accomplished in two ways, by removing material from the high places and by using it to fill in the low places. Removal from high places is called degradation, filling the low places is called aggradation. The gradational processes consist of weathering, masswasting, and erosion; the aggradational processes consist of deposition, sometimes called sedimentation.

Weathering

Weathering consists of a complex set of passive processes by which rocks are disintegrated and decomposed. Weathering goes on all about us, not only affecting the works of nature but the works of man. The crumbling of buildings and their foundations, the rusting of bridges and all things made of iron or steel, the blurring of inscriptions on gravestones and monuments, and the heaps of boulders at the bases of cliffs, all attest to the slow but inexorable processes of disintegration and decomposition. The agents of weathering cannot be neatly and precisely enumerated. They have been listed in a preceding paragraph. The processes of weathering may be divided into two groups, those that accomplish disintegration by mechanical or physical means, and those that accomplish decomposition by chemical means.

Chemical weathering is brought about by the processes of hydration, carbonation, and oxidation. Hydration, the union of water with other elements in the mineral, is most important, for neither oxidation nor carbonation can be effective without it. Through these processes new minerals are formed from the old; the new minerals are more stable than the old under the conditions that exist at the surface of the earth. Minerals that are already stable do not weather chemically. The chemical weathering of the feldspars has been discussed in Chapter XXXIX. Chemical weathering is necessary for the production of soil (Fig. 43-1).

Mechanical weathering consists of those processes that break up rock into smaller pieces without changing the composition. In temperate latitudes or at high elevations where there is considerable alternate freezing and thawing during the late fall, winter, and early spring, this is best done by frost wedging. Rain water or water from melting snows fills the pores and crevices of rocks. When it freezes, it expands, exerting a wedging effect, which, on steep slopes or cliff faces, may cause blocks of rock of all sizes to loosen and roll down the slopes to form talus slopes (Figs. 43-2 and 43-3). Roots of trees, growing on such slopes, grow down into cracks to help the wedging process along during the non-freezing months.

The volume changes brought about by the chemical weathering of minerals also cause a wedging effect that pries mineral fragments loose. The volume changes are brought about by union of the minerals being weathered with atmospheric moisture,

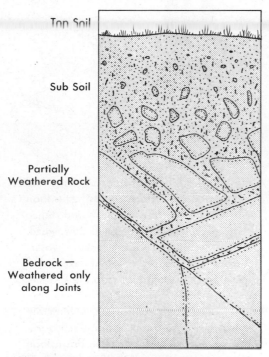

Fig. 43-1.   Residual Soil Profile.

carbon dioxide, and oxygen. Since rocks broken into smaller fragments expose a larger surface area to the action of the atmosphere than larger fragments, mechanical weathering enables chemical weathering to proceed at a faster pace.

Masswasting

This term refers to the downslope movements of weathered rock debris under the

Fig. 43-2.   Mechanical Weathering of Columnar Basalt, Devil's Post Pile, Sierra National Forest, California. The columnar structure is joints formed by contraction on cooling of an approximately horizontal igneous body. The mechanical weathering process is that of frost wedging. The pile of debris is called a talus. (Photograph by United States Forest Service.)

influence of gravity alone. The energy transformations are from potential to kinetic to heat. The effects of masswasting are especially noticeable at the foots of cliffs or steep slopes where heaps of angular boulders of "sliderock" loosened from the cliff by frost or root wedging accumulate. This sliderock forms a talus slope.

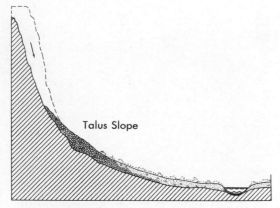

Fig. 43-3. Masswasting, the Downslope Movement of Weathered Material. Jointed blocks of rock, loosened by frost wedging and root wedging of trees, fall and accumulate in heaps near the bottom of the cliff, forming a talus composed of sliderock. From then on, chemical weathering and the slow downward creep of the weathered material, which is slowly becoming soil, dominate. Rainwash plays an important role in transporting the soil into the stream, which may carry it to the sea. (Modified from C. F. S. Sharpe, *Landslides and Related Phenomena*.)

More important but far less obvious is the slow movement (*creep*) of soil formed by chemical weathering down slopes (Fig. 43-4), especially where the debris is subject to soaking rains followed by alternate freezing and thawing. The net effect of creep is to make the soil cover thinner on and near the tops of hills than it is farther downslope.

More spectacular but far less important are the landslides, in some of which millions of tons of rock and rock debris may move distances of a mile or more in a matter of seconds. They are largely confined to steep mountain regions. Masswasting of any type is obviously lacking in a level region. The net effect of masswasting is to reduce the land areas to gentler slopes

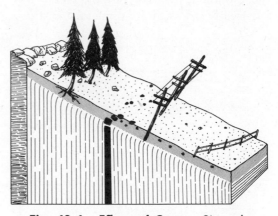

Fig. 43-4. Effects of Creep. Since the soil nearest the surface creeps faster than that at depth, trees, poles, and fence posts anchored in it are tilted downward. When the soil on such a surface is water-soaked and freezes at night, expansion takes place at right angles to the surface, not vertically upward. When melting takes places, the contraction is vertically downward. The result is that each particle moves a tiny bit farther downslope after each melting. (Modified from C. F. S. Sharpe, *Landslides and Related Phenomena*.)

that are not strikingly higher than the level of the floor of the valley which lies at the foot of the slopes (Fig. 43-3). Much of the load of rock debris carried by streams is furnished by masswasting.

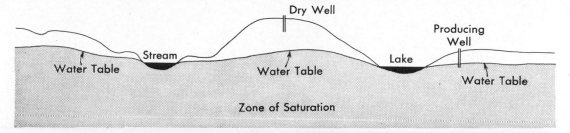

Fig. 43-5. Water Table. The water table is the upper surface of the zone of saturation. This surface, misnamed a table, is a subdued replica of the land surface, i.e., it rises and falls with the topography but not so greatly. To obtain water a well must be sunk below the water table in rock or sediments that are permeable to water. Note that the water table intersects the surface of all permanent streams and lakes. Therefore it is the source of most of their water.

Groundwater

The only important source of groundwater is the rainwater or meltwater of snows that sink into the ground to fill the crevices and pore spaces in soil and rocks. The amount depends on a number of factors, such as the slope of the land, the amount and kind of vegetation, the porosity and permeability of the soil and rocks, and how rapidly the rain falls. If there is sufficient rainfall, the water that soaks down through the soil and rocks reaches the water table (Fig. 43-5), which is the surface below which the soil and rocks are saturated. The depth to the water table increases or decreases with the amount of rainfall. If the water table is at the surface, a swamp develops.

The geologic work of groundwater is largely confined (1) to carbonate rocks such as limestone and marble, and (2) to the solution of the soluble salts formed during the process of chemical weathering. Pure water is ineffective in dissolving the (calcium) carbonate rocks, but rain falling through the atmosphere dissolves some CO_2, forming a weak solution of H_2CO_3 (carbonic acid), which is effective. Almost all caverns and caves are formed by solution in limestones and marbles.

Sinkholes (Fig. 43-6) are extremely abundant in some limestone regions. Limestones and marbles were originally formed by precipitation from solution of the soluble products of weathering. The products, largely salts of various kinds, are carried by groundwater into streams, the streams carry them to the sea. This is the reason that the seas are salty. The Mississippi River alone carries nearly a quarter of a million tons of dissolved material down to the sea each year. Thus, the seas get a bit saltier each year.

Groundwater is of extreme importance to man, for without it few areas of the earth would be inhabitable. In large areas of the earth man is completely dependent on well water for his existence. In other areas he is dependent on streams and lakes for his fresh water, which, in their turn, are largely dependent on groundwater for their supply. The availability of fresh water for human and animal consumption has long been a limiting factor in popula-

Fig. 43-6. Sinkhole in Limestone. Groundwater, seeping along joints in the rock slowly dissolved the calcium carbonate of which limestone is composed. Of the common rocks only limestone and marble are soluble enough for sinkholes to develop in them. (Courtesy United States Geological Survey.)

tion growth in many areas, and as the population increases, it is becoming an important factor almost everywhere. The possibility of ever desalting ocean waters at a cost that makes their use for purposes *other* than personal human consumption or in industry practicable is largely wishful thinking. The amount of water needed per acre for agricultural purposes even under highly controlled conditions is enormous. At $1.00 per 1000 gal at the plant, the cost per acre would range up to $100 or more. To the cost of desalting there would have to be added the cost of distribution, which is always uphill from sea level. Moreover, the areas that need water for agricultural purposes are arid to semi-arid where the loss by evaporation is exceptionally high.

Stream Erosion

Streams are the chief means of returning the water evaporated from the ocean and which falls on the land, to the ocean again. The energy of a stream is both potential and kinetic. As it flows, potential energy is converted into kinetic, and kinetic energy is converted partly into work as rock debris is transported downstream, and partly into heat. Man uses the energy of running water for transportation and for generating hydroelectric power.

The erosional work of a stream consists of the removal of rock debris, the transportation of this load downstream, and its ultimate deposition, usually in deltas or on the continental shelf. The removal is accomplished in several ways, (1) by washing loose material away just as water from a hose can be used to remove a pile of sand from a sidewalk, (2) by abrasion, and (3) by solution. Most important in the early stages of a stream is abrasion. This is accomplished by the sand or pebbles striking against the bottom or sides of the channel. By such abrasive action the stream acts like a saw as it cuts its valley deeper and deeper (Figs. 43-7 and 43-8). The rapidity of the cutting depends on the volume of water, its velocity, the hardness of the rocks in which the valley is being cut, and the quantity and kind of sand by which the cutting is done. The latter acts as a necessary tool, for water by itself can do no cutting. The faster the flow, the more rapid the cutting. Doubling the velocity not only doubles the number of particles of sand striking bedrock per unit of time, but causes them to strike twice as hard. Moreover, the water can carry not only

more particles per unit volume, but larger particles as well. Since the velocity of a stream increases greatly with an increase

Fig. 43-7. Gully Development on Grassy Slope in California. This tributary to some larger stream is slowly extending itself up the slope. It is also being widened and deepened. There is water in its channel only during, and a short time after, a rain. When the channel has been cut below the water table, it will be a permanent stream. (Courtesy United States Geological Survey.)

in volume (due to heavy rains), it is no wonder that streams do most of their work during high-water stages.

As the stream cuts its valley deeper, it reduces its average gradient (slope measured in feet per mile), for streams in most

Fig. 43-8. Gullying at Ducktown, Tennessee. The forest and vegetation cover has been destroyed by the sulphurous fumes of a nearby copper smelter. With nothing to anchor the soil in place, erosion has been rapid. Note the intricate system of branching gullies. (Courtesy United States Geological Survey.)

Fig. 43-9. Valley Development. The stages shown are (**a**) early youth, (**b**) late youth, (**c**) early maturity, (**d**) full maturity. In early youth the stream valley is V-shaped, either straight or with irregular curves. Note that in **b, c** and **d** the stream is eroding the valley walls on the outsides of the curves—which are slowly being transformed into sweeping meanders. By maturity the original narrow V-shaped valley has been altered to a wide flat-floored valley. (Modified from Longwell, Knopf and Flint, *Physical Geology*, John Wiley and Sons, New York, 1939.)

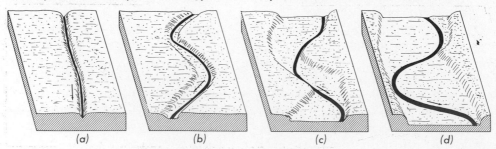

(a)   (b)   (c)   (d)

Fig. 43-10. Meanders in Trout Creek Yellowstone National Park. One or the other of two cutoffs is imminent. (Courtesy United States Geological Survey.)

regions cannot cut below sea level. In reality, they can reduce their channels to sea level only in their lower parts, for a stream must have a gradient, however gentle, down which to flow. The level below which a stream cannot cut is called base level. As a stream nears base level in its downcutting, it begins to swing more and more from side to side, thus widening its valley (Fig. 43-9), changing it from a V-shape to a flat-floored valley which slowly gets wider and wider. In the process the stream itself accentuates any original irregular curves into smooth-swinging curves called meanders, thus lengthening the stream (Fig. 43-10).

Meanwhile, the many tributaries and their subtributaries, etc., have been devel-

oping into a full-fledged drainage system. Weathering, mechanical and chemical, have been slowly going on in all of the interstream areas, and masswasting has been slowly moving the weathered debris down the slopes into countless rills and brooks and creeks, which carry it via the larger tributaries into the master stream. The master stream carries the load, most of it in suspension, down to its mouth and usually into the sea, where it is deposited to form a delta which is built out across the continental shelf. Ocean waves and currents may drift part of the mud and sand for many tens (and even hundreds) of miles, spreading them far and wide across the continental shelf. Thus, the continental shelves become the great reposi-

Fig. 43-11. Uplifted Peneplane, Canyon de Chelly. The upper surface is the peneplane. Note the strata are inclined (dipping) to the right, and that the peneplane truncates their upturned edges. After peneplanation the area was uplifted, and a new cycle of erosion initiated. If the uplift had not occurred, the erosional effects seen in the foreground could not have occurred.

tories of the sediments eroded from the lands. The lands themselves become lowered, reduced eventually to a gently undulating surface called a peneplain (almost a plain). Here and there erosional remnants called monadnocks [1] may be left standing well above the surrounding region, either because they are of harder rock, or because there always has to be some last part to be removed.

The time necessary to peneplane an area is highly variable, but it is always measured in millions, more commonly tens of millions, of years. Vulcanism and diastrophism may interrupt the process before

it is complete, thus initiating a new cycle of erosion. Even if peneplanation is accomplished, diastrophism, possibly accompanied by vulcanism, eventually gets the upper hand, thus rejuvenating the streams by elevating and tilting the area. This has been done fairly recently, geologically speaking, and so there are no true peneplains anywhere at present (Fig. 43-11).

The rock debris that forms the load of streams is not transported downstream in one fell swoop, but is picked up and deposited, picked up again, etc., because the flow of the stream is turbulent. For a given velocity a stream can carry only so much of a load; any decrease in velocity will cause it to drop part of it. The amount carried by large streams in time of high

---

[1] In dry regions where the rock layers are essentially horizontal, they are called mesas if flat-topped, or buttes if they are otherwise.

water is enormously greater than at low water. Fast-flowing streams may carry boulders a foot or more in diameter, and they may roll boulders several feet in diameter along their bottoms. Blocks of concrete, weighing thousands of tons, from broken dams have been carried a mile or two downstream.

Any decrease in velocity causes a fully loaded stream to deposit. Thus, a heavily loaded stream coming down out of mountains where the gradient is steep onto a more level area at the foot of the mountain, will have its velocity suddenly checked by the abrupt change in gradient. The stream will dump most of its load, filling up the channel. It then spills over, forming a new channel, fills it up, and repeats the process over and over again. Thus a fan-shaped deposit is built up, called an alluvial [2] fan (Fig. 43-12), which is sometimes likened to a delta built on land. As the mountains will in time be lowered by the processes of gradation, fan-building will also cease. Eventually the fan will itself be removed, as all of the rock and rock debris that lie above base level are removed to a more or less final resting place in the delta at the mouth or elsewhere on the continental shelf.

Glaciers

For a glacier to form, all that is needed is to have more snow fall in winter than can possibly melt in summer over a long enough period of time. Glaciers can even exist in equatorial regions if the mountains are high enough. The residue accumulated over the years becomes packed and otherwise transformed into ice. When the

[2] Alluvium is a general name for stream deposits of any kind.

accumulation is big enough it will start to move under its own weight. If the region of accumulation is at the heads of mountain valleys (Fig. 43-13), glaciers of the alpine type (also called mountain glaciers or valley glaciers) will move down the val-

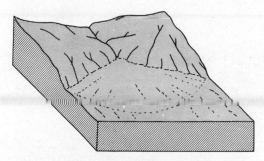

Fig. 43-12. Alluvial Fan. The steep gradient of a mountain stream is abruptly reduced as it leaves the mountain. As a result its velocity, and hence its transporting ability, is greatly diminished. It cannot carry all of its load; it drops some, filling up its channel, and swings over into a new one. Swinging back and forth from one mountain wall to the other builds up the deposit in the shape of a fan. The fan consists of gravel (closer to the mountains), sand, and clay (farther out).

ley until the rate of melting of the ice front equals the rate of advance. Such valleys were originally made by streams while the mountains were being uplifted. The glacier transforms them from V-shaped to U-shaped valleys (Fig. 43-14), straightens them out, and otherwise alters them in a characteristic manner, so much so that after the glaciers have disappeared the region bears the unmistakable marks of glaciation for tens of thousands of years.

If the region of accumulation is not in

Fig. 43-13. Birthplace of Alpine Glaciers. The snow accumulates high up in the mountains, avalanching from the higher slopes down into the heads of the valleys. Much of it gets transformed into ice. If more snow falls every winter than can melt in the summer, it accumulates until the whole mass begins to move under its own weight. Note the rock debris formed by frost wedging. (Courtesy United States Geological Survey.)

the mountains but, say, in a relatively level area of some tens of thousands of square miles in extent, the ice will eventually spread out in all directions under its own weight. The great ice sheets of the Pleistocene period, the last of which disap-

peared from the United States less than twelve thousand years ago, did just this. Accumulating in the area a bit south of the Arctic Circle, these great sheets, a mile or two thick, moved north, south, east, and west. The scratches (glacial striae) left on the bedrock they passed over attest to these directions of movement. They moved down into northern United States, reaching New York City in the East, and the Ohio and Missouri rivers in the Midwest. The mountain glaciers of Glacier National Park (Montana), of Mt. Rainier, Mt. Baker, Mt. Shasta, and others are shrinking remnants of this last ice age.

Glacial erosion is accomplished chiefly by the great weight of the ice pressing down on boulders and pebbles that it is dragging along beneath it as it very slowly advances. These boulders and pebbles are ground to pieces, to fine rock flour as in a great grinding mill; new ones are being constantly picked up as the glacier moves forward like a giant bulldozer. A glacier's farthest line of advance will be located where the rate of the melting back of the ice front equals the rate of advance. It is here that the terminal moraine is formed

Fig. 43-14. U-Shaped Valley, Wasatch National Forest, Utah. Valleys of this shape are never formed by streams. This was once a V-shaped stream valley that was remodeled into a U-shape during the last ice age. Glaciers do not originate their own valleys. (Photograph by United States Forest Service.)

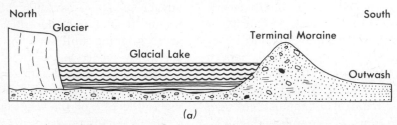

(a)

Fig. 43-15. Terminal Moraine and Outwash Plain. The great ice sheet moved southward until the rate of melting of the ice front equaled the rate of advance. The glacier was then *apparently* motionless but its movement dragged debris along the bottom, piling it up in the form of a ridge (terminal moraine) paralleling the ice front. The moraine is composed of glacial till. It consists of boulders, gravel, sand, and clay, unsorted and unstratified. **(a)** Eventually the rate of melting exceeded the rate of advance and the glacier began an apparent retreat. A glacial lake developed between the ice front and the terminal moraine. When melting was rapid the lake overflowed in countless places, washing the finer debris (mostly sand and clay) out, depositing it far and wide beyond the moraine. Thus an outwash plain is built. **(b)** The terminal moraine (in New York City and vicinity) accounts for the hilly character of northern Long Island, and the outwash plain for the flat terrain of southern Long Island. Beneath these glacial deposits lie sedimentary rocks that are missing in Manhattan and the Bronx. Beneath the sedimentary rocks, however, are the same metamorphic rocks (gneiss, marble, schist) that form the foundation rocks of Manhattan and the Bronx. Countless coarse-grained granite dikes (pegmatite dikes) intrude them.

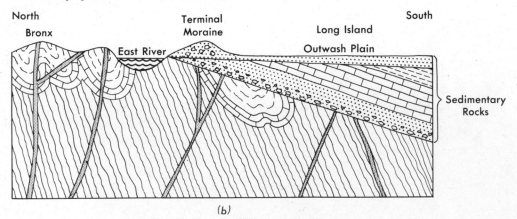

(b)

(Fig. 43-15), a great deposit of unsorted and unstratified boulders, pebbles, sand, and clay (called glacial till). The form is highly irregular but is generally ridgelike.

The terminal moraine of the last ice sheet can be traced from the eastern end of Long Island to the Rocky Mountains; stretches of it have been removed in places. The area to the north bears abundant evidences of glaciation, that to the south, none. Glaciers of the ice sheet type smooth out the topography by removing loosened material from the high places and depositing it in the low places. In doing so they form innumerable lake basins by irregular gouging and deposition. The vast majority of the lake basins of the world are glacial in origin. Alpine glaciers, on the other hand, make the topography more angular (Fig. 43-16); the result is some of the most spectacular scenery on earth.

Wind

As we have already stated the climatic and indirect effects of the wind greatly exceed their direct geologic effects. There are few places in the world where wind erosion is more important than stream erosion. Essential conditions are a truly arid climate, strong winds, and a supply of hard sand grains, e.g., quartz, to do the abrasive work. Since winds blow more sand along the ground than higher up, projecting pieces of rock get cut away at the bottom faster than higher up, producing erosional features called pedestal rocks.

In dry areas where the vegetation cover has been removed, the soil may be picked up and carried away, causing dust storms. This process is called deflation. Wind-blown hollows formed by it are called blowouts. Sand deposits made by the wind are called dunes. They may be irregular in form or crescent-shaped (Figs.

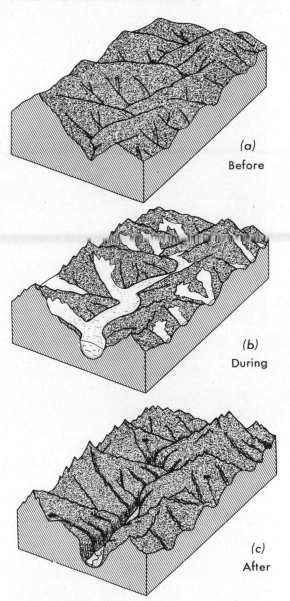

(a)
Before

(b)
During

(c)
After

Fig. 43-16. Before, During, and After Alpine Glaciation. Compare the more rounded topography resulting from stream erosion in **(a)** with the highly angular topography resulting from glacial erosion in **(c)**. Note also the change in the main valley from a V-shape to a U-shape.

Fig. 43-17. Crescent-Shaped Sand Dunes, Biggs, Oregon. Such dunes, called barchans, are formed in regions where the supply of sand is not too great, and the wind is constant in direction. Here the wind was blowing from left to right. (Courtesy United States Geological Survey.)

43-17 and 43-18). Dunes may be formed at times in humid climates if there is an abundance of sand not anchored down by vegetation, as along some beaches.

Ocean Waves and Currents

Both of these erosional agents are caused by the wind. They are effective only along the edges of the lands, continents, or islands, or along the shores of very large lakes. Most of the erosional work of waves is accomplished during heavy storms. Strong waves can pick up pebbles and boulders and throw them at cliffs. Gradually the cliffs are eroded back, the broken debris being broken further and ground finer until the outgoing undertow (return current) can carry it farther out to sea,

where it is eventually dropped into water too deep for waves to disturb it (Fig. 43-19). The chalk cliffs of Dover have been eroded back more than two miles since the time of the Norman conquest in 1066.

Winds blowing at an angle to the shore set up currents that run parallel to the shore but some little distance from it. These are the longshore currents. They drift sand along the bottom, often piling it up in submarine bars across the mouths of bays. In time of storm the submarine bar may be built up above normal sea level. It is then called a spit. Some well-known spits along the Atlantic Coast are Sandy Hook (across the mouth of New York Bay), Rockaway spit (across Jamaica

Bay, Fig. 43-20), and Cape Cod. To protect these spits from destruction by the agent that built them, man builds jetties at right angles to the shore. They keep the longshore currents away from the shore.

SUMMARY

The constructional processes of vulcanism and diastrophism elevate the continents, forming plains and plateaus, and form fold, fault block, and complex mountains. They are opposed by the forces of gradation which reduce the elevated lands to surfaces of low relief. The gradation forces start their work early in the cycle and, in the case of mountains, have eroded deeply before the constructional forces have ceased. Given time enough and interruption, the gradational forces of weathering, masswasting, and erosion by streams will reduce whole continents to a surface of low relief, a peneplain. The other gradational agents—groundwater, glaciers, ocean waves and currents, and the wind—aid the peneplanation processes locally but are incapable of the reduction of continents unless given infinite time.

The gradational agents derive their energy from the sun, largely through use of its heat energy to evaporate water from the oceans, and, by unequal heating of the earth, to cause winds which transport the water vapor, and distribute the heat. Secondarily involved are the gravitational forces, for once the evaporated moisture falls as rain or snow, streams

Fig. 43-18. Ancient Sand Dune Deposit, Utah. The sandstones that form the towering cliffs in Zion National Park were deposited as dunes by the wind 125 million years ago. Note the irregularity of the beds (cross-bedding), a characteristic of dune deposits. (Courtesy United States Geological Survey.)

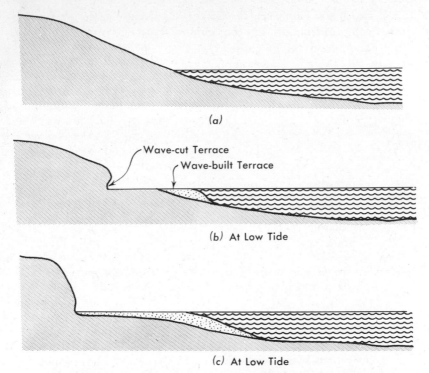

Fig. 43-19. Wave Erosion. (a) Hypothetical newly submerged area in which no wave erosion has yet taken place. (b) The waves have cut the land back forming a wave-cut cliff and a wave-cut terrace. The wave-built terrace consists of the debris removed to form the cliff and the wave-cut terrace. (c) A later stage. As the cliff is cut back farther and farther the waves lose more and more energy as they drag over the long terraces, thus reducing the rate of cutting.

and glaciers may be formed. They move down slopes because of the gravitational forces, doing work as they do by expenditure of kinetic energy. All of the agents except groundwater do most of their work by abrasive action of rock particles (boulders, pebbles, sand). These particles are produced largely by mechanical weathering processes, aided to some extent by chemical weathering and by the erosional processes themselves. During the chemical weathering process new minerals are produced, minerals that are more stable under surface conditions than the old. In general, igneous and metamorphic rocks are more susceptible to chemical weathering than sedimentary rocks, because most sedimentary rocks are the products of a previous cycle of chemical weathering. Masswasting plays its role by moving the weathered material down slope into streams, which in turn carry it to sea where it is deposited on the continental shelves, either directly or after being reworked and transported by waves and currents.

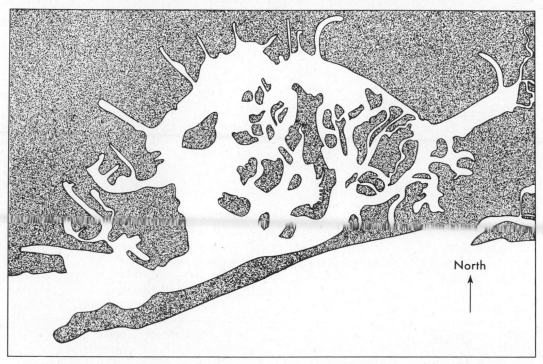

Fig. 43-20. Spit Formation.   Long-shore currents from the right have drifted sand across the mouth of the bay building at first a submarine bar, which later, in time of storm, was built up above sea level.   This particular split is the Rockaway split in south Brooklyn and Queens, New York City.   The bay is Jamaica Bay.   Man-made features have been largely eliminated.

EXERCISES

I. TERMS AND CONCEPTS

Degradation
Aggradation
Constructional forces
Destructional forces
Agent of gradation
Process of gradation
Chemical weathering
Mechanical weathering
Hydration
Carbonation

Frost wedging
Sliderock
Talus
Deflation
Dune
Blowout
Longshore current
Spit
Masswasting
Creep

Permeability
Water table
Zone of saturation
Sinkhole
Abrasion
Gradient
Base level
V-shaped
   valley
Flat-floored
   valley
Delta
Fan
Alluvium

Peneplain
Monadnock
Mesa
Butte
Alpine gla-
   cier
Ice sheet
Striae
Terminal
   moraine
Till
Pedestal
   rocks

II. PROBLEMS

1. Mountain ranges never reach their greatest potential height. Why?

2. Distinguish between an agent and a process of gradation, and between a depositional feature and an erosional feature.

3. Classify the following as agent, process, erosional feature, or depositional feature. State the particular agent and the particular process.

atmospheric moisture	valley
hydration	creep
masswasting	frost wedging
talus	fan
delta	peneplain
canyon	monadnock
sinkhole	striae
dune	abrasion
longshore current	deflation
moraine	spit
decomposition	disintegration

4. If the agents of gradation are effective in reducing the lands, and the earth is so old, why is the whole earth not a peneplain?

5. Trace *all* of the energy transformations that result in a delta being formed by a stream.

6. A dark-colored feldspar in an igneous rock contains some calcium and oxygen, among other things. Eventually some of these two elements end up as $CaCO_3$ (calcium carbonate) in the ocean waters. List the intervening events.

7. Distinguish carefully between mechanical and chemical weathering.

8. Quartz does not weather chemically. Neither does the mineral calcite. Why?

9. What is a talus? How is it produced?

10. In humid climates the slopes of hills are more rounded (less angular) than they are in dry climates. Moreover, bedrock is less likely to be exposed in the lower half of the hills. Explain.

11. How deep (not in feet) must a well be to furnish a steady supply of water?

12. The greatest of all water reservoirs on the lands is the soil and rocks of the earth's outer crust. Explain.

13. In a region where there is plenty of rainfall what would determine the lower limit of the water table?

14. Mammoth Cave in Kentucky was carved by what agent? In what kind of rock? Why not some other kind?

15. List three ways by which a stream erodes. Which is most important where the channel is cut in bedrock?

16. Through one five-mile section of the Grand Canyon the Colorado River drops about 62.5 ft. What is its gradient?

17. How are stream valleys widened at the bottom? At the top?

18. Most streams in humid climates keep flowing steadily even though it may not have rained for a month or two. Where do they get their supply of water?

19. How does a stream carry most of its load? What causes a stream to deposit?

20. How and where is an alluvial fan built? A delta?

21. Ice is a soft mineral, softer than most rock minerals, yet a glacier erodes the bedrock beneath it. How?

22. Alpine glaciers never originate new valleys; they only remodel pre-existing valleys. Explain.

23. When a geologist sees a deposit made directly by a glacier, he need rarely ask, "Could some other agent have made it?" Why is this so?

24. Of what sorts of materials are terminal moraines made?

25. How do glaciers form lake basins?

26. Northern New Jersey was glaciated by a great ice sheet but southern New Jersey was not. List as many pieces of evidence as you can that would tend to prove this statement.

27. The indirect erosional effects of the winds are vastly more important than their direct erosional effects. Explain.

28. By what two methods do winds erode? Name one erosional feature produced by each method.

29. Explain how a spit is formed.

30. The earth is more than 3 billion years old, yet it is highly unlikely that any river flowing today is much more than 60 to 70 million years old, and most are much less than that. Explain.

CHAPTER XLIV

The Search for the Past

. . . no vestige of a beginning, no prospect of an end.—JAMES HUTTON (*Father of Modern Geology*)

It is easy to see that the science of geology insofar as we have dealt with it so far is to a very large degree the application of the principles of physics and chemistry. The study of rocks and minerals is almost exclusively a study of the principles of chemistry. The study of the interior of the earth and the three fundamental processes acting to alter the face of the earth involve many of the principles of physics. It is only the application that is different.

That part of historical geology that deals with paleontology, the science of ancient life, depends in large part upon the science of biology, for anyone who wishes to make a detailed study of the life of the past must first study the life of the present. Geology, however, is not entirely the application of the principles of other sciences, for none of them attempts to decipher past events. The geologist is concerned with questions that the physicist, the chemist, and the biologist would not think of asking

unless he was consciously trying to be a geologist also.

Consider a mountain range. The chemist would be concerned with the composition of the minerals that form the rocks, their origin, etc. The physicist would be concerned with the forces that caused the mountain range to be formed, the conditions at depth that would allow such a range to stand so high above the surrounding region, and similar problems. The biologist would be concerned chiefly about the fossils the strata contained. On the other hand the geologist would be concerned not only with all of these problems, but with many others, for example: Why are many mountain ranges composed of sedimentary rocks on their flanks, with igneous rocks in their cores? What sequence of events preceded the making of the mountain range that allowed the enormous thicknesses of both continental and marine sediments that form the mountains to be deposited? What sequence of events followed the making of the mountains that allows the individual ridges to always be composed of resistant rock and the intervening valleys of weaker rock? And many more.

These questions involve the methods and principles of the search for the past, a search that we more formally call historical geology. Because the pages that we can devote to it are few, we will confine our discussion to a few of these methods and principles rather than to the facts of historical geology.

The problem of accumulating the facts and arranging them in a proper time sequence are many and complex. The earth is unimaginably old, more than 3 billion years old. The history of man, civilized and uncivilized, becomes more and more fragmentary, and dimmer and dimmer the farther back we go in time, until we lose all trace of him except for the fossils of his distant ancestors. Just so, the history of the earth becomes dimmer and more fragmentary until we have little or no record of its first billion years.

Think of a book originally with at least four thousand pages, and with a million years of earth history recorded on each page. For the first two thousand pages there is not a single complete page. Moreover, all of the earlier chapters have been forever destroyed. It is not until we reach the last eighth of the book that we begin to have complete chapters, but even there many of the pages are fragmentary and some are missing. We might more properly say that all the pages are fragmentary, but that their fragments have been scattered over all of the earth, some forever destroyed, some still in existence although still undiscovered. The great majority of these later pages have, however, been discovered and pieced together to give us a reasonably coherent history of the last one-sixth of geologic time.

It is the problem of the trained geologist to collect the missing fragments for each region if they are still in existence, and if not, to try to reconstruct as best he can the record of the missing parts from the evidence he has and from that of neighboring regions. Considerable amounts of the missing records now lie buried beneath younger sediments, either in our plains and plateaus where the strata are horizontal, or beneath younger strata on the continental shelves.

ORDERLY SEQUENCE OF DEPOSITION

We might very well ask how so much of the record came to be destroyed. Before answering, we might better ask what the record consists of. Suppose that two billion years ago the area now occupied by North America consisted of two great highland areas one in the east and one in the west with a great lowland area in between. Suppose also that this lowland area consisted of a great central shallow seaway with a broad comparatively lowland area on each side between it and the highland areas. Streams flowed down from the highlands and into the sea, carrying with them the products of weathering and erosion, and depositing them. To keep pace with the filling, let the floor of the seaway slowly sink, not so much because of the weight of the sediments but because of the action of the forces that caused the basin in the first place. Let uplift of the highland area keep pace with erosion, and let us assume that once sediments were deposited they remained uneroded to the present day.

Assume that life evolved in the sea, first plants, then simple marine invertebrates, then more complex invertebrates, and finally finned vertebrates. Let these be followed by plant life on the land and land-dwelling invertebrates. Eventually came the land-dwelling vertebrates, first the amphibians, then the reptiles, and then the birds and the mammals almost together. In all cases the remains of the hard parts of many of these plants and animals would be preserved in the sediments. Quick burial by fine-grained sediments after death would preserve some of each group. If

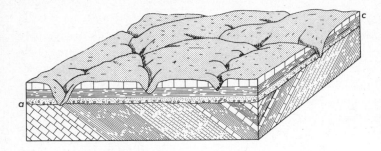

Fig. 44-1. Block Diagram Showing an Unconformity. It is clear that the horizontal strata could not have been present when the inclined layers were folded. After folding the area was peneplaned. This erosion surface is indicated by *ac*. Later the horizontal sediments were deposited on the erosion surface. Thus, the surface, *ac*, is a *surface of erosion* that separates younger from older beds. Such surfaces are unconformities. An unconformity indicates a time gap in the orderly sequence of deposition. This gap may be millions, tens of millions, or even hundreds of millions of years long. The fossils in the horizontal layers (if any) will be different from those in the folded layers, because plants and animals are continually evolving.

this situation existed, the sediments would contain a reasonably complete record, not only of their own history but much of that of the highland areas that supplied the sediment. Entombed in the sediments would be a complete record of the evolution of life. Since sedimentation was continuous, with no erosion of the sediments, there would be no gaps in the record (Fig. 44-1). Our only problem would be to get at the record, for there would be many tens of thousands of feet of sediments, all more or less in horizontal layers.

If this seaway prevailed today, and we were here to contemplate it, we would ac-

tually know less than we do about the history of the earth, for most of it would be unavailable. But the record would still be there, fully preserved, instead of fragmentary; there would be no gaps in the orderly sequence of deposition.

From this hypothetical situation we should gain some understanding of what the record of earth history consists of and how it is preserved. Such a record would be complete as far as life is concerned, but the igneous and metamorphic history would be incomplete. There is no hypothetical picture that we can think of that would allow all phases of earth history to be preserved, because you cannot have sediments deposited without erosion, and you cannot have erosion without some destruction of the record.

AVAILABILITY OF THE GEOLOGIC RECORD

In fact, diastrophism followed by erosion is responsible for the availability of much of the geologic record. Consider the Grand Canyon area (Fig. 44-3). The rocks exposed at the surface on the north side of the canyon are limestones containing fossils of marine animals. They are now a mile and a half above sea level. Other rock formations once above them have been removed by erosion. The forces of diastrophism elevated these limestones (and all the associated rocks) at least a mile and a half. Yet these limestones would not now be exposed to man's observations if erosion had not removed the overlying rocks, and the rocks below the limestones would be hidden if the Colorado River had not cut a deep canyon into them.

Fig. 44-2. The Geologic Time Scale, and the Order of Succession of Animal Life as Revealed by Fossils. Note that the total time shown is 3,500,000,000+ years.

Era	Period		Type of Life	Approximate Length of Each Interval (years)
CENOZOIC	TERTIARY	RECENT	Invertebrates, fishes, amphibians, reptiles, birds, mammals (including man)	1,000,000 +
		PLEISTOCENE		
		PLIOCENE		
		MIOCENE	Invertebrates, fishes, amphibians, reptiles, birds, modernized mammals (except man)	20,000,000
		OLIGOCENE		
		EOCENE	Invertebrates, fishes, amphibians, reptiles, birds, and "archaic" mammals	125,000,000
		PALEOCENE		
	CRETACEOUS			
MESOZOIC	JURASSIC		Invertebrates, fishes, amphibians, reptiles, and primitive mammals	35,000,000
	TRIASSIC		Invertebrates, fishes, amphibians, and primitive reptiles	70,000,000
PALEOZOIC	PERMIAN			
	PENNSYLVANIAN		Invertebrates, fishes, and primitive land-dwelling vertebrates — the amphibians	65,000,000
	MISSISSIPPIAN			
	DEVONIAN			
	SILURIAN		Invertebrates, and primitive vertebrates—the fishes	90,000,000
	ORDOVICIAN			
	CAMBRIAN		Marine invertebrates	120,000,000
PRECAMBRIAN ERAS			No certain fossil record of animal life	3,000,000,000 +

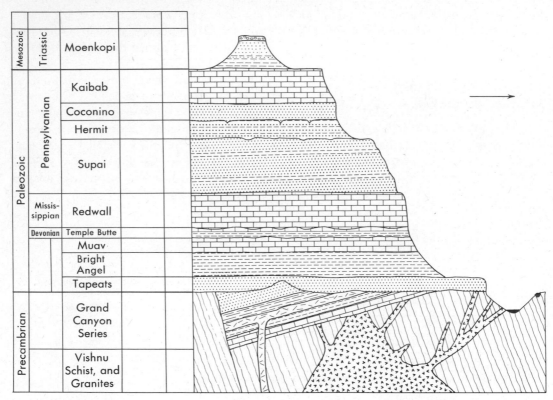

Mesozoic	Triassic	Moenkopi
Paleozoic	Pennsylvanian	Kaibab
		Coconino
		Hermit
		Supai
	Mississippian	Redwall
	Devonian	Temple Butte
		Muav
		Bright Angel
		Tapeats
Precambrian		Grand Canyon Series
		Vishnu Schist, and Granites

Fig. 44-3. Grand Canyon. Much of the geologic history of the Grand Canyon area is decipherable from the rocks exposed on the south wall. We cannot possibly present it all here. None of the last 100 million years and more is portrayed, and there are great gaps in the record represented by unconformities. The greatest is that between the Cambrian and the Precambrian. Another exists within the Precambrian itself. You can locate others if you know the geologic time scale (Fig. 44-2). Much about the conditions of deposition can be inferred from the fossils. All formations contain a few at least except the Precambrian. The formations below the Supai contain marine fossils, indicating the presence of the sea in the area. The Supai and Hermit show evidences of stream deposition, not only by fossils, but also by other characteristics; the Cocconino is obviously a dune deposit of sand made by the wind. The Kaibab indicates the return of the sea, and the Moenkopi a retreat of the sea again. Later chapters of the history of the region are contained in rocks to the north. The cutting of the canyon itself was started about 1 to 2 million years ago.

Thus, streams cutting their valleys into rocks expose them to our view. Still, deep valleys like the Grand Canyon are few, and even the deepest are cut little more than a mile into the earth. If horizontally deposited sediments[1] are folded and then eroded (Fig. 41-10), then the older layers may be exposed at the surface even though the surface is level. Note in the figure that if erosion had cut only to the line *dp*, no formations below 3 would be exposed. Erosion to *fg* exposes them all. The result is that one can walk across the surface from *f* to *g* and see formations exposed right at the surface that in *A* may have been as much as three miles below the surface.

In New York City the schists and gneisses that represent the roots of an ancient mountain range are exposed in the parks of Manhattan and the Bronx, while across the East River on Long Island these rocks are buried by younger sediments of varying thicknesses (Fig. 43-15*b*). The schists and gneisses are intruded by countless pegmatite dikes but none of them penetrates the younger sediments. Thus, the older rocks reveal something of the igneous and metamorphic history of a region that was once a highland area, but on Long Island where the younger rocks have not yet been eroded away, the story the older rocks have to tell is hidden from us. Erosion, therefore, is both detrimental and useful to man's search for the past.

GEOSYNCLINAL CONCEPT

We used a hypothetical North America to demonstrate some of the problems that

[1] Most sediments are deposited in nearly horizontal layers.

man has in gaining access to the geologic record. There were elements of truth in the situation presented. Beginning some 500,000,000 years ago there was a highland area in eastern North America, a highland area broken up into a chain of volcanic islands, and to the west of them there was

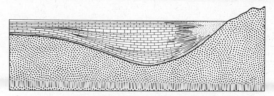

Fig. 44-4. The Geosynclinal Concept. To the right (east or southeast in the case of the Appalachian Geosyncline) was the borderland area, the source of the sediments which were produced as the result of weathering, masswasting and stream erosion. Streams carried them down into the periodically subsiding basins, building great deltas out into them. When filling got ahead of sinking, the sea was driven out; when sinking got ahead of filling, the sea returned. Note that the coarser sediments are nearest the source.

a shallow trough in which sediments eroded from the islands accumulated in great thicknesses. Such a trough is called a geosyncline. Its bottom sank from time to time to keep pace more or less with filling (Fig. 44-4).

At times sinking got ahead of filling and a shallow sea covered the floor of the geosyncline in whole or in part. At other times filling got ahead of sinking and so the sea was driven out for some millions of years. Coupled with such advances and retreats of the sea were other advances and retreats caused by diastrophism as the

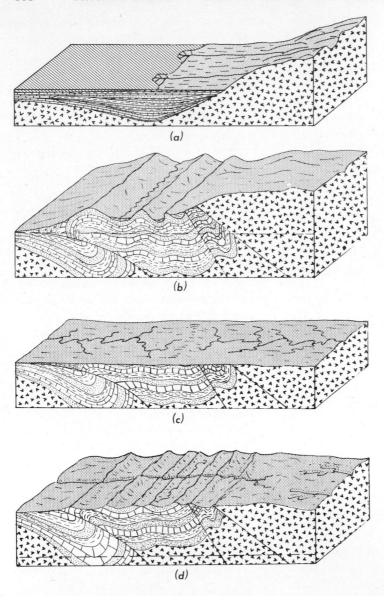

(a)

(b)

(c)

(d)

Fig. 44-5. Generalized Abbreviated History of Appalachian Mountains. **(a)** Streams from highland areas (Appalachian) transported sediments to the Appalachian Geosyncline where they accumulated in thicknesses up to 40,000 ft. over a period of some 300 million years. **(b)** Lateral compression from the southeast caused the weakest rocks (the sediments) to crumple into anticlines and synclines, and to fault, forming the original Appalachians. **(c)** Peneplanation of the area. **(d)** Uplift of eastern North America initiated a new cycle of erosion. The weaker rocks were eroded out faster than the more resistant (see Fig. 41-11), leaving the latter standing up as ridges. (Actually there have been at least three peneplanations with an uplift following each.)

highland areas were uplifted from time to time after being eroded down almost to the peneplain stage. While the sea was absent the previously deposited sediments were subject to erosion, so that there are now gaps in the geologic record.

This series of events were spread over some 300 million years, during which time the total thickness of sediments deposited in some parts of the geosyncline reached 40,000 ft. In the end these sediments were folded (Fig. 44-5) into a great mountain range, the remnants of which we today call the Appalachian Mountains.

The folding was completed about 225 million years ago. Curiously enough, the mountains were highest in those areas where the sediments accumulated in greatest thicknesses. Careful study reveals that most of the other great mountain ranges of the earth were formed from great thicknesses of sediments accumulated in other geosynclines. Therefore if we understand the history of one of these ranges, we understand, in general, the history of them all. It is chiefly the details that are different. The original Appalachians have since been peneplaned, uplifted, peneplaned again, uplifted, and peneplaned a third time. Once again uplift came, and they are at present undergoing a fourth peneplanation. Since the last uplift erosion has cut deeply into the belts of weaker rocks, leaving the more resistant ones to stand up as ridges (Fig. 41-11).

LAW OF SUPERPOSITION

We have already noted that sedimentary rocks are deposited in successive layers that are usually not far from the horizontal. It follows that in any sequence of sedimentary rock formations not disturbed by diastrophic forces other than uplift, the oldest strata will be at the bottom, the youngest at the top. This is sometimes referred to as the Law of Superposition. In cases where the strata have been deformed by folding or faulting, the law still holds. In some cases the strata have been so complexly folded that the folds have been overturned; older strata have come to lie on younger strata, or they may simply stand vertically. One type of fault can also produce the same result. In such cases the law does not hold. Usually the geologist can apply

some method or principle to give him the relative ages.

LAW OF IGNEOUS INTRUSION

We have also noted that the rocks of New York City are intruded by countless dikes but that on Long Island there are younger strata with no evidence of such intrusions (Fig. 43-15b). It follows that the dikes were intruded before the younger strata were deposited. It also is self-evident that the dikes are younger than the schists and gneisses. This is an example of the law of igneous intrusion, which simply states that the intrusive rock is always younger than the intruded rock. In Fig. 41-6 an igneous body lies between layers of sedimentary rock. If it is intrusive, then it is not only younger than the rocks below it but also younger than the rocks above. The problem is to prove that it is intrusive, for there is a possibility that it could have been poured out on the surface as a lava flow, or series of lava flows, and then buried by later sediments.

If we note the projections extending from the sill into both the rocks above and below, we see that it must be intrusive. Moreover, the sediments in contact with the sill at its top show the effects of the heat of the igneous body. They must therefore have been present earlier.

PRINCIPLE OF UNCONFORMITY

We have already spoken about the gaps in the record that have been caused by erosion. If the eroded strata have been covered by younger strata, the surface between the two series of strata is called an unconformity. Formally defined, an unconformity is a surface of erosion or nondeposition that separates younger from older beds. Consider Fig. 43-15*b*. It is obvious that there is a great gap in the geologic record between the time of the formation of the original rocks from which the schist and gneiss were derived, and the time of deposition of the strata in contact with them on Long Island. During that time the original rocks must have been folded, metamorphosed to schist and gneiss, and peneplaned. (Actually far more has happened than that but a study of these rocks alone will not reveal it.) Other unconformities are shown in Figs. 41-4, 44-1, and 44-2. The gap in the record indicated by the unconformity may vary from hundreds of thousands of years to a billion or even more.

LAW OF ORGANIC CORRELATION

Assemblages of fossils, and sometimes single fossils, may be used to determine the relative ages of formations in one area with respect to those in other areas. The principle assumes [2] that evolution has taken place, so that the differences in the fossils in marine strata at the bottom of a high cliff and those in marine strata at the top of the cliff are explainable by the changes that evolution has wrought during the time the whole sequence was being deposited.

Consider the geosyncline described earlier in this chapter. Suppose the sea has been present for a long time. Marine animals have lived and died, and the remains of many have become entombed in the

---

[2] Whether evolution has or has not taken place is no longer subject to question among scientists. It is an accepted fact because of the overwhelming amount of evidence that has been accumulated. Scientists may argue about how evolution has taken place but never whether it has taken place or not.

sediments. Now let the sea retreat for some millions of years. Evolution goes steadily on during these millions of years, and when the sea returns, it brings with it all the new forms of marine life that have evolved. Some of them will be preserved as fossils in the new sediments, fossils that will be different from those in the beds below them.

Millions of years later, perhaps hundreds of millions of years later, suppose that two groups of strata are exposed to investigation by geologists. A geologist in Georgia collects fossils from the two series of strata, carefully listing and describing them and the formations in which they are found; he eventually publishes his findings. Another geologist in Pennsylvania reads the article and finds the fossils described are identical for the most part with some he has collected from two series of strata in his state. He assumes that his strata are the same age as those in Georgia. He is simply using the Law of Organic Correlation, which states that if two sedimentary formations have the same assemblages of fossils, they are the same age.

This Law of Organic Correlation has been established and verified by thousands of geologists working in all parts of the earth during the last hundred and fifty years. By use of the law the geologist can determine the distribution of land and sea at various times during the past. In other words, he can construct paleogeographic maps. Unfortunately not all sedimentary rocks contain fossils, so that correlation with other formations are not always possible. Moreover, strata containing fossils of land dwellers cannot ordinarily be correlated with strata containing fossils of marine dwellers. However, indirect correlations can be made in some cases.

UNIFORMITARIANISM vs. CATASTROPHISM

All of the early peoples of the earth believed in some form of special creation for both the earth and themselves. In Western Europe the belief that the earth was created essentially as is prevailed even among most men of science until near the beginning of the nineteenth century. It was heresy for Christians to believe that the earth was more than 6000 years old. Mountains were believed to have originated within a short span of time, a few weeks at most, with catastrophic results in the surrounding regions. Great cataclysms split the earth wide open in places, forming the great canyons that some rivers flowed in. Great floods were called on to explain the location of strata containing marine fossils on the tops of mountains, the distribution of boulders that we now know to have been left by one of the great ice sheets, and many other geologic phenomena.

The fact that fossils in some strata were entirely different from those in strata directly above created a problem that was "solved" by assuming a catastrophe that wiped out the earlier forms, necessitating another creation. As more knowledge was gained, more and more catastrophes were called for, until the number reached 27. Long before, however, almost all geologists and biologists had forsaken the catastrophism concept, for even the most casual dabbling in geology had revealed indisputable evidence that the earth was more than 6000 years old.

The first important dissenter from the catastrophism concept was the Scotsman, James Hutton, the founder of modern geology. Hutton obtained his facts first and drew his conclusions afterwards, as do all true scientists. He could find no evidence of any process that took place in the past that was not going on at present. He could find "no vestige of a beginning, no prospect of an end." He came to the conclusion that the present is the key to the past. No great floods, no great cataclysms were needed, but only the processes that are operating today. This is the essence of the concept of uniformitarianism. Hutton's work was carried on by Sir Charles Lyell, who championed Hutton's ideas and added much evidence of his own. Shortly after Darwin had advanced his theory of evolution in 1859 (a theory that introduced into the field of biology the same general concept of uniform change), the Law of Uniform Change (uniformitarianism) was widely accepted. It involves the fewest awkward assumptions, and so gives the simplest explanation of all the available facts.

SUMMARY

The search for the past is chiefly a search for fossils combined with a study of the environmental conditions under which the original organisms lived. The search is made only in sedimentary rocks or slightly metamorphosed rocks that were once sedimentary, except rarely. Only those rocks that are exposed at the earth's surface by the processes of erosion are available for study, except for the rock cores of wells and the rocks in some quarries and mines. Thus no thorough search of all sedimentary rocks is possible. The best places to search are among the strata exposed in cliffs and canyons, and in the sedimentary rocks exposed in deeply eroded fold mountain areas (Fig. 41-10); in level areas of horizontal rock only the top layer is exposed.

From the fossils the trained geologist can deduce the habitats. Easiest is that of a marine or continental environment. If marine, the geologist knows that a shallow sea once covered that area, etc. Given sufficient information from enough fossils and from other sources, the geologist can infer the distribution of land and sea at various times in the past. In the absence of fossils the task is more difficult, but intelligent use of such features as "fossil" ripple marks and mudcracks, stratification, cross-bedding, grain size and composition, etc., will reveal much information. The laws of superposition, igneous intrusion, organic correlation, and the principles of uniformitarianism, unconformity, and many other laws and principles not mentioned, are all used by the geologist in his search for the past. The fossils also reveal that life has indisputably evolved from simpler forms.

From a study of the thickness and kinds of strata deposited in folded mountain regions, e.g., the Appalachians, as compared with adjacent areas of horizontal strata, geologists have deduced the geosynclinal concept, a concept that is valid for all folded mountain chains, simple or complex. Essentially the concept explains the much greater thickness of strata in these mountain regions than in the adjacent regions of horizontal strata, by deposition of sediments derived from a nearby highland region in a great, shallow, much elongated trough (the geosyncline) whose bottom sank to more or less keep pace with filling. Eventually the constructional forces began to dominate the destructional ones, with the final result that the geosynclinal rocks were folded into a great mountain range (Fig. 44-4). Long before this folding and elevation is completed, the forces of gradation are at work to level the area. Thus, what was once an area of deposition has become an area of erosion, with the sediments derived from it being deposited somewhere else. Today those areas are chiefly the continental shelves that surround all the large land areas of the earth.

EXERCISES

I. TERMS AND CONCEPTS

Geosyncline
Principle of superposition
Law of Igneous Intrusion
Principle of unconformity
Law of Organic Correlation
Law of Uniformitarianism (uniform change)

II. PROBLEMS

1. What is meant by the geologic record?

2. Explain how erosion and diastrophism have together made more of the record available, while they at the same time have destroyed much of it.

3. List the order in which the various types of life, plant and animal, invertebrate and vertebrate, appear in the fossil record. Does this succession support the concept of evolution? Explain.

4. What is meant by a gap in the orderly sequence of deposition? What causes the gaps?

5. Much of the geologic record that has been preserved is unavailable to man, and always will be as far as modern man is concerned. Explain by stating where these records may be and why they are unavailable.

6. Where would you expect to find the best record of geologic events during a 500,000,000-year interval preserved and available to man, in a level plain or plateau, or in a rugged mountain region? Explain.

7. In Fig. 44-1, why are the upper rocks on Long Island not folded as are the lower ones? What do you call the surface separating the folded rocks from those above them?

8. What is a geosyncline? How can such a shallow trough accumulate so great a thickness of sediments?

9. List the general sequence of events from the time of formation of a geosyncline

until its final destruction. In what way was it destroyed? (Note that what had so long been an area of deposition finally became an area of erosion.)

10. Study Fig. 44-2 carefully, noting that the ridges in *B* (what is a ridge?) are the upfolds, whereas in *D* they are composed of the resistant sandstones and conglomerates; the valleys in *B* are the downfolds, whereas in *D* they are composed of the weaker shales and limestones.

11. Can one apply the Law of Superposition to vertical strata? Why or why not?

12. The question as to whether a dike is intrusive or not never arises, but every sill has to be carefully checked. Explain.

13. What is an unconformity? What is its significance as far as the geologic record is concerned?

14. Locate an unconformity in Fig. 44-3.

15. An area is vertically uplifted a few tens of feet above sea level. The uplifted sediments contain fossils. It remains that way for some millions of years. Would it be an area of erosion or an area of deposition, or neither? Finally it sinks beneath the sea again for a long period of time, and is then again uplifted. A geologist examines the rocks thousands of years later. Could he find a record of the first uplift? If so, what would it be? Could he estimate the length of time of the first emergence? How?

16. Do fossils give us the absolute age of rocks? Explain.

17. Would you expect to find fossils of dinosaurs and horses in the same formation? Why or why not?

18. A newspaper carried an account of fossil bones being found in a nearby area. They were reported to be dinosaur bones. A local geologist, who had not read the account, was asked about it. His first question was the whereabouts of the locality of the find. On being told, he said, "They can't possibly be dinosaur bones; they are probably mastodon bones." His listeners, all nongeologists, protested that he was much too dogmatic in his answer. Yet he turned out to be right. Any geologist familiar with the local geology would have given the same answer, and just as quickly. Can you think of a reason why?

19. Why was the concept of catastrophism necessary to those who believed the earth to be only 6000 years old?

20. State the Law of Uniformitarianism (Law of Uniform Change).

PART

VIII

THE ENERGY WITHIN ATOMIC NUCLEI*

We now return to the structure of the atom. Whereas our previous concern was chiefly with the arrangement of the electrons, our present concern will be entirely with the nucleus. The arrangement of the electrons in the outer shells of atoms led us directly into the electronic theory of chemical bonding; we were forced to by-pass further study of the nucleus, for at most it plays a passive role in chemical reactions. The only alternative is to by-pass the electronic theory, and return to it later. Our method is better, we believe, for a consideration of the energy of the nucleus leads us directly into the energy within stars, our closing topic.

That there was considerable energy within the nucleus was made evident by the phenomena of radioactivity. The ejection of both alpha particles and beta rays at high speeds and the emission of high-energy gamma rays, the most penetrating of all electromagnetic radiation could mean only that considerable energy resided in the nucleus. The fact that large numbers of positive charges were packed tightly in nuclei suggested that large amounts of energy were needed to hold them together. Einstein,

---

* That which makes stars possible is the energy within atomic nuclei. Therefore we will include the chapter on stellar astronomy in this section instead of in a separate section by itself.

in his discussion of relativity in 1905, had stated the equivalence of mass and energy in his now famous equation

$$E = mc^2$$

where m is mass and c is the velocity of light $(3 \times 10^{10}$ cm/sec$)$. If they are equivalent, then under certain circumstances they should be interconvertible. Our problem is to see what these circumstances are.

CHAPTER XLV

Natural Radioactivity and Modern Alchemy

The value of "useless science" must be stressed. I should like to be able to make people see research in science as one of the great achievements of the human mind, an activity more allied to the arts.—SIR GEORGE THOMSON (*Nobel Prize, Physics, 1937*)

We now return to the structure of the atom to learn something of the energy that lies within its nucleus. Our concern with atomic structure previously was with the electrons and their arrangements about the nucleus. It is the distribution of energy in the outer shells that undergoes changes during chemical reactions—in fact, it is these changes that constitute a chemical reaction. During these changes the role of the nucleus was a passive one, except in the case of the hydrogen atom. Hydrogen is the exception because it is the only reactive atom with only one shell, and it is the only atom whose nucleus (in ordinary hydrogen) consists of one proton only, and has a bare nucleus for its positive ion. The role of this nucleus has been discussed in acid–base reactions.

We have seen how Moseley (1913–1914) (Chapter XVIII), by means of the progressive shift of X-ray spectra with increasing atomic number, was led to the conclusion that "there is in the atom a fundamental quantity, which increases by regular steps as we pass from one element to the next. This quantity can only be the charge on the central positive nucleus, of the existence of which we already have proof. Thus, the number of charges on the nucleus is always equal to the atomic number. The letter Z is commonly used to indicate atomic number.

These discoveries made it possible to define *an element as a substance whose atoms all had the same atomic number, i.e., the same charge on the nucleus.*

DISCOVERY OF THE PROTON

Research on the structure of the nucleus was continued by Rutherford and others, chiefly by bombarding various kinds of atoms with alpha particles (doubly charged helium ions) from a radioactive source. Rutherford used such ions to bombard nitrogen atoms in a closed tube. The approximate atomic weights of helium and nitrogen are 4 and 14, respectively. Now a light ball with a fixed velocity that strikes a much heavier ball head on cannot propel that heavier ball nearly as far as it could if it struck a ball lighter than itself (Law of Conservation of Momentum). Therefore Rutherford expected to find that the alpha particles would be stopped by collisions (even if not head on) with the heavier nitrogen atoms.

To see if they were, he placed a movable fluorescent screen in the tube. Alpha particles cause a flash of light (scintilla-

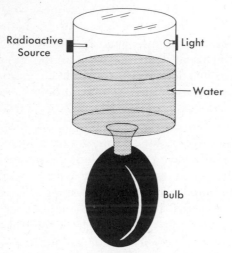

Fig. 45-1. Wilson Cloud Chamber. The enclosed air above the water is saturated with vapor. Squeezing the bulb compresses the vapor, heating it slightly. A wait of a few seconds allows this heat to be dissipated, so that when the bulb is released, cooling takes place as the vapor expands. The air is then supersaturated because of the drop in temperature, so that condensation occurs about any particles in the air, particularly charged particles. The charged alpha particles shot out from the source at high speed ionize the air molecules. The condensing vapor collects on them, so that the train of ions in the wake of the alpha particle appears as a cloud trail visible to the naked eye.

tions) to be emitted when they strike the screen. Few flashes could be observed farther than a distance of about 7 cm. These few could be observed when the screen was more than 30 cm away. This could happen only if the particles causing the flashes had greater velocity than the alpha particles. Momentum considerations ruled out the possibility that they could be nitrogen atoms.

Rutherford tried other gases, but found they produced no long-range scintillations. For all of them, alpha particles had very nearly the same range. Clearly then, the effect was one related to the particular gas, nitrogen, and, equally clearly, the particles causing the long-range scintillations were particles smaller than alpha particles. The only particles smaller than alpha particles that could produce this effect are hydrogen nuclei, which have masses about one-fourth those of alpha particles. He therefore isolated [1] some of the unknown particles and tested their behavior in a magnetic field. He found that they had the same charge and the same mass as hydrogen nuclei. They must therefore be hydrogen nuclei.

The next problem was their source. He first had to eliminate the possibility that hydrogen could be present in water vapor mixed with the nitrogen, or could get into his apparatus in any other way. Eventually he became convinced that the only source was nitrogen nuclei. He used Wilson's newly invented cloud chamber (Fig. 45-1) to show the paths of the alpha particles through the nitrogen. The cloud chamber is a device that makes the paths of charged particles visible and photographable. The final conclusion was that in some way the helium nuclei (alpha particles) were absorbed by nitrogen nuclei, and the product transformed into some-

[1] The separation is effected by passing the contents of the tube through electric and magnetic fields. (See Chapter XXVI.)

thing else, as shown by the following nuclear reaction: [2]

$$_7N^{14} + {}_2He^4 \rightarrow {}_9F^{18} \rightarrow {}_1H^1 + {}_8O^{17}$$

(Eq. 45-1)

Note that the nitrogen nucleus momentarily absorbed the helium nucleus, making the charge on the new nucleus 9 (which by definition must be that of fluorine), and giving it a mass number of 18. This is not regular fluorine with a mass number of 19, but an isotope (for which see later) which is unstable. The assumption that a nitrogen nucleus can absorb an alpha particle is bolstered by the fact that radioactive atoms eject alpha particles. F^{18} at once splits into two unequal parts, one a hydrogen nucleus (to which Rutherford applied the term proton) and the other an isotope of oxygen. This is the old dream of the alchemist—a transformation of one element into another—although it was not that of a baser element into gold.

DISCOVERY OF THE NEUTRON

The mass number of the hydrogen nucleus (a proton) is 1, whereas that of

[2] In nuclear equations the subscripts refer to atomic numbers and the superscripts to mass numbers. The mass number of an atom is the whole number nearest the atomic weight. It should be carefully distinguished from an atomic mass unit (amu). If 6×10^{23} atoms of C^{12} weighs 12 gm, then one atom of C^{12} weighs $12/(6 \times 10^{23})$ gm. A new unit equal to $\frac{1}{12}$ of this weight is called an atomic mass unit: $\frac{1}{12}$ of $12/(6 \times 10^{23}) = 1.66 \times 10^{-24} = 1$ amu. The mass number of ordinary hydrogen is 1 and its atomic weight is 1.0070 (under the new atomic weight scale, p. 248). The actual mass of the hydrogen atom is, therefore, 1.007 (1.66×10^{-24}) gm. Like chemical equations, nuclear equations must be balanced; both the sum of the subscripts and the sum of the superscripts on the two sides must be equal.

helium is 4. If it is the proton that carries the positive charge, then helium's two protons account for only half of its mass. What constitutes the other half? That there were two particles each approximately equal to 1 amu instead of one particle of 2 amu could be inferred from the fact that beryllium with 4 protons has a mass number of 9. It has 5 mass numbers to be accounted for, which can be done by 5 of the unknown particles of 1 mass number each, but not by unknown particles of 2 mass numbers each. The unknown particle was first inferred to be some sort of a proton-electron combination. Such a particle would be about the right size, it would be electrically neutral, and it would account for the source of the beta particles (electrons) emitted during natural radioactivity. It would also explain why the ejection of a beta particle would increase the atomic number of the atom by one; the proton left behind, with no electron to neutralize it, would add an extra charge to the nucleus. This hypothetical proton-electron combination was named the neutron even before it was discovered.

Search for it continued for years. In 1930 the daughter of Marie Curie and her husband (F. Joliot) were bombarding the metal beryllium with alpha particles. No protons were ejected, but a new type of radiation of greater energy than any yet known was detected. If a plate of paraffin (a hydrocarbon) was placed in its path, the new radiation ejected protons from it. This new radiation did not leave tracks in a cloud chamber and it was wholly unaffected by electric and magnetic fields. The discoverers came to the conclusion that this radiation was electromagnetic in character.

In 1932 Chadwick, a former assistant of

Rutherford's, proved that the high energy of this radiation could not be accounted for by assuming that it was wavelike, but that it could be explained by assuming that it was a particle with a mass slightly greater than that of a proton but with no

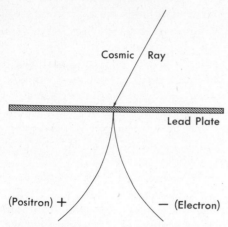

Cosmic / Ray

Lead Plate

(Positron) +   — (Electron)

Fig. 45-2. Discovery of the Positron. A cosmic ray from outer space entered the lead plate and passed close to the nucleus of a lead atom. The intense electric field of this nucleus caused the ray (probably a gamma ray photon in this case) to disintegrate into an electron and a positron. A magnetic field below the plate caused these oppositely charged particles to diverge.

charge. It turned out to be the long sought for neutron. The reaction can be written as follows:

$$_4Be^9 + _2He^4 \rightarrow _6C^{12} + _0n^1$$

where $_0n^1$ is the neutron.

The difficulty of its detection lies in its tiny size and in its electrical neutrality. Because of these properties it has great penetrating ability; neutrons cannot be contained in any container. Having no charge

a neutron does not ionize a gas except by a direct hit and so does not readily lose its energy (since the bulk of the atom is empty space), and it experiences no electrical force of repulsion or attraction on approaching a nucleus. In a head-on collision with a proton, all or nearly all of its energy is transmitted to the proton. The neutron has a mass number of 1 and zero charge; it is therefore represented by $_0n^1$.

We can now redefine atomic mass number as the sum of the masses of the protons, the neutrons, and the electrons in a nucleus. If we use the term *nucleon* to refer to either a proton or a neutron, we can say that the mass number is the number of nucleons in the nucleus. Since the atomic number, given by the subscripts in nuclear formulas, is the number of protons in the nucleus, the difference between the atomic and the mass numbers represents the number of neutrons.

DISCOVERY OF THE POSITRON

The fundamental particles of the atom, electrons, protons, neutrons, are all accounted for. There were, however, less fundamental particles to be discovered. Among them was the positron, a particle with the mass of an electron but the charge of the proton. The positron was discovered by observing photographs of cloud tracks (in a Wilson cloud chamber) made by the "smashing" of an atom by cosmic rays.[3] Along with the positron there occurred an electron. In passing through a

[3] Cosmic rays are a very penetrating radiation coming from outer space. That they are extremely penetrating means they have very high energies. Not all cosmic rays are alike. Most are probably atomic nuclei. The problem of cosmic rays is much too complex to be presented here.

magnetic field the paths of the two are curved in opposite directions (Fig. 45-2).

The explanation given, and now accepted, is that, a high-energy cosmic ray, probably a gamma ray photon, entered the cloud chamber through a lead sheet, passed close to the intense electric field of a nucleus of a lead atom, and was transformed into an electron and a positron. This is known as pair production and is the first *transformation of energy into matter* that we know about. The life of a positron is very short. As it loses kinetic energy (by passing near charged particles), it will move towards an electron; they join together and annihilate each other, producing a gamma-ray photon in the process. This, of course, is the reverse of pair production; it is the *transformation of matter into energy*.[4]

Other particles have been recognized, in all about 30. At least one fits into the theory of nuclear binding forces. Most are strange particles that have no place in the scheme of the atom as presented here. Most appear to be disintegration products of protons and neutrons. The situation is rather chaotic at present. Research still goes on in the hopes that order will eventually replace the present confusion.[5]

[4] Positrons are not to be considered elementary particles in the same sense that electrons, protons, and neutrons are. A proton can disintegrate into a neutron and a positron.

[5] One of the strange things about these particles is that half of them are classified as anti-matter. Thus, the positron is the same as the electron but with opposite charge. It could be called an anti-electron. There are anti-protons, anti-neutrons, etc. The anti-particles are produced by interactions between particles. They are short-lived, for if an anti-particle meets up with one of its counterparticles, both are annihilated by conversion of their matter into electromagnetic energy.

ISOTOPES

As far back as 1815 William Prout, an English physician, was impressed by the prevalence of whole numbers and nearly whole numbers among the atomic weights. He therefore suggested that the hydrogen atom with an atomic weight of 1 was the fundamental particle; other atoms were made up of hydrogen atoms combined in some unknown way. The idea had to be abandoned as greater accuracy in atomic weight determinations were made. The idea was revived in the early 1900's with the discovery of isotopes.

Isotopes are different forms of the same element; they have the same atomic number but different mass numbers. It had been known since about 1912 that not all atoms of the same element had the same atomic weight. The story goes back to the 1880's when an investigator discovered positive rays (Chapter XXVI) in gas discharge tubes. These rays were ionized atoms or molecules. Experiments to determine their charge-to-mass ratio ran into trouble because not all had the same mass nor the same velocity.

The difficulty was overcome by first passing the ions through a velocity selector [6] which separates those of one particular velocity from those having other velocities. Thus, we get ions whose only difference is in their masses. Once through the veloc-

[6] A velocity selector is an arrangement of an electric and a magnetic field at right angles to each other. The strengths of the fields are adjusted so that the net force exerted on a particular charged particle moving at a particular velocity is zero, so that the particle passes straight through without deviation. However, if particles of other velocities enter the fields, they will be deflected out of the line of flight of the particular particle.

ity selector, these selected ions continue to move at a uniform speed because there is no net force acting on them to change the speed. They are, however, passed through a magnetic field which changes their direction but not their speed. They, therefore, move in circles whose radius depends on the values of m, v, and e.[7] Since v and e for all are the same, the radius depends only on m. Those with the most mass will be deflected the least and so move in a circle with the largest radius (Fig. 45-4).

This sorting out is made apparent by allowing the deviated particles to impinge on a photographic film, where they produce lines somewhat analogous to those of spectral lines as seen in a spectroscope. An instrument that accomplishes this is called a mass spectrograph (because it separates ions according to their masses), and the series of lines is called a spectrogram. The mass spectrogram of neon, whose isotopes were the first to be separated, is shown in Fig. 45-3b. It reveals the three isotopes of neon with their respective atomic weights. The width and intensity of the spectrogram line indicates the proportions of each.

About 90 per cent of ordinary neon is Ne^{20}, which accounts for its atomic weight being close to 20 (20.2). These proportions are constant for any natural source of neon, as it is for all other elements. For oxygen there are also three isotopes with mass numbers of 16, 17, and 18. However,

99.76 per cent of all oxygen is O^{16}. Tin has 10 isotopes. Hydrogen has three, $_1H^1$, $_1H^2$ (deuterium) and $_1H^3$ (tritium); these are the only well-known isotopes with special names. The mass of any isotope can now be calculated with very great precision (to six and seven significant figures). The mass numbers of isotopes are always within less than 1 per cent of their true masses. Chemical processes *never* separate isotopes, so that the chemist is rarely concerned with the concept.

RADIOACTIVITY

Radioactivity, as we have already indicated (Chapter XXVI), involves the spontaneous disintegration of certain types of atoms to form atoms of other elements by the emission of either an electron or a helium nucleus from the nucleus of the disintegrating atom. In either case, the remaining part of the disintegrating atom is a new element. It is therefore a natural transmutation. Consider the emission of an alpha particle (helium nucleus) from ordinary uranium:

$$_{92}U^{238} \rightarrow _{90}Th^{234} + _2He^4$$

(The arrow indicates that the helium nucleus has escaped.) The emission of the helium nucleus causes a loss of two positive charges. Hence the atomic number drops from 92 to 90. The emission also causes a loss of four nucleons (2 protons and 2 neutrons) so that the mass number of the new element is 234. The thorium atom now emits an electron (beta ray).

$$_{90}Th^{234} \rightarrow _{91}Pa^{234} + _{-1}e^0$$

[7]
$$\frac{mv^2}{r} = Hev$$

(see p. 389). Whence $r = \dfrac{mv}{He}$

Since v, H, and e are the same for all of these ions, r depends only on m.

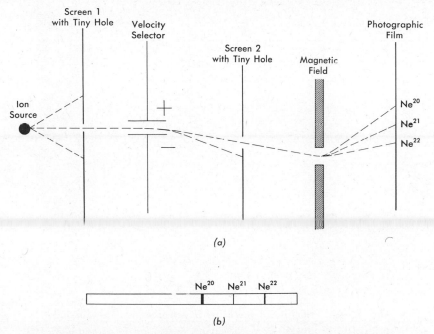

Fig. 45-3. Principle of Mass Spectrograph (Spectrometer) Used in Separation of Isotopes. **(a)** Atoms must first be ionized. The screens let only those ions which strike the holes to pass through, thus insuring a narrow beam. The velocity selector consists of an electric field (shown) and a magnetic field arranged at right angles to it (not shown). This insures that all ions passing through Screen 2 will have the same velocity and the same charge. Thus, any differences in the amount of deviation on passing through the second magnetic field will be due to differences in mass only. **(b)** The developed film shows the impacts of the three isotopes of neon as lines whose densities are proportional to the amount present in natural neon. Most of it is Ne[20], as is predicted by its atomic weight of 20.183.

The mass number of the new element (proactinium) remains unchanged because the mass of the electron is negligible. The atomic number increases by one because a neutron has split into a proton and an electron; the escape of the electron leaves an additional positive charge in the nucleus.

Ejection of another electron (from proactinium) then takes place, followed by the ejection of five helium nuclei, one after the other.

$$_{91}\mathrm{Pa}^{234} \rightarrow \, _{92}\mathrm{U}^{234} + \, _{-1}e^{0}$$

$$_{92}\mathrm{U}^{234} \rightarrow \, _{90}\mathrm{Th}^{230} + \, _{2}\mathrm{He}^{4}$$

$$_{90}\mathrm{Th}^{230} \rightarrow \, _{88}\mathrm{Ra}^{226} + \, _{2}\mathrm{He}^{4}$$

and so on.

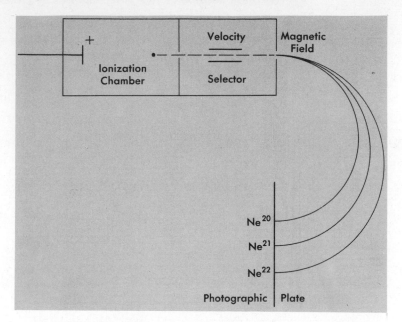

Fig. 45-4. Principle of the Mass Spectrometer. The curving paths are produced by a continuous deflection in a magnetic field. The lighter atoms are deflected more than the heavier ones.

In all, $_{92}U^{238}$ ejects eight alpha particles and six beta particles before the nucleus becomes stable. The final product is $_{82}Pb^{206}$, which is one of several isotopes of lead.

When atoms of $_{92}U^{235}$, one of the natural isotopes of uranium, disintegrates, the final product is also an isotope of lead, $_{82}Pb^{207}$. During the process of the disintegration of uranium 235, one or more isotopes of all of the elements with atomic numbers 81 or higher are created.[8] It was Rutherford,

who, while working on the identification of alpha particles, conceived the idea that other elements should be present in every uranium sample, elements lighter than uranium. By long and careful work he determined the order in which the elements were created for each isotope of uranium. This is a natural transmutation of the elements, but not a transmutation of baser elements into gold. It is much more nearly the reverse, i.e., the transmutation of more valuable (to man) elements to the less valuable ones.

Half-Life

Each radioactive element gives off its rays (i.e., decays) at a definite rate. A definite number of particles are emitted

[8] Lead is the only nonradioactive element whose atomic weight varies with the place where it is found. U^{238}, U^{235} and Th^{232} all disintegrate radioactively into three different isotopes to form 98.5 per cent of all lead. Since U and Th do not necessarily occur together, lead from different areas will have different atomic weights.

per second *for any given quantity of the element*. This means that if we change the quantity of the element, we change the *rate* at which the particles are emitted. Consider a number of piles of widely different masses of a radioactive element. Whether the size of the pile is 1 oz, 1 lb, or 1 ton, the time for half of the atoms in each pile to decay is the same. Thus, the rate depends on the size of the pile. As the number of undecayed atoms gets less and less, the rate becomes slower and slower, so the time for complete decay to take place is infinite for each pile.

Thus, to speak of the "life" of a radioactive element is meaningless. The half-life, however, is an actual easily determinable span of time. Nothing that man can do, either physically or chemically, to radioactive atoms can cause them to change the half-life. This half-life is a property of the atoms of a given radioactive element, and it varies enormously from element to element. (See Table 45-1.)

TABLE 45-1

HALF-LIFE OF RADIOACTIVE ELEMENTS

U^{238}	4.5×10^9 yr	Po^{218}	3.05 min
U^{235}	7.1×10^8 yr	Pb^{214}	26.8 min
U^{234}	2.5×10^5 yr	At^{218}	1.5–2.0 sec
Th^{234}	24.1 days	Po^{214}	1.64×10^{-4} sec
Ra^{226}	1620 yr	Pb^{210}	22 yr
Rn^{222}	3.82 days	Pb^{207}	Stable
		Pb^{206}	Stable

A few moments perusal of the table should make it apparent that any fresh sample of a uranium-bearing mineral will consist mostly of uranium and lead. Of the other elements, only radium will be present in comparatively readily determinable quantities.

Radioactivity as a Time Clock

Consider the following facts: (1) uranium has a long half-life, 4.5×10^9 years; (2) the rate at which it decays is constant for any given quantity of it; (3) it is a mineral that is formed when certain magmas crystallize; and (4) it may in places be found in fresh unweathered igneous intrusive rocks and so contains what is left of its original uranium plus all of the lead that is the end-product of the disintegration. From these facts there arose the possibility of using the ratio of the number of atoms of lead to the number of atoms of uranium to tell the age of the sample. After long and careful work to eliminate all possible sources of error, an equation was worked out that yielded reasonably satisfactory results. Thus, the minimum age of the earth has been determined.[9]

Carbon Dating

The C^{14} method of dating is confined to more precise dating of geologic and anthropologic events of the last 50,000 years. C^{14} is a radioactive isotope that is formed in the atmosphere by high-energy particles from outer space (cosmic rays) striking nitrogen atoms, transmuting them to C^{14} with a half-life of 5600 years. There is an equilibrium in the atmosphere between the rate of C^{14} formation and the rate of disintegration. All living things contain carbon obtained from the atmosphere, and so also contain an amount of C^{14} that is in

[9] Other methods of minimum age determinations exist, all by radioactivity of one sort or another. Their results are used as a check for the accuracy for the determinations listed above.

equilibrium with that in the atmosphere. When death comes to any plant or animal, the intake ceases but the radioactive decay of C^{14} to C^{12} goes on. Thus, old dead organic matter, be it straw, wood, or bones, contains less C^{14} than new wood. By measuring the concentration of C^{14}, the time since death can be computed. By this means it has been determined that the retreat of the last great ice sheet in North America began only some 10,000 years ago.

We have left a number of questions about radioactivity unanswered. We will concern ourselves here only with two. Why should one atom of a radioactive element, say uranium, emit an alpha particle at one instant, and another one alongside of it not emit one until several billions of years later? At present we do not know. The other is, whence comes the energy? We do know that alpha particles are emitted at a velocity of about 10,000 mi/ sec. Again, we do not know, but the study of radioactivity led naturally to a study of the energy within the nucleus in a search for possible answers.

SUMMARY

The ejection of alpha and beta particles from radioactive atoms at extremely high speeds made it evident that there must be enormous amounts of energy inside the nucleus. Einstein, solely from mathematical considerations in his work on his relativity theory, had deduced the equation $E = mc^2$. During the 1930's various nuclear experiments were made by many investigators in many countries which revealed much about the nucleus. The discovery of the neutron had given the physicists a new tool, a new "bullet" to fire at atoms of many kinds. Such experiments revealed that some elements could be transmuted into other elements, some normally nonradioactive elements could be made radioactive, and, finally, that the atoms of U^{235} could be fissioned. They allowed experimental tests of Einstein's equation to be made; it proved correct.

The stage was then set for the development of the atomic bomb, the so-called A-bomb, a development that would not have even been seriously thought of had not World War II already started in Europe. This then was the climax of research into the structure of the atom, research that had begun in the early 1900's as a purely intellectual investigation. After the war the possibility of nuclear fusion of light elements was investigated, and in the early 1950's became a reality. The fusion of hydrogen to helium accounts for the energy of the sun and the stars.

Thus, the dream of the alchemists, that of changing one element into another, was realized, but, ironically, the possibility of turning gold into the baser metals, iron in particular, is vastly greater than that of turning iron into gold. This is because iron has the largest binding energy per nucleon of all the elements, and therefore the energy to transmute it is the highest of all.

A number of elements of higher atomic weight than uranium have been made in the laboratory (in the so-called atom-smashing machines). These all have too short half-lives to be found today in nature. Plutonium, with a half-life of 24,000 years, is the only one that at present seems to be useful to man. It is fissionable, as is U^{235}, and can be made in nuclear reactors from U^{238} (the abundant isotope of uranium) to supplement the supply of the relatively rare U^{235}. The heat developed in nuclear reactors where fission can be controlled can be used to generate electricity via a steam engine and dynamo. There is little hope at present of using the energy of atomic fusion for a similar purpose.

EXERCISES

I. Terms and Concepts

Proton	Cosmic ray
Neutron	Isotope
Nucleon	Mass spectrograph
Wilson cloud	Spectrogram
chamber	Deuterium
Nuclear reaction	Tritium
Mass number	Half-life
Positron	Carbon dating

II. Problems

1. Alpha particles ejected from radioactive atoms do not travel more than about 7 cm through air, although they are ejected at 10,000 miles/sec. Why?

2. What caused Rutherford to suspect that the particles causing the long-range scintillations (in his bombardment of nitrogen with alpha particles) were smaller than alpha particles? At that time what particles were known that were smaller than alpha particles? How did he prove what his unknown particles were?

3. The discovery and identification of the neutron was more difficult than that of the proton. Why?

4. The neutron had been postulated and named long before its discovery. Explain.

5. What is an atomic mass unit (amu)? How does it differ from mass number?

6. The neutron turned out to be a more energetic "bullet" with which to bombard atoms than were protons and alpha particles. Why?

7. Neutrons are radioactive. What is their half-life? What are their decay products?

8. How many neutrons are there in $_8O^{16}$, $_{16}S^{32}$, $_{26}Fe^{56}$, $_{82}Pb^{208}$, $_{92}U^{238}$, $_1H^1$, $_1H^2$, $_1H^3$?

9. What is a positron? What happens to it when it meets an electron?

10. What is an isotope? Tin (Sn) has 10 natural isotopes. Seven have atomic weights ranging from 113.9 to 119.9. Write the nuclear formula for each of them.

11. Natural chlorine has an invariable atomic weight of 35.45. Explain why it is not closer to 35 or 36.

12. What is the underlying principle used to separate isotopes? Why can they not be separated chemically?

13. Radium is a disintegration product of U^{238}. Why is it considered an element?

14. Radium disintegrates into radon and helium. The atomic number of radium is 88 and its mass number is 226. What is the atomic number of radon? (Do not look it up.) What is its mass number?

15. What happens to the atomic and mass numbers of a radioactive nucleus when it emits a beta particle? Explain.

16. The ultimate end-products of all natural radioactivity are what? Are the end-products of U^{238} and U^{235} the same? Explain.

17. Explain what is meant by half-life. Why is the half-life meaningful whereas the "full life" meaningless?

18. You have 10 gm of a radioactive isotope which has a half-life of 64 days. How much do you have left at the end of 2 days? Three days? Six days? Eleven days?

19. All natural aluminum atoms have the same mass number. When it is bombarded with alpha particles, Si^{30} and a proton are "created." Write the equation, showing both intermediate and final products.

20. What precautions must be taken to insure a reliable result in the dating of rocks by radioactive methods? Why can C^{14} not be used to give a minimum age of the earth?

CHAPTER XLVI

Nuclear Energy: Atomic Fission and Fusion

. . . all science as it grows towards perfection becomes mathematical in its ideas.
—A. N. WHITEHEAD (1911)

The discovery that radioactive atoms emit alpha, beta, and gamma rays with enormous amounts of energy raised the exciting possibility that man could somehow tap that rich supply. Einstein, at nearly the same time, equated mass to energy in his equation, $E = mc^2$. At the time (1905) this was a mere speculation, resulting from his relativity theory; there was not an experimental shred of evidence to support it. Skepticism about the validity of the equation was not so strong when it was learned that a single alpha particle was emitted with millions of electron volts (ev),[1]

[1] An alpha particle ejected from a radioactive atom creates enormous numbers of ions in passing through two inches of air, at a cost of about 6×10^6 ev of energy. These ions, in returning to the neutral state, ultimately deliver this energy in the form of heat. It is therefore expected that radioactive minerals in rocks gradually cause the

whereas the energy from oxidizing carbon to CO_2 is only about 4 ev per carbon atom. We can "shoot" electrons at helium atoms in a gas discharge tube with high enough energy to strip both electrons from the helium atom, converting it into an alpha particle. This takes only about 80 ev. Whence comes the millions of electron volts with which an alpha particle is emitted from a radioactive atom?

Consider a uranium atom with its 92 protons. Ejection of an alpha particle means that two protons and two neutrons are emitted as a single particle. At the instant of ejection there is a repulsive force between 90 protons and 2 protons. Is this force great enough to eject the alpha particle with a speed of 10,000 mi/sec? The charge on the proton in electrostatic units is 4.8×10^{-10} and the distance between the two protons is about 10^{-13} cm. Applying Coulomb's Law we have

$$F = \frac{q_1 q_2}{d^2} = \frac{(4.8 \times 10^{-10})(4.8 \times 10^{-10})}{(10^{-13})^2}$$

$$= 23 \times 10^6 \text{ dynes} \qquad \text{(Eq. 46-1)}$$

A dyne is a very small unit of force, but 23,000,000 dynes is an enormous force for particles so small to exert; it is equivalent to a 23,000-gm force. Thus, it seems that the repulsive forces can account for the energy of ejection of alpha particles.

This leaves us not much better off, for we are now confronted with other questions. How can any nucleus hold together even an instant in the face of such forces? Why does one uranium atom eject an alpha particle at once and another one alongside it not do so for billions of years? Where

temperature of the rocks to rise if the heat cannot escape fast enough.

did the uranium nucleus get its energy in the first place?

Perhaps Einstein's equation is correct; perhaps the source of the energy is matter itself. The equation states that the energy released for each gram of matter that is annihilated is equal (in ergs) to the square of the velocity of light (in centimeters per second). Thus,

$$E = mc^2 = 1 \times (3 \times 10^{10})^2$$

$$= 9 \times 10^{20} \text{ ergs} \qquad \text{(Eq. 46-2)}$$

This is enough energy to raise a 50,000-ton battleship 100 mi in the air. In a bomb it is equivalent to more than 20,000 tons of TNT.

We will diverge a moment to consider units and instruments. An accelerator is an instrument in which charged particles (ions) gain kinetic energy by being repelled by one electrode and attracted by the other. The higher the potential difference the higher the energies imparted. One unit of such energy is the electron volt. This is an extremely small unit. Nuclear physicists use the larger units, Mev (million electron volts) and Bev (billion electron volts). When one atomic mass unit (amu) is converted into energy, 931 Mev are released.[2]

---

[2] Consider 1 gm of hydrogen ions (approximately 1 mole or 6×10^{23} protons). Converted to energy according to the equation $E = mc^2$, it is equal to $1 \times (3 \times 10^{10})^2$ ergs, or 9×10^{20} ergs. One atomic mass unit (approximately equivalent to the mass of a proton) is equivalent to $1/(6 \times 10^{23})$ gm (see footnote 2, p. 647). Hence 1 amu converted to energy is equal to

$$\frac{1}{6 \times 10^{23}} \times 9 \times 10^{20} = 1.5 \times 10^{-3} \text{ ergs}$$

How many ev (or Mev) is this? The charge on the electron is 1.6×10^{-19} coulombs, and a volt is a joule per coulomb. Hence, 1 ev = $1 \times 1.6 \times 10^{-19}$

THE COCKCROFT-WALTON EXPERIMENT

Now let us return to the previous paragraph. The energy is there if the equation is valid. The first experimental check on it came in 1932 when Cockcroft (England) and Walton (Ireland) bombarded lithium with high-energy protons (protons accelerated by a high voltage) in what is now called an ion accelerator. In the process alpha particles were produced.

$$_3\text{Li}^7 + {}_1\text{H}^1 \rightarrow {}_4\text{Be}^8 \rightarrow$$

$$_2\text{He}^4 + {}_2\text{He}^4 + \text{energy} \qquad \text{(Eq. 46-4)}$$

The energies of the alpha particles could be calculated by measuring their range in air.[3] The energy turns out to be 8.6 Mev for each, a total of 17.2 Mev for both alpha particles. The lithium was at "rest" and the proton that was fired at the lithium had an energy of about 0.5 Mev. How could it impart an energy of 17.3 Mev to the alpha particles? Whence came the energy? Perhaps some mass was converted into energy. We can check this by calculating the masses on the two sides of the above equation:

Mass of proton + mass of lithium

+ input energy in amu

= 2(Mass of alpha particle)

+ output energy in amu   (Eq. 46-5)

---

joules, which is equal to $1.6 \times 10^{-19} \times 10^7 = 1.6 \times 10^{-12}$ ergs (since 10^7 ergs = 1 joule). It follows, then, that 1 amu is equivalent to

$$\frac{1.5 \times 10^{-3} \text{ ergs}}{1.6 \times 10^{-12} \text{ ergs/ev}} = 931 \times 10^6 \text{ ev} = 931 \text{ Mev}$$

(Eq. 46-3)

[3] This is analogous to measuring the energy of a bullet from a gun by measuring the thickness of a board that it will penetrate.

The input energy is the kinetic energy of the proton and the output energy is the kinetic energy of the two alpha particles.

Now if no mass has been converted into energy, the following equation should apply:

Mass of proton + mass of Li atom

$$= 2 \times \text{Mass of an alpha particle}$$

$$\text{(Eq. 46-6)}$$

One of the two equations (46-5 or 46-6) must be wrong. Let us substitute the actual masses in each, doing so in Eq. 46-6 first.

$$1.0076 \, \text{amu} + 7.0166 \, \text{amu}$$

$$= 4.0028 \, \text{amu} + 4.0028 \, \text{amu}$$

$$8.0242 \, \text{amu} = 8.0056 \, \text{amu} + ?$$

The difference is

$$8.0242 - 8.0056 = 0.0186 \, \text{amu} \quad \text{(Eq. 46-7)}$$

Does the question mark have any significance? It might be argued that the difference is within the limits of error. However, the masses of atoms are now known (by means of the mass spectrograph) to five and six decimal places. We have listed them only to four; the difference here is in the second decimal place. It seems that some mass was converted into energy. Let us substitute in Eq. 46-5 to see if this is so.

$$1.00760 \, \text{amu} + 7.01657 \, \text{amu} + 0.00016 \, \text{amu}$$

$$= 4.00278 \, \text{amu} + 4.00278 \, \text{amu}$$

$$+ 0.01826 \, \text{amu}$$

Total masses: $8.02417 = 8.02382$

$$\text{(Eq. 46-8)}$$

Rounding off, $8.024 = 8.024$

$$\text{(Eq. 46-9)}$$

This agreement in Eq. 46-8 is within the limits of experimental error.

Let us now take the difference in masses (Eq. 46-7) and convert it to energy by means of Einstein's mass–energy equation, and see if there is agreement with the observed energies of the alpha particles.[4] The difference in mass is 0.0186 amu.

$$E = mc^2 = 0.0186 \times (1.67 \times 10^{-24})$$

$$\times (3 \times 10^{10})^2 \, \text{ergs}$$

or (using the conversion factor)

$$0.0186 \times 931 = 17.3 \, \text{Mev} \quad \text{(Eq. 46-10)}$$

This turns out to be in very close agreement with the measured energies of the two alpha particles, 17.2 Mev. Einstein's mass–energy equation seemed valid. To check, Cockcroft and Walton bombarded fluorine with protons, with the following result:

$$_1\text{H}^1 + {}_9\text{F}^{19} \rightarrow {}_{10}\text{Ne}^{20} \rightarrow$$

$$_8\text{O}^{16} + {}_2\text{He}^4 + \text{energy} \quad \text{(Eq. 46-11)}$$

Again they measured the energies of the oxygen and fluorine atoms, and set up the mass–energy equation to find the energy liberated. They then divided the energy between the oxygen and the alpha particle in accordance with the laws of Conservation of Momentum and Energy. The agreement between the measured and the computed values were as good as in the previous case. Einstein's mass–energy equation was no longer subject to doubt. Thus, the great significance of the Cockcroft-Walton experiment was established.

[4] We did this in arriving at Eq. 46-6 but in a less direct manner. As previously stated the energy equivalent to 1 amu is 931 Mev.

STABILITY OF NUCLEI

We still wonder, however, how the protons and the neutrons can remain tightly packed together to form stable nuclei. Let us compare the combined masses of two free protons and two free neutrons with the mass of a helium nucleus which consists of four such particles bound together in some way.

Mass of two free protons

$$2 \times 1.00814 = 2.01628 \text{ amu}$$

Mass of two free neutrons

$$2 \times 1.00898 = 2.01796 \text{ amu}$$

Total Mass $= 4.03424 \text{ amu}$

The mass of a helium nucleus is 4.00387 amu. The difference is 0.03037 amu. This means that when two protons and two neutrons combine to form a helium nucleus, there is a loss of 0.03037 amu. Now a helium nucleus is very stable. We have seen that they can be used to smash other atoms without themselves being broken up. This must mean that a great deal of energy is used to hold them together.[5] This 0.03037 amu corresponds to 0.03037×931 28.3 Mev. This is the energy that holds the four particles together in the helium nucleus. It is called binding energy.

[5] Let us calculate this energy in other units. How much energy is released if 2.01628 gm of protons and 2.01796 gm of neutrons were to combine to form 4.00307 gm of alpha particles? The difference in mass is 0.03037 gm.

$$E = mc^2 = 0.03037 \times (3 \times 10^{10})^2 = 2.73 \times 10^{19}$$

$$\text{ergs} = 2.73 \times 10^{12} \text{ joules}$$

$$= \frac{2.73 \times 10^{12} \text{ joules}}{4.18 \text{ joules/cal}} = 653 \text{ billion}$$

$$\text{calories} = 26 \text{ million kilowatt-hours}$$

Since this is the energy that is released when about 2 gm of neutrons and about 2 gm of protons are combined to form helium nuclei, it is the energy that must be supplied to break 6×10^{23} nuclei (of helium) up into free protons and free neutrons. In the process this *energy* would be converted into matter. It is no wonder that alpha particles are so stable.

Much as this may convince us that the energy to hold stable nuclei together can be accounted for, it still fails to offer any satisfying pictorial model as to how it overcomes the mutual repulsion of the protons or how neutrons can be attracted either to protons or to one another. Gravitational attractions are billions of billions times too small.

To better understand the problem, let us consider the nucleus of deuterium, an isotope of hydrogen ($_1H^2$). It contains one proton and one neutron, and so is the simplest nucleus that contains a neutron. Deuterium is a very stable isotope; like the helium nucleus, its mass is less than the combined mass of a free proton and a free neutron. There is no force of electrical attraction between the proton and the neutron in deuterium. Yet there *must* be a force of attraction between them. Whether we understand the nature of this attraction or not, we must accept the concept of very large attractive forces between protons and neutrons when they are extremely close together.

We have used the relationship between the combined masses of free protons and free neutrons and the mass of a nucleus to explain stability of nuclei. We note that stability is increased by a decrease in mass, just as atoms with their electrons in a lower energy state are more stable than when they are in a higher energy state. Now let us see if we can also use the mass difference to explain instability. Let us begin with the neutron.

A free neutron has a mass equal to 1.008986 amu. A free proton has 1.007595 amu and an electron 0.000550 amu. Together the mass of the proton and the electron is 1.008145 amu. This is 0.000841 amu *less* than the mass of the neutron, i.e., a neutron has a *greater* mass than the sum of its free parts. The neutron may therefore be considered as existing in a *higher energy* state than the proton and the electron. We should suspect, then, that the neutron should be less stable than either a proton or an electron. This turns out to be the case, for the half-life of a neutron is about 13 minutes, whereas protons and electrons can exist in the free state forever. We remember that a radioactive atom may eject a beta ray (electron) with a very high energy and that a proton was created in the process without changing the mass number of the atom. The energy represented by the 0.000841 amu difference mentioned above corresponds to the energy of the emitted beta ray. Here we have another confirmation of the concept that the beta ray is ejected *from a neutron* in radioactive atoms.

The instability of radioactive atoms is more complicated. We need to consider the total binding energy of nuclei—or perhaps we should say "unbinding energy," for it is defined as the energy required to separate a nucleus into free (isolated) protons, neutrons, and electrons. It is calculated as the difference between the actual mass of a given nucleus and the total mass of the free protons and free neutrons of which it consists. This difference in mass is expressed either in atomic mass units or in energy units—ergs or calories or electron volts—usually electron volts.

Note carefully that binding energy is the energy that a nucleus *does not have* in comparison to the total energy of its separate parts, and that this energy is measured in terms of differences in mass according to the equation $E = mc^2$. An examination of the periodic chart reveals that as we pass from the lighter to the heavier elements, the ratio between the atomic weight and the atomic number increases. This means that the number of neutrons relative to the number of protons increases. It is also apparent that the *total binding energy* per nucleus is greater for the heavier elements simply because there are more particles to be held together (or isolated). The *binding energy per nucleon*, however, is about constant for the heavier elements, as can be seen from Fig. 46-1. For the lighter elements the binding energy per nucleon increases rapidly up to nuclei of mass number of about 40. It increases more slowly up to elements of mass numbers of about 55 to 60, changes little in those with mass numbers between 60 and 70, and then very slowly increases for the rest of the elements with higher mass numbers (Fig. 46-1).

Note that the greater the binding energy, the more energy per nucleon needed to break a nucleus up into its constituent nucleons. Note also that iron, a "base" metal has the greatest binding energy per nucleon of all of the elements, which means that it is therefore the most stable. Others with about the same binding energy as iron are manganese, cobalt, nickel, copper, and zinc. These elements have the most stable nuclei, and therefore are least likely to be broken up, i.e., fissioned. Note that in Fig. 46-1 the arrows alongside the curve both point downward towards the low point of the curve. This means that to attain greater binding energy per nucleus, the heavier elements must disintegrate,

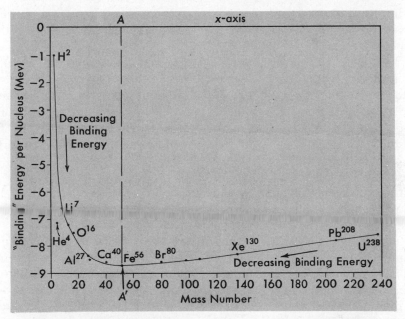

Fig. 46-1. Binding Energy per Nucleon vs. Mass Numbers of a Few Stable (or Near-stable) Isotopes. Note that the binding energy *per nucleon* (not total binding energy of the nucleus) is almost constant for elements with mass numbers greater than A^1. The distance between the curve and the *x*-axis (top of diagram) is proportional to the energy per nucleon that would be required to take the nucleus apart. Note that this distance is greatest in Fe^{56} (the distance AA^1). Thus, the curve is concave upward from a minimum at mass number 56. *This means that more energy is required to take the nucleus of iron apart than for any other element.* Note: In the actual graph the *x*-axis has been dropped down so that it intersects the *y*-axis at -9 instead of at the usual 0. This makes the graph easier to read.

either by emitting nucleons (in the form of alpha particles) or by fissioning. It also means that the lighter elements must fuse to form heavier elements if greater binding energy per nucleon is to be attained. *In either case energy is released* by some amount of matter being converted into energy. This follows from the definition of binding energy. The amount released

is greatest when 26 protons and 30 neutrons combine to form iron.

The graph shown in Fig. 46-1 gives us a clue to the reason for the limit to the number of naturally occurring elements. All of the naturally radioactive elements are at the right in the graph—and all those at the right of the graph are radioactive. If there ever were any elements heavier than uranium 92, they must have been very unstable and so have long since disintegrated. Eleven elements beyond atomic number 92 have been artificially created by man; all are highly unstable, with short half-lives compared to the age of the earth. If they ever existed they have long since decayed to the radioactive elements we find naturally or to stable lead.

Another clue to the stability of nuclei may be found in the relative numbers of protons and neutrons they contain. In the lighter elements the number of neutrons equals the number of protons. In iron the number of neutrons is 15 per cent larger than the number of protons; in lead the number is just over 50 per cent and in uranium, there are 58.7 per cent more neutrons than protons in the nucleus. Seemingly the more protons in a nucleus, the more neutrons necessary to maintain stability, and when the number rises above 82 (that of nonradioactive lead), no number of neutrons can counteract the repulsive effect of the protons for one another. It may be that the neutrons act as a sort of a nuclear cement to hold the nucleons together. Isotopes with an even number of protons and an even number of neutrons seem to be more stable than those with an odd number of one and an even number of the other, and the latter are in their turn more stable than those with an odd number of each.

We will conclude this section on stability of the nucleus by stating that whatever the attractions between neutrons and protons may be, it appears to be very strong at extremely short distances but extremely weak at any other distance, much more so than is the case with gravitational or electrostatic forces.

From this discussion and from the binding energy curve (Fig. 46-1), there emerge the two methods by which energy may be released quickly and in large amounts from the nuclei. One is by the distintegration of the heavier atoms, i.e., by fission, and the other is by combination of lighter elements to form heavier ones, i.e., by fusion. We will now turn our attention to them.

NUCLEAR FISSION

From the discussions it is apparent that nuclear physicists realized that large amounts of energy were stored within the atom, and that this energy was emitted from the nuclei of certain atoms of high atomic weight. The problem was to learn how to release this energy and to control it. The search for the means of obtaining nuclear energy and bringing it under control so as to build atomic bombs was not, as so many people seem to believe, something that came about as a result of World War II, but instead was a conclusion to the sequence of events that began with the discoveries of Becquerel, the Curies, Thomson, Einstein, and Rutherford in the 1890's and early 1900's. The wartime research merely did on an enormous scale what scientists in their research laboratories had been doing on a small scale. Actually the war brought about little new fundamental research, i.e., few additions to basic knowledge were made. Scientists were much too busy hastening to put to practical use the knowledge they already had.

The discovery of the neutron gave the nuclear physicists a new "bullet" to bombard atoms. The neutron has about the same mass as the proton and about one-fourth that of the alpha particle. It had one great advantage over either in that it could penetrate into the nuclei of atoms, scoring direct hits, because it had no charge, and so would experience no repulsion. They are ejected from some artificially radioactive atoms at high speeds. A typical reaction was that caused by bombarding boron with alpha particles. A radioactive isotope of nitrogen and a neutron were produced

$$_5B^{10} + _2He^4 \rightarrow _7N^{13} + _0n^1$$

They lose energy in passing through matter only by direct collisions. In some of these collisions the neutrons will be absorbed or captured by nuclei, especially after they have been slowed down. A neutron captured by a nucleus adds one nucleon to it, thus creating a new isotope. Isotopes that are not found in nature are always unstable —which is the reason that they are not found in nature.

Once a source of neutrons had been established, they were used to bombard other atoms. Fermi bombarded uranium with them in 1934, Hahn and Strassman in early 1938. Presumably they obtained fission, but it was not recognized as such until early in 1939. The fission was found to result in the formation of two elements near the middle of the period chart, barium and krypton, or antimony and niobium, or strontium and xenon, etc. In all cases the atomic numbers of the two elements add up to 92, but their mass numbers are always larger than those of their stable isotopes, i.e., they contain excess neutrons and so are radioactive. It is these radioactive isotopes that constitute the "fall-out" from nuclear explosions. A typical fission reaction is

$$_{92}U^{235} + _0n^1 \rightarrow _{92}U^{236} \rightarrow$$
$$_{54}Xe^{140} + _{38}Sr^{94} + 2_0n^1 + \text{gamma ray}$$
$$+ 200 \text{ Mev}$$

U^{235} is the only isotope of uranium that can be fissioned by low-energy neutrons. This isotope is present in natural uranium only in the proportion of 1 to 140. In every case a number of neutrons are produced by the fission, the average number per fissioned atom being 2.5. This meant that the reaction could be self-sustaining, i.e., neutrons from the outside would not be needed to keep it going. A chain reaction would be possible if not too many neutrons escaped to the outside or were absorbed. (A chain reaction is like a chain letter, with which you are all doubtless familiar.) The amount of U^{235} in ordinary uranium was not enough to start a chain reaction; too many neutrons were absorbed by the U^{238}. It became necessary to separate them. This is impossible chemically because all isotopes of the same element behave exactly alike chemically. Two methods were developed, both based on the difference in mass numbers, and both very expensive. Once this was done the atomic (A) bomb became possible.

If the mass of U^{235} is below a certain critical size, the chain reaction will not take place; too many neutrons escape to the outside without causing fission. Conversely, if the mass is above the critical size, the chain reaction operates spontaneously and the bomb explodes instantly. The problem is to control it. This is done by separating the U^{235} into two or more parts, each part a bit below the critical size. To set the bomb off, all that has to be done is to bring the parts together. No source of neutrons is necessary to start the reaction because cosmic rays are constantly creating neutrons in the atmosphere. Despite their half-life of 13 minutes, there are always enough around to start the reaction. The temperature generated in the heart of the bomb is enormous, many millions of degrees centigrade. The maximum size of the A-bomb is strictly limited by the number of masses of fissionable material, each below the critical size, that can be brought together at the same instant to form a single mass above critical size. Only a small part of each atom is converted into energy, i.e., only the energy representing the difference between the mass of the uranium atom and the combined masses of the products is released. The amount per gram of mass converted is given by $E = mc^2$.

If we examine the graph (Fig. 46-1) we can see that the fission products with their mass numbers around 90 and 140, are nearer the base of the curve than uranium. This is always true. It is therefore not possible to fission elements at the low part of the curve. Several of the other radioactive elements, notably Th^{233}, can be fissioned under proper circumstances.[6]

[6] The most important fissionable atom is plutonium 239, an element that does not occur in nature but which is made synthetically by bombarding U^{238} with neutrons. The reaction is as follows:

$$_{92}U^{238} + _0n^1 \rightarrow _{92}U^{239}$$
$$_{92}U^{239} \rightarrow _{93}Np^{239} + _{-1}e^\circ$$
$$_{93}Np^{239} \rightarrow _{94}Pu^{239} + _{-1}e^\circ$$

The intermediate element, neptunium, has a half-life of only 2.3 days whereas that of Pu (plutonium) has one of about 24,000 years. It is therefore stable enough to be used. It is fissionable just as is U^{235}. It is "made" in an atomic pile under controlled conditions. Unlike U^{235} it can be separated from U^{238} by chemical means, for it is a different element.

ATOMIC FUSION

The discovery of atomic fission put a new light on the source of the energy radiated from the sun. It had long been known that the enormous energy radiated could not possibly be accounted for by normal chemical processes. Could it be that atoms were being fissioned in the sun? Analysis of the spectrum of the sun reveals comparatively few atoms that are fissionable, whereas it reveals large amounts of hydrogen and helium. Inspection of the curve in Fig. 46-1 shows that these could not be produced by fission of larger atoms. The curve does, however, suggest that the elements to the left of the low point of the curve might be fused to form elements whose energy per nucleon is greater than either of the elements to be fused.

It was in 1939 that Bethe of Cornell proposed the carbon cycle (so-called because carbon serves as a sort of nuclear catalyst) to account for the source of the sun's energy. In this cycle hydrogen is converted into helium,[7] as follows

$$_6C^{12} + _1H^1 \rightarrow _7N^{13} + \text{energy}$$
$$_7N^{13} \rightarrow _6C^{13} + _{+1}e^0$$
$$_6C^{13} + _1H^1 \rightarrow _7N^{14} + \text{energy}$$
$$_7N^{14} + _1H^1 \rightarrow _8O^{15} + \text{energy}$$
$$_8O^{15} \rightarrow _7N^{15} + _{+1}e^0$$
$$_7N^{15} + _1H^1 \rightarrow _6C^{12} + _2He^4 + \text{energy}$$

Note that the starting components were carbon and hydrogen, that the end-products were the same carbon plus helium, and that the only element added during the

[7] It was the English astronomer, Eddington, who first suggested (1927) that conversion of hydrogen to helium takes place in the sun.

intervening steps was hydrogen. The net effect is

$$4(_1\mathrm{H}^1) \rightarrow {}_2\mathrm{He}^4 + 2(_{+1}e^0) + 24.7 \text{ Mev}$$

Each of the nuclear reactions listed had been accomplished in the laboratory before Bethe proposed the cycle. It is estimated that nearly half the energy of the sun is generated during the carbon cycle. The source of the remainder is the same conversion of hydrogen to helium but by another method, similar in principle to that of the hydrogen bomb. The details of the bomb are not available to the public but we can make an educated guess.

There are two isotopes of hydrogen in addition to ordinary hydrogen, $_1\mathrm{H}^2$ (deuterium) and $_1\mathrm{H}^3$ (tritium). Tritium is radioactive but its half-life is 12.5 years and so it may be stored for a time. It is very rare in nature but can be transmuted from lithium at a very high cost. This reaction is

$$_3\mathrm{Li}^6 + {}_0n^1 \rightarrow {}_1\mathrm{H}^3 + {}_2\mathrm{He}^4$$

The most probable reaction to produce helium is

$$_1\mathrm{H}^2 + {}_1\mathrm{H}^3 \rightarrow {}_2\mathrm{He}^4 + {}_0n^1 + 17.6 \text{ Mev}$$

This reaction needs a fantastically high temperature to activate it, 15,000,000° C at least. This temperature can be obtained only by use of an A-bomb. To make the H-bomb a small A-bomb is surrounded by a quantity of liquefied deuterium and tritium, which in turn is surrounded by a quantity of LiH^2. The "firing" of the A-bomb supplies the heat to start the fusion reaction. Since the activation energy of the fusion process is so extremely high, there is no upper limit to the size of the H-bomb except perhaps due to technical difficulties. Bombs equivalent to 50,000,-000 tons of TNT have been exploded. Any radioactive fall-out from the H-bomb is due entirely to the A-bomb used to trigger it.

Note that the most usable energy that can be obtained from nuclear reactions of any kind is heat. Nuclear reactors (sometimes called piles) are simply devices in which the fission (not fusion) of plutonium atoms (footnote 6) is not allowed to reach chain reaction proportions. The heat given off is used to heat water to run a steam engine which in turn runs a dynamo to generate electrical energy. Atomic reactors are very large and heavy, for they must be surrounded with several tons of shielding material to absorb the deadly radiations. There is no other way at present to use atomic power, nor is there likely to be. There is no way at present to use the energy of fusion, nor is the possibility at all promising.

SUMMARY

The nucleus of the atom has remained essentially a passive particle, or group of particles, in all of our discussions to date. The discovery of the proton and the measurements of its mass and charge showed conclusively that the nuclei of all atoms other than hydrogen contained another particle (or other particles) and that this particle could not carry an electric charge. It was named the neutron even before it was discovered in 1932.

The discovery of the neutron quickly led to the explanation of the variation in mass among atoms of the same element. Neon was separated into atoms with three different atomic weights, 20, 21, and 22. Ne^{21} contains one more neutron than does Ne^{20}, and Ne^{22} contains two more. Since in nature the proportions of these three isotopes are constant, the atomic weight of natural neon is explained by the relative proportions of the three isotopes. Thus, an old puzzle was resolved.

Radioactivity, the spontaneous disintegration of certain kinds of atoms, had been known since the late 1890's. Further research revealed that most of the heavier elements, i.e., those with atomic weights greater than lead, were disintegration products of uranium, the heaviest naturally occurring element. All radioactive elements have a half-life, which is defined as the time it takes for half of any given quantity of an element to disintegrate to form a more stable element. This time is the same regardless of the quantity. The half-life for different elements ranges from some billions of years for U^{238} to fractions of a second (for Po^{214}). Because of the constancy of radioactive decay under any condition whatsoever, the rate serves as a geologic time clock.

EXERCISES

I. TERMS AND CONCEPTS

Ion accelerator	Chain reaction
Mev, Bev	A-bomb
$E = mc^2$	Fusion
Binding energy	H-bomb
Fission	Carbon cycle

II. PROBLEMS

1. Einstein's mass-energy equation is a general one, and so can be applied to chemical as well as nuclear reactions. Nothing useful is learned by doing so, for the uncertainty in m (in $E = mc^2$) far exceeds the value of E. Thus, in chemical reactions, we assume that mass and energy are conserved separately. On p. 517 is the equation $2Na + Cl_2 \rightarrow 2NaCl + 196,800$ calories. Considering all that has been said so far, what is the source of the energy that appears on the right? Explain.

2. Approximately how many atomic mass units are there in 1 gm (i.e., gm) of protons?

3. What was the significance of the Cockcroft-Walton experiment?

4. The mass of a proton is 1.00814 amu, that of a neutron is 1.00898 amu and that of an electron is 0.00055 amu. We have already learned (p. 660) that a neutron may decay into a proton and an electron. How do you explain that the sum of the masses of a proton and an electron do not equal the mass of the neutron?

5. What is meant by binding energy? Is it released or absorbed when free protons and free neutrons combine to form nuclei of other atoms? Is the total mass of the free protons added to the total mass of the free neutrons equal to the total mass of the protons and neutrons in the nuclei formed? Explain.

6. To explain the above how do we rewrite the Law of Conservation of Mass and the Law of Conservation of Energy?

7. Calculate the amount of energy released per molecule of helium formed in equation 46-11. Use the following atomic masses: F = 19.00445, O = 16.00000.

8. What elements have the greatest binding energy per nucleon (Fig. 46-1)? Why does this graph start with $_1H^2$ rather than $_1H^1$?

9. What relationship is there between binding energy and stability of a nucleus?

10. How does the ratio of the number of protons to the number of neutrons in atomic nuclei change as we proceed to higher and higher atomic numbers? Can you suggest a reason for this, and relate it to natural radioactivity?

11. All atoms can be made artificially radioactive by bombardment with one sort of particle or another. There are thus hundreds of artificially radioactive isotopes. If our theories of origin of the elements from hydrogen ions, by processes like those described for our sun, are correct, then it seems likely

that very large numbers of these radioactive isotopes were also made. Assuming this to be correct, how do you explain their absence (for the most part) from nature today?

12. In our previous discussions we have seen how protons, neutrons and alpha particles have been ripped loose from atoms by nuclear bombardment. Why are these not referred to as nuclear fission?

13. What is it that fissions certain types of atoms? What is the source (or sources) of the "fissioner"? What are the products?

14. Can you suggest a possible reason for U^{235} being fissionable but not U^{238}? (Refer to your answer to problem 10.)

15. What is a chain reaction?

16. What is meant by a mass of U^{235} of critical size? Explain why there should be a critical size.

17. Suggest a reason for their being no atomic explosions in uranium mines.

18. Fermi, Cockcroft and Walton, and others obtained nuclear fission in various experiments well before 1939 but failed to recognize the new discovery because of the influence of preconceived concepts. Explain their failure.

19. Give one method (not necessarily practical) for separating U^{235} from U^{238}.

20. In what form does the great bulk of the energy in an atomic explosion appear? In what ways may this energy be used *directly*?

21. Would an automobile powered by atomic energy be practicable? Give more than one reason. Explain.

22. Nonscientists have said that the home of the future would have a small atomic power plant built into it, from which the energy to run the home could be obtained for generations at no cost and without any attention. Discuss both sides of this problem.

23. In what fundamental ways do A-bombs differ from H-bombs? Which can be most destructive? Why?

24. What is radioactive fallout? What is its source? (Be specific.)

CHAPTER XLVII

The Universe Beyond the Solar System

At the midnight in the silence of the sleep time
When you set your fancies free . . .
—ROBERT BROWNING

The number of stars that the average big-city dweller can see even on the clearest, darkest night would probably not add up to more than a few hundred. The number that can be seen from a high mountain top far from the obscuring effects of city lights is probably five thousand or more. With a small telescope one can see several times as many and with the largest, the number runs into the billions. Each star is a brightly glowing sphere like our sun.

The vast majority of them are so far away that they show no parallax. Our knowledge of any of them is obtained entirely by means of the small amount of light received from them, light that has been traveling through space at the speed of 186,000 mi/sec for times varying from a minimum of 4.2 years to hundreds of thousands and even millions of years. The principal instruments by which we gain this knowledge are our telescopes of varying sizes. By means of larger and larger telescopes astronomers are able to gather greater and greater amounts of the feeble light that reaches them so that it can be analyzed with other delicate instruments. Chief among them are the camera and the spectroscope. In our search for knowledge of the stars we will be concerned chiefly with their distances, their brightnesses, their temperatures, their sizes, their masses, their densities, and their motions. All are determined by calculations made from direct observations.

DISTANCES OF THE NEAR STARS

The early Greeks, despite their other achievements in astronomy, had no concept of the actual distances to the stars. This is not surprising, for even today after more than a hundred years of knowing, we still find the actual distances inconceivable. Since they could detect no parallax they concluded that the earth was stationary. Copernicus had the same difficulty; he could only state that the lack of parallax was due to their great distances. He was right, but he had no evidence. Newton made the first attempt to calculate the distance to the stars. He assumed that all of the stars had about the same intrinsic brightness as the sun, and that they appeared less bright only because they were so much farther away. He knew that the intensity of light varies inversely as the square of the distance from its source (Fig. 6-1). He therefore could calculate how far away the sun would have to be to have the same *apparent* brightness as a particular star. Of course, many stars have intrinsic brightnesses that are very different from the sun, but a great many do have about the same brightness, and for these, his estimates were reasonable.

About 1835 Bessel made the first measurement of parallax on one of the nearest stars. This is done by trigonometric methods involving the measurement of a base line and an angle (Fig. 1-5). The longest base line available to man is the diameter of the earth's orbit (186,000,000 mi). To use the base line two observations are made on the same star six months apart. The angle is extremely small even for the nearest star, being only a small fraction of a degree. Today the measurement is made on photographs, taken six months apart, by a micrometer. Proxima Centauri, the nearest star, is nearly 25 trillion miles away. This is equal to 4.2 light years; a light year is the *distance* light travels in a year. Only about forty stars are less than 16 light years away. The method of parallax can be used for stars up to 300 light years away, perhaps somewhat more with the 200-in. telescope on Mt. Palomar. For those farther away indirect methods must be used; these will be described later.

APPARENT BRIGHTNESS

The apparent brightness of a star, aside from its location with respect to other stars, was the only basic item of information to be had previous to 1835. What we see is a star's brightness relative to other stars as we see them from the earth. The star with the greatest apparent brightness, aside from our sun, is Sirius, the dog star. The apparent brightness (to the unaided eye) of stars ranges from that of Sirius down to those barely visible under the most ideal conditions.

The stars were classified according to

their apparent brightness by Hipparchus.[1] The twenty stars with the greatest apparent brightnesses are called first-magnitude stars. Those barely visible to the unaided eye are stars of the sixth magnitude. The light reaching us from first-magnitude stars is about 100 times as bright as that from sixth-magnitude stars. With our best telescopes stars can be photographed that are 100 million times dimmer than those of magnitude one. On the magnitude scale the apparent brightness of our sun is -26.7.

The apparent brightness today is measured by the amount of darkening of a photographic plate in a specified time under specified conditions. Some stars are too dim to be recorded on a photographic plate. They are known only because they eclipse other stars. It is possible that some stars with high intrinsic brightness are so far away that they cannot be photographed even by the 200-in. Mt. Palomar telescope.

INTRINSIC BRIGHTNESS (LUMINOSITY) [2]

Intrinsic brightness is defined as the total amount of light emitted. It is a property of the star itself, i.e., it does not depend upon the distance. It is dependent upon

[1] The magnitude of a star thus has no necessary relationship to its size. Consistent with the meaning of the term magnitude are the terms giant and dwarf insofar as they refer to stars. They refer only to the amount of light emitted, not to size. A star may appear bright either because it is very near (as our sun) or because it is very big or because it has a high intrinsic brightness, or because of a combination of all three.

[2] Other terms used for intrinsic brightness are true brightness, absolute brightness, absolute magnitude, absolute luminosity, etc. By luminosity we will always means absolute luminosity.

temperature and size. The temperature determines the amount of light each square centimeter of its surface emits per second, and the size determines the number of square centimeters there are to emit. Stars may thus have a high luminosity either because they are very hot or very big. If they are both, their luminosity will be very high. Most giant stars have high luminosity because they are big, not because they have high temperature. (They are not, however, called giant stars because of their size.) Dwarf stars are, as their name indicates, stars with low luminosity, either because they are relatively cool, small, or both. Canopus, 180 light years distant, has an intrinsic brightness 5200 times that of our sun. Others are only $\frac{1}{10,000}$ times as bright as the sun.

The intrinsic brightness of a star may be calculated from the apparent brightness and its distance in those cases where the distance can be determined by parallax. All that needs to be done is to figure out, by use of the inverse-square law, how bright a star would have to be at its known distance to send us the observed amount of light. The relationship may be expressed as follows:

$$\text{Apparent brightness} = \frac{\text{Intrinsic brightness}}{(\text{Distance})^2}$$

The proper units, of course, must be used.

This equation shows us that the distance can be calculated if the apparent and the intrinsic brightnesses are known. As already indicated, the apparent brightness is never a problem. The problem is to use some other method for determining the intrinsic brightness. Because this other method involves the spectroscope, we will postpone discussion of it until later.

STAR TEMPERATURES AND SPECTRA

The temperature of the surface of a star is easily measurable since precise measurements are not needed. A fair and useful estimate can be made by color alone.

Red	cool	2000°–4000° C
Orange	warm	4000°–5000° C
Yellow	moderately hot	6000°–7000° C
White	very hot	10,000°–12,000° C
Blue	extremely hot	15,000° C and up

Our sun is a yellow star; Vega is a white star. There are, of course, all gradations in between—orange-yellow, yellow-white, blue-white, etc.

A more accurate determination of the temperature can be made by comparing the spectra of stars. In Chapter XXIV we learned that spectra are the fingerprints of atoms. These lines show that the stars are largely composed of hydrogen (about 75 per cent on the average). Next in abundance is helium, followed by various metals. In the cooler red stars some compounds are present. We also learned that the spectrum of an incandescent body also depends upon the temperature, the frequencies emitted shifting from the red end of the spectrum towards the blue end as the temperature rises (Fig. 24-1a). Since there are no pronounced differences in the compositions of stars, spectral differences are due chiefly to temperature differences.

At the high temperatures of yellow, white, and blue stars, no compounds can exist; all matter is dissociated into atoms. These atoms are in "excited" states, more so in the white and blue than in the yellow stars. They emit radiation as they return to less excited states. The greater the difference between these two states, the higher the frequencies emitted. The number of possible frequencies is also increased. The excitation comes from within the star where the temperatures are vastly higher than at or near the surface. Cooler atoms at the surface absorb energy coming from within the star, and reradiate it in all directions. Atoms of different substances differ in their capacities to absorb radiation at different temperatures. The effect is to produce dark (absorption) lines where the bright lines would normally appear (p. 363).

Thus, the hydrogen lines (bright or dark) in the spectrum of hydrogen or any other element in a blue star are not all exactly the same as those in the spectrum of a white star. Moreover, the intensity of the lines, bright or dark, vary with the temperature. It is therefore possible to classify the spectra into types according to the lines (bright or dark) present. The types are listed as O, B, A, F, G, K, M, R, N. Blue stars have O-type spectra. Our sun is a G type; M, R, and N are red types. Blue stars emit 20 or more times the radiation per unit area that our sun does, whereas a red type may emit as little as $\frac{1}{20}$ as much per unit area (or even much less).

Using the spectral type, the temperature may be determined by use of Wien's Law. Intensity of the emitted energy is plotted against wavelength (Fig. 24-1a), and the curve drawn. The temperature of the star is directly proportional to the frequency (inversely proportional to the wavelength) at which most of its radiation is given off, i.e., to the high point of the curve.

We can now understand how the intrinsic brightness of a star can be determined even if its distance is not known. For stars of any one spectral class, and whose intrinsic brightnesses are known, it was observed that the relative intensities of certain spectral lines depended on the intrinsic brightness. In other words, the relations among the intensities of spectral lines change as the intrinsic brightness changes. So pronounced are the differences in these relations that it was possible to predict the intrinsic brightness of a star by examining its spectrum. The validity of the method was established by applying it to the stars whose intrinsic brightnesses are known from the apparent brightnesses and the distances. If this is valid for *all* of them, it should be valid for the more distant stars.

DISTANCES OF THE REMOTE STARS

We may now return to the equation,

$$\text{Apparent brightness} = \frac{\text{Intrinsic brightness}}{d^2}$$

Since we have developed a method for determining the intrinsic brightness that does not depend on the distance, we can now use it in conjunction with apparent brightness to determine the distance to those stars too far away to use the parallax method. The validity of the method, of course, is tested by applying it first to those stars whose distances are known by the parallax method. If it holds for them, it should hold for those that are farther away. This is an accepted method of procedure among scientists.

Another method of calculating distances, especially useful for the most distant stars, makes use of the period of pulsation for certain stars called the Cepheid variables. The name comes from a pulsating star in the constellation Cepheus. These stars change in brightness more or less periodically, reaching a maximum and then fading to a minimum, over and over again. The period ranges from a day or so to a month or more. By a study of a sufficient number of stars, it was determined that the Cepheids with the longer periods had the greater intrinsic brightnesses. This correlation held for the few Cepheids whose distances could be readily calculated by methods already described. The problem was to correlate the period with intrinsic brightness, i.e., to establish a scale by which period could be translated into intrinsic brightness. The method by which this was done is too complex for us here. Once done, however, distances to the Cepheids could be calculated.

SIZE

The size of the star may be calculated if we know both the amount of light emitted per unit of surface area and the total amount of light emitted. The Stefan-Boltzmann Law (Chapter XXIV) is useful here for it states that the total energy radiated from an ideal radiator varies as the fourth power of the absolute temperature. Stars are not ideal radiators, but the error introduced by using the law is small.

$$\frac{\text{Total energy radiated}}{\text{Amount radiated per unit area}}$$
$$= \text{Total area of surface}$$

From the total surface area, both the diameter and the volume of the star is easily calculated.

Calculation of the sizes of the stars yields some startling figures. Canopus turns out to have a diameter a bit greater than the radius of the earth's orbit about the sun, and Antares, a red star, has a diameter of 400,000,000 mi! Any astronomer would be happier if he could check this figure by some other method. This was done by Michelson, who used an ingenious method involving interference. His figure was 428,000,000 mi. At the other end of the scale is a star that revolves about Sirius, the dog star. This star is a white dwarf only 25,000 mi in diameter, about the same as the planet, Uranus. It is appropriately named the Pup. Some of the white dwarfs are even smaller than the earth.

DENSITY AND MASSES

Despite this great range in diameters the range in masses is remarkably small. The mass of most stars ranges from 5 times that of the sun to $\frac{1}{5}$ of it. A few run to as much as 100 times that of the sun. It follows that the stars with the greatest diameters (volumes) must have low densities. Antares, e.g., has a density less than that of the atmosphere here on earth. On the other hand the density of the Pup is about 61,000 times that of water. A pint of it would weigh over 30 tons. If we remember that most of the atom is empty space, that the nucleus of a hydrogen atom occupies only a millionth of a millionth of the volume of the atom, we can begin to understand how matter could be as dense as that in the Pup.

How do astronomers ascertain the masses of stars? None of the methods so far used for investigation of stellar phenomena will give it to us. The matter would be enormously more difficult if there were not so many double stars. In all of them, each star revolves about the other. If the period can be determined, then by the application of the Law of Gravitation, the mass of the system can be determined. This was done first with Sirius and the Pup. By more complex calculations the mass of each was determined. Once this was known, the

Pup's density of 61,000 gm/cm³ was calculated. Some dwarf stars have vastly greater densities.

THE MASS-LUMINOSITY LAW

If we plot the luminosity (intrinsic brightness) of stars against their spectral classes, a diagram like that in Fig. 47-1 results. Most of the stars fall along a diagonal band called the main sequence. Note that the hot stars are on the left, the cooler on the right. Note also that there is nothing on the diagram that directly tells you anything about the mass or size of stars.

Now stars owe their intrinsic brightness first to their temperature, and then to their size. From the position of the red giants we see that they have high intrinsic brightness even though they are relatively cool. We conclude that this is possible only because they are giants in size as well as in magnitude. From the position of the white dwarfs we see they have low intrinsic brightness even though they are very hot. We conclude that they must be dwarfs in size as well as in magnitude. Note carefully that neither the giants nor the dwarfs fall in the main sequence. Why do the stars other than the giants and the dwarfs fall in a band such as the main sequence? This must be because there is a relationship between mass and luminosity. In general stars have high luminosity because they are both big and hot, and others have low luminosity because they are smaller and cooler. The sun falls almost in the middle of the main sequence. It is moderate in size, in luminosity, and in temperature. More formally, the law states that the stars in our galaxy that have the same mass have the same intrinsic brightness (except for the white dwarfs and the red giants).

STELLAR EVOLUTION

These relationships can hardly be accidental. Why should there be such a sequence? Do the stars in such a graph fall along such a band because they are in different stages of evolution? Perhaps we should ask another question first. What starts a star shining in the first place? In brief, we can say that any aggregation of gaseous matter *in sufficient quantity* cannot help but contract and get hot as the energy liberated by contraction is converted to heat. If this gaseous matter is hydrogen, when the temperature gets high enough, it will begin to be converted to helium as indicated in the previous chapter. This conversion raises the temperature and maintains it as long as any hydrogen is left. The high temperature causes the star to emit light in the manner explained by the Bohr theory, i.e., for the same reason that an iron rod will glow if it is hot enough.

We might therefore speculate on the possibility that the red giants are young stars in which the conversion of hydrogen into helium has scarcely begun, and then only in their deep interiors. As the temperature rises the rate of conversion increases, causing a still further rise in temperature. Eventually a sort of equilibrium is reached, and the star settles down to a long period (measured in billions of years) of maturity. The mass becomes less, due to the conversion of some of it into radiant energy as hydrogen is transmuted into helium. Eventually the hydrogen present becomes so reduced that the rate of conversion to helium is decreased; the high temperature cannot be maintained. Now in the old age stage, the star begins to contract. If the size of the star was not too

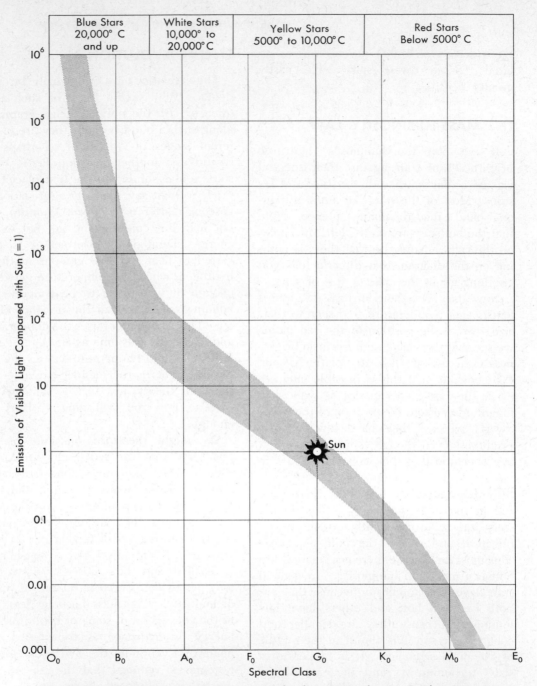

Fig. 47-1. Hertzsprung-Russell Diagram (color luminosity chart). Brightness is correlated with temperature, color, and spectral class. Sun is assigned a brightness of 1. Stars below it emit less visible light than it, those above it more. Stars to the left are hotter and whiter or bluer, those to the right cooler and redder. The vast majority of stars fall in the curved band known as the main sequence. Stars seem to begin their existence near the bottom of the band and evolve upward along it.

big to begin with, this contraction rather quickly leads to the white dwarf stage. In this stage its luminosity is maintained for some millions of years by the conversion of mass to energy as elements of *greater mass than helium* are formed. Eventually it cools, grows dark, and becomes cold.

For the very large stars the story is somewhat different and cannot be so clearly estimated. During the process of contraction it may explode, sending out great parts of its mass into space in a great burst of brilliance (a nova). That part of its mass which remains ultimately becomes a white dwarf. Both the early and the late parts of a star's career are passed through comparatively quickly. Most stars should therefore be in the mature stage; these are the main sequence stars.

Our sun is a comparatively young star; it still has lots of hydrogen left to convert to helium. If our summary of the life history of a star is correct, it should increase in temperature until all life on earth is impossible—but several billion years will pass before that stage occurs. In time old age will surely arrive and our sun will become a tiny white dwarf. Several billions of years later it will become a cold dead body. This account is, of course, highly speculative because man has not been around long enough to observe any sizable stage of stellar evolution. It is, however, in accord with present ideas, both of energy production in stars and in the present explanations of the main sequence diagram.

STELLAR MOTIONS

If Ptolemy were to come back to earth today he would have no trouble recognizing the constellations. In fact, he would note no differences in the positions of stars relative to one another, unless he made careful measurements. In the time since he measured it, Sirius has moved only half a degree. Others have moved as much as a degree. The motion of any star may be described by giving its *radial motion* (motion directly towards or away from the observer) and its *proper motion* (motion at right angles to a line between the star and an observer). The latter is obtained by direct observation. Even for stars that have high velocities, the proper motion is very small because of the great distances. Radial motion is detected by the so-called red shift of the spectral lines. The principle involved is the Doppler effect (Fig. 22-4), a principle that applies to all wave motion.

If the star is approaching the observer, the spectral lines are all shifted slightly towards the violet end of the spectrum. If the star is moving away from the observer, the shift is towards the red end. In the first case the wavelengths are apparently shorter, in the latter they are apparently longer. The amount of shift from the wavelengths as observed in the laboratory from a stationary source will give the speed towards or away from the observer. That such shifts do occur can be checked by the spectrum of the Pup as it revolves about Sirius. Along part of its orbit it is moving towards us and in another part it is moving away. The spectral lines shown corresponding shifts in position. The spectra of pulsating stars—the pulsation is due to alternate contraction and expansion of the star—also show such shifts. From such shifts the radial motion of any star, no matter how far away, can be detected. Observation of the proper motion, on the other hand, is limited, because as the distance increases, the amount of motion across the line of sight decreases so that it is imperceptible for most stars, unless very

Fig. 47-2. Spiral Nebula in the Constellation Virgo. The spirals are composed of countless stars, the brightest of which appear as definite points of light. Note the spiraling arms. (Courtesy Mt. Wilson and Palomar Observatories.)

long periods of time are taken. One hundred thousand years from now the proper motions of the stars forming the Great Dipper will have been so great that the name, if still applied, will no longer be at all descriptive. Speeds of stars in our galaxy up to 30 or 40 mi/sec are not uncommon.

GALAXIES

Even the unaided eye can detect the fact that the stars in the heavens are not uniformly distributed throughout space. A pair of binoculars or a low-power telescope will make this fact far more evident. Most of the stars we see are grouped in a belt that approximates the plane of the ecliptic. This is the belt that contains the constellations of the zodiac (Fig. 2-10). This distribution suggests the form of a wide disc with a comparatively small thickness. It also suggests that our solar system is located somewhere inside the disc, perhaps near the center. Thus, we see a great many stars looking in directions parallel to the plane of the disc, whereas looking in directions at right angles to it we see far fewer, probably only $\frac{1}{100}$ as many. An aggregation of stars such as this is called a galaxy. Ours is, of course, named the Milky Way.

It is in the form of a giant wheel, 80,000 to 100,000 light years across and about 10,000 in thickness. Modern research has revealed the following important items of information: (1) that the disc is spiral in form (Fig. 47-2) with great "arms" curving in the plane of the disc; (2) that our solar system is not at the center of the disc but is 27,000 light years from it, in one of the spiral arms; (3) that there are within it and near it a number (about 100) of globular star clusters, of perhaps 100,000 stars each, which act as single gravitational systems; (4) that our galaxy is revolving like a giant pinwheel, and (5) that there

Fig. 47-3. Great Spiral Nebula in the Constellation Andromeda. Andromeda is of the order of 1 to 1.5 million light years away, yet the Great Spiral Nebula can be seen with the naked eye. It is the largest known spiral. (Courtesy Mt. Wilson and Palomar Observatories.)

Fig. 47-4. Another Spiral Nebula in Andromeda, Seen Edgewise. (Courtesy Mt. Wilson and Palomar Observatories.)

are great clouds of interstellar gas and "dust," very irregularly distributed, and which obscure our vision of some parts of the sky. These "dark" parts of the sky are now being investigated by radioastronomy. The period of revolution of the Milky Way is between 200,000,000 and 250,000,000 years. The speed of our solar system due to this revolution is about 180 mi/sec.

Outside the Milky Way, and removed from it by distances varying from 70,000 to more than 2 billion light years, are other great galaxies. They are often called nebula because with any except the largest of telescopes, they appear as nebulous clouds of light. The best telescopes resolve this cloud into vast numbers of stars like those in our own galaxy. The great spiral in Andromeda (Figs. 47-3 and 47-4) is an example. It is 1,500,000 light years away but is easily visible to the naked eye. It is an "island universe" consisting of 100 billion stars, and is somewhat bigger than the Milky Way. There are tens of thousands of galaxies within the range of our 200-inch telescope at Mt. Palomar, California.

THE "EXPLODING" UNIVERSE

As we have already seen, the speeds of stars that are moving towards or away from us are calculated from the Doppler shift of the spectral lines. Our previous discussion was confined to the stars within our own galaxy. When observance of the Doppler shift was extended to other galaxies, it was found that the shift *in all cases* was away from us, i.e., the lines were shifted towards the red end of the spectrum. This means, if the interpretation of the shift is valid, that all galaxies are receding from us. Moreover, it was discovered that the greater the distance, the greater the velocity of recession. Double the distance and the speed was doubled.

Let us imagine their directions to be reversed so that all would move towards our galaxy, maintaining their present speeds as they do so. Given time enough they would all join together into one huge mass. Since the farther ones would be moving faster than the near ones, they would all reach this central area at the same time. That time would be some 5 billion years from now. What does it all mean?

The evidence seems to point to the conclusion that some 5 billion years ago, this huge mass of hot gaseous matter exploded into a vast number of huge fragments. Each one of these fragments would in time become a galaxy. Local condensations within the galaxy would give rise to star or star systems, some of which developed into solar systems during the process. This is, of course, based on the interpretation placed upon the red shift. Could something else cause it?

A host of other questions arise at once. How did all the matter in the universe ever get together in the first place? How long had it been together before the explosion took place? How long will the universe keep expanding? Is it finite or infinite? Etc., etc., etc. All we can say is that the universe is at least 5 billion years old, and it is not likely that it is as much as 10 billion. Will we ever know more than that? Perhaps not; only time will tell.

SUMMARY

Most of our information about the stars comes from photographs taken in conjunction with telescopes and from their spectra. From direct observations with these instruments we learn something of their distances, their brightnesses, their temperatures, their sizes, their masses, their densities, and their motions. Distance is related both to apparent and intrinsic brightness, so that if any two are known the third can be calculated. The temperature of stars is related both to their color and to their spectral class. From the spectra we also learn something about their composition. The intensity of spectral lines have been found to be an indication of the intrinsic brightness. Thus, the spectroscope is an aid in the determination of the distance to those stars too far away to determine by means of parallax.

Many of the above-listed relationships are made apparent by the Hertzsprung-Russell diagram, which is essentially a graph in which intrinsic brightness is plotted against spectral class or temperature. From it the important mass–luminosity law is derived. It also indicates that not all stars are the same age. In fact, there are stars of all ages in the heavens, and so we can deduce the life history of a star just as the life history of an average human being can be deduced from a study of babies, children, adolescents, mature, and old human beings.

The fixed stars are not fixed, but moving, some of them moving at high speeds. The motions may be resolved into two components at right angles to each other; one is radial, the other proper motion. Proper motion, across the line of sight, can be detected only by careful comparison on photographs taken at long intervals. Radial motion, towards or away from us, is detected by the spectroscope by observing the Doppler effect. The so-called red shift is used as the basis for the exploding universe.

EXERCISES

I. TERMS AND CONCEPTS

Apparent brightness	Proper motion
	Radial motion
Intrinsic brightness	Galactic red shift
	Globular clusters
Luminosity	Galaxy
Magnitude	Spiral nebula
Spectral class	Interstellar "dust"
Giants and dwarfs	Expanding universe
Main sequence	Intrinsic brightness = $d^2 \times$ apparent brightness
Mass–luminosity law	Magnitudes from spectral class

II. PROBLEMS

1. How can you prove that the stars shine by their own light, whereas the moon and the planets shine only by reflected light?

2. How bright would the sun appear to be relative to its present apparent brightness if it were removed to the position of Jupiter (about 50 times as far away)?

3. Which is brighter, a star of magnitude 1 or one of magnitude 2?

4. A light year is a unit of what? How far is a light second?

5. How may intrinsic brightness be determined if the distance cannot be determined by parallax?

6. How may distance be determined if a star is too far away to be calculated from its parallax?

7. Explain the relationship between temperature and spectral class.

8. Distinguish between a giant, a dwarf, and a star in the main sequence.

9. The spectra of the sun and the other stars show many dark lines superimposed on a continuous spectrum. What is the cause of the dark lines?

10. Explain, in terms of the Bohr theory, why the spectral lines of hydrogen in a very hot star differ from those of a cool star.

11. What are stars composed of?

12. The sun is losing mass every day by the conversion of 4,000,000 tons of its matter into radiation each *second*. (The same is true of every other star except that the amount may differ.) If its present mass is of the order of 10^{34} gm, what percentage of its mass will be left in 5 billion years, assuming a constant rate of loss? (There are about 1,000,000 gm in a long ton, and 31,500,000 sec in a year.)

13. What is a Cepheid variable? Of what use are they in the study of stars?

14. Compare the diameters of the Pup, Antares, and the sun. Which is nearer the average for all stars? Compare the masses of these three stars.

15. What is a double star? What information do we need to determine the mass of a double star system?

16. What is meant by main sequence stars? What stars lie outside the main sequence? Why?

17. How may masses of stars not in double (or triple) star systems be estimated?

18. What is a galaxy? Name one besides our own. What is a spiral nebula?

19. Galactic nebulae are great irregular masses of diffuse material (gas and fine "dust") within our galaxy that shine probably from reflected light of nearby stars. (Do not confuse them with spiral nebulae.) What might the "dust" consist of?

20. What is meant by the "red shift"? Explain the principle involved. Does it have the same significance applied to stars in our own galaxy as it does to other galaxies? Explain.

CHAPTER XLVIII

Conclusion

A time to look back on the way we have come and forward to the summit whither our way lies.
—J. H. BADLEY

It is not at all strange that we should conclude our explorations in the major fields of physical science in the heavens where we began. The heavens early excited man's imagination in a way that his mundane surroundings never could. He probably became aware of such regularities of nature as the round of the seasons, the rise and fall of the tides, the phases of the moon, etc., as soon as he began to think, but centuries were to elapse before he separated the solar system from the stars. Still another score of centuries were to pass before he realized the tremendous isolation of this solar system in space.

By this time he had gained a nearly complete knowledge of planetary motions, and reasonably accurate knowledge of distances, sizes, satellites, etc., but the stars were still largely a mystery. Despite the discovery of the telescope, stellar astronomy did not advance much beyond the cataloging stage until Fraunhofer had turned his newly invented spectroscope on the sun and stars, and Bessel had discovered stellar parallax. Even so, the astron-

omers made little progress in providing explanations until the physicists had unraveled the structure of the atom, accomplished atomic fission, reasoned the likelihood of atomic fusion, and made it a reality in the early 1950's. Stellar astronomy therefore most fittingly belongs at the end of our account just as solar astronomy belongs at the beginning.

The Copernican hypothesis as modified by Kepler described the motions of the planets and their satellites well enough but failed completely to assign an adequate cause. We therefore investigated the concepts of force and the laws of motion as developed by Galileo and Newton. The law of gravitation came as a great integrating concept, welding all that went before into a rational and significant whole.

A study of force and motion leads naturally into a study of work and energy. Although to us heat and work are obviously related via heat engines, it was by no means obvious that heat was a form of energy and not a substance; it took long and careful work to prove its relationship to mechanical energy. This investigation into the nature of heat introduced us to the world of molecules by way of a study of gases, and finally led us to another great integrating concept, the kinetic-molecular theory of matter.

Having been introduced to the finer state of matter via gaseous molecules, we proceeded to investigate the nature of matter in a more detailed manner. We learned, oddly enough, that a proper concept of the process of combustion was the gateway that led to the Law of Conservation of Mass, the Law of Definite Proportions, the Law of Multiple Proportions, and shortly to the atomic theory of Dalton which integrated them all. The Law of Combining

Volumes, however, remained a thorn in the side of the atomic theory for fifty years, until Cannizzaro removed it by resurrecting the suggestion made by Avogadro shortly after the first recognition of the disagreement. With the atomic theory seemingly fully established, the science of chemistry with the aid of Mendelyeev's periodic chart advanced rapidly, until it ran into troubles of a very different sort, troubles that arose as a result of investigations into two apparently different aspects of matter. One arose out of the revelation that all matter was electrical in nature. Because of it, we delved into the nature of electricity, and here, more than anywhere else in this book, we went beyond the immediate need of understanding the nature of matter and energy. The justification is that electricity touches our daily lives in so many ways, and more obviously than any of the other major provinces of physical science. The first quantitative measurements of the charge associated with atoms were made by Faraday in his work which culminated in his laws of electrolysis. Just how this electricity was associated with atoms remained an unsolved problem for decades.

The other arose out of the seemingly unrelated problem of spectra, bright line spectra in particular. To understand spectra we had to have some knowledge of light, the pursuit of which led us into a study of wave motions. That light was a wave motion was indisputably proved by Young as early as 1805, but the source (i.e., the vibrator needed to produce it) was not discovered for more than a century. Maxwell's electromagnetic theory was a great step forward, for it showed how light could be transmitted from the sun and stars through empty space, and without loss of energy. The work of Hertz, Marconi, and Roentgen helped to put it on a firm basis. Yet it contained no answer for the problem of spectra.

Two events very late in the nineteenth century spelled doom for the old belief in the indivisibility of the atom. These were the discovery of radioactivity as the spontaneous disintegration of certain kinds of heavy atoms at the far end of the periodic table, and the discovery of the electron as a universal constituent of all matter. These were quickly followed by Planck's quantum theory of radiation, based on sound experimental evidence but in apparent contradiction to Maxwell's theory. Here Einstein, probably the greatest coordinator of facts from various fields of science that ever lived, first appears on the scene with his photon theory of light (based on Planck's quantum theory) and his special theory of relativity. A little later Rutherford put forth his nuclear theory of the atom.

At this stage there were many threads hanging loose that needed tying together if man was ever to understand such phenomena as light, spectra, photons, electrons, and their relations to atoms. There was a critical need for another of these great integrating theories which had been so successful in the past. It came when Niels Bohr, a young Dane not long out of graduate school, put forth his theory of the hydrogen atom. At once the relationships of electrons to atomic nuclei, the problems of spectra, the reason for the emission of light according to the photon theory, the explanations of chemical reactions, and other problems were well on their way towards final solution. True, there remained much detailed work, chiefly of the drudge sort, before the mists were cleared away.

In the process Bohr's original theory as applied to atoms other than hydrogen was modified almost beyond recognition. This should not detract from Bohr, for without the original theory none of the modifications could have been made. Bohr's original theory still stands as one of the greatest conceptual schemes ever devised by the mind of man.

As far as the atom is concerned in our study there is left only the nucleus. It obviously contained the necessary positive charges to give the atom electrical neutrality, and it soon became apparent that it contained a neutral particle to give the atom the mass necessary to account for the atomic weight. Eventually these two particles, the proton and the neutron, were discovered and their masses determined. These turned out not to be fundamental particles for they can be "smashed," giving rise to a number of other particles that need not concern us here. Those of us who are not nuclear physicists can consider neutral atoms to be made of protons, neutrons, and electrons.

From a study of the energy given off in natural radioactivity, and the data from certain laboratory experiments involving nuclear bombardment, there arose the conviction that matter could be converted into energy in accordance with Einstein's equation, $E = mc^2$. Atomic fission was accidentally discovered in experiments during nuclear bombardment of U^{235} atoms with neutrons just as World War II started. Atomic fusion on the other hand was no accident; it was considered to be possible from mathematical considerations, and needed only an experiment to prove it.

Once the Bohr theory was modified to account for the spectra of all atoms, the explanation of the periodicities in the periodic chart was at hand, and with it, the basis was laid for the understanding of the physical and chemical properties of all of the elements. The electronic theory of chemical bonding was the integrating thread throughout our long discussion of the chemical behavior of different kinds and states of matter.

The discussion of carbon compounds was, in part at least, a deviation from the integrating thread running through the entire book, but is justified on two grounds. First, the chemistry of life makes a study of carbon compounds a necessary background for biological science, and second, thousands of new carbon compounds are being made every year, many of them of great importance to man.

No book on the nature of matter and energy would be complete without the section on geology and meteorology. The earth contains all of the natural elemental kinds of matter known to man. The form in which these elements occur are dealt with in our study of rocks and minerals. A general view of the earth helps to provide an adequate understanding of geological processes. Diastrophism and vulcanism are caused by transformations of nuclear and gravitational energy into heat, and of heat into mechanical energy of faulting, folding, uplift, and volcanic intrusions and extrusions. The processes of weathering and erosion represent transformations of the radiant energy of the sun on gigantic scales. This is true for the processes involved in meteorology.

The chapter entitled "Search for the Past," is again a bit removed from our integrating thread, but is justified by natural curiosity about the history of this floating island abode of ours. We learn something about how matter and energy have operated in the past here on earth, and how the record of it that is written in the rocks is deciphered.

We have included much of the history of science so that you may have a better understanding of the processes of scientific discovery, that you may see that human folly has played its part in the field of science just as it has in other fields, and that you may gain wisdom by learning how difficult it is for any man to step outside the intellectual climate of his time.

Throughout all we have kept the emphasis on principles rather than on the practical side, for this has been a course in science rather than a course about science. There is little intellectual discipline in the latter, little that will help you to see farther and more dispassionately in other fields. If you now think back about the scientists mentioned in this book, you will not be able to find one of them who was trying to invent anything of practical use at the time he made his discovery. This is not to say that none of them invented anything. Perhaps they did, but, if so, none are remembered because of that. We stress the value of what has been called "useless science" over that of practical science simply because the practical scientist, e.g., Edison, depends almost wholly on "useless science" for ideas. The hall of fame is replete with the names of men who made facts significant, who integrated them into a conceptual scheme, but contains the names of few men who were mere discoverers of facts. No practical scientist ever won a Nobel prize.

Because the fruits of science have been used to make devastating weapons, many people are inclined to blame the scientist for these weapons. "Why did they have to make the bomb?" they ask. The work

on the structure of the atom began as a purely intellectual endeavor. No one could know where it would lead. Once this work was started the bomb was inevitable if the political climate was ripe for it. Those who blame scientists for *not* refusing to work on the bomb, should ask themselves the question, "What would I think of our scientists who refused to aid in the development of the bomb if Hitler's scientists had developed it first?"

What of the future? Will science ever solve all of the mysteries of the universe? No scientist really thinks so. The solution of every problem creates new problems. The ignorant have no conception of what they do not know; the learned are humbled because they know so little. Will our present theories all be overthrown some day, to be replaced by different ones? Some will, some will undergo revision, and some will stand very much as they are. In general, the older theories stand the best chance of retention intact. The laws, however, will always hold within the limits placed upon them. Newton's laws apply to the phenomena of motion, including those of artificial satellites, just as they always have.

One of the outstanding differences between the science of today and that before World War II is its relation to the public. Science no longer can be considered the business of scientists only. It has become everybody's business. Let us forget for a moment about bombs. What the scientists do in the next few decades will have an important influence on the lives of us all, for science has become a great natural resource which will probably change the lives of many of us. Can an intelligent citizen afford to be ignorant of science? Can he afford to leave the use that is to be made of scientific discoveries to men who are ignorant of science and its methods? The only alternative is for every intelligent citizen to become familiar with science and its methods.

Perhaps you are disappointed by the lack of answers in this book to ultimate problems. You will find many answers to the "how" of things, few to the "why." Ultimate problems are the province not of science, but of philosophy and religion. The scientists say, "Give us matter to start with and we will tell you how it will behave." They cannot answer the question, "Why is there a universe in the first place?" None of the methods known to science can be applied to any degree at all in providing an answer. If a scientist attempts to answer that question, he has stepped out of his role as a scientist to become a philosopher or a theologian.

APPENDIX

Units of length (metric system):
>.10 millimeters (mm) = 1 centimeter
>>(1 mm = approx. .04 in.); (1 cm = approx. .4 in.)
>100 centimeters (cm) = 1 meter (39.37 in.)
>1000 meters (m)   = 1 kilometer (.62 mi)
>>*Note:* 1 in. = 2.54 cm; 1 ft = about 30 cm.

Units of volume (metric system):
>1 cu cm   = 1 milliliter (ml), very nearly.
>1000 cu cm = 1 liter, very nearly.
>>*Note:* 1 liter is slightly more than one quart (1.06 qt).

Units of weight (metric system):
>1 gram (g or gm) = very nearly the weight of 1 cu cm (1 ml) of water at 4° C. The difference is in the 6th decimal place.
>1000 gm   = 1 kilogram (2.20 lb)
>>*Note:* 1 ton = 907 kg.

Other units based on metric system:
>1 micron   — 1 millionth (10^{-6}) meter
>>1 ten-thousandth (10^{-4}) millimeter
>1 millimicron   = 1 millionth (10^{-6}) millimeter
>1 Angstrom (A) = 10^{-8} cm (1 ten-millionth $[10^{-9}]$ millimeter), the order of magnitude of the diameter of an atom

Other useful numerical data:

Astronomical unit (AU)	= 93,000,000 miles (distance from earth to sun)
Light year	= 6×10^{12} miles
Velocity of light	= 3×10^{10} cm/sec (186,400 mi/sec)
Velocity of sound in air	= approx. 1100 ft/sec (varies with density and temperature)
Atmospheric pressure at sea level	= 14.7 lb/in^2 = 760 mm mercury = 10^6 dynes/cm^2
Mechanical equivalent of heat (J)	= 4.18/joules/cal
1 joule	= 10^7 ergs
1 electron volt (ev)	= 1.6×10^{-19} joules = 1.6×10^{-12} ergs = $.38 \times 10^{-19}$ cal
1 Mev	= 10^6 ev

1 atomic mass unit (amu) = 931 Mev

1 gram mass (converted to energy) = 9×10^{20} ergs = 9×10^{13} joules = 2.15×10^{13} cal

1 kilowatt hour (kwh) = 3,600,000 joules

Avogadro's number = 6×10^{23}

Charge on the electron = 4.8×10^{-10} electrostatic units (esu) = 1.6×10^{-19} coulombs

Number of electrons in one coulomb = 6×10^{18}

Number of esu in one coulomb = 3×10^9

1 faraday = 96,500 coulombs = 3×10^{14} esu = 6×10^{23} electrons

Weight of hydrogen atom = 1.67×10^{-24} gm

Weight of electron = 9.1×10^{-28} gm = $\dfrac{1}{1835}$ weight of hydrogen atom

Planck's constant = 6.6×10^{27} erg sec

Wavelength of visible light = 3.8×10^{-5} cm (violet) to 7.6×10^{-5} cm (red) = 1.5×10^{-5} in. to 3.0×10^{-5} in. = 3800 A to 7600 A.

Frequencies of visible light = 8×10^{14} vib/sec (violet) to 4×10^{14} vib/sec (red)

INDEX

The letter n, written as a superscript, refers to a footnote.